27

GENERAL AND INDUSTRIAL CHEMISTRY SERIES

Edited by

H. M. BUNBURY, M.SC., F.R.I.C.

THE PETROLEUM CHEMICALS INDUSTRY

THE PETROLEUM CHEMICALS INDUSTRY

by

RICHARD FRANK GOLDSTEIN

B.Sc., Ph.D. (Lond.), F.R.I.C., F.Inst.Pet.

Second, revised and enlarged edition

NEW YORK

JOHN WILEY & SONS INC.

440 Fourth Avenue

1958

First edition 1949
Second, revised edition 1958

Printed in Great Britain at the Pitman Press, Bath

PREFACE TO THE SECOND EDITION

SINCE the first edition was published, the petroleum chemicals industry has become established on a world wide basis and the major products and lines of development have become much clearer. In writing the second edition, the problem has been to avoid expanding the book unduly by inclusion of new material without corresponding elimination of obsolete matter.

Since the petroleum chemicals industry is primarily a new source of bulk raw materials for the chemical industry, I have concentrated on the major products and have aimed to indicate their commercial outlets and to explain the basic chemistry of the processes used. Some smaller products previously included, which have not lived up to their earlier hopes, have been left out. Two new chapters on the history of the petroleum chemicals industry and on economics and statistics have been included, and more than half the former chapters have been largely or completely re-written. This edition is up-to-date to approximately the end of 1956.

I am indebted to Dr. M. A. Matthews, who has once more read the whole of the manuscript. It is a pleasure to thank Dr. R. D. Thrower for assistance in correcting the proofs, Dr. F. Din for recalculating all the thermodynamic data on hydrocarbons, the Petroleum Information Bureau and Mr. N. G. W. Luitsz for help with some of the statistics, and British Oxygen Research and Development Limited, for facilities in consulting their library.

R. F. GOLDSTEIN

London, *August*, 1957.

FOREWORD TO THE FIRST EDITION

by Professor SIR ROBERT ROBINSON, *M.A., D.Sc., LL.D., P.R.S.* (1949)

AT a comparatively early period in my professional career I asked Honours B.Sc. Candidates the following question:
"Write the introduction to a new text-book of organic chemistry and use the opportunity to indicate your views on the present trend of the science." Only one answer was submitted and this started as follows: "It was only at the earnest solicitations of my students and colleagues that I took up my pen to add yet another to the already too large number of text-books of organic chemistry." He went on to deplore the excessive complications such as aromatics, heterocycles, etc., etc., which only confused the beginner and decided to devote his book exclusively to compounds in which carbon exercised its proper valency of four in a respectable, saturated manner.

This was an amusing sarcasm but it did express the somewhat widely spread view that the saturated hydrocarbons present few problems, that their chemistry is simple and their behaviour predictable. Nothing could be further from the truth for, as Dr. Goldstein's monograph clearly shows, many of their transformations are exceedingly difficult to understand and the mechanism of reactions in this group includes more unsolved mysteries than are found in most of the other series.

Thus, to take one example of many possible, we are at a loss to explain in a convincing manner the curious syntheses of the 'alkylation' process, of such great practical importance in the manufacture of higher grade fuels. Naturally one reason for the surprise evoked by the strange reactions of paraffins is that the conditions of temperature and pressure can be so different from those usual in the practice of organic chemical laboratories. We have developed most of our ideas from experiments at $-15-100°$ C. or perhaps a little higher, and at the atmospheric pressure. But though it is not simple, petroleum chemistry is slowly getting on its theoretical feet, and that is true even in respect of the phenomena of heterogeneous catalysis. Dr. Goldstein has given an excellent account of the facts that call for explanation although his main concern has undoubtedly been to describe the scope of the industry; what has been done and how it was done.

This work deserves to be termed monumental because of the labour which its preparation must have involved and because of the completeness of the survey which it affords. It will certainly find a place on my desk rather than on the shelves.

But it is timely too, because the present opportunity to develop the industry of petroleum chemicals in this country has been seized in more than one quarter. We may well be at the beginning of a new era of progress in this field of national effort and hence the provision of such an excellent *vade-mecum* is a valuable service for which all chemists will be most grateful. As a member of the Ayre Committee, to which the author refers in his Preface, I am one of those who have been convinced by the evidence that the future prosperity of the chemical industry cannot be assured unless we strive with all our might to take our full share in the manufacture of chemicals from petroleum.

Moreover it is not merely a question of economics, of profit and turnover, but national security is also involved. We must be prepared to face any possible changes in the availability of sources of carbon compounds and chemists must be adaptable, ready to use coal for oil, or oil for coal.

Dr. Goldstein has done his part—let us hope that the stimulus he has given will penetrate even the most pachydermatous of academic quarters and that his effort will so quicken the interest of pure chemists and University authorities that the scientific, technological, industrial and national importance of petroleum and its multitude of derivatives will receive in the future the greater attention which they so richly deserve.

R. ROBINSON

PREFACE TO THE FIRST EDITION

THE petroleum chemicals industry is concerned with the manufacture of synthetic organic chemicals based on petroleum as the starting material. This is the third and newest of the three principal key materials, coal, vegetable matter and mineral oil, from which all or almost all industrial organic compounds are manufactured.

The petroleum chemicals industry is only about twenty-five years old; for obvious reasons, it was developed originally in America, and practically no chemicals were manufactured from oil in Great Britain up to the outbreak of the recent war. This was in part a consequence of the duty on hydrocarbon oils; the realisation of the future importance of this industry led Sir John Anderson, then Chancellor of the Exchequer, to set up a Committee in 1944 to consider the effect of the Hydrocarbon Oils Duty on the chemical industry of Great Britain. This Committee, the Ayre Committee, recommended that imported hydrocarbon oils used for chemical synthesis be freed from duty, and their recommendation has since been accepted by the Government. The removal of these duties, coupled with world changes in the sources of cheap oil, opens up the petroleum chemicals industry to Great Britain on equal or almost equal terms with any other country.

The chemistry of petroleum derivatives up to 1937 has been fully documented in two volumes by Carleton Ellis, 'The Chemistry of Petroleum Derivatives', *Reinhold Publishing Corporation*, Vol. 1, 1934; Vol. 2, 1937. It has not proved practicable merely to carry on where Ellis left off; the changes have been so rapid and so comprehensive that no readable account could have been presented. Indeed, as explained in the Introduction, the decision on what is a petroleum chemical and what is not has been very difficult, and the ultimate decision has had to be both highly selective and highly personal. Again, no attempt has been made to give a complete set of references on all subjects since 1937; they would be out of date before the book could be published owing to the steady release of accounts of work carried out in the Allied countries during the war, and the continuing flow of reports on the German chemical industry. What has been aimed at is to give a clear and reasonably comprehensive picture of the state of the art on each subject dealt with, special emphasis being laid on developments during the last ten years. To this end, patents have been treated as journal information, and no particular attempt has been made to allocate priorities to any company or country, or to give a complete picture of the patent position on any subject. Whilst the bulk of the manuscript was written in 1946, additions and amendments have been made so as to bring the subject matter up to date to the end of 1947.

The lay-out of the book is explained in the Introduction; to assist in grasping the possibilities and problems of the industry, statistics both on petroleum and on petroleum chemicals are included in Appendices.

I acknowledge with thanks permission to reproduce Figs. 17 and 18 from Berkman, Morrell and Egloff, 'Catalysis', *Reinhold Publishing Corporation*, 1940.

It is my pleasant duty to express my thanks to Dr. M. A. Matthews, who has read the whole of the manuscript and made many valuable suggestions, to Mr. E. Penny and Dr. C. A. Pulley for help in the arduous task of correcting the proofs, to the Institute of Petroleum for facilities for obtaining certain of the statistics, and to the Publishers for their continued helpfulness and guidance in preparing the manuscript for publication.

Finally, I record my appreciation to the Directors of Imperial Chemical Industries, Ltd., for providing many facilities for writing this book.

R. F. GOLDSTEIN

London, *January*, 1949.

CONTENTS

ABBREVIATIONS

JOURNALS

Angew. Chem.	Angewandte Chemie
Ann.	Annalen der Chemie
Ann. Rep.	Annual Reports on the Progress of Chemistry
Ber.	Berichte der Deutschen Chemischen Gesellschaft
Brennstoff-Chem.	Brennstoff-Chemie
Brit. Chem. Abs.	British Chemical Abstracts
Brit. Plastics	British Plastics
Bull. Soc. Chim. Belg.	Bulletin de la Société Chimique de Belgique
Can. J. Res.	Canadian Journal of Research
Chem. Abs.	Chemical Abstracts
Chem. Age	Chemical Age
Chem. Eng.	Chemical Engineering (formerly Chemical & Metallurgical Engineering)
Chem. Eng. News	Chemical and Engineering News
Chem. Eng. Prog.	Chemical Engineering Progress (before 1947, Transactions of the American Institute of Chemical Engineers)
Chem. Ind.	Chemical Industries
Chem. and Ind.	Chemistry and Industry
Chem. Ind. Week	Chemical Industries Week
Chem. Ing. Tech.	Chemie Ingenieur Technik
Chem. Met. Eng.	Chemical and Metallurgical Engineering
Chem. Rev.	Chemical Reviews
Chem. Trade J.	Chemical Trade Journal
Chem. Week	Chemical Week
Compt. Rend.	Comptes Rendus hebdomadaires des Séances de l'Académie des Sciences
Ind. Chem.	Industrial Chemist
Ind. Eng. Chem.	Industrial and Engineering Chemistry
I.R.W.	India Rubber World
J. Amer. Chem. Soc.	Journal of the American Chemical Society
J. Appl. Chem.	Journal of Applied Chemistry
J. Chem. Soc.	Journal of the Chemical Society
J. Inst. Fuel	Journal of the Institute of Fuel
J. Inst. Pet.	Journal of the Institute of Petroleum
J. Inst. Pet. Tech.	Journal of the Institution of Petroleum Technologists
J. Soc. Chem. Ind.	Journal of the Society of Chemical Industry

Nat. Pet. News	National Petroleum News
Oil Gas J.	Oil and Gas Journal
Pet. Proc.	Petroleum Processing (*National Petroleum News*, Refinery Number, prior to Sept. 1946)
Pet. Refiner	Petroleum Refiner
Pet. Times	Petroleum Times
Proc. Roy. Soc.	Proceedings of the Royal Society
Rec. Trav. Chim.	Receuil des Travaux Chimiques des Pays-Bas
Trans. Amer. Inst. Chem. Eng.	Transactions of the American Institute of Chemical Engineers
Trans. Faraday Soc.	Transactions of the Faraday Society
World Pet.	World Petroleum
World Pet. Proc.	World Petroleum Proceedings
Z. Elektrochem.	Zeitschrift für Elektrochemie und angewandte physikalische Chemie
Z. Physikal. Chem.	Zeitschrift für Physikalische Chemie

COMPANIES

Air Reduction	Air Reduction Co.
Armour	Armour and Co.
Bakelite	Bakelite Corporation
Barrett	Barrett Co.
B.P.M.	N.V. de Bataafsche Petroleum Maatschappij
Battelle Mem.	Battelle Memorial Institute
Brit. Celanese	British Celanese Co.
Brit. Oxygen	British Oxygen Co.
B.T.H.	British Thomson-Houston Co.
Carbide and Carbon	Carbide and Carbon Chemicals Company
Cities Service	Cities Service Oil Co.
Commercial Solvents	Commercial Solvents Corporation
Cons. f. Elektrochem.	Consortium für Elektrochemische Industrie G.m.b.H.
Degussa	Deutsche Gold und Silber Scheide-Anstalt vorm. Roessler
Distillers	Distillers Co.
Dow	Dow Chemical Co.
du Pont	E. I. du Pont de Nemours and Co.
Eastman-Kodak	Eastman-Kodak Co.
Goodrich	B. F. Goodrich Co.
Hooker	Hooker Électrochemical Co.
Henkel	Henkel et Cie. A-G.
I.C.I.	Imperial Chemical Industries
I.G.	I-G. Farbenindustrie A-G.
Monsanto	Monsanto Chemical Co.

Phillips Pet.   Phillips Petroleum Co.
Procter and Gamble   Procter and Gamble Co.
Rhône Poulenc   Société des Usines Chimique Rhône-Poulenc
                          S.A.
Roessler and Hasslacher   Roessler and Hasslacher Co.
Rohm and Haas Co.   Rohm and Haas Co. (Philadelphia)
Rohm und Haas A-G.   Rohm und Haas A-G. (Darmstadt)
Ruhrchemie   Ruhrchemie A-G.
Shawinigan   Shawinigan Chemicals Co.
Shell Development   Shell Development Co.
Soc. Carbochimique   S.A. Carbochimique
Standard Oil Development Standard Oil Development Co.
Standard Oil Ind.   Standard Oil Company of Indiana
Texaco   Texaco Development Co.
Union Carbide   Union Carbide and Carbon Corporation
U.O.P.   Universal Oil Products Co.
U.S. Ind. Chem.   United States Industrial Chemicals Co.
Usine de Melle   les Usines de Melle S.A.
Wacker   Dr. Alex. Wacker Gesellschaft für Elektro-
                          chemische Industrie G.m.b.H.
Wyandotte   Wyandotte Chemicals Corporation

REPORTS ON THE GERMAN CHEMICAL INDUSTRY

B.I.O.S.   British Intelligence Objectives Sub-Committee
C.I.O.S.   Combined Intelligence Objectives Sub-Com-
                          mittee
F.I.A.T.   Field Investigation Agency, Technical (U.S.
                          Group, Central Council for Germany)

THE PETROLEUM CHEMICALS INDUSTRY

INTRODUCTION

1. The scope of the petroleum chemicals industry

THE three main sources of synthetic organic chemicals are coal, oil and vegetable products. Such is the ingenuity of the organic chemist that any one of these basic raw materials could supply all that industry requires; indeed, every synthetic organic chemical listed in Beilstein can be made in some way or other starting from methane, or for that matter, from coal or coke. The technologist is concerned, however, both with what is possible and what is the most economic route. Choice of the most economic route depends on new technological discoveries and on the fluctuating availability and costs of raw materials. The natural resources of industrial countries differ and these differences may be augmented or cancelled for reasons of State policy; examples are the support given to ethyl alcohol in Great Britain for many years, and the autarkic policy of the Third Reich, which led to immense developments of acetylene chemistry in Germany.

Every one of the three starting materials for synthesising organic compounds has its own peculiar advantages; but the indications are that in countries with free access to oil, it will have a large and growing share of the field; compared with coal, oil has the advantage that it already is combined with the hydrogen which is an essential component of hydrocarbons. Compared with vegetable products, it is more readily transportable, and a given weight of oil will give a higher yield of synthetic chemical than the same weight of vegetable product.

Whilst the main objective of this monograph has been to survey those fields of industrial organic chemistry in which oil is the most economic starting material, in several cases oil is used alongside coal or vegetable products. For example, in America and in the United Kingdom ethyl alcohol is manufactured both from oil via ethylene and by fermentation processes; in America, Germany and Italy acetylene is made both by partial combustion of natural gas methane and from coal via calcium carbide.

To try to make the competitive position reasonably clear, information on alternative non-petroleum routes has been included where appropriate. It has also been considered worth while including subjects where the oil route has not yet been established as the most economic one but where minor improvements in technique may swing the balance in its favour.

Other difficulties have presented themselves in deciding what is a petroleum chemical and what is not. It has been mentioned above that every organic chemical can be made from methane, and the availability of benzene, toluene, naphthalene, etc., from petroleum means that the whole field of synthetic aromatic compounds, including dyestuffs, medicinals, explosives and so on could be regarded as part of the field of petroleum

1

chemicals. To keep this book within bounds, the choice of subject matter
has had to be highly selective. Of the three main divisions of organic
chemistry, aliphatic, aromatic and heterocyclic, the chemistry of petroleum
derivatives leads predominantly to aliphatic compounds. The manufacture
of aromatic hydrocarbons from petroleum is dealt with in some detail, but
aromatic chemistry has been limited to those recent developments which
have been based on petroleum aromatics; in the same way, the manufacture
of raw materials for the high polymer industry is referred to where they
arise from petroleum, but the polymerisation step is not discussed. The
chemistry and technology of the petroleum industry, which deals mainly
with the manufacture of fuels and lubricants from crude petroleum, has
been discussed only in so far as it bears on the petroleum chemicals industry; manufacture of carbon black, which is based almost exclusively on
petroleum but which does not lead to synthetic organic chemicals, has not
been included.

The monograph is divided as follows: Chapter 1 gives a summary of
the history of the petroleum chemicals industry. Chapter 2 deals with the
source materials of the petroleum chemicals industry, the hydrocarbons
present in crude petroleum or produced as by-products in the refining
operations of the petroleum industry itself, and the general methods of
separation of hydrocarbons. Chapters 3–6 deal with the chemistry of the
paraffins, and Chapters 7–11 with the manufacture of olefins and the chemical developments based on them. The manufacture of the other important
classes of hydrocarbons – diolefins, naphthenes, aromatics, and acetylene
– are discussed in Chapters 12–15. In Chapters 16–20, the manufacture and
reactions of the principal classes of petroleum chemicals are considered.
Chapter 21 gives a brief summary of the chemical by-products – usually
non-hydrocarbon – arising from refinery operations. Chapter 22 gives a
brief conspectus of the economics of the petroleum chemicals industry – the
effect of locality on choice of raw material and route, and the main end uses.
Appendices contain the boiling points of the simpler hydrocarbons, general
information and charts, and statistics of world petroleum production and
consumption and of the manufacture of synthetic organic chemicals of
non-coal tar origin in the United States, where adequate figures are
available.

2. Nomenclature and physical and physico-chemical data employed

(a) NOMENCLATURE

The nomenclature of organic compounds is based on the trivial names
commonly adopted in the petroleum chemicals industry; otherwise, the
nomenclature of the Heilbron-Bunbury 'Dictionary of Organic Compounds',
Eyre and Spottiswoode, Vol. 1, 1943, is used.

Numbers are used in preference to Greek lettering. The numbering of aliphatic compounds commences at the end carbon atom nearest to the shortest side chain:

$$\underset{4}{CH_3}\underset{3}{CH_2}\overset{\overset{\displaystyle CH_3\ 3'}{|}}{\underset{2}{CH}}\underset{1}{CH_3}$$

2-methylbutane
(isopentane)

In olefinic or acetylenic compounds, the unsaturated bond is given the lowest number possible, the acetylenic bond taking the lowest number in compounds containing both types of unsaturation:

$$\underset{4}{CH_3}\underset{3}{CH_2}\underset{2}{CH}:\underset{1}{CH_2}$$

1-Butene

$$\underset{4}{CH_2}:\underset{3}{CHC}\overset{..}{\underset{2}{C}}:\underset{1}{CH}$$

3-Buten-1-yne
(monovinylacetylene)

The common names, ethylene and propylene, are used throughout but for the C_4 and higher olefins, the names butene, pentene, etc., are adopted.

The order of substituents is:

> Halogen (F, Cl, Br, I)
> NO_2
> OH
> NH_2 and substituted NH_2
> Alkyl
> Aryl
> Acyl

CN, CHO, COOH, SO_3H, etc., are treated as suffixes; with compounds containing these groups, numbering commences at the carbon atom carrying the suffix; on the other hand, with primary alcohols, numbering commences at the carbon atom belonging to the CH_2OH group, *e.g.*,

$$\overset{\overset{\displaystyle CH_3\ 3'}{|}}{\underset{3}{CH_3}}\underset{2}{CH}\underset{1}{CH_2COOH}$$

2-Methylbutyric acid

$$\overset{\overset{\displaystyle CH_3\ 4'}{|}}{\underset{4}{CH_3}}\underset{3}{CH}\underset{2}{CH_2}\underset{1}{CH_2OH}$$

3-Methyl-*n*-butyl alcohol

$$\underset{4}{HOOCCH_2}\underset{3}{CH_2}\overset{\overset{\displaystyle COOH}{|}}{\underset{2}{C}}:\underset{1}{CH_2}$$

1-Butene-2 : 4-dicarboxylic acid

In naming compounds, cyclo, iso and neo are treated as part of the name. Double and triple derivatives take the prefixes di- and tri-, also treated as part of the name. *n*-, *sec*-, *tert*-, *o*-, *m*-, and *p*- are not treated as part of the name.

No special mention need be made of the nomenclature of alicyclic, aromatic and heterocyclic compounds, as their chemistry is dealt with only in the briefest way.

(b) PHYSICAL DATA

Data on boiling points, melting points, etc., are from the usual reference books such as 'Handbook of Chemistry and Physics', *Chemical Rubber Publishing Co.*, 30th Ed., 1950–51, or Perry, 'Chemical Engineers' Handbook', *McGraw Hill*, 3rd Ed., 1948. Data on hydrocarbons have been taken from A.P.I. Research Project No. 44, 'Selected Values of Physical and Thermodynamic Properties of Hydrocarbons and related Compounds', *Carnegie Press*, 1953. Use has also been made of the publications of some of the manufacturing companies.

The physical units employed conform in general to those used in BS. 813. The principal units are as shown below:

mm.	millimetre
cm.	centimetre
m.	metre
in.	inch
ft.	feet
g.	gram
kg.	kilogram
lb.	pound
gal.	gallon (Imperial)
bbl.	barrel
l.	litre
atma.	atmosphere (absolute pressure)
psi.	pounds per square inch (absolute pressure)
g. cal.	gram calorie
k. cal.	kilogram calorie
kWh.	kilowatt hour

In equations, the letters (l) and (g) in brackets indicate that the molecule is respectively in the liquid state or in the vapour state. This convention is not used for substances normally gaseous at room temperature, such as hydrogen.

Long tons have been employed throughout the body of the text, except in Appendix 3 which deals with the statistics of the production of petroleum and petroleum fractions. In conformity with general practice, it has been judged wise to adhere to the usual procedure of quoting these figures in metric tons.

Useful conversion factors between the common systems of units are given at the beginning of Appendix 3.

(c) THERMODYNAMICS; SYMBOLS AND METHOD

The thermodynamic symbols used in this book are based on those approved by the Joint Committee of the Chemical Society, the Faraday

Society and the Physical Society. which issued agreed recommendations in 1937.[1]

T Temperature, absolute scale, ° K.
t Temperature, Centigrade scale, ° C.
P, p Pressure.
H Enthalpy, total heat content.
G Free energy of Lewis and Randall.
S Entropy.
C_p Heat capacity per mol at constant pressure.
R   Gas Constant.
K Equilibrium Constant $= \dfrac{\{\text{Products}\}}{\{\text{Reactants}\}}$.
k Velocity Constant of reaction.

Changes in thermodynamic quantities are represented by the prefix Δ:

ΔH Increase in total heat content in any reaction in going from the left hand side of the equation to the right hand side.
ΔG Increase in free energy.
ΔS Increase in entropy.

For exothermic reactions, ΔH has a negative sign; for endothermic reactions, ΔH has a positive sign.

Natural logarithms are represented by 'ln', logarithms to the base ten, by 'log'.

The thermodynamic treatment has deliberately been kept as simple as possible, and has been restricted to illustrating the broad effects of changes in the principal conditions of reaction – pressure, temperature and concentration – on the equilibrium.

The equilibrium constant in a chemical reaction carried out at constant temperature and pressure is given by the relationship:

$$\ln K_p = \frac{-\Delta G}{RT} \qquad . \qquad . \qquad . \qquad . \qquad (1)$$

where K_p is the equilibrium constant, expressed as $\dfrac{[\text{products}]}{[\text{reactants}]}$, the concentrations of the participating species being expressed as partial pressures.

ΔG at constant temperature is also given by the relationship:

$$\Delta G = \Delta H - T\Delta S \qquad . \qquad . \qquad . \qquad (2)$$

where ΔH and ΔS are respectively the increase in total heat content and in entropy in the reaction.

---

[1] *Chem. and Ind.*, 1937, **15**, 860.

The chief value to us of the concept of free energy is as a means of predicting equilibrium conditions. The change in free energy, ΔG, can be obtained from equilibrium measurements by means of equation (1), but is more often calculated from equation (2) which requires thermal data.

This second method calls for a knowledge of heat capacities of the individual components from absolute zero up to the temperatures involved, of the changes in enthalpy accompanying changes in state between these temperatures, and of the heats of formation of each component from its elements at some temperature.

In the following series of equations, (3) to (6), all differential equations are partial differentials at constant pressure.

The change in enthalpy with temperature is related to the difference in specific heats, ΔC_p, by the equation:

$$\frac{\mathrm{d}\Delta H}{\mathrm{d}T} = \Delta C_p \quad . \qquad . \qquad . \qquad . \quad (3)$$

The heat capacities of most solids, liquids and gases can be expressed by empirical equations of the form:

$$C_p = a + bT + cT^2 \quad . \qquad . \qquad . \qquad . \quad (4)$$

where a, b, c are constants.

Integrating (3) with the aid of (4),

$$\Delta H = \Delta H_o + \Delta aT + \tfrac{1}{2}\Delta bT^2 + \tfrac{1}{3}\Delta cT^3 \qquad . \qquad . \quad (5)$$

where ΔH_o is a constant, the change in enthalpy at the absolute zero, and Δa, Δb, Δc are the sums of the individual a, b, and c terms for the products minus the corresponding sums for the reactants.

Entropy is related to heat capacity by the equation:

$$\mathrm{d}S = C_p \frac{\mathrm{d}T}{T} = C_p \mathrm{d}\ln T.$$

A knowledge of C_p from absolute zero, and of the entropy changes accompanying changes in state, combined with the assumption that the entropy of pure crystalline compounds at the absolute zero is nil, enables the entropy of any particular compound to be evaluated at any temperature. This gives the second term on the right hand side of equation (2) and enables the free energy to be computed.

The change of free energy with temperature is given by the Gibbs-Helmholtz equation:

$$\Delta G = \Delta H - T\frac{\mathrm{d}\Delta G}{\mathrm{d}T}$$

an alternative form of which is:

$$\frac{d\left(\dfrac{\Delta G}{T}\right)}{dT} = -\frac{\Delta H}{T^2} \qquad . \qquad . \qquad . \qquad . \qquad (6)$$

From equation (5), equation (6) can be evaluated in terms of data depending only on heats of reaction or formation and of heat capacities. Integrating (6) gives:

$$\Delta G = \Delta H_o - \Delta aT\ln T - \tfrac{1}{2}\Delta bT^2 - \tfrac{1}{3}\Delta cT^3 + IT \qquad . \qquad (7)$$

where I is the constant of integration.

Equation (7) is the general form of the variation of change in free energy with temperature. Over a limited temperature range, it is more convenient to express (7) in the approximate linear form:

$$\Delta G = A + BT \qquad . \qquad . \qquad . \qquad . \qquad (8)$$

where A and B are constants which are not identical with ΔH_o and I of equation (7).

This treatment is very convenient in considering the inter-relationships of the hydrocarbons; given the free energies of formation of the individual hydrocarbons, the free energy change from one hydrocarbon to another can at once be obtained by algebraic summing of the equations for the free energies of formation. From the free energy change, the equilibrium constant is obtained by equation (1).

Consider the dehydrogenation of ethane to ethylene:

$$C_2H_6 \rightleftharpoons C_2H_4 + H_2 \qquad . \qquad . \qquad . \qquad . \qquad (9)$$

From Chapter 7, Table 22, p. 92, the free energies of formation of ethane and of ethylene from their elements (in the form of graphite and of hydrogen gas) are related to the absolute temperature over the range $700°–1,000°$ K. by the equations:

$$\Delta G_{C_2H_6} = -24,640 + 50 \cdot 8T,$$
$$\Delta G_{C_2H_4} = 9,670 + 18 \cdot 6T.$$

The free energy change, $\Delta G_{(9)}$, for reaction (9) is then:

$$\Delta G_{(9)} = -(-24,640 + 50 \cdot 8T) + (9,670 + 18 \cdot 6T)$$
$$= 34,310 - 32 \cdot 2T.$$

At $T = 1,066°$ K. (793° c.), ΔG for this reaction is 0.

From equation (1), $\ln K_p = \dfrac{-\Delta G}{RT}$, or $\log K_p = \dfrac{-\Delta G}{4 \cdot 57T}$,

At $T = 1,066°$ K., $\log K_p = 0$, or $K_p = 1$, *i.e.*, $\dfrac{p_{C_2H_4}p_{H_2}}{p_{C_2H_6}} = 1$.

At 1 atmosphere pressure, assuming we form x mols of ethylene from 1 mol of ethane:

$$C_2H_6 \rightleftharpoons C_2H_4 + H_2$$

$$1 - x \qquad x \qquad x \qquad \text{Total mols, } 1 + x.$$

$$\frac{1-x}{1+x} \qquad \frac{x}{1+x} \qquad \frac{x}{1+x} \qquad \text{Partial pressures}$$

Therefore, at 1,066° K.,

$$K_p = 1 = \frac{\left(\dfrac{x}{1+x}\right)^2}{\left(\dfrac{1-x}{1+x}\right)}, \ i.e., \ \frac{x^2}{1-x^2} = 1 \text{ from which } x = \sqrt{\tfrac{1}{2}} = 0{\cdot}71.$$

That is to say, at this temperature, conversion is 71%,* and the partial pressure of the ethylene in the gases at equilibrium is $\dfrac{0{\cdot}71}{1{\cdot}71}$, or 0·415 atma.

The conversion of ethane and the partial pressure of ethylene can be calculated in the same way at any other temperature.

In using partial pressures to express K_p, it is implicitly assumed that the components obey the Gas Laws. This is not true in practice, especially at high pressures, and it is more accurate to use the concept of fugacity. In view of the approximations made in the derivation of the free energy equations, it has not been considered worth while to introduce this further refinement. Details of this method of calculation of equilibrium constants can be found in the standard text-books of thermodynamics such as Lewis and Randall.[2]

(d) THERMOCHEMICAL DATA

Knowledge of the thermochemistry of hydrocarbons is now extensive, due to the interest and support of the petroleum industry. Thermal and free energy data on the more important hydrocarbons and hydrocarbon series up to 1952 have been collected by A.P.I. Research Project No. 44,[3] and we have kept to their data as far as possible.

Information on non-hydrocarbon compounds is much more scanty. We have drawn on the excellent summary compiled by Parks and Huffman in 1932.[4] Heats of combustion of most of the important non-hydrocarbon compounds are known,[5] from which heats of formation can be calculated.

___

* Throughout the main text of the book "per cent" has been written out in full wherever the term is used as a substantive, *e.g.*, sixty per cent of olefins, and the symbol "%" employed in all cases in which the term is used adjectivally, *e.g.*, a 60% solution.

[2] 'Thermodynamics and the Free Energy of Chemical Substances', *McGraw-Hill*, 1923.

[3] 'Selected Values of Physical and Thermodynamic Properties of Hydrocarbons and Related Compounds', *Carnegie Press*, 1953.

[4] 'The Free Energies of some Chemical Compounds', *Chemical Catalog Co.*, 1932.

[5] See, *e.g.*, Perry, 'Chemical Engineers Handbook', *McGraw-Hill*, 3rd Ed., 1948.

What are lacking are entropy data and data on change in heat capacity with temperature; there are now available empirical, semi-empirical, and special theoretical methods of calculating the required information without actual experimental measurements.

In fact, we may repeat the suggestion that the time is now ripe for some expert in thermodynamics to collect and review the large amount of thermal and free energy data on non-hydrocarbon organic compounds which have been published since the time of Parks and Huffman's monograph.

CHAPTER 1

HISTORY OF THE PETROLEUM CHEMICALS INDUSTRY[1]

1. Petroleum chemicals in America 1920 to 1940

THE petroleum chemicals industry started in the United States in 1919–20; it was created from research work carried out during the first world war. In the 1920's and 1930's the industry was concerned mainly with the methods of making and of using the simple olefins – ethylene, propylene, and the butenes. The first olefin, ethylene, was made by direct cracking of liquid petroleum fractions or of propane. Propylene and the butenes were obtained either simultaneously with ethylene in these direct cracking processes or as by-products of refinery operations, particularly as these became more and more akin to chemical processes with the adoption of thermal reforming and later of catalytic cracking and catalytic reforming.

For separation of the olefins, reliance was placed largely on efficient fractional distillation under pressure, using techniques now familiar to the petroleum industry; the unusual feature was the low temperature required for concentration of ethylene. The main olefin reactions developed were hydration with sulphuric acid to give the alcohol, which was then dehydro-genated to the corresponding aldehyde or ketone, and conversion to the olefin oxide via reaction with hypochlorous acid. The ready commercial availability of ethylene oxide and propylene oxide led to a continuous stream of new products, such as the glycols, glycol ethers, and alkanol-amines.

This indicates the two-fold function of petroleum chemicals; on the one hand, the hydration of olefins led to alcohols and to the family of derivatives of alcohols already made from other sources; on the other hand, the olefin oxides and their derivatives were new industrial chemicals not previously made.

Ethylene was and, in fact, still is the most important olefin. Although it is believed that isopropyl alcohol was actually the first petroleum chemi-cal, as it was made on a limited scale in 1919–1920, the outstanding feature of this period was the launching of the derivatives of ethylene oxide into the industry and their establishment on a firm and proved basis. These chemicals found new uses mainly in the automobile industry. Ethylene glycol was the basis of the first permanent antifreeze, while the glycol ethers were used in the new surface coatings being developed for automobiles. Simultaneously, ethyl alcohol was being made from ethylene by hydration

---

[1] Based on Goldstein, 'Advances in Chemistry Series', *American Chemical Society*, 1954, **10**, 321.

with sulphuric acid, using a process the chemistry of which had been worked out many years before but which had not been economically successful.

The bulk utilization of ethylene was soon followed by that of propylene and then by the butenes, which were converted to ketones via the alcohols made by the same hydration step as for ethyl alcohol. The ketones and their derivatives also found outlets in the automobile and solvents industries.

These developments progressed steadily up to the outbreak of the second world war. This can be shown in Table 1,[2] which shows how the number of ethylene and propylene chemicals marketed by only one firm, Carbide and Carbon Chemicals Corporation, increased between 1926 and 1939. The figures are approximate.

TABLE 1

Number of individual aliphatic compounds from olefins made by Carbide and Carbon Chemicals Co.

Year	Number of compounds derived from ethylene	Number of compounds derived from propylene	Total
1926	5	2	7
1929	15	4	19
1934	35	15	50
1939	41	27	68

Derivatives of the butenes had been introduced from about 1930, though not by the company named.

At the same time, other work was in hand which was the basis of many of the later developments dealt with in the following section.

2. Petroleum chemicals in America 1940 to 1955

Whilst the first world war was responsible for the creation of the petroleum chemicals industry, the second world war led to its widespread expansion. Firstly, more types of hydrocarbons were used as the raw materials of the industry. Secondly, the end uses were enlarged from the limited outlets of the first period.

The techniques of preparation and of separation of hydrocarbons were improved. New construction materials led to cracking being conducted under more severe conditions, to increase the amount of olefins produced. This also permitted a partial change from propane to ethane as the raw material for ethylene synthesis. Aromatics became available from petroleum naphthenes. Diolefins and acetylene were manufactured from petroleum sources.

Methods of separation of hydrocarbons became more diversified. Fractional distillation was improved by the use of azeotropic and extractive

---

[2] U.S. Tariff Commission reports, Census of Production, Synthetic Organic Chemicals.

distillation. Liquid-liquid solvent extraction, already used in petroleum refining, was adapted to the concentration and purification of some of the raw materials for petroleum chemicals. Continuous adsorption on solids such as active charcoal or silica gel was established.

Olefins were the main building blocks of the industry during the first period. The second period brought into the picture the paraffins, the di-olefins, acetylene, and the aromatic hydrocarbons. The magnitude of utilization of the olefins increased *pari passu* with that of the other hydro-carbons, but they were no longer the only type.

Although the initial work had in some cases been carried out earlier, important new olefin reactions established since 1940 were:

Direct oxidation of olefins to olefin oxides (discovered in Europe in 1929), partly replacing the hypochlorous acid route.

Direct hydration of olefins to alcohols without the use of sulphuric acid (known for many years but never successful until the discovery of new catalysts both in Europe and in U.S.A. at the end of the second world war).

Reaction of olefins with carbon monoxide and hydrogen, leading directly to primary alcohols with one more carbon than the initial olefin (discovered in Germany in 1938).

High temperature substitutive chlorination of olefins, leading to syn-thetic glycerol and to new intermediates for the plastics industry (dis-covered in America, 1936 to 1939).

Methane from natural gas was used as a source of petroleum chemicals for making synthesis gas (carbon monoxide and hydrogen) and hydrogen, by reaction with water (methane-steam process) or with oxygen (methane-oxygen process). Methane from natural gas thus became the raw material for synthetic methyl alcohol and for synthetic ammonia. The synthetic ammonia synthesis had been worked out in Germany just before the first world war and synthetic methyl alcohol followed in the 1920's, both from coal. Similarly the methane-steam and methane-oxygen processes were European developments using by-product methane from coke oven gas separation or from coal hydrogenation.

In America methane has now largely displaced coal as the raw material for synthetic methyl alcohol and ammonia. It is being used as the starting material for the synthesis of liquid fuels, using an improved method of conducting the Fischer-Tropsch process, which could give a considerable tonnage of petroleum chemicals as co-products. Toward the end of this second period, methane is being established for the manufacture of acety-lene, again using a European process of the 1930's, which used methane from coal.

Propane and butane are directly oxidised with air to a range of oxygen-ated compounds, principally formaldehyde, methyl alcohol, acetaldehyde and acetic acid. This is a development of work initiated in the 1930's, although an oxidation process of this type was first tried out in America in 1926.

At the same time as the lower paraffins were being pressed into service, the second world war led to the manufacture of aromatics from petroleum. New methods of isolating, isomerizing, and dehydrogenating petroleum naphthenes were devised on the basis of petroleum techniques. During the war, manufacture of toluene and xylene was established; since then, benzene has been added, because the growing demands of the chemical industry in the U.S.A. could not be met from the conventional source, coke-oven tar.

Simultaneously with this diversification of types of hydrocarbons, new industries were being created which turned to petroleum for many of their raw materials. These included synthetic rubbers, synthetic fibres, plastics, and detergents.

Synthetic rubber led to the development of specific petroleum routes to butadiene, from *n*-butane and 1- and 2-butenes, and to styrene, from benzene and ethylene. The techniques used were refinements of those already established by the petroleum industry for the manufacture of high octane gasoline.

The growth of synthetic fibres has led to the devising of syntheses from petroleum of the chemical intermediates required for this new industry. Leaving aside acetic anhydride from ethylene via synthetic ethyl alcohol and from propylene via acetone, already established and used for cellulose acetate in the 1930's, nylon has called for the isolation of petroleum cyclohexane and for the discovery of a route from butadiene to nylon salt; Terylene (Dacron in the United States) has led to the isolation of *p*-xylene from petroleum xylene, and the nitrile fibres require the synthesis of acrylonitrile from ethylene or acetylene.

Plastics need such a wide variety of raw materials that it is difficult to select the major petroleum chemical developments. Styrene, vinyl chloride, and polyethylene from ethylene, formaldehyde from petroleum methyl alcohol, and urea from petroleum ammonia are the chief contributions of petroleum chemicals.

Detergents, which now equal or surpass soap in demand, are based largely on petroleum; the variety of structures which confer detergent properties have led to some interesting syntheses. Alkylaryl sulphonates are made by alkylation of benzene either with chlorinated kerosene or with a highly-branched olefin made from propylene. Long chain olefins for secondary sulphates are made from paraffin wax. Secondary alkyl sulphonates are made by direct sulphonation of paraffins with sulphur dioxide and chlorine, a reaction discovered in America in the 1930's.

3. Other countries

Aside from one or two relatively minor operations, there was no petroleum chemicals industry outside America until after the second world war. The potential importance of the new chemical industries based on petroleum, augmented by the growth of home oil refineries, then led to the creation of petroleum chemical industries in several European countries and in Canada. In the few years available, it is not surprising that most of these countries are still in the first stage of American development; that is to say, their industries are directed primarily to making and using the lower olefins.

There are two factors which distinguish operations in some of these countries from American practice. In the first place, in the absence of natural gas, petroleum chemicals have to be made from imported liquid hydrocarbon fractions. Secondly, compared with America, many of the European countries are well placed on aromatic compounds as by-products from coal processes and the relative price structure does not make manufacture of aromatics from imported oil attractive.

The United Kingdom has, at present, the largest petroleum chemicals industry outside America. It is based mainly on imported liquid fractions and is directed largely to the manufacture and use of olefins. The position in France is similar, but in Italy, with new natural gas discoveries and no coal, manufacture of chemicals from methane is of equal importance. Germany is basing her petroleum chemicals industry both on the lower olefins and on her limited but growing supplies of natural gas. Canada can hardly be termed the most recent entrant to this field, as she participated in the manufacture of synthetic rubber from petroleum during and since the second world war. The postwar developments so far have, however, been on the European pattern.

4. By-products

The main by-products from petroleum refining are sulphur compounds, oxygen compounds, and nitrogen compounds.

The principal oxygen compounds are naphthenic acids and phenols. These are present only in particular crude oils in significant amounts. Naphthenic acids were found in considerable quantities in the early days of the oil industry in crude oils from Roumania and from Russia. These have been used in Europe before the first world war. By-product petroleum cresylic acids have been industrial products in America since the 1930's.

Nitrogen compounds are present only in certain crude petroleums and are not of industrial significance.

The main interest in sulphur compounds used to be in their removal in order to upgrade the quality of petroleum fractions. In recent years the recovery of sulphur from the hydrogen sulphide present in natural and refinery gases has reached the status of a major industry. The processes used employ methods worked out in the nineteenth century in the coal gas industry. In the petroleum industry, the method was first used in Iran before the second world war; it is now being adopted throughout the world, partly because of the sulphur shortage and partly to avoid effluent nuisance.

Industrial sulphur compounds also occur at the other end of the refining industry, in working up of white oils and related products. Manufacture involves drastic treatment with sulphuric acid, giving rise to sulphonic acids, which are useful on account of their surface active properties. They have been known for many years, but their constitution is still uncertain.

5. Alternative routes to petroleum chemicals

The importance of alternative routes to petroleum chemicals was discussed on p. 1. The position on the more important chemicals is summarised in Table 2.

TABLE 2

Alternative routes to principal petroleum chemicals

Chemical	Petroleum source	Alternative sources (Europe, except where stated)
Methane	Natural gas	Coal, as by-product of separation of coke oven gases (1920–30) or of coal hydrogenation (1930–40)
Ammonia	Methane	From coal via producer gas (1910–20)
Methyl alcohol	Methane	From coal via producer gas (1920–30); from methane (from coal) by methane-steam and methane-oxygen processes (1930–40)
Ethylene	Pyrolysis of gaseous or liquid hydrocarbons	Dehydration of ethyl alcohol (original route). By-product in fractional distillation of coke oven gas (1925–35). Hydrogenation of acetylene (1940–45)
Acetylene	Methane	Calcium carbide (original route). Methane from coal by partial combustion and by arc process (1935–45)
Ethylene glycol	Ethylene	From ethylene made as above (1925). In America from coal via carbon monoxide and formaldehyde (1935–40)
Ethyl alcohol	Ethylene	Fermentation of molasses (original route)
Acetaldehyde	Synthetic ethyl alcohol. Co-product of paraffin gas oxidation	Fermentation ethyl alcohol or acetylene from carbide (1900–10)
Acetone	Propylene	Wood distillation (original process). Pyrolysis of acetic acid (1920–30) or by acetylene-steam reaction (1930–40)
Glycerol	Propylene	By-product of soap manufacture (original process)
Butadiene	1- and 2-Butenes, synthetic ethyl alcohol	Ethyl alcohol (1915); acetaldehyde via 1:3-butanediol (1920–30); acetylene and formaldehyde from coal via 1:4-butanediol (1940–45); from 2:3-butanediol by fermentation (1940–45)
Aromatic hydrocarbons	Aromatic rich fractions, naphthene rich fractions	By-products of coal tar distillation

CHAPTER 2

THE SOURCES OF PETROLEUM HYDROCARBONS

THE starting materials for the petroleum chemicals industry are obtained from crude petroleum in one of two general ways. They may be present as such in crude petroleum and concentrated or isolated by purely physical methods such as distillation, solvent extraction or crystallisation. The second source is the chemical operations now carried out in petroleum refineries on an ever increasing scale, by which saturated and aromatic hydrocarbons present only in traces in crude are synthesised as main products, and unsaturated hydrocarbons not initially present at all are manufactured as intermediates.

1. Composition of crude petroleum

Crude petroleum consists essentially of mixtures of paraffinic, naphthenic and aromatic hydrocarbons. The naphthenic hydrocarbons are based on cyclopentane and on cyclohexane or on fused C_5 and C_6 rings. There is no evidence that cyclopropane, cyclobutane, cycloheptane or higher rings are present in crude petroleum. Olefins, diolefins and acetylenes are absent. The aromatic hydrocarbons are mainly benzene derivatives; naphthalene, tetralin and their substituted derivatives have been isolated in a few cases.

Crude petroleums may be broadly classified as paraffinic, naphthenic or aromatic depending upon the type of hydrocarbon which preponderates. It should be made clear as early as possible that in the higher fractions of petroleum all these hydrocarbon types are present together, sometimes in the same molecule. In general, the aromatic and naphthenic hydrocarbons are almost invariably substituted by paraffinic side chains, and in addition the two ring types may co-exist as condensed or linear rings in the same molecule.

This classification omits the asphaltic crudes, a petroleum rich in asphalts or bitumens, usually associated with aromatic hydrocarbons; actually crudes are usually mixtures of two or more of these four fundamental types. Sachanen[1] suggests the classification as shown in Table 3.

Crude petroleum varies widely in composition from country to country, from state to state and even in some cases from adjoining wells. If a broad generalisation could be attempted, we may say that American petroleum is predominantly paraffinic; Russia and Roumania produce mixed aromatic-naphthenic types, Iran a paraffin-naphthene type, Borneo aromatic. Petroleum from the English field at Eakring is a paraffinic-base type with

---

[1] Sachanen, 'Chemical Constituents of Petroleum', *Reinhold*, 1945.

a high content of paraffin wax[2] and so on. This picture is an over-simplification, as Table 3 indeed shows; fuller information on composition of crude petroleums may be found in the literature.[1,3]

TABLE 3

Classification of crude petroleums

Class	Composition	Examples where produced
Paraffinic .	75% or more paraffins or paraffinic side chains	Pennsylvania
Naphthenic .	70% or more naphthenes	Russia (Emba-Dossor)
Aromatic .	50% or more aromatics	—
Asphaltic .	60% or more resins or asphalts	Bitumen of natural asphalt
Paraffinic-naphthenic	Paraffins, 60–70%; naphthenes at least 20%	Many American crudes
Paraffinic-naphthenic-aromatic	Per cent of paraffins, naphthenes, aromatics about equal	Russia (Maikop)
Naphthenic-aromatic	Naphthenes and aromatics, each at least 35%	California
Naphthenic-aromatic-asphaltic	Naphthenes, aromatics and asphaltic compounds each at least 25%	California
Aromatic-asphaltic	Aromatics and asphaltic compounds each at least 35%	Russia (Ural)

Crude petroleum consists essentially of hydrocarbons but small amounts of organic sulphur, nitrogen and oxygen compounds are present in appreciable amounts in certain petroleums (see Chapter 21). Crude petroleum is always associated with natural gas, the lower gaseous paraffins (see p. 19).

The primary separation of crude petroleum is carried out by distillation; the liquid products boil over a wide range of temperature and consist of no single individual compound. The main fractions are:

Fraction					*Boiling Range*
Petrol	.	.	.	.	20–200° c.
Kerosene		.	.	.	about 175–275° c.
Gas oil	.		.	.	about 200–400° c.
Lubricating oil		.	.	.	about 300° c.; distillable only *in vacuo*.
Fuel oil	.		.	.	—
Pitch or coke	.		.	.	—

The composition of the fractions of petroleum boiling up to about 100° c. is known with some accuracy, but above that temperature, although the simpler aromatics can be identified, the increasing number of isomers present makes full analysis impossible. For determining the proportions of

---

[2] Dickie, *Times Trade and Engineering*, Nov. 1946, p. 8.

[3] 'Science of Petroleum', *Oxford University Press*, Vol. 2, 1938, p. 839; Vol. 5, part 1, 1950, p. 1.

paraffins, naphthenes and aromatics in the higher fractions of petroleum, reliance is usually placed on Waterman's method.[4] This is based upon measurement of the aromatic content by hydrogenation or by determination of aniline point; after hydrogenation, the ratio of naphthenes to paraffins is determined by specific gravity and refractive index measurement. This method does not give an absolute measure of the hydrocarbons present but is the best method so far devised.

Average composition by this method of 'straight run' fractions of petrol (*i.e.*, petrol isolated by distillation and not prepared by heat treatment or other chemical processing of petroleum) of end point 150–200° c. is:

Hydrocarbon type	% by vol.
Aromatics	6–22
Naphthenes	20–50
Paraffins	40–75

In the majority of cases, the composition of the petrol corresponds to the composition of the crude petroleum, a highly paraffinic crude giving a highly paraffinic petrol. The percentage of aromatics and naphthenes usually increases as the boiling range of the petrol fraction increases. This is illustrated in Table 4, which gives the distribution of hydrocarbons in a Pennsylvania straight run petrol.

TABLE 4

Chemical constitution of Pennsylvania petrol

Fraction ° c.	Aromatics % by vol.	Naphthenes % by vol.	Paraffins % by vol.
38–70	0	3	97
70–100	4	18	76
100–150	8	22	70
above 150	12	26	62
Total fraction	7	18	75

Petrol contains hydrocarbons from C_4 to about C_{12}, kerosene, from C_9 to about C_{16}. The hydrocarbons in gas oil are probably in the range C_{15} to C_{25}. Waterman analysis of gas oils boiling in the range 260–382° c. gave 43–74 per cent paraffins, 19–35 per cent naphthenes, and 7–22 per cent aromatics. Lubricating oils have a molecular range of 300 to 1,000, *i.e.*, about C_{20} to C_{70}; this fraction contains paraffin wax and aromatics which are usually removed during the refining processes. Lubricating oils are hydrogen deficient and are therefore of fused ring type. A typical paraffin base lubricating oil (Viscosity Index, 100) analysed 75 per cent paraffins (presumably as side chains) and 25 per cent naphthene and aromatic rings. A naphthenic base lubricating oil (Viscosity Index, − 30) analysed 45 per cent paraffins and 55 per cent rings. In both cases, the paraffin chains are probably branch chain and not straight chain.

---

[4] Waterman *et al.*, *J. Inst. Pet. Tech.*, 1935, **21**, 661, 701.

Most attention has been directed to the chemical constituents of petrol both because of their importance from the standpoint of octane number and because of the comparative simplicity of the problem. Detailed studies of many American, Russian and other petrols have been described in the literature by various workers. We shall limit ourselves here to the hydrocarbons identified in an American depentanised straight run petrol from Ponca City (for boiling points of the lower hydrocarbons, see Appendix 1).

TABLE 5

Hydrocarbons present in Ponca City petrol

Hydrocarbon	% in crude (by vol.)
1. *Paraffins*—	
2 : 3-Dimethylbutane	0·06
2-Methylpentane	0·12
3-Methylpentane	0·25
n-Hexane	0·7
2 : 2-Dimethylpentane	0·04
2-Methylhexane	0·35
3-Methylhexane	0·2
n-Heptane	1·1
2-Methylheptane	0·5
n-Octane	1·0
2 : 6-Dimethylheptane	0·1
2 : 3-Dimethylheptane	0·05
4-Methyloctane	0·06
2-Methyloctane	0·2
3-Methyloctane	0·06
n-Nonane	1·0
n-Decane	0·8
2. *Naphthenes*—	
Methylcyclopentane	0·25
Cyclohexane	0·35
1 : 1-Dimethylcyclopentane	0·05
trans-1 : 3-Dimethylcyclopentane	0·2
trans-1 : 2-Dimethylcyclopentane	0·3
Methycyclohexane	0·3
trans-1 : 3-Dimethylcyclohexane	0·15
Ethylcyclohexane	0·1
1 : 2 : 4-Trimethylcyclohexane	0·1
3. *Aromatics*—	
Benzene	0·08
Toluene	0·3
Ethylbenzene	0·03
p-Xylene	0·04
m-Xylene	0·12
o-Xylene	0·22
Isopropylbenzene	0·03
1 : 3 : 5-Trimethylbenzene	0·02
1 : 2 : 4-Trimethylbenzene	0·2
1 : 2 : 3-Trimethylbenzene	0·06

2. Natural gas

In favoured localities, natural gas is available in vast quantities from many of the oil wells producing crude petroleum; certain wells actually are gas wells, producing no oil at all but only natural gas. Natural gas consists of methane and the higher paraffins up to C_5, associated in some areas with small amounts of hydrogen sulphide, nitrogen and helium. Statistics of production and outlets in the United States of America and analyses of some natural gases are given in Tables 6 and 7.

TABLE 6

Production and uses for natural gas in the United States

		Year			
		1944	1948	1951	1954
1. *Production*, long tons × 10^6 . . .		80	111	161	191
2. *Outlets*					
Field uses . . . . . %		23	20	19	18
Heating (domestic and commercial) %		21	24	26	29
Carbon black . . . . %		10	9	6	3
Industrial outlets, including chemicals %		46	43	44	46

The tonnage figures given in this table are based on 48·5 lb./1,000 ft³ natural gas. The percentage figures for 1948, 1951 and 1954 do not add up to 100% because of storage and transmission losses.

The weight of natural gas produced in the United States in 1954 compares with their production of 600,000,000 long tons of coal and about 700,000,00 long tons of crude petroleum.

TABLE 7

Analyses of natural gases[5]

Type	'Dry' gas	'Wet' gas	Sweet gas	Sour gas	From Panhandle	Iran N.P. gas
CH_4 . .	99·2	87·0	73·1	58·7	91·8	81·0
C_2H_6 . .	—	4·1	23·8	16·5	2·9	16·0
C_3H_8 . .	—	2·6	—	9·9	2·0	—
C_4H_{10} . .	—	2·0	—	5·0	0·9	—
C_5H_{12} . .	—	3·4	—	3·5	0·5	—
N_2 . .	0·6	—	2·8	—	1·8	1·4
O_2 . .	—	—	—	—	0·3	—
H_2S . .	—	—	—	6·4	—	0·9
CO_2 . .	0·2	1·1	—	—	—	0·7

The analyses for various natural gases are taken more or less at random and relate mainly to American natural gases. These consist essentially of methane with varying amounts of the higher paraffins; the amount of these higher paraffins in the natural gas as used depends in part on how efficiently they have been removed in the preliminary operations, but certain natural gases consist solely of methane.

From the tonnage point of view, the major constituent of natural gas

[5] Bowen, 'Science of Petroleum', *Oxford University Press*, Vol. 2, 1938, p. 1500.

is methane. Ethane is usually obtained mixed with methane or with propane; its separation in the pure form presents the same sort of problem as the separation of ethylene from cracked gas, the gas obtained as a by-product in cracking processes (see Chapter 7, p. 110).

Propane and the butanes can be isolated from natural gas by scrubbing with a petroleum oil under pressure, followed by fractional distillation, also under pressure. These gases are referred to as LPG ('liquefied petroleum gases'). Consumption and uses for liquefied petroleum gases in the United States are summarised in Table 8.[6]

TABLE 8

Consumption and uses of liquefied petroleum gases in the United States, 1945–54

	Year			
	1945	1948	1951	1954
	long tons × 10^6			
Total consumption　.　.　.　.　.	2·7	5·8	9·0	11·0
	%			
Usage—				
Domestic and motor fuel .　.　.	42	53	58	63
Industrial and miscellaneous　.　.	20	10	6	7
Gas manufacture　.　.　.　.　.	4	9	7	4
Synthetic rubber　.　.　.　.　.	16	8	9	6
Other chemical outlets　.　.　.	18	20	20	20

The chemical outlets for these lower paraffins from natural gas are dealt with in detail in the next four chapters. For chemicals, ethane is used almost wholly for making ethylene by pyrolysis. Propane is used for making ethylene and propylene by pyrolysis and oxygenated products by air oxidation. Of the butanes, about two-thirds are dehydrogenated to butenes and the remaining third oxidised with air.[7] Natural gas is a source of these chemicals only near the point of production or within the economic limits of piping.

3. Separation of crude petroleum

The first separation of crude petroleum into the six broad cuts referred to on p. 17 is only a very rough fractionation. A simplified flowsheet of this 'primary distillation' is given in Fig. 1.

---

[6] Benz, Tucker and de Voe, *Pet. Proc.*, 1955, **10**, 198.
[7] *Chem. Week*, June 12, 1954, p. 89.

The first step is called stabilisation, the removal of some of the C_4 hydrocarbons and the whole of the C_3 and lighter fractions which would confer an undesirably high vapour pressure on the petrol fraction. This operation is usually carried out under a moderate pressure, say 3–5 atma. From this operation, a liquid distillate of C_5 and lighter hydrocarbons is obtained; this can itself be stabilised in a second fractionation to give the *n*- and isopentanes.

The next operation is distillation at atmospheric pressure. From this column, several side-streams are taken off, as shown. The bottoms from this column are further separated by vacuum distillation, sometimes in the

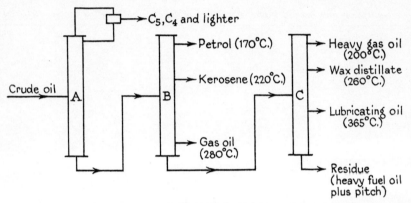

FIGURE 1

Primary distillation of crude oil

presence of steam, to isolate distillable but high boiling fractions from the undistillable heavy residues. The temperatures at which the various fractions may be taken off are indicated; for the vacuum column, the temperatures are at the operating pressure of the column (50–75 mm.).[8]

This primary distillation gives mixtures, as would be expected from the method of carrying it out. The simpler hydrocarbons present can be isolated from the first fractions by using refined and improved methods of distillation.

The boiling points of the lower paraffins, naphthenes and aromatics are given in Appendix 1. Most of the hydrocarbons listed in these classes have already been identified in one source or another of crude petroleum. Derivatives of cyclopropane and cyclobutane are omitted since there is no evidence of their presence in crude petroleum, or for that matter in any refinery product.

All the paraffin hydrocarbons up to and including C_5 can be separated from one another by fractional distillation, but above C_5, the increasing

---

[8] Condensed from Gruse and Stevens, 'Chemical Technology of Petroleum', *McGraw-Hill*, 1942.

number of isomers and the presence of naphthenes and aromatics make simple distillation ineffective. It is worth while emphasising the point that, in ascending any homologous series of hydrocarbons, the increasing number of isomers makes the isolation of the higher members by simple physical methods almost impossible. The individual complex hydrocarbon has to be built up from simpler units, which is one reason why the lower paraffins and olefins are so important in the petroleum chemicals industry.

Neglecting geometrical isomers, the number of possible isomers in the three series under consideration is as follows:

TABLE 9

Number of isomers in the paraffin, naphthene and aromatic series

Total number of carbon atoms	Paraffins	Naphthenes (C_5 and C_6 rings only)	Aromatics (Benzene rings only)
1	1	—	—
2	1	—	—
3	1	—	—
4	2	—	—
5	3	1	—
6	5	2	1
7	9	5	1
8	18	14	4
9	35	38	8
10	75	—	22
20	366,319	—	—
30	$4 \cdot 1 \times 10^9$	—	—

We therefore have to consider in detail the methods of separating petroleum hydrocarbons.

SEPARATION OF HYDROCARBONS

The methods of separation used or available can be divided into the following types:

(*i*) Liquid-vapour systems. This covers distillation methods which are the most widely used, and absorption in liquid solvents.

(*ii*) Liquid-liquid systems such as solvent extraction.

(*iii*) Liquid-solid systems. This includes solid adsorption and crystal- lisation processes.

(*iv*) Solid-vapour systems. This covers the two new adsorption pro- cesses, hypersorption and molecular sieves.

Compound formation, which is not a physical process, is used only with reactive hydrocarbons. The only important example is as one of the methods of separating butadiene (Chapter 12, p. 203) but it has also been fully considered for ethylene (Chapter 7, p. 103) and for acetylene.

(i) Liquid-vapour systems

This comprises straight fractional distillation, superfractionation, modified distillation methods, and absorption in liquid solvents.

An example of the sizes of columns and column conditions usual in the petroleum industry is the method used for separation of propane and the butanes from the C_2–C_5 liquefied condensate from primary distillation.[9]

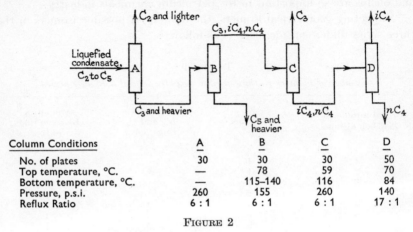

Column Conditions	A	B	C	D
No. of plates	30	30	30	50
Top temperature, °C.	—	78	59	70
Bottom temperature, °C.	—	115–140	116	84
Pressure, p.s.i.	260	155	260	140
Reflux Ratio	6 : 1	6 : 1	6 : 1	17 : 1

FIGURE 2

Separation of propane and the butanes

The C_5 fraction can be separated in a similar column to give isopentane and *n*-pentane of 99% purity. This lay-out gives an indication of the operating conditions and the scope of separation used in the petroleum industry. These standard methods are inadequate for separation of hydrocarbons above C_5. For these higher hydrocarbons, more powerful methods are now used.

In the first place, straight fractional distillation has been improved by provision of columns containing between fifty and a hundred or more theoretical plates (super-fractionation). By this means, hydrocarbons boiling as close as 3° c. apart can be separated so long as they do not form mixtures with abnormal vapour pressures; if the boiling points are closer than 3° c., fractionation is not practicable. An account of the large scale application of super-fractionation to the preparation of 'isohexane' and 'isoheptane' concentrates is given by Birch, Docksey and Dove;[10] these concentrates do not consist entirely of one individual hydrocarbon but are narrow boiling mixtures, substantially freed from the normal paraffins.

Finer methods of separation depend upon selecting conditions of operation to produce deviations from Raoult's Law, so as to create an appreciable difference in the relative volatilities of the compounds to be separated.

⁹ From Harts, *Nat. Pet. News*, 14 May, 1941.
¹⁰ *J. Inst. Pet.*, 1946, **32,** 167.

Relative volatility is a direct measure of the ease of separation of components by a distillation process. Where Raoult's Law is obeyed, the relative volatility is proportional to the vapour pressures of the components. If two components boil at the same temperature and obey Raoult's Law, they are inseparable by distillation.

In practice, however, Raoult's Law is not obeyed exactly and deviations may be increased artificially by the methods of azeotropic distillation or extractive distillation. The relative volatility of paraffins to aromatics boiling at the same temperature may be increased from one to two or even three, which will easily permit separation by fractionation.

In the typical azeotropic distillation, a third component is added to a close boiling binary mixture. This third component forms minimum boiling azeotropes with one or both of the components of the binary mixture, giving an increase in the difference of boiling points; it therefore alters the relative volatilities of the two original components to one another.

The liquids usually chosen to form azeotropes with hydrocarbons belong to the polar classes of compounds, *e.g.*, amines, alcohols, ketones, water; aromatics sometimes form azeotropes themselves with paraffins and naphthenes. The azeotrope forming liquid increases the relative volatilities of hydrocarbons in the order paraffins > naphthenes > olefins > diolefins > aromatics. This is one way of extending the scope of fractional distillation and of separating hydrocarbons of the same boiling range into five constitutional classes.

There are two types of azeotrope forming liquids (entrainers), termed non-selective entrainers and selective entrainers. Methyl alcohol forms azeotropes with all the paraffins, naphthenes, olefins and aromatics boiling in the range 100–110° c. and is a non-selective entrainer. Methyl ethyl ketone forms azeotropes with the paraffins, naphthenes and olefins but not with toluene; it is therefore a selective entrainer for the separation of toluene.

Choice of entrainer is limited by the following considerations. It should boil 0–30° c. below the hydrocarbon to be separated so that the difference in boiling points between the azeotropes, or between the azeotrope and the non-azeotrope forming hydrocarbon, is adequate to serve as the driving force of separation. It should give large deviations from Raoult's Law and give minimum boiling azeotropes with one or more of the hydrocarbons to be removed. In addition, it has to be soluble in the hydrocarbon at the distillation temperature and for a few degrees below, inexpensive, stable, unreactive, and easy to separate from the hydrocarbons with which it forms azeotropes. The two usual methods of separation are by partial immiscibility at low temperature, *i.e.*, separation into two phases, or by washing out with water.

Extractive distillation consists of fractionation in presence of a selective solvent which has a much higher boiling point than the hydrocarbon mixture to be separated and which is added to alter the ratio of the relative volatilities. This gives one more degree of freedom than azeotropic distillation, since the phase composition is not fixed solely by temperature and pressure, permitting the concentration of the solvent to be maintained at the desired optimum.

As with azeotropic distillation, the selective solvent is usually a polar compound; it may be one of several hundred organic compounds, including most of the solvents used for refining kerosene or lubricating oil. The solvents commonly employed are phenol, acetone and furfural; aniline is

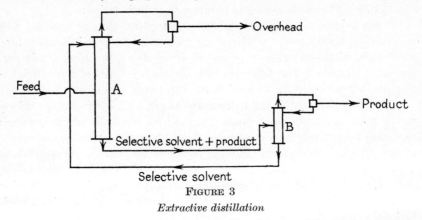

FIGURE 3
Extractive distillation

sometimes used. The basic flowsheet of extractive distillation is given in Fig. 3.

The selective solvent is fed into the top of a conventional fractionating column, A, into the middle of which the feed is introduced. This solvent passes down from plate to plate, extracting the feed component of lowest relative volatility (aromatics, etc.). The overhead is freed of this component. From the bottom of column A a mixture of the selective solvent and the less volatile component passes to a small column, B, from which the product hydrocarbon is taken overhead and the selective solvent recycled to the head of the main fractionating column, A. The selective solvent therefore is never taken overhead.

Extractive distillation has been used for the separation of aromatics from naphthenes, etc., the separation of naphthenes from paraffins, and the separation of diolefins from olefins.

For example, the relative volatility of *n*-heptane (b.p. 98·4° c.) to methylcyclohexane (b.p. 100·3° c.) is normally 1·08, but in presence of 92 mol per cent aniline it is raised to 1·52. Similarly, the relative volatility of *n*-hexane (b.p. 68·8 c.) to methylcyclopentane (b.p. 71·9° c.) is 1·10; in presence of 80 mol per cent aniline, this is raised to 1·45. The azeotrope between cyclohexane and benzene can be resolved and pure cyclohexane obtained overhead by extractive distillation with more than 100 mol per cent aniline. Examples of extractive distillation are given in Chapter 7, p. 117 (Separation of C_4 hydrocarbons) and Chapter 12, p. 200 (Separation of butadiene).

General articles bearing on the development and relative advantages of extractive and azeotropic distillation are by Benedict and Rubin,[11] Colburn and Schoenborn[12] and Griswold, Andres, van Berg and Kasch.[13]

Absorption of the more soluble constituents of hydrocarbon gas mixtures in solvent liquids, usually higher hydrocarbon mixtures, is used as an alternative method in certain separations, such as in the concentration of ethane and propane from natural gas. The solvent oil is introduced at the

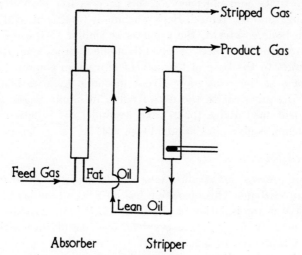

FIGURE 4
Liquid vapour absorption

head of the absorption column, and the 'fat oil' from the base of this column passes to the desorption column where the dissolved gases are disengaged, the lean oil from the base of this column being cooled and recycled to the head of the first column (Fig. 4).

The separation which this method gives can be improved by returning some of the product gas from the head of the desorption column to the base of the absorption column where it helps to strip out any stripped gas dissolved in the 'fat oil'; it functions in the same way as provision of reflux in fractional distillation.

(ii) Liquid-liquid systems

The standard method here is solvent extraction, first used in the petroleum refining industry to remove harmful aromatic material from kerosene

[11] *Trans. Amer. Inst. Chem. Eng.*, 1945, **41**, 353.
[12] *Trans. Amer. Inst. Chem. Eng.*, 1945, **41**, 421.
[13] *Ind. Eng. Chem.*, 1946, **38**, 65.

and lubricating oil. The method is equally applicable to the lower molecular weight hydrocarbons in petrol, as it is nearly independent of molecular weight and boiling point. Low temperatures are required to give two liquid phases. The solvents used include sulphur dioxide, nitrobenzene, di-2-chloroethyl ether, furfural and phenol; propane is also employed. Solvent extraction gives an extract (hydrocarbon soluble in solvent) and a raffinate (hydrocarbon relatively insoluble in solvent) in which the C : H ratio is respectively high and low. That is to say, aromatics can be extracted from mixtures with paraffins and naphthenes; this is the usual technical separation.

The selectivity and efficiency of this process has been improved by 'back washing' and by 'reflux'. Back washing is treatment of the raffinate with a high boiling solvent, the same as or similar to the main solvent, which removes the last traces of solvent-soluble hydrocarbon. Reflux is recycling extract to the base of the solvent extraction column to strip out the last trace of the relatively solvent insoluble hydrocarbon from the extract; it is equivalent to the use of reflux in liquid-vapour absorption processes mentioned above (p. 27). An example, the isolation of toluene from petroleum, is given in Chapter 14, p. 234.

(iii) Liquid-solid systems

The main process is crystallisation, used for isolation of relatively high melting hydrocarbons. This operation has long been familiar in the petroleum industry in the isolation of paraffin wax. It is used in the petroleum chemicals industry for isolating p-xylene from admixture with other C_8 aromatics (Chapter 14, p. 237).

Adsorption on a solid from the liquid state is a well-known physical process. It is used in one petroleum chemical process, the Arosorb process, in which aromatic hydrocarbons are adsorbed on silica gel from mixtures with paraffins, and subsequently desorbed. An example is given in Chapter 14, page 237.

A different type of liquid-solid separation is that known in the petroleum industry as extractive crystallisation; it is dependent on formation of the so-called inclusion compounds.

About 1940, it was discovered by Bengen in Germany that straight chain paraffins formed solid adducts with urea in methyl alcohol solution whilst branch chain paraffins of the same and similar molecular weight did not.[14, 15] The separation depended upon the fact that there was sufficient room inside the crystal molecules of urea for straight chain paraffins, but branch chain paraffins were too big. These inclusion compounds are not compounds in the conventional sense; there is no definite ratio between

---

[14] Bengen, *D.R.P. Anm.*, OZ,12438 (March 18, 1940).
[15] Schlenk, *Angew. Chem.*, 1950, **62**, 299; *Ann.*, 1949, **565**, 204.

the number of urea molecules and the number of paraffin molecules, but the adducts contain about 0·65–0·7 mols of urea for each CH_2 group in the hydrocarbon. The inclusion compounds can be separated by filtration and are readily decomposed by heating, by dilution with water and so on. This method permits separation of straight chain paraffins from C_6 to over C_{20} from complex mixtures.[16] It has been developed to the pilot stage; the method is not limited to urea as the including compound or to methyl alcohol as the solvent. Thus thiourea forms inclusion compounds with highly branch chain paraffins and with cyclic compounds.[17]

This process, though of considerable potential interest, has not so far passed beyond the pilot trial stage for chemicals.

For purifying hydrocarbon fractions, a plant is being built in Germany to remove paraffins from spindle oil using urea with a capacity of 50 tons/day spindle oil. In the process equal parts of charge stock, methylene dichloride and aqueous urea saturated at 70° c. are mixed at 35–40° c.[18] A similar plant is under construction in America.[19]

(iv) Solid-vapour systems

This method covers only adsorption processes, which are applied to low molecular weight hydrocarbons and other light gases where condensation methods are not too easy to employ.

The two methods of interest to the petroleum chemicals industry are adsorption on charcoal and adsorption on synthetic zeolites (complex silicates).

Charcoal adsorption has been mechanised to make it continuous in the Hypersorption process. This process is illustrated in Fig. 5.

The carbon is moved continuously down the vertical reactor (the Hypersorber). At the top, it is cooled and dried; in the first section, the heavier constituents of the feed are adsorbed, the lighter constituents being discharged. Below the feed, the carbon encounters a reflux of heavier components liberated by the stripper, and intermediate constituents can be removed as a side-cut. Steaming and a stripper section, where the carbon is heated, remove the heavier constituents as the 'make'. The carbon is then elevated mechanically or by gas-lift to the top of the Hypersorber.

An example of its use in the separation of natural gas is given in Table 10.

Hypersorption has been used for separation of methane from ethane and of methane from nitrogen.[20] An example of its use for separation of

---

[16] Zimmerschied, Dinerstein, Weitkamp and Marschner, *Ind. Eng. Chem.*, 1950, **42**, 1300; Redlich, Gable, Dunlop and Millar, *J. Amer. Chem. Soc.*, 1950, **72**, 4153.

[17] Redlich, Gable, Beason and Millar, *J. Amer. Chem. Soc.*, 1950, **72**, 4161.

[18] *Chemische Industrie*, English Edition, 1955 (No. 2), p. 67.

[19] *Chem. Week*, 4 August, 1956, p. 82.

[20] Berg, *Trans. Amer. Inst. Chem. Eng.*, 1946, **42**, 665; Berg, Fairfield, Imhoff and Multer, *Pet. Refiner*, 1949, **28** (**11**), 113.

ethylene from the methane rich overhead in ethylene fractionation is given in Chapter 7, p. 103.

Adsorption on synthetic zeolites is the most recent solid-vapour process. The zeolites can be made to have graded size pores so that molecules of

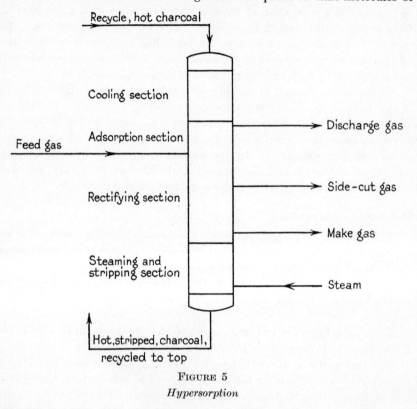

Recycle, hot charcoal

Cooling section

Feed gas → Adsorption section → Discharge gas

Rectifying section → Side-cut gas

→ Make gas

Steaming and stripping section ← Steam

Hot, stripped, charcoal, recycled to top

FIGURE 5
Hypersorption

different sizes can be separated by appropriate choice of adsorbent – a method first adumbrated by R. M. Barrer in England and rather resembling in results the technique of extractive crystallisation described on p. 28.

TABLE 10
Separation of natural gas by hypersorption

Gas	Feed % by vol.	Discharge % by vol.	Side-cut % by vol.	Make % by vol.
CH_4 . . .	78·1	81·5	—	—
C_2H_6 . . .	13·4	18·3	0·4	—
C_3H_8 . . .	6·9	0·2	96·4	0·8
C_4H_{10} . .	1·3	—	2·9	81·1
C_5's + . . .	0·3	—	0·3	16·1

Both these adsorption methods have the potentiality of separating molecules of the same number of carbon atoms but in practice neither of them can do it. They handle only molecules of three or less carbon atoms; and it so happens that the C_2 hydrocarbons have about the same size and do not differ very much in boiling point or adsorbability. The separation between them which can be achieved by adsorption methods is indicated in Table 11.[21]

TABLE 11

Adsorption of C_2 gases at 20° C. and 100 mm.

	C_2H_6	C_2H_4	C_2H_2
	wt. % adsorbed		
'Type 4A' molecular sieve .	3·8	7·8	7·7
Activated charcoal . .	5·9	4·8	3·5
Silica gel	0·7	2·4	2·2

Adsorption is therefore available and is used as an additional method of separating gases of different numbers of carbon atoms; but one usually falls back on more conventional methods for isolation of a pure hydrocarbon from mixtures with hydrocarbons of the same number of carbon atoms.

4. Paraffin wax

The term wax is applied to paraffins melting above 34° c. Two types of wax derived from crude petroleum are recognised, paraffin wax and microcrystalline wax. Both are saturated aliphatic hydrocarbons, C_nH_{2n+2}.

Paraffin wax is a mixture of essentially straight chain paraffins with from eighteen to thirty-five carbon atoms, and with a setting point up to 70° c.; the usual paraffin wax melts at 40–60° c. and is a mixture of C_{22} to C_{30} normal paraffins.

Paraffin wax is usually isolated from waxy distillates (Fig. 1, p. 22) by solvent extraction or precipitation followed by sweating or emulsion de-oiling. World production, excluding U.S.S.R., of paraffin wax in 1949 was 500,000 tons. The American production in 1949 was 400,000 tons, of which about 60 per cent was used in paper coating, 7 per cent in candles, 6 per cent for chemicals and the remainder in a variety of end-uses, including fireworks, adhesives and crayons. The principal chemical outlet is in chlorinated waxes, but the wax content of waxy distillates is a source of long chain olefins for detergents, etc. (Chapter 11, p. 181); oxidation of paraffin wax to long chain fatty acids (Chapter 4, p. 60) seems now to be declining.

Microcrystalline waxes are partly branch chain paraffins; they have a higher molecular weight (400–800), higher melting range (up to 90° c.) and higher viscosity than the paraffin waxes. They are usually isolated from residues (not distillates) by methods similar to those used for paraffin wax.

[21] *Pet. Proc.*, 1955, **10**, 79.

American production is about one-quarter of that of paraffin wax. One of their principal outlets is in the paper industry; they are not used for making chemicals.

5. Other refinery products

Besides the physical processes of distillation and solvent treatment which do not alter the chemical composition of the constituents of crude petroleum, chemical processes for the treatment of petroleum or of its simple fractions have been growing in importance with the increasing demands for motor spirit over the last twenty-five years, and have been given a further impetus by requirements, during and since the war, for aviation petrol and for synthetic rubber. These chemical processes give rise to a further series of hydrocarbons not present in crude petroleum but equally important to the petroleum chemicals industry.

The principal chemical processes used are:
(1) Thermal and catalytic cracking
(2) Thermal and catalytic reforming
(3) Alkylation
(4) Isomerisation
(5) Polymerisation

In cracking, the principal reaction is the rupture of a paraffin molecule to give one molecule of an olefin and one molecule of a paraffin each containing fewer carbon atoms than the starting paraffin:

$$C_{n+m}H_{2(n+m)+2} \rightarrow C_nH_{2n} + C_mH_{2m+2}$$

Dehydrogenation takes place simultaneously with cracking and by catalytic means can be made the sole or main reaction; this gives an olefin of the same number of carbon atoms as the starting paraffin:

$$C_nH_{2n+2} \rightarrow C_nH_{2n} + H_2$$

Cracking and dehydrogenation are the principal routes to olefins, the most important raw materials of the petroleum chemicals industry. These processes are discussed in detail in Chapter 7.

Whilst in cracking processes the objective is to reduce the average number of carbon atoms in the molecules, in reforming processes, the aim is to keep the size of the molecules the same, but to alter their shape – to produce branched chain paraffins from straight chain paraffins and aromatics from naphthenes. The first reforming process, thermal reforming, was therefore carried out at moderate temperature and relatively high pressure. Catalytic reforming processes were designed originally to dehydrogenate C_6 naphthenes to aromatics but have more recently been extended to combine isomerisation of straight chain paraffins to branched chain paraffins. and of C_5 naphthenes to C_6 naphthenes with simultaneous dehydrogenation of the naphthenes to aromatics. There may also be some conversion of paraffins to aromatics.

In alkylation, an olefin, usually a butene, is alkylated with isobutane at ordinary temperatures under acid conditions using either sulphuric acid or hydrofluoric acid. The formal equation is:

$$\begin{array}{c} CH_3 \\ {\diagdown} \\ {}\diagup \\ CH_3 \end{array}\!\!C:CH_2 + \overset{\displaystyle CH_3}{\underset{\displaystyle CH_3}{\overset{|}{\underset{|}{CHCH_3}}}} \rightarrow \begin{array}{c} CH_3 \\ {\diagdown} \\ {}\diagup \\ CH_3 \end{array}\!\!CHCH_2\overset{\displaystyle CH_3}{\underset{\displaystyle CH_3}{\overset{|}{\underset{|}{CCH_3}}}}$$

Alkylation can also be carried out in the vapour phase under completely different conditions, *e.g.*, ethylene and isobutane react at high temperatures and pressures to give 2 : 2-dimethylbutane (neohexane):

$$CH_2:CH_2 + \overset{\displaystyle CH_3}{\underset{\displaystyle CH_3}{\overset{|}{\underset{|}{CHCH_3}}}} \rightarrow CH_3CH_2\overset{\displaystyle CH_3}{\underset{\displaystyle CH_3}{\overset{|}{\underset{|}{CCH_3}}}}$$

This process has now been displaced by the liquid-phase alkylation of isobutane with ethylene in presence of aluminium chloride at about 40° c. and 20–25 atm. pressure, to give 2 : 3-dimethylbutane:

$$\overset{\displaystyle CH_3\,CH_3}{\underset{}{\overset{||}{CH_3CHCHCH_3}}}$$

Aromatic hydrocarbons are alkylated somewhat more readily to give products used both for chemical synthesis and in fuels, *e.g.*,

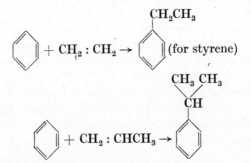

The alkylation of aromatics is dealt with in Chapter 14, p. 248 *seq.*

Isomerisation is the rearrangement of *n*-paraffins to isoparaffins under the influence of aluminium chloride or other type of Friedel-Crafts catalyst, *e.g.*,

$$CH_3CH_2CH_2CH_3 \rightleftharpoons CH_3CH\!\!\begin{array}{c} {\diagup}CH_3 \\ {\diagdown}CH_3 \end{array}$$

Isomerisation is applied technically to *n*-butane, *n*-pentane and *n*-hexane; it can be carried out either in the liquid phase or in the vapour phase at moderate temperature and pressure. Both isomerisation and alkylation are very important reactions for the oil industry; with the exception of isomerisation between cyclopentanes and cyclohexanes (Chapter 13, p. 220), and processes for making specific xylenes, the hydrocarbons made by these reactions have not yet found outlets in the chemical industry.

Polymerisation is the self-combination of two or more molecules of an olefin to give an olefin of higher molecular weight. In the petroleum industry, it has been used for isooctane from isobutene via diisobutene which is subsequently hydrogenated; this route has been largely displaced by alkylation:

$$\underset{\overset{|}{\underset{CH_2}{\parallel}}}{\overset{CH_3}{\underset{|}{CH_3C}}} + \underset{\overset{|}{\underset{}{}}}{\overset{CH_3}{CH_3C : CH_2}} \rightarrow \underset{\overset{|}{\underset{CH_3}{}}}{\overset{CH_3 \quad CH_3}{CH_3CCH_2C : CH_2}} \xrightarrow{+ H_2} \underset{\overset{|}{\underset{CH_3}{}}}{\overset{CH_3 \quad CH_3}{CH_3CCH_2CHCH_3}}$$

Further information on polymerisation as a route to olefins for chemical synthesis is given in Chapter 7, p. 124.

Diolefins and acetylenes have not so far been mentioned. Diolefins are present in low concentration in the products of high temperature cracking; their isolation and *ad hoc* manufacture is dealt with in Chapter 12. Acetylene is produced in traces in cracking operations carried out at the highest temperatures, 700° c. or higher; manufacture of acetylene from hydrocarbons is discussed in Chapter 15. Substituted acetylenes are not produced in more than traces in any refinery operation; possible synthetic routes from petroleum sources are outlined on p. 272.

In considering the types of hydrocarbon made by the current processes of refinery operations, it should be underlined that these processes have been worked out to make fuels of high octane value suitable for the internal combustion engine. Different fuels are being developed for other types of prime mover such as the gas turbine.

The development of these new fuels may make other types of hydrocarbons available as by-products for chemical syntheses. The older types, for which manufacturing processes have already been established, will always be available, though not necessarily as by-products.

CHAPTER 3

SYNTHESIS AND REACTIONS OF CARBON MONOXIDE-HYDROGEN MIXTURES

1. Synthesis of carbon monoxide-hydrogen mixtures

THE manufacture of carbon monoxide-hydrogen mixtures and of the range of products obtainable from these mixtures was first established industrially starting with coal or coke. By the well-known water gas reaction:

$$C + H_2O \rightarrow CO + H_2,$$

a carbon monoxide-hydrogen mixture in which the ratio of the gases is approximately 1 : 1 is obtained. By reacting the whole or a part of this mixture with excess of steam, the carbon monoxide reduces the steam to hydrogen by the water gas shift reaction:

$$CO + H_2O \rightleftharpoons CO_2 + H_2,$$

so that, after removal of carbon dioxide, any ratio of $CO : H_2$ from pure hydrogen to the 1 : 1 ratio in water gas can be obtained.

If pure carbon monoxide is wanted, it can be isolated from water gas or from other gases containing it by standard methods, for example lique-faction and fractionation, or selective absorption under high pressure in solutions of cuprous salts such as cuprous ammonium formate-carbonate.[1] A whole range of important syntheses, such as synthetic ammonia, synthetic methyl alcohol, and coal hydrogenation, has been built up on these gas reactions.

Similar gas mixtures can be obtained from saturated hydrocarbons by two main reactions, treatment with steam at high temperatures in the presence of catalysts – the methane steam process; and partial oxidation with oxygen – the methane-oxygen process. The processes are named after methane, which is the hydrocarbon most widely used, but they can be operated with the higher paraffins. The availability of methane, and altera-tions in the relative costs of coal and oil, make these reactions of consider-able importance for the synthesis of heavy chemicals from the paraffin gases.

(a) THE METHANE STEAM PROCESS

The first stage is the reaction between the paraffin and steam; exem-plified with methane, the reactions which can occur are:

$$CH_4 + H_2O \rightleftharpoons CO + 3H_2. \quad \Delta H = + 49 \text{ k. cal.} \qquad (1)$$

followed by

$$CO + H_2O \rightleftharpoons CO_2 + H_2. \quad \Delta H = - 10 \text{ k. cal.} \qquad (2)$$

---

[1] See, *e.g.*, Thorpe, 'Dictionary of Applied Chemistry', *Longmans Green*, 4th Ed., Vol. 2, 1938, p. 345.

so that the total overall reaction may be:

$$CH_4 + 2H_2O \rightleftharpoons CO_2 + 4H_2. \quad \Delta H = + 39 \text{ k. cal.} \qquad . \quad (3)$$

The equilibrium constants for these reactions in the range 700–1,000° K. are:

for reaction (1), $\log K_1 = -\dfrac{11,600}{T} + 13\cdot1$

for reaction (2), $\log K_2 = \dfrac{1,900}{T} - 1\cdot8$

for reaction (3), $\log K_3 = -\dfrac{9,700}{T} + 11\cdot3$

The numerical values of K_1 and K_3 increase with rising temperature. K_2 decreases with rise in temperature.

For the methane steam reaction (1), the equilibrium concentration of reactants at different temperatures are given in Table 12.

TABLE 12

$CH_4 + H_2O \rightleftharpoons CO + 3H_2$. *Calculated equilibria*

Temperature ° c.	CH_4 % by vol.	H_2O % by vol.	CO % by vol.	H_2 % by vol.
500	44·9	44·9	2·6	7·7
580	31·6	31·6	9·2	27·6
635	19·8	19·8	15·1	45·3
710	8·8	8·8	20·6	61·8
835	2·2	2·2	23·9	71·7
940	0·8	0·8	24·6	73·8

This means that reaction (1) should proceed practically to completion above about 900° c. Theoretically, reaction (3) should also proceed to completion about this temperature level, but the water gas shift reaction (2) is unfavourable, and in practice the main carbon compound at high temperature is still carbon monoxide, even in presence of excess steam.

For the equilibrium in the combined reactions (1) to (3), the following gas compositions have been calculated.[2]

TABLE 13

Equilibrium compositions,† reactions (1) to (3)

Temperature ° c.	CH_4 % by vol.	CO_2 % by vol.	CO % by vol.	H_2 % by vol.
816	0·1	4·7	19·1	76·1
927	—	3·8	20·3	75·9

† Dry basis.

The methane steam process is used industrially for two purposes, the

[2] Reed, *Trans. Amer. Inst. Chem. Eng.*, 1945, **41**, 453.

manufacture of hydrogen and the manufacture of carbon monoxide-hydrogen mixtures. Where hydrogen is the objective, reaction is carried out in two stages, the water gas shift reaction being carried out subsequently to the methane steam reaction, with added steam and at lower temperatures (450–500° c.), to push the equilibrium to the right hand side. As hydrogen is wanted mainly for ammonia and for hydrogenations, it is only incidentally a source of new carbon compounds; this does not apply to carbon monoxide-hydrogen mixtures, however, and the manufacture of these gas mixtures from methane calls for further consideration.

Inspection of equation (1) and of the data in Tables 12 and 13 shows that the reaction conditions should be as follows. Pressure is adverse, since two molecules of reactant give four molecules of product. Excess of steam will tend to push the equilibrium in favour of carbon monoxide and, at low enough temperature, will give some carbon dioxide. The reaction is highly endothermic and the equilibrium moves favourably with rise in temperature. With equimolar mixtures of methane and steam, optimum temperature lies in the range 800–1,000° c.

In practice, the theoretical equilibrium is approached by the use of catalysts, of which the most common is nickel promoted with magnesia or alumina and mounted on an inert support. The reaction is believed to proceed in two steps:

$$CH_4 \rightleftharpoons C + 2H_2$$
$$C + H_2O \rightleftharpoons CO + H_2$$

This is supported by the fact that catalysts active for the methane steam process are also active for the decomposition of methane into its elements under the same working conditions.

The methane steam reaction has been operated since the early 1930's. Methane and steam were passed through a gas-fired multitubular reactor packed with catalyst, at about 870° c. and atmospheric pressure; the exit gases consisted of hydrogen and carbon monoxide with only 2 per cent unreacted methane. The catalyst was sulphur sensitive, and the feed gases had to be freed from sulphur compounds before reaction. After the methane steam stage, the carbon monoxide was converted to hydrogen and carbon dioxide by a further treatment with steam at 460° c. over a water gas catalyst (iron oxide promoted with chromium oxide and basic oxides), giving hydrogen sufficiently pure for hydrogenations after removal of carbon dioxide.[3] A later development is the operation of the methane steam process at elevated pressures (6–7 atma.).

Higher hydrocarbons can be used in place of methane, and the equilibrium is slightly more favourable. They also give a higher ratio of carbon monoxide to hydrogen, *e.g.*, with propane:

$$C_3H_8 + 3H_2O \rightleftharpoons 3CO + 7H_2 \ (CO : H_2, 1 : 2·33)$$

---

[3] Byrne, Gohr and Haslam, *Ind. Eng. Chem.*, 1932, **24**, 1129.

Reed[4] gives an account of the thermodynamics and practice of the propane-steam reaction; in this case, pure hydrogen was the objective. With the higher paraffins, there is an increased tendency to carbon formation but, nevertheless, petrol, kerosene, and even gas oil can be reacted with steam to give carbon monoxide-hydrogen mixtures. Olefins are stated to be undesirable constituents of hydrocarbon gases for the methane steam process as their presence leads to rapid fouling of the catalyst; their removal by hydrogenation has been suggested.

With a growing shortage of cheap methane from natural gas, there is an incentive to develop processes using the next cheapest by-product of oil refining, residual fuel oil. Processes are already in the development stage, but the indications are that fuel oil will be converted to synthesis gas by the combined action of oxygen and steam (see p. 40).

A modification of the methane steam process is the reaction between methane and carbon dioxide:

$$CH_4 + CO_2 \rightleftharpoons 2CO + 2H_2; \quad \Delta H = + 59 \cdot 1 \text{ k. cal.}$$

The theoretical equilibrium concentration of reactants at atmospheric pressure are given in Table 14.

TABLE 14
$CH_4 + CO_2 \rightleftharpoons 2CO + 2H_2$. *Equilibrium composition*

Temperature ° c.	CH_4 % by vol.	CO_2 % by vol.	CO % by vol.	H_2 % by vol.
450	49·4	49·4	0·6	0·6
550	43·3	43·3	6·7	6·7
650	22·8	22·8	27·2	27·2
750	7·0	7·0	43·0	43·0
850	2·0	2·0	48·0	48·0
900	1·2	1·2	48·8	48·8

The reaction therefore requires similar temperatures to the methane steam process; the same type of catalyst can be used. There are a considerable number of patents on this reaction, presumably because of the importance of flexibility of ratio of carbon monoxide and hydrogen; it is not known how extensively it is operated in practice.

(b) METHANE OXYGEN PROCESS

In this process:

$$CH_4 + \tfrac{1}{2}O_2 \rightarrow CO + 2H_2; \quad \Delta H = - 8 \cdot 5 \text{ k. cal.}$$

the heat needed to supply the endothermic requirements of the ordinary methane steam process (49 k. cal.) is supplied by burning part of the

---

[4] Reed, *Pet. Refiner*, 1945, **24**(9), 119.

methane internally instead of externally. If air is used as the source of oxygen, the products are contaminated with nitrogen which is disadvantageous for most purposes. Use of pure oxygen adds to the materials cost of the process. The reaction is considered to proceed in two well defined steps; firstly, complete reaction of the oxygen with some of the methane to give water and carbon dioxide, followed by slower reaction of the carbon dioxide and the water with the excess of methane to give mixtures of carbon monoxide and hydrogen, so that the sum total of the reactions occurring is:[5]

$$CH_4 + 2O_2 \rightarrow CO_2 + 2H_2O$$

followed by

$$CH_4 + CO_2 \rightarrow 2CO + 2H_2$$

and

$$2CH_4 + 2H_2O \rightarrow 2CO + 6H_2$$

Total

$$4CH_4 + 2O_2 \rightarrow 4CO + 8H_2$$

The partial combustion reaction is therefore usually completed under similar conditions to the methane steam and methane carbon dioxide reactions, *i.e.*, with nickel catalysts and in the temperature range, 800–1,000° c.

In one of the methods of operation in Germany,[6] methane and steam, preheated to 650° c., were mixed with oxygen and passed downwards through a reactor, the lower portion of which was packed with nickel catalyst to convert unreacted methane to carbon monoxide and hydrogen. Maximum temperature in the combustion chamber was 1,200–1,500° c.; the gases left the catalyst section at 800–900° c. Their composition was CO, 23·8 per cent, H_2, 69 per cent, CO_2, 7 per cent, CH_4, 0·2 per cent.

Alternatively, use of some oxygen in the methane steam reaction has been advocated to supply a portion of the endothermic heat of reaction. Another method suggested to overcome the problem of provision of heat is to operate on the regenerative furnace principle. The methane steam process is carried out in presence of a contact mass which functions as a heat accumulator, the heat being supplied by intermittent blasting with an oxygen or air hydrocarbon flame to raise the contact mass to a high temperature.

The process has now been established in America, taking advantage of the availability of methane under pressure. The process is operated at 8–15 atma., giving the CO—H_2 mixture at about the same pressure. This saves part or all of the cost of compression for the processes in which the products are used, the Hydrocol process which is operated at 15 atma., or synthetic ammonia which usually requires a pressure of at least 200 atma.

[5] Prettre, Eichner and Perrin, *Trans. Faraday Soc.*, 1946, **42**, 335.
[6] F.I.A.T. 426.

Where natural gas is freely available it is the logical raw material for synthesis gas from petroleum sources. Elsewhere, as mentioned on p. 38, residual fuel oil is likely to be used. As the ratio of carbon to hydrogen is increased in going from methane to fuel oil, a point is reached at which the oxygen necessary to react with the carbon is more than enough to bring the product mixture to the necessary temperature. At this point, steam is used to supply part of the total oxygen and to hold the reaction temperature at the desired level. This process has been worked out by the Texaco Development Company.[7] With methane, the reaction with oxygen under pressure is carried out at 230 p.s.i., using a ratio of natural gas to oxygen of 1 : 0·83 by volume, and gives a product gas containing 38 per cent of carbon monoxide and 60 per cent of hydrogen. With residual fuel oil the pressure is 360 p.s.i. Typical feed ratios are oil: oxygen: steam of 1 : 1 : 0·4 by weight. The reaction temperature is held at 1,100° c. to bring the residual methane down to 1 per cent. The exit gases, containing 48 per cent of carbon monoxide and 47 per cent of hydrogen, are quenched with water before the water gas shift reaction. Sulphur in the feed appears mainly as hydrogen sulphide with traces of carbon oxysulphide and carbon disulphide. It is understood that this process will shortly be in operation in Great Britain.

An earlier version of the pressure gasification of residual fuel oil with oxygen and steam involved a two stage process.[8] In the first stage, fuel oil and oxygen at 1,100–1,320° c. and 15–30 atma. in a packed reactor gave a mixture of hydrogen, carbon monoxide and carbon; in the second stage, the carbon was burnt off with steam and oxygen.

2. Outlets of carbon monoxide-hydrogen

The main outlets in the chemical industry of the gas mixtures obtained by these methods of reforming methane are the manufacture of hydrogen for synthetic ammonia, the methyl alcohol synthesis and its variants, the Fischer-Tropsch reaction and the Oxo synthesis. The last named process is dealt with in Chapter 11, p. 183; the first three are discussed here.

(a) SYNTHETIC AMMONIA

The steps in making synthetic ammonia involve preparation and purification of the gas mixture, $N_2 + 3H_2$, the synthesis step itself, and the recovery of ammonia and recycling of unchanged gases.

The carbon monoxide-hydrogen mixtures obtained from methane are converted to carbon dioxide and more hydrogen by reaction with excess steam in the water gas shift reaction. The carbon dioxide is removed by scrubbing with water at 25 atma., or with ethanolamine solutions, the mixture further compressed to operating pressure, and carbon monoxide

[7] Eastman, *Ind. Eng. Chem.*, 1956, **48**, 1118.
[8] Texaco, B.P. 672165.

removed by scrubbing with cuprous ammonium formate. The gas mixture is then ready for synthesis. Nitrogen is supplied either by liquefaction of air, in which case the oxygen can be used for partial combustion of the methane, or alternatively the methane-steam process has been operated at 700°C., so as to leave an appreciable proportion of unreacted hydrocarbon. The hot gas mixture is mixed with sufficient air to give eventually the required hydrogen-nitrogen ratio, and burnt in a combustion furnace to give mainly hydrogen and carbon monoxide. The carbon monoxide is converted to carbon dioxide and hydrogen by the water gas shift reaction, and the carbon dioxide and residual carbon monoxide removed by the usual methods, giving ammonia synthesis gas.

Synthesis gas, whether from coal or oil, is not the only source of ammonia synthesis gas. Ammonia is also made from hydrogen obtained either electrolytically, where water power is cheap, or from by-product hydrogen, *e.g.*, from petroleum refinery catalytic reformers, or from cracking of methane to thermatomic black. In those cases, the nitrogen required is usually, but not invariably, supplied from air liquefaction plants.

The synthesis step is operated at elevated temperature to obtain a reasonable rate of reaction at the cost of partial conversion.

The change of equilibrium with temperature and pressure in the reaction:

$$\tfrac{1}{2}N_2 + \tfrac{3}{2}H_2 \rightleftharpoons NH_3. \quad \Delta H_{298} = -9 \cdot 5 \text{ k. cal.}$$

is given in Table 15, which shows the percentage of ammonia by volume at equilibrium under different conditions.

TABLE 15

Variation of equilibrium of ammonia synthesis with temperature and pressure

Percentage of ammonia (by volume)

Temperature ° C.	10 atm.	100 atm.	300 atm.	1,000 atm.
	%	%	%	%
400	4	25	47	80
450	2	16	36	70
500	1	10	26	57
550	0·8	7	19	41
600	0·5	5	14	31

At low temperatures, the speed of reaction is too slow, and for technical processes one has to accept partial conversion with recycling of unreacted gases. The first processes operated adiabatically at about 250 atm. pressure. There is a 17° c. rise for each 1 per cent conversion to ammonia and the practical limit of conversion was then 8–9 per cent. Some modern processes aim to operate as far as possible adiabatically and achieve conversions as high as 40 per cent.

Most processes use promoted iron as catalyst, the usual promoters being alumina and potassium oxide.

The purified 3 : 1 hydrogen nitrogen mixture is raised to full pressure, mixed with recycle gas, passed through oil filters and cooled to condense out ammonia, then raised to temperature in heat exchangers and passed into the reactors. After reaction, the gases are cooled to $- 10°$ c to $- 20°$ c. to condense most of the ammonia, part of the gas purged to remove inerts, recompressed and mixed with make-up gas. The overall yield of most processes is about 85–90 per cent.

The salient features of the various systems are summarised in Table 16.

TABLE 16
Synthetic ammonia processes

Name	Pressure atm.	Temperature ° c.	Conversion %	Comments
Haber-Bosch .	200–250	550	8–9	—
Casale .	600	500	15–18	—
Fauser .	200	500	12–23	—
Claude .	900–1,000	500–650	40–85	No recirculation; a series of converters used
Mont-Cenis .	100	400–425	9–20	Iron cyanide catalyst

In America there has been an almost complete switchover from coke to natural gas as the source of hydrogen since the end of the war. In 1930, only 2 per cent of synthetic ammonia was made from petroleum sources; the percentage made from natural gas was 88 per cent in 1949 and 90 per cent in 1953. Natural gas or its equivalent is now the chosen raw material for synthetic ammonia wherever it is available, as in Italy, Canada and the Middle East.

Production of synthetic ammonia in the United States in 1952 was 2,000,000 tons as nitrogen; of this, some 70 per cent was used in fertilisers, 25 per cent in industrial outlets, and 5 per cent went for export or in military uses.

The industrial uses are very diverse; about half of the 25 per cent were used in explosives, plastics and acid manufacture. The remainder went into at least ten different outlets.[9]

Urea and ammonium nitrate are not included in the industrial outlets of ammonia; they require special mention because of the scale on which they are made and because they are usually made in association with

---

[9] Windisch, *Chem. Eng.*, November 1955, p. 260.

synthetic ammonia; several of the latest ammonia from natural gas plants in America have planned to convert much of their ammonia direct to urea.

Urea is made by the reactions:

$$2NH_3 + CO_2 \rightarrow NH_2COONH_4 \rightarrow NH_2CONH_2 + H_2O$$

The carbon dioxide is available from making and purifying the ammonia synthesis gas. The conversion to urea is only partial, leaving ammonia and/ or carbon dioxide to be recovered and recycled.

The reaction is carried out in the liquid phase, with excess of ammonia over that stoichiometrically necessary. Reaction conditions are 180–210° c. at 200–400 atm. pressure, with ratios of ammonia to carbon dioxide varying from 2 : 1 to 6 : 1. Reaction time is about 2 hours and conversion of ammonia per pass is from 25–50 per cent, depending on the excess used. The intermediate ammonium carbamate is extremely corrosive and the equipment is normally silver lined. The latest processes use stainless steel or even lead.[10]

The first major outlet for urea was in the synthetic plastics field; fertiliser uses are now more important and growing faster.

Ammonium nitrate is another product which, like urea, is geared to synthetic ammonia and which has expanded with the expansion of synthetic ammonia from methane. It is made by direct reaction between ammonia and aqueous nitric acid, the nitric acid being obtained by air oxidation of ammonia.

$$4NH_3 + 5O_2 \rightarrow 4NO + 6H_2O$$
$$2NO + O_2 \rightarrow 2NO_2$$
$$3NO_2 + H_2O \rightarrow 2HNO_3 + NO$$

In the oxidation step, ammonia and air containing about 10 per cent by volume of ammonia and either at 1 atma. or 6 atma. pressure is passed over a platinum rhodium gauze catalyst at 750–1,000° c. The hot gases are cooled and the nitric oxide oxidised to nitrogen dioxide with more air in a water scrubbing tower in which the nitric acid is made. The acid is obtained as an aqueous solution of 50–65 per cent strength. Ammonium nitrate is used as a component of explosives and for making nitrous oxide; its principal world outlet today is as a fertiliser.

Carbon dioxide is another by-product of synthetic ammonia; its availability on site is one of the factors leading to expansion of urea manufacture. Other outlets are for solid carbon dioxide, carbonated beverages and as an industrial refrigerant. American production in 1954 was 700,000 tons, of which a considerable proportion was made directly from petroleum or indirectly from synthetic ammonia from methane.[11]

---

[10] *Chem. Week*, Nov. 27, 1954, p. 88.
[11] *Chem. Week*, 9 April, 1955, p. 89.

(*b*) SYNTHESIS OF METHYL ALCOHOL AND HIGHER ALCOHOLS

The methyl alcohol synthesis:

$$CO + 2H_2 \rightleftharpoons CH_3OH. \quad \Delta H = -26 \text{ k. cal.} \qquad . \qquad . \qquad (4)$$

is well known and has been carried out industrially in several countries for over twenty years. The process resembles the synthesis of ammonia in that (*i*) the equilibrium moves adversely with rise in temperature, (*ii*) technical catalysts operate only at the upper temperature levels, at which the equilibrium at normal pressure is unfavourable, (*iii*) conversion and equilibrium are greatly assisted by working at high pressure, (*iv*) actual operating conditions involve only partial conversion.

The effect of temperature on the equilibrium constant, K_p, is shown below:[12]

Temperature, ° c.	K_p
200	$1 \cdot 7 \times 10^{-2}$
250	$1 \cdot 6 \times 10^{-3}$
300	$2 \cdot 3 \times 10^{-4}$
350	$4 \cdot 5 \times 10^{-5}$
400	$1 \cdot 1 \times 10^{-5}$

At 300° c., the effect of pressure on conversion at equilibrium is given in the same reference as:

Pressure, atm. at 300° c.	Conversion to liquid methyl alcohol in one pass %
10	nil
50	8·0
100	24·2
200	48·7
300	62·3

The usual conditions of reaction in industry are pressures of 250–350 atm., and temperatures in the range 300–400° c. The catalysts employed are based on zinc oxide, which is usually mixed with other less basic oxides to give long life and resistance to high temperature. The usual promoting oxide is chromium oxide; copper oxide is sometimes used in addition to or in place of chromium oxide.

The reaction is strongly exothermic and under the conditions selected will give only partial conversion of carbon monoxide and hydrogen to methyl alcohol. The usual conversion is 12–15 per cent. The methyl alcohol is condensed out, and unreacted gases, with fresh make-up gas, recycled to the convertors. The process is operated in conventional ammonia convertors; besides a common source of raw materials, synthesis gas, this is a second reason why manufacture of synthetic ammonia and of synthetic methyl alcohol is usually integrated. The yield of methyl alcohol on carbon monoxide : hydrogen reacted is high.

Most of the world's methyl alcohol has hitherto been obtained from coal or coke. In America, the availability of natural gas has led to a change

---

[12] Ewell, *Ind. Eng. Chem.*, 1940, **32**, 147.

over from coke to natural gas as a source of synthesis gas. In 1946, 29 per cent of American methyl alcohol was made from natural gas. By 1949, this had risen to 77 per cent and in 1953, over 90 per cent was made from natural gas. Methyl alcohol was formerly obtained as one of the products of wood distillation; it is also manufactured as one of the products of the pressure air oxidation of the lower paraffins (see Chapter 4, p. 59).

The end-use pattern for methyl alcohol in America in 1954 is estimated as follows on a total consumption of 485,000 tons :[13]

Outlets	% offtake
Formaldehyde	48·5
Anti-freeze	27·8
Chemical syntheses	8·6
Solvent and aviation fuel	8·8
Exports and miscellaneous	6·3
	100·0

The principal products included in chemical syntheses are methylamines, which account for about half this usage, methyl chloride and methyl methacrylate.

There seems to be limited use for methyl alcohol as an anti-freeze in Europe, where its main outlet is for formaldehyde.

By minor changes in the conditions of running the methyl alcohol synthesis, a series of higher alcohols can be obtained as by-products. The principal alteration is addition of a small amount of alkali, for example 1 per cent potassium oxide, to the methyl alcohol catalyst; the higher alcohols synthesis is also carried out at a somewhat higher temperature, 400–450° c.

The higher alcohols synthesis gives a considerable amount of water alongside the alcohols. In the Leuna process[14] synthesis gas was circulated over a zinc oxide-chromic oxide catalyst containing 1 per cent potassium oxide at 450° c. and 300 atm., giving a crude product of the following composition:

TABLE 17

Composition of products from 'higher alcohols' synthesis

Product	% by wt.
Methyl alcohol	50–55
Water	22–25
Dimethyl ether	1–3
n-Propyl alcohol	1–2
Isobutyl alcohol	11–12
C_5 alcohols	2
C_6 and C_7 alcohols	2·5
C_8 and C_9 alcohols	1–2
C_{10-14} alcohols	1
Higher alcohols	1–2

[13] *Chem. Week*, Nov. 27, 1954, p. 43.
[14] C.I.O.S., 32/107.

This mixture was worked up into its components by a complex train of fractionating columns. The C_6 and higher fractions contained a certain proportion of aldehydes, ketones and hydrocarbons.

Of the higher alcohols, the main product was isobutyl alcohol, used for making isobutene, the outlets for which are discussed in Chapter 7, p. 121, and for making isobutyraldehyde (Chapter 16, p. 298). In countries where isobutene is more cheaply available from petroleum, isobutyl alcohol is used as a solvent and intermediate. The higher alcohols were converted to acetates and phthalates, and to acids, depending on their molecular weight and the outlets required. The recovered methyl alcohol was recycled.

The ratio of methyl alcohol to the higher alcohols varies with the reaction conditions, decreasing with increasing time of contact, but complete suppression of formation cannot be effected. The higher alcohols obtained are ethyl alcohol, *n*-propyl alcohol, isobutyl alcohol, 2-methyl-*n*-butyl alcohol, 2-methyl-1-pentanol, 2 : 4-dimethyl-1-pentanol, 4-methyl-1-hexanol, isopropyl alcohol, 3-methyl-*sec*-butyl alcohol and 2 : 4-dimethyl-*sec*-butyl alcohol. Traces of aldehydes and ketones corresponding to the higher alcohols are also present. Ethyl alcohol, *n*-propyl alcohol and the secondary alcohols are formed in small or very small quantities, isobutyl alcohol and higher branch chain primary alcohols being the main products.

Various explanations of the mode of formation of these higher alcohols have been put forward, but the difficulty is to explain why the primary alcohols formed are branch chain and not straight chain. One explanation, advanced by Graves,[15] is that the alkalised oxide catalyst brings about a Guerbet type condensation between the alcohols. The Guerbet reaction is the interaction of alcohols, RCH_2CH_2OH with the corresponding sodium alkoxide at 250° c. under pressure to give a branch chain primary alcohol by elimination of sodium hydroxide, the hydrogen being abstracted from the 2-methylene group:

$$RCH_2CH_2OH \quad \rightarrow RCHCH_2OH + NaOH$$
$$+ \qquad\qquad\qquad |$$
$$NaOCH_2CH_2R \quad\quad CH_2CH_2R$$

According to Graves, the higher alcohols synthesis starts off by condensation of two molecules of methyl alcohol to give ethyl alcohol; this condenses with another molecule of methyl alcohol to give *n*-propyl alcohol, which undergoes condensation on the methylene group next to the CH_2OH group with methyl alcohol to isobutyl alcohol, and with ethyl alcohol to 2-methyl-*n*-butyl alcohol; the higher alcohols are built up in the same way.

The main product of the higher alcohols synthesis is isobutyl alcohol. As a manufacturing process, it is of declining importance because isobutyl

---

[15] Graves, *Ind. Eng. Chem.*, 1931, **23**, 1381.

alcohol is now made from propylene and synthesis gas by the Oxo reaction (Chapter 11, p. 184) without the range of other alcohols obtained simultaneously in the higher alcohols process.

(c) THE FISCHER-TROPSCH REACTION

The Fischer-Tropsch reaction is the catalytic condensation of carbon monoxide and hydrogen to give high molecular weight hydrocarbons with elimination of water. The main reaction is:

$$CO + 2H_2 \rightarrow \frac{1}{n}(CH_2)_n + H_2O(g). \quad \Delta H_{298} = -46 \text{ k. cal.} \quad . \quad (5)$$

It was discovered in 1925 and was originally intended as a route from coal to petrol and the higher petroleum hydrocarbons; it was used on a very extensive scale for this purpose in Germany during the recent war. Nevertheless, its ramifications have been so widely developed that under conditions where synthesis gas is cheaply available from paraffin gases, the Fischer-Tropsch synthesis is available as a petroleum route for the manufacture of hydrocarbons and of oxygen compounds. The Germans have admitted that under conditions of free economy, this synthesis starting with coal is not an attractive route to fuels, and they consider its chief interest would be for special chemicals or for upgraded products commanding a higher premium than fuel.

This now appears to hold for petroleum methane as well, but the process is being developed in South Africa to make petroleum products from coal. Here, the conditions are unusual; the plant is sited close to Johannesburg, near some of the cheapest coal in the world, and with relatively high cost petroleum products, owing to the absence of indigenous petroleum and the distance from the sea.

The main Fischer-Tropsch reaction has been indicated above; the hydrocarbons obtained are mixtures of paraffins and olefins, the ratio depending on the reaction conditions and on the ratio of carbon monoxide to hydrogen in the synthesis gas. In addition, two side reactions can take place, both involving loss of higher hydrocarbons:

$$CO + 3H_2 \rightarrow CH_4 + H_2O. \quad \Delta H = -49 \text{ k. cal.} \quad . \quad . \quad (6)$$
$$2CO \rightarrow CO_2 + C. \quad \Delta H = -41 \text{ k. cal.} \quad . \quad . \quad (7)$$

Carbon dioxide formation involves wastage of the valuable carbon monoxide but can be avoided by suitable choice of catalyst. Methane formation also represents loss; it can never be avoided, but careful choice of reaction conditions can minimise it.

Although reactions (5) and (6) are about equally exothermic, there is a large difference in the free energy change. The free energy equations for various possible reactions are calculated on the basis of one mol of carbon monoxide as shown (all products gaseous):

$$CO + 3H_2 \rightarrow CH_4 + H_2O. \qquad \Delta G = -53,000 + 59\cdot8T$$
$$CO + 2\tfrac{1}{2}H_2 \rightarrow \tfrac{1}{2}C_2H_6 + H_2O. \qquad \Delta G = -44,700 + 59\cdot7T$$
$$CO + 2H_2 \rightarrow \tfrac{1}{6}C_6H_{12} + H_2O. \qquad \Delta G = -35,200 + 54\cdot1T$$
$$CO + 2\tfrac{1}{6}H_2 \rightarrow \tfrac{1}{6}C_6H_{14} + H_2O. \qquad \Delta G = -40,500 + 59\cdot7T$$
$$CO + 2\tfrac{1}{8}H_2 \rightarrow \tfrac{1}{8}C_8H_{18} + H_2O. \qquad \Delta G = -40,000 + 59\cdot7T$$

The change of free energy with temperature for these possible reactions

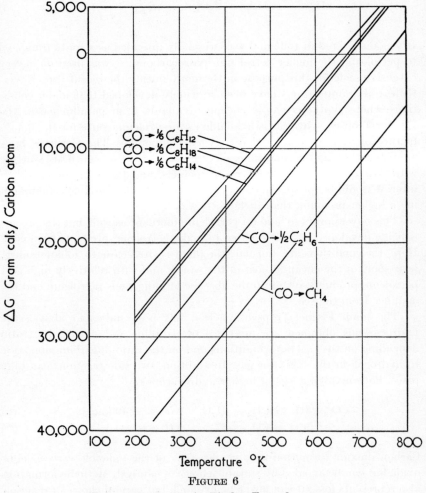

FIGURE 6

Free energy changes in Fischer-Tropsch processes

is shown in Fig. 6. Formation of the higher normal paraffins and olefins is thermodynamically possible up to about 400° c. at atmospheric pressure.

The characteristic feature of the Fischer-Tropsch reaction is that the hydrocarbons obtained, whether saturated or olefinic, are almost entirely straight chain, very little branching occurring; the olefins have the double bond at or near the end of the carbon chain. This straight chain configuration is of value in chemical synthesis, as it is possible to segregate individual compounds or mixtures consisting of only a few similar chemical compounds up to quite high molecular weights. In the case of crude or cracked petroleum, it is possible to do this only up to about C_6, before the complications introduced by the rapidly increasing number of isomers make further separation impracticable.

Perhaps the clearest way to explain how this reaction can be used for making synthetic chemicals is to outline the process for making fuels[16] and to indicate the variations in reaction conditions which give different proportions of products or which entirely alter the chemical nature of the products obtained.

The two vital factors in the successful operation of the Fischer-Tropsch process are accurate control of temperature and provision of an active and long-lived catalyst.

The main Fischer-Tropsch reaction, (5), and the two side reactions, (6) and (7), are all strongly exothermic, and the synthesis goes in the desired direction only within a narrow temperature band. If the temperature is not controlled very closely, the side reactions leading to methane and carbon dioxide formation, and to deposition of carbon on the catalyst, take charge and the reaction runs away. Temperature is controlled by provision of very elaborate methods of cooling and by working to small throughput to limit the amount of heat to be disposed of. The catalysts employed are metals of Group 8, such as cobalt or iron.

Reaction is carried out either at normal pressure or at about 10 atma. pressure (medium pressure process). The normal pressure reactors comprise rectangular steel boxes, about 20 ft. long, 9 ft. high and 6 ft. wide. The heat of reaction is removed by water cooling provided by numerous small finned water tubes running horizontally through the reactor. The catalyst is on the outside of the cooling tubes, filling the whole space of the reactor between the fins. The catalyst charge occupies 10 m.^{3}, weighs about three tons and contains about one ton cobalt.

The synthesis gas is passed downwards through the reactor, the product being taken out at the bottom. Reaction temperature is usually 180–200° c., the heat of the reaction being used to raise steam in the water tubes. The temperature is controlled by the pressure on the steam drum. In effect, the reactor is functioning as a multi-tubular steam generator. The usual gas rate was 1,000 nm.^{3}/hour/reactor (1 nm.^{3} = 1 m.^{3} synthesis gas measured at N.T.P.). By 'synthesis gas' is meant $CO + H_2$ alone; the gas usually

---

[16] B.I.O.S., Overall Report No. 1.

employed contained 15–20 per cent inerts. By working a multi-stage system with two or three reactors in series, the overall yield was 150–160 g. liquid products (C_3 and higher) per 1 nm.³ synthesis gas; the theoretical yield is 208 g./nm.³ Assuming this yield could be obtained in one passage through a single reactor, each reactor could give a maximum of 3·5 tons liquid products per day. This output is small compared with the output from many other technical catalytic processes.

In the medium pressure process, the more conventional multi-tubular type of reactor is used in which the catalyst is inside the tubes and the cooling medium, again water, is outside. However, to provide as much cooling surface as possible, annular tubes are used, the catalyst being in the annulus, and the water circulating outside the tubes and inside the annular ring. The annular tubes are 44 mm. outside diameter and 24 mm. inside diameter. Each reactor contains some 2,200 of these tubes, which are about 4·5 m. long, giving a catalyst volume of about 10 m.³ The same cobalt catalyst is employed as for the normal pressure process. Temperature limits, throughput, yield, and nature of product are also similar.

On a thermal balance, 30 per cent of the heat content of the unpurified synthesis gas is recovered in the primary products (C_3 and higher); however, allowing for the steam raised in the reactors (80–90 per cent of the heat of reaction is recovered as steam at 10 atma.), and for the methane content of the tail gases, altogether 55 per cent of the initial heat content is usefully recovered. 4·5–5·5 tons of coke are required per ton of primary product.

Hall[17] gives the following average composition of the various fractions obtained (expressed as weight per cent of C_3 and higher):

TABLE 18

Average composition of Fischer-Tropsch products

Product	Normal pressure		Medium pressure	
	Weight % of total	% olefins on fraction	Weight % of total	% olefins on fraction
C_3 and C_4 . . .	14	43	10	40
Petrol, 30–165° c. . .	47	37	26	24
Middle Oil, 165–230° c. .	17	18	24	9
Heavy Oil, 230–320° c. .	11	8	13	—
Soft wax, 320–460° c. .	8	—	17	—
Hard wax, above 460° c. .	3	—	10	—

The yield of methane on synthesis gas was 14 per cent in the normal pressure process, falling to 10 per cent in the medium pressure process.

17 *Chem. Age*, 18 January, 1947, p. 115.

The products from the Fischer-Tropsch synthesis, whether carried out at normal or at medium pressure, are worked up by condensation or adsorption followed by fractional distillation. No lubricating oil fraction is produced in this synthesis; the fraction above the diesel oil is wax.

The crude wax is worked up by topping at 320° c. *in vacuo* to remove the heavier components of the diesel oil fraction, and then separated by fractional distillation and sweating into slab wax, m.p. 50–52° c., soft wax, m.p. 30–33° c., and hard wax, with a m.p. as high as 90° c. The slab wax is similar in molecular range to the paraffin wax from petroleum, *i.e.*, about C_{20} to C_{30}. The hard wax has an average molecular weight of about 600, corresponding to C_{40}, and is of higher molecular weight than the usual wax obtained from crude petroleum.

From the point of view of fuel outlets, the petrol fraction is of low octane rating and has to be further processed to give high grade petrol; the diesel oil, on the other hand, is of exceptionally high cetane number and quality. The absence of a lubricating oil fraction is made good by synthesis, by polymerising some of the lower olefins produced in the process, or of olefins made by thermal cracking of the wax fraction.

This reaction can be varied to alter the types and ratios of the different hydrocarbon fractions produced, and to give non-hydrocarbon materials as the main products. In the first place, the proportion of olefins can be raised by increasing the ratio of carbon monoxide to hydrogen in the synthesis gas.

For high olefin content, a higher ratio of carbon monoxide-hydrogen than 1 : 2 is required.

Secondly, choice of catalyst may drastically alter the composition of the product. Iron usually gives more wax, sometimes more olefins,[18] and more ethane than cobalt; it suffers from the drawback of considerably higher carbon dioxide production. The iron catalysts developed in Germany were promoted with copper and calcium oxides, and were operated at rather higher temperatures and pressures than cobalt catalysts (205–230° c. at 15–20 atma.). Minor changes in conditions of preparation of these iron catalysts led to formation of alcohols as the principal products of reaction. With iron catalysts at 200° c. and 200 atm. pressure the main products, amounting to 80 per cent of the total, were alcohols, principally C_7 to C_{12} primary alcohols.

Somewhat similar to this Ruhrchemie work on iron catalysts to give alcohols is the I.G. 'Synol' synthesis.[19] In this process, carbon monoxide-hydrogen in the ratio 1 : 0·8 was passed over the sintered iron catalysts used in ammonia synthesis (Fe_3O_4 containing 2·5 per cent alumina and a trace of potassium oxide, reduced with hydrogen at 450° c.) at 18–25 atma.

---

[18] *e.g.*, Union Carbide, U.S.P. 2717259.
[19] C.I.O.S. 32/107; Asinger, *Ber.*, 1944, **77**, 73.

and 190–200° c. The yield of liquid products was 155–165 g./nm.^{3} synthesis gas. The approximate composition was:

Composition	%
Alcohols	35–50
Olefins	25–40
Paraffins	20–35

Of the total product, 30–40 per cent boiled in the range 50–100° c., 35–45 per cent from 100–200° c. and 25–30 per cent from 200–350° c.; the highest alcohol concentration was in the range 150–200° c. The alcohols were believed to be entirely straight chain primary alcohols. They were separated from the hydrocarbons by forming their boric esters at about 100° c., and distilling out the hydrocarbons, the boric esters boiling about 200° c. higher than the initial mixture. The esters were easily hydrolysed back to the alcohols by dilute aqueous boric acid. The process had not been taken on to the large scale.

Another alternative catalyst is ruthenium; according to Pichler,[20] with ruthenium at 150 atm. and 195° c., a high yield of hydrocarbons was obtained consisting largely of waxes melting at 118–119° c.; on solvent extraction, a considerable proportion of a wax melting at 130–134° c. was isolated. This wax had a molecular weight corresponding to 200 to 600 carbon atoms per molecule; later work gave waxes of molecular weight 23,000, corresponding to 1,650 carbon atoms per mol.[21]

As a by-product in the usual medium pressure synthesis, about $\frac{1}{2}$–1 per cent of directly synthesised fatty acids is obtained, about half of which is present in the diesel oil fraction (C_{11} to C_{18}). This portion is worked up for soaps. The yield of acids can be increased to 2 per cent.

The main chemical outlets developed in Germany for the various products have been dictated by their war-time shortages of alternative starting materials. Owing to the position on natural fats, three fractions of the Fischer-Tropsch products were turned into substitute materials. The diesel oil fraction, saturated C_{10} to C_{18} paraffins, was converted to detergents both by the Reed reaction (Chapter 6, p. 85), and by chlorination, condensation with benzene and sulphonation (Chapter 5, p. 75). The waxes were oxidised to long chain fatty acids for soaps (Chapter 4, p. 62); they can give rise to fatty acids of higher molecular weight than those obtainable by the oxidation of paraffin wax from crude petroleum. The C_{10} to C_{18} olefins were converted to aldehydes and primary alcohols by the Oxo reaction (Chapter 11, p. 183), for sulphation to the long chain primary sulphates. The C_3 and C_4 olefins were hydrated to the corresponding alcohols for conversion to the C_3 and C_4 ketones (Chapters 8, p. 136, and 17, pp. 303, 320). Other outlets in Germany involved the conversion of the primary products to products required in the fuel industry, *e.g.*, synthetic lubricating oils, and are outside the scope of this book.

---

[20] *Brennstoff-Chem.*, 1938, **19**, 226.
[21] Pichler and Buffleb, *Brennstoff-Chem.*, 1940, **21**, 285.

Although these processes are now in abeyance, it is true to say that the Fischer-Tropsch process is a route to medium and high molecular weight paraffins and olefins which are not accessible directly from crude petroleum or from the chemical refinery operations carried out as part of the petroleum industry.

In America, a modified version of the Fischer-Tropsch process has been developed, based upon methane from natural gas as the raw product, and carrying out the synthesis stage using a fluidised iron catalyst at about 300–330° c. and 15–20 atma. pressure. This process has been worked out and developed by the Hydrocol Corporation.[22] The products consist of about 70–75 per cent petrol of high octane rating, 10–15 per cent of diesel oil and fuel oil, and about 20 per cent of oxygenated compounds, chiefly alcohols, aldehydes, acids and ketones. Half these oxygenated compounds are water soluble and it is this half which is a potential source of chemicals. At least fifteen different low molecular weight compounds in these classes were produced, making the problems of isolation and disposal analogous to that of working up coal tar. The principal compounds were ethyl alcohol (40 per cent of total water-soluble oxygenated compounds), acetic acid (16 per cent), *n*-propyl alcohol (10 per cent) and acetaldehyde, propionic acid and acetone (each about 6–7 per cent).

(*d*) OTHER REACTIONS OF CARBON MONOXIDE

Although outlets for synthesis gas and for carbon monoxide other than for ammonia, methyl alcohol and the Fischer-Tropsch reaction are dealt with in later chapters, it is convenient to summarise them here and to give references to where these reactions can be found later in this volume.

The most important new reaction of synthesis gas is its direct addition to olefins to give aldehydes, the so-called Oxo reaction:

$$RR_1C : CR_2R_3 + CO + H_2 \rightarrow \underset{\underset{CHO}{|}}{RR_1CCHR_2R_3} \text{ and } \underset{\underset{CHO}{|}}{RR_1CHCR_2R_3}$$

Details of reaction conditions and an indication of its uses are given in Chapter 11, p. 183.

Synthesis gas is also a source of pure carbon monoxide by extraction with ammoniacal cuprous salts using techniques fully worked out by the chemical industries based on coal.[1] Some of the methods by which carbon monoxide can be used in industrial organic synthesis are:

$$RCH : CH_2 + CO + H_2O \rightarrow \underset{\underset{COOH}{|}}{RCHCH_3} \qquad . \qquad . \qquad \text{(Chapter 11)}$$

$$2RCH : CH_2 + CO + H_2 \rightarrow (RCH_2CH_2)_2CO \qquad . \qquad \text{(Chapter 11)}$$

$$CH : CH + CO + H_2O \rightarrow CH_2 : CHCOOH \qquad . \qquad \text{(Chapters 15 and 18)}$$

$$RCHO + CO + H_2O \rightarrow RCH(OH)COOH \qquad . \qquad \text{(Chapter 16)}$$

$$ROH + CO \rightarrow RCOOH \qquad . \qquad . \qquad \text{(Chapter 18)}$$

---

[22] Keith, *Pet. Processing*, 1947, **2(5)**, 390.

CHAPTER 4

OXIDATION OF PARAFFINS

THIS chapter is limited to the direct production of organic compounds by oxidation of paraffins. Manufacture of carbon monoxide and of acetylene by reaction between paraffins and oxygen at high temperature is dealt with in Chapters 3, p. 38, and 15, p. 266.

The oxidation of paraffins can be carried out using either the oxygen of the air or chemical oxidising agents. The availability of the gaseous paraffins has led to a large expenditure of effort on the development of air oxidation of these paraffins to a technical process. There are three serious practical difficulties which appear to have been overcome only in the last two decades. Firstly, it is necessary to work outside the explosion limits of the hydrocarbon-air mixture; this means using either a large excess of air or of the paraffin. With excess air, the volatile products are present in low concentration in the exit gases, involving costly recovery problems; with excess paraffin, only low conversions per pass can be obtained involving recovery and recycling of the excess paraffin. Secondly, in all cases, except perhaps with methane, mixtures of products are obtained. These are expensive to separate and involve the problem of finding markets for a whole range of by-products produced in a more or less fixed ratio. Thirdly, overall yields of useful products are not high, owing to loss of carbon as carbon monoxide or carbon dioxide.

Air oxidation of the higher paraffins in the liquid phase is free of the first difficulty and to some extent simplifies the second and third; the liquid phase air oxidation of paraffin wax has been operated on an industrial scale for a considerable period. The liquid phase oxidation of paraffins has also been carried out with chemical oxidising agents and is being developed with air.

1. Mechanism of air oxidation

Since the mechanism of oxygen attack on paraffins is essentially the same whether reaction is carried out in the vapour phase or in the liquid phase, it is appropriate to discuss it before dealing with specific examples of oxidation.

The current view is that oxidation proceeds by a chain mechanism involving formation of a hydrocarbon peroxide, the peroxide decomposing to give the oxidation products. The basic mechanism is:

$$R^{\times} + O_2 \rightarrow RO_2^{\times} \qquad \cdot \qquad \cdot \qquad \cdot \quad (1)$$
Radical 1 Radical 2

$$RO_2^{\times} + RH \rightarrow RO_2H + R^{\times} \cdot \qquad \cdot \quad (2)$$
Radical 2 Hydrocarbon Peroxide Radical 1

This reaction chain is self-sustaining. Various chain starting and chain ending mechanisms have been suggested; vapour phase and liquid phase oxidation may differ widely in these respects.

The peroxide, RO_2H, will decompose in different ways according to its structure, the general reaction conditions and the presence of catalysts.[1]

(i) Tertiary alkyl peroxides

These decompose first by fission of the O—O bond and then by fission at the weakest C—C bond on the α carbon atom, *e.g.*,

$$CH_3-\overset{\overset{\displaystyle CH_3}{|}}{\underset{\underset{\displaystyle CH_3}{|}}{C}}-O\vdots OH \rightarrow CH_3\overset{|}{\underset{CH_3}{C}}O + CH_3^\times + OH^\times$$

With unsymmetrical *tert*-alkyl peroxides, the weakest C—C bond is that attached to the largest alkyl group.

(ii) Secondary alkyl peroxides

These decompose in several ways. At low temperatures they give rise to ketones; particularly in the presence of polyvalent metal catalysts, alcohols are formed simultaneously, *e.g.*,

$$\begin{array}{c} CH_3 \\ \diagdown \\ CH_3 \end{array}\!\!CHOOH - \boxed{M^+} \begin{array}{l} \longrightarrow \begin{array}{c} CH_3 \\ \diagdown \\ CH_3 \end{array}\!\!CO + H_2O \qquad \qquad (3) \\ \longrightarrow \begin{array}{c} CH_3 \\ \diagdown \\ CH_3 \end{array}\!\!C\!\!\begin{array}{c} H \\ \diagup \\ \diagdown \\ O^\times \end{array} + OH^- + M^{++} \quad (4) \end{array}$$

$$\begin{array}{c} CH_3 \\ \diagdown \\ CH_3 \end{array}\!\!C\!\!\begin{array}{c} H \\ \diagup \\ \diagdown \\ O^\times \end{array} + \begin{array}{c} CH_3 \\ \diagdown \\ CH_3 \end{array}\!\!CHOOH \rightarrow \begin{array}{c} CH_3 \\ \diagdown \\ CH_3 \end{array}\!\!C\!\!\begin{array}{c} H \\ \diagup \\ \diagdown \\ OH \end{array} + \begin{array}{c} CH_3 \\ \diagdown \\ CH_3 \end{array}\!\!C^\times OOH \quad (5)$$

However, at higher temperatures in the gas phase, rupture occurs at the O—O bond and the weakest adjacent C—C bond as with tertiary peroxides, to give aldehydes:

$$\begin{array}{c} CH_3 \\ \diagdown \\ CH_3 \end{array}\!\!CH-O\vdots OH \rightarrow CH_3CHO + CH_3^\times + OH^\times \qquad (6)$$

(iii) Primary alkyl peroxides

These decompose in the same way as the secondary peroxides. They can give rise to aldehydes or primary alcohols, or undergo fission in the gas phase at higher temperatures, *e.g.*,

$$CH_3CH_2OOH - \begin{array}{l} \longrightarrow CH_3CHO + H_2O \qquad \qquad (7) \\ \longrightarrow CH_3CH_2OH + O^\times \qquad \quad (8) \\ \longrightarrow CH_3CH_2O^\times + OH^\times \qquad \quad (9) \end{array}$$

$$\downarrow$$
$$CH_3^\times + CH_2O$$

The decomposition (8) probably proceeds via a peroxide radical,

---

[1] Walsh, *Trans. Faraday Soc.*, 1946, **42**, 269.

CH₃CHOOH, by collision with a second peroxide molecule as in reactions (4) and (5).

In the gas phase decomposition (9), the radical RCH_2O has been recognised from mirror experiments and is known to decompose easily to formaldehyde. This type of decomposition is probably one of the main sources of the formaldehyde which is always such a prominent product in the gas phase oxidation of the lower paraffins.

The initial point of attack of oxygen on the hydrocarbon molecule is in accordance with the ideas of the organic chemist, carbon being attacked in the order tertiary > secondary > primary, which is the order of decreasing bond strength of the C—H bond.

In Rice's work on the thermal decomposition of hydrocarbons, he assumed the reactivities of tertiary, secondary and primary carbon atoms were 33 : 3 : 1 at 300° c. and 10 : 2 : 1 at 600° c. Reactivity in the liquid phase will follow the same general order but, in the normal temperature region of about 100–150° c., the spread between tertiary and primary carbon atoms will probably correspond to gas phase reaction at a very much higher temperature.

2. Air oxidation—gas phase

In few fields can the journal and patent literature be so confusing and conflicting as in the vapour phase oxidation of the normally gaseous paraffins. The explanation is that minor changes in operating conditions and the presence of catalytic materials exert a major effect on the extent and nature of the oxidation. It has therefore been necessary to select what appear to be well authenticated oxidation results and to give a brief résumé of the general picture.

In general, methane and the higher hydrocarbons react with oxygen in the vapour phase at temperatures from about 250° c. upwards to give most of the possible oxidation products—alcohols, aldehydes or ketones, acids and oxides. With the higher hydrocarbons, chain rupture always occurs and frequently the oxidation products with the same number of carbon atoms as the starting hydrocarbon represent the smallest percentage of the useful products obtained. The difficulty of oxidation of paraffins decreases in the order methane > ethane > propane > butanes, methane being the most difficult to oxidise. Pressure is advantageous by increasing output and limiting to some degree the extent of oxidation. There is usually an induction period before onset of oxidation; solid contact catalysts and presence of water vapour have little effect on the course of oxidation. A parallelism with vapour phase nitration (Chapter 5) will be noticed in these respects and it is significant that nitration with nitric acid is always associated with considerable oxidation.

Turning now to methane, according to Blair and Wheeler[2] it is not

---

[2] *J. Soc. Chem. Ind.*, 1922, **41**, 303.

oxidised at an appreciable rate below 600° c. at atmospheric pressure, whereas formaldehyde begins to decompose considerably below this temperature. The reactions which may occur are:

$$CH_4 + \tfrac{1}{2}O_2 \rightarrow CH_3OH \quad . \quad . \quad . \quad . \quad . \quad (10)$$
$$CH_3OH + \tfrac{1}{2}O_2 \rightarrow CH_2O + H_2O \quad . \quad . \quad . \quad (11)$$
$$CH_2O \rightarrow CO + H_2 \quad . \quad . \quad . \quad . \quad (12)$$
$$CH_2O + \tfrac{1}{2}O_2 \rightarrow CO + H_2O \quad . \quad . \quad . \quad (13)$$
$$CH_2O + O_2 \rightarrow CO_2 + H_2O \quad . \quad . \quad . \quad (14)$$

Blair and Wheeler suggested that the main difficulty in getting high yields of formaldehyde lay in suppressing the oxidation reaction (13) and not the thermal decomposition reaction (12). At ordinary pressures, formaldehyde production greatly exceeds methyl alcohol production. At high pressures and with low air-methane ratios, methyl alcohol is the main product.

To limit the side reactions (12), (13) and (14), involving waste of methane, it has been found necessary to operate with low conversions per pass and with very short contact time. Catalysts do not have a major effect on the reaction; both solid catalysts such as metal phosphates, and vapour phase catalysts such as oxides of nitrogen and hydrogen chloride have been tried and claimed to be beneficial.

The Germans have examined various methods of direct oxidation of methane to formaldehyde on the pilot scale. In one process, methane and air were reacted at 400–600° c. in presence of 0·1 per cent of nitric oxide as a gaseous catalyst; the yield of isolated formaldehyde was 10 per cent on the methane reacted. Another process used oxygen containing 1 per cent of ozone at 110–120° c. over a catalyst of barium peroxide promoted with silver oxide; the yield of formaldehyde claimed was 90 per cent[3] on methane reacted.

Extensive laboratory and pilot plant work on oxidation of saturated hydrocarbons has been carried out by Wiezevich and Frolich;[4] unfortunately interpretation of their results is rendered somewhat confusing by their choice of mixed gases as starting materials. Oxidation was carried out in metal tubes, with metallic catalysts such as iron, aluminium or nickel, at about 400° c. and 130 atm. Methane containing 2 per cent ethane and 6 per cent propane gave methyl alcohol as the main useful product, but the yield on oxygen consumed was only 15 per cent.

The oxidation of ethane has been examined by Newitt and Townend.[5] Using an ethane-oxygen ratio of 88·2 : 11·8 at 262·2 c. and 100 atm. with a reaction time of forty minutes, Newitt and Townend were able to account for 67 per cent of the carbon consumed as condensed organic compounds.

---

[3] F.I.A.T. 1085.
[4] *Ind. Eng. Chem.*, 1934, **26**, 267.
[5] *World Pet. Cong.* (*London*), 1933, **2**, 847.

Reaction was so sensitive that at 278·0° c., contact time was reduced to five minutes and only 44 per cent of the carbon of the ethane consumed was accounted for. The composition of the two condensates is given in Table 19.

TABLE 19

Air oxidation of ethane at 100 atm.

Product	Conditions	
	262·2° c. for 40 min.	278° c. for 5 min.
	% wt.	% wt.
Ethyl alcohol	24·3	28·6
Methyl alcohol	15·5	42·3
Acetaldehyde	6·3	20·9
Acetic acid	52·3	5·5
Formaldehyde and formic acid . .	1·6	2·7

Propane commences to react with oxygen at even lower temperatures; according to Wiezevich and Frolich, at 150 atm. reaction starts at as low as 112° c. These workers carried out an extensive investigation of propane oxidation at high pressures. A typical run with a mixture of 92·1 per cent propane and 7·9 per cent oxygen, at ten seconds' reaction time and 350° c. (chosen because of the very short reaction time), gave a yield of 43 per cent of oxygen converted to useful condensation products:

Product	% by wt.
Acetaldehyde and formaldehyde . . .	23
Acetone	7
Methyl alcohol	24
Ethyl alcohol	20
Isopropyl alcohol	18
Acetic acid (and formic acid)	7

Pease and Munro[6] examined the slow oxidation of propane-oxygen mixtures at 400° c. and atmospheric pressure in order to detect the primary products; they worked with relatively high oxygen-propane ratios (1 to 3 : 1); of the organic carbon compounds, the major products reported were propylene, peroxides, aldehydes and some ethylene. The peroxide had the approximate formula $CH_3CH(OH)(OOH)$ and decomposed to formaldehyde. Even under these mild conditions, considerable chain scission had taken place.

The non-catalysed oxidation of the lower gaseous paraffins by a deficiency of oxygen has been examined further by Bataafsche Petroleum Maatschappij. Reaction in a resistant metal container at about 400–500° c., the surface of the reactor being kept below 200° c., gave the Pease type of organic peroxide,[7] but minor changes in reaction conditions led to formation

[6] *J. Amer. Chem. Soc.*, 1934, **56**, 2034.
[7] B.P. 541110.

of aqueous hydrogen peroxide as the principal active oxygen product. For example with a 90 per cent propane/10 per cent oxygen mixture, wall temperature 150° c., actual temperature 470° c., reaction time, 5 seconds, the principal oxygenated product is hydrogen peroxide, obtained as a 3–4 per cent aqueous solution.[8] This route to hydrogen peroxide appears to have given way to direct oxidation of isopropyl alcohol (Chapter 8, p. 137).

An alternative method of oxidation with oxygen, which really depends on bromination, has been worked out by Shell Development Co. This depends on oxidation in the presence of a little hydrogen bromide, which permits the reaction to be carried out at much lower temperatures than with straight paraffin-oxygen mixtures and gives simpler mixtures and individual compounds in high yield.

Probably the most likely technical process is with isobutane. A mixture of isobutane : oxygen : hydrogen bromide in the ratio 10 : 10 : 1 gives at 160° c. a 75% yield of *tert*-butyl hydroperoxide with some isobutyl alcohol and di-*tert*-butyl peroxide:

$$(CH_3)_2CHCH_3 + O_2 \rightarrow (CH_3)_3COOH$$

Both *tert*-butyl hydroperoxide and di-*tert*-butyl peroxide are commercial products, used as catalysts in polymerisation processes.

Hydrocarbons containing both secondary and primary C—H bonds give ketones; propane reacts at 190° c. to give acetone. Ethane gives acetic acid at a higher temperature, 220° c.; methane does not react.[9]

The direct oxidation of natural gas is operated in America by two companies. Cities Service Oil Co. have a plant at Tallant, Okla., in which natural gas is oxidised at moderate temperature and pressure to give a mixture of equal weights of methyl alcohol and formaldehyde, with smaller quantities of acetaldehyde and methyl acetone;† a flowsheet of the plant is given.[10] According to this company's patents[11] natural gas containing C_1 to C_4 hydrocarbons mixed with about 10 per cent by volume of air was reacted at 460° c. and 20 atma. pressure over a contact catalyst; this was originally platinised asbestos, but later aluminium phosphate plus copper oxide on an inert support was used. The products of oxidation were isolated by cooling and the last traces extracted from the gases by scrubbing below 0° c. with some of the liquid condensed at higher temperatures. Only partial oxidation was effected, the oxygen being completely used up; the spent gases were recycled after adding make up gas, or were burnt. Typical liquid composition is given as 5–6 per cent acetaldehyde, 34–36 per cent methyl

---

[8] Shell Development, U.S.P. 2376257.

[9] Rust and Vaughan, *Ind. Eng. Chem.*, 1949, **41**, 2595.

† This term covers mixtures of acetone, methyl alcohol and methyl acetate containing up to 75 per cent acetone.

[10] *Chem. Met. Eng.*, 1942, **49**(9), 154.

[11] U.S.P. 2007115, 2007116, 2042134, 2186688.

alcohol, 20–23 per cent formaldehyde together with water and small amounts of oxygenated compounds of higher molecular weight. Reaction time is limited to a few seconds, sometimes less than one second, and temperature control is by controlling the preheat of the entering gas to about 50° c. below the desired reaction temperature. Pressure is limited to 20 atm. to give as much formaldehyde as possible; at 50 atm. methyl alcohol is the main product. According to statements in the patents, much of the methane passes through unchanged, the oxidation products arising from attack on the higher hydrocarbons.

It is understood that Cities Service also now carry out the oxidation of propane and butane and operate a process similar to that of Celanese Corporation of America. This firm oxidises propane and butane with air by a non-catalytic process. Excess of hydrocarbon is used; the temperature is in the range 350–450° c., at pressures from 3–20 atma. Butane reacts more readily than propane and is the preferred feedstock. The products are worked up for recovery of condensable organic products, the non-condensables being recycled; a purge is taken to prevent build-up, but propane and butane are recovered from the purge and returned to process, the utilisation of hydrocarbon being 100 %. At least 15–20 per cent of the hydrocarbon is lost as carbon oxides. A complex mixture of organic compounds is obtained; they include formaldehyde, methyl alcohol, acetaldehyde, acetic acid, n-propyl alcohol, methyl ethyl ketone, and the oxides of ethylene, propylene, and butene. This process is operated at Bishop, Texas, and Edmonton, Canada.

A second Celanese process, operated at Pampa, Texas, oxidises butane with air in the liquid phase in a solvent. The main products are methyl alcohol, acetaldehyde, and acetic acid, with the acid predominating; the conditions can be changed to give methyl ethyl ketone as the main product. This process should properly be discussed in Section 3 below.

The scale of operations of these oxidation processes is indicated by the estimate that in 1954 the combined usage of propane and butane was as high as 230,000 tons. 7 per cent of American methyl alcohol and 25 per cent of American formaldehyde were made in 1954 by direct oxidation of propane and butane.[12]

3. Air oxidation—liquid phase

The liquid phase air oxidation of paraffins proceeds by the same primary mechanism as the gas phase oxidation but there are two important differences. The homogeneous gas phase explosive decomposition does not take place, and the primary products usually undergo further oxidation to acids:

$$> CH_2 \xrightarrow{\;O_2\;} > CHOOH \begin{cases} \rightarrow > CO \longrightarrow acids \\ \rightarrow > CHOH \rightarrow acids \end{cases}$$

---

[12] *Chem. Week*, June 12, 1954, p. 89; *Chem. Eng.*, Sept., 1955, p. 266.

According to Burwell,[13] the first attack of oxygen is on the 2-carbon atom of the paraffin chain, followed by attack on the 3-carbon atom and so on to the centre of the molecule. Only traces of dibasic acids are formed. The chief lower acids are formic and acetic acids. Simultaneously or subsequently, oxygen is attacking other parts of the molecule, so that, besides the simple long chain fatty acids, keto- and hydroxy acids, lactones and estolides are also formed. The first stages of oxidation were therefore represented by him:

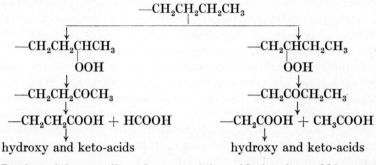

In view of the complicated course of the oxidation, it would be expected that simpler mixtures of products would result from the oxidation of paraffin wax, which is a mixture of the straight chain normal paraffins, than from the oxidation of normally liquid petroleum fractions such as kerosene, which contain normal and branch chain paraffins, and other types of hydrocarbons. This is in fact the case. Nevertheless, both types of hydrocarbons are oxidised industrially, although the oxidation of paraffin wax is carried out on a considerably larger scale.

In the Alox process,[14] highly paraffinic hydrocarbon fractions with boiling ranges from petrol up to paraffin wax are used, depending on the nature of the products required. Oxidation is carried out batchwise in stainless steel reactors with air at 10–20 atma. pressure, the temperature being within the range 100–180° c. The reaction is initiated with heavy metal soaps and with some of the high molecular weight alcohols and ketones from a previous batch. The oxygen content of the air is completely consumed.

The oxidation product is worked up by treatment with caustic soda which separates the acids, alcohols and ketones floating to the top and being removed. The acids are split out by acidification, and usually used as obtained. They contain a considerable percentage of hydroxy acids which decompose to unsaturated acids on distillation.

The Alox Corporation plant at Niagara Falls, N.Y., has a capacity of 9,000 tons p.a. hydrocarbon raw material, giving approximately an equal weight of oxidised product. About 30–40 per cent of this is organic acids,

[13] *Ind. Eng. Chem.*, 1934, **26**, 204.
[14] Zabel, *Chem. Ind.*, 1946, **59(5)**, 821.

the remainder being alcohols and ketones. The products are used in a wide variety of applications, such as greases, oil additives, wetting agents, plasticisers, anti-corrosives, etc., where their complex composition is not a drawback. The process does not seem to have been expanded since the war.

On the other hand, the oxidation of paraffin wax can be made to give a high yield of one class of product, the straight chain carboxylic acids. The most successful conditions, using air as the oxidising agent, were indicated over seventy years ago by Schaal and improvements have been made since then only in detail. Oxidation is carried out in the temperature range 100–150° c. in presence of both a basic material and a polyvalent metal catalyst, and preferably under increased pressure (4–10 atma.).

In Germany the oxidation was carried out on the large scale with about 0·1 per cent potassium permanganate as catalyst at 130° c. (110–140° c.) under a pressure of about 10 atma. in aluminium reactors, the oxidation being terminated after between fifteen and thirty hours.[15] Paraffin waxes of molecular range C_{20} to C_{30} were chosen to give the desired molecular range of acids. The off-gases which contained 10–15 per cent oxygen carried away all the acids up to C_5 and some of the C_6—C_8 acids; they were scrubbed with water and these lower acids recovered from the water solution.

The oxidation product, consisting of a mixture of unchanged wax, alcohols, ketones, acids, hydroxy and keto-acids, wax esters and lactones, was worked up by saponification with alkali under pressure at 150–170° c. This hydrolysed the esters and lactones, giving two layers.

The upper layer was returned to the oxidiser for the next oxidation. The lower layer, still containing some alcohols and ketones, was heated further to 200° c. at 80–120 atm.; this dehydrated the alcohols to olefins and split some of the ketones to acids:

$$-CH_2CH_2CH_2CO\vdots CH_2CH_3 \rightarrow -CH_2CH_2CH_2COONa + C_2H_6$$
$$NaO\vdots H$$

the carboxy group remaining attached to the larger alkyl fragment.

The product was then flashed to atmospheric pressure, giving steam volatiles (alcohols, ketones, hydrocarbons) and the molten anhydrous soap. The acids were isolated by acidification followed by vacuum distillation at 3 mm. pressure using water injection by the Wecker method.

Three main fractions were obtained. The first fraction, C_4 to C_{10} acids, was obtained in a yield of 16 per cent by weight on the wax oxidised. The second and main fraction, C_{10} to C_{20} acids, was obtained in a yield of 45 per cent by weight. The third fraction, C_{21} to C_{28} acids, represented 10 per cent by weight. The C_{10} to C_{20} fraction was used for soaps; the C_4 to C_{10} acids were converted to esters for solvents and plasticisers. The higher fraction was used for lacquers. The soap made from the main fraction had

---

[15] B.I.O.S. 805; B.I.O.S. 1560.

normal washing properties but was unsuitable for toilet use owing to the odour the soap imparted to the human skin. To augment their supply of soap from natural fats, there were three plants for oxidation of waxes in Germany, with a total capacity for treating 80,000 tons p.a. wax, at Witten, Oppau and Heydebreck. Most of the raw material was Fischer-Tropsch wax, but Oppau also handled hydrogenated brown coal wax and German petroleum wax.

Both odd and even numbered straight chain acids are present in approximately equal amounts. Stossel[16] gives the following analysis of the acids from oxidation of a Fischer-Tropsch slack wax (C_{16}–C_{28}). Of the total acids formed, about one-fifth were C_1 to C_8; the remaining four-fifths had the following approximate composition:

Acids	% by wt.
up to C_7–C_8	11·2
C_9	5·7
C_{10}	7·4
C_{11}	6·2
C_{12}	7·6
C_{13}	8·3
C_{14}	8·8
C_{15}	9·0
C_{16}	6·7
C_{17}	6·2
C_{18}	4·2
above C_{18}	18·2

It has been mentioned that some alcohols and ketones are always formed; the proportion of alcohols isolated can be considerably increased by oxidation of wax in presence of weak acids such as boric or acetic acid which esterify the alcohol and inhibit or slow down further oxidation. For example, on oxidation at 175° c. of wax containing 5 per cent boric acid with air saturated at room temperature with acetic acid, a yield of 44 per cent of alcohols was obtained in three hours.

These technical processes of oxidation depend upon use of normal paraffins as starting materials. Isoparaffins give low molecular weight acids and oxyacids; substituted naphthenes give naphthenic acids of particularly objectionable odour.

4. Oxidation with chemical oxidising agents

Although such drastic oxidising agents as potassium dichromate and sulphuric acid have been tried on paraffin wax, the only technical alternative to air is nitric acid or its equivalent, nitrogen oxides; the nitric acid or nitrogen dioxide is reduced to nitric oxide which is reoxidised by air to nitrogen dioxide. The nett effect therefore is that the nitrogen dioxide is acting as a carrier for the oxygen of the air.

This method has been examined in Germany; their process[17] was carried

---

[16] *Oil Gas J.*, August 15, 1945, p. 145.
[17] C.I.O.S. 27/69.

out by passing nitrogen dioxide containing gases from ammonia oxidation into a stirred mixture of wax and nitrosyl sulphuric acid at 125° c. for 8–12 hours. The product was saponified with aqueous alkali, unchanged wax extracted with a solvent and recycled. A C_{40} wax, m.p. 90–95° c., from the Fischer-Tropsch process (p. 47) gave acids of an average chain length of C_{20}. With recycling of wax, the yield of acids was about 80 per cent wt./wt. (72 per cent of theory on the assumption that one mol of wax gives two mols of acid).

Some doubt has been expressed on the chain length and yield of acid obtained.[18]

---

[18] B.I.O.S. 447.

CHAPTER 5

CHLORINATION OF PARAFFINS

Technically, the only important halogenation reaction is chlorination. Bromination and iodination of paraffins are not carried out industrially. The important saturated fluorine compounds, such as Freon 12, CF_2Cl_2, are usually made from chloroparaffins by reaction with fluorine compounds.[1] It has, however, been judged worth while to add at the end of this Chapter a section summarising the war-time American work on the synthesis of fully fluorinated paraffins by direct fluorination processes.

Chlorination is carried out either in the vapour phase or in the liquid phase. In most technical chlorinations of paraffins, the object is to make the mono-chloro derivative; in these circumstances, chlorination is always carried out in presence of a large excess of hydrocarbon, to repress formation of polychlorides as much as possible, since the monochloride chlorinates at about the same rate as the starting hydrocarbon. Reaction is carried out to give complete utilisation of chlorine, to avoid problems in the disposal of free chlorine. In vapour-phase chlorinations, use of excess hydrocarbon, which is essential, involves chemical engineering problems in isolation of the monochloride from the large excess of hydrocarbon, and in recovery and recycling of the hydrocarbon with minimum heat loss. Chlorination under pressure considerably simplifies these problems, and at the same time provides other operating advantages.

Hass and his collaborators have formulated ten general rules for chlorination of paraffins into which most reactions fit.[2]

Rule 1

Carbon skeleton rearrangements do not occur during photochemical or thermal chlorinations if temperatures and catalytic conditions at which pyrolysis may take place are avoided.

Rule 2

At low and moderate temperatures, hydrogen atoms are substituted at rates which are in the order primary < secondary < tertiary, and at any given temperature are independent of the hydrocarbon. For example, vapour phase chlorination of propane, isobutane, pentane or isopentane at 300° c. gives relative rates of 1·00 for primary hydrogen atoms : 3·25 for secondary : 4·43 for tertiary.

---

[1] Ellis, 'Chemistry of Petroleum Derivatives', *Reinhold*, Vol. 1, 1934, p. 708; Vol. 2, 1937, pp. 733, 747, etc.
[2] *Ind. Eng. Chem.*, 1935, **27**, 1190; 1936, **28**, 333; 1937, **29**, 1335.

RULE 3

At higher temperatures, the rates of substitution of the hydrogen atoms approach equality in the vapour or liquid phase.

RULE 4

Liquid phase chlorination gives relative rates of primary, secondary and tertiary substitution obtainable only at much higher temperatures in the vapour phase. There is some evidence that low temperature, liquid phase, chlorination of normal paraffins tends to attack first the methylene groups near the end of the chain.

RULE 5

Moisture, carbon surfaces, catalysts and light do not appreciably affect the ratio of substitution.

RULE 6

Excess temperature or time of reaction cause pyrolysis of the mono-chlorohydrocarbons, the order of stability being primary > secondary > tertiary.

RULE 7

Under constant conditions of chlorination, the ratio of monochlorides to polychlorides formed is related to the ratio of hydrocarbon to chlorine reacted by the equation:

$$X = KY$$

where X is the weight ratio of monochlorides to polychlorides,
    Y is the molar ratio of hydrocarbon to chlorine,
    K is a constant for the particular hydrocarbon and set of conditions used.

RULE 8

Dichlorides are obtained by two mechanisms, (a) loss of hydrogen chloride followed by addition of chlorine, (b) progressive substitution.

Slow thermal chlorination favours mechanism (a). Rapid liquid phase or vapour phase single pass chlorination favours mechanism (b) and represses mechanism (a).

RULE 9

In vapour phase chlorination, the presence of a chlorine atom on one carbon atom tends to decrease slightly the anticipated rate of reaction on the carbon atom which is already substituted.

RULE 10

In vapour phase chlorination, increased pressure increases the relative rate of primary substitution.

In the vapour phase, the velocity of reaction is appreciable only above 250° c. Since even momentary high temperatures lead to pyrolysis, efficient mixing of the chlorine with the hydrocarbon is essential; the chlorine is usually introduced into the hydrocarbon stream through jets at velocities greater than the speed of propagation of flame.

A further refinement is the introduction of chlorine in a series of jets arranged along the path of the hydrocarbon stream.

Photochemical chlorination brings about chlorination at lower temperatures, and in this respect is similar to liquid phase chlorination. The importance of primary substitution will make liquid phase chlorination of increasing importance; with the lower hydrocarbons, this means operating either under high pressure or in a solvent such as carbon tetrachloride.

According to Hirschkind,[3] photochemical chlorinations are used technically only to a limited extent; this process gives no unsaturated products, carbon or tar and there is no induction period. The products from liquid or vapour phase photochemical chlorinations are very similar. Drawbacks are high capital cost and problems with electrical supply.

Materials of construction of the reactor are important only insofar as catalytic agents capable of leading to pyrolysis or rearrangement of the carbon skeleton are avoided. For this reason, steel is not usually used for the chlorinator. The usual austenitic steels are also unsuitable; high chrome steel or monel metal can be used. Technical chlorinations are sometimes operated under pressure, not only because of the simplification of the problem of recovery of product from the excess hydrocarbon, but also because pressure reduces the volume of gases to be handled and increases the output from a given size of equipment.

The usually accepted mechanism of chlorination is based upon the formation of free alkyl radicals, initiated by the presence of chlorine atoms, which are themselves formed thermally or by photochemical means:

$$Cl_2 \rightarrow Cl^\times + Cl^\times$$
$$RH + Cl^\times \rightarrow R^\times + HCl$$
$$R^\times + Cl_2 \rightarrow RCl + Cl^\times$$

This mechanism is supported by the inertness of water, light, catalysts,

---

[3] *Ind. Eng. Chem.*, 1949, **41**, 2749.

etc., in altering the ratios of substitution, and by the effect of oxygen in retarding or inhibiting chlorination.

1. Chlorination of methane

Methane is the most difficult of the paraffins to chlorinate but, at a sufficiently high temperature, reaction proceeds normally.[4] By introducing chlorine along the reaction path, so that excess of methane or of partially chlorinated methanes was always present, mixtures from over 90 per cent methyl chloride to pure carbon tetrachloride could be obtained. The best temperature range was 400–440° c. Results are summarised in Fig. 7, which is based on Hirschkind's paper.[3]

In all cases the efficiency of utilisation of chlorine was 93–96 per cent.

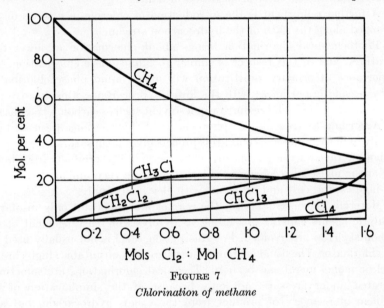

FIGURE 7
Chlorination of methane

It is particularly important to avoid any local concentration of chlorine as, besides overchlorination, the carbon black reaction:

$$CH_4 + 2Cl_2 \rightarrow C + 4HCl$$

could take place.

This reaction has been operated in Germany for the manufacture of both methyl chloride and methylene dichloride. Five mols of methane, 99·5% pure and freed from ethylene by a hydrogenation treatment, mixed with one mol of chlorine were introduced cold into large cement lined reactors maintained at 390–410° c. by external heating. Hydrochloric acid was removed by washing with hot water, the chlorinated products isolated by

---

[4] Hass, McBee, Neher and Strickland, *Ind. Eng. Chem.*, 1942, **34**, 296.

compression and refrigeration and separated by fractionation. The crude condensed reaction mixture contained 50 per cent methyl chloride, 35 per cent methylene dichloride, and 15 per cent more highly chlorinated compounds. When methylene dichloride was required as the main product, methyl chloride was recycled up to a maximum of 20 per cent by volume on the total hydrocarbon gas fed. Exceeding this figure led to excessive carbon formation.[5]

Methyl chloride is used as a refrigerant and as a methylating agent. Outlets in the chemical industry include its use as an intermediate in the manufacture of silicones. Methylene dichloride, despite its low boiling point (40·1 c.), is of growing importance as a solvent, for example in the manufacture of cellulose acetate and Butyl rubber.

In America, chlorination of methane has been operated to make as the end products of the process chloroform and carbon tetrachloride, the lower chlorinated intermediates being recycled. The usual route to carbon tetrachloride is by chlorination of carbon disulphide; chloroform is made by reduction of carbon tetrachloride, or from ethyl alcohol or acetone. One of its newer uses is as the starting point for making tetrafluoroethylene and its polymer (Fluon or Teflon):

$$CHCl_3 + 2HF \rightarrow CHF_2Cl \xrightarrow{-HCl} CF_2 : CF_2$$

The main outlets for carbon tetrachloride are as an intermediate for Freon 12, CF_2Cl_2, as a pest control chemical and as a solvent. It can be used for making tetrachloroethylene, C_2Cl_4, by pyrolysis, an interesting example of going from the C_1 to the C_2 series:

$$2CCl_4 \rightarrow C_2Cl_4 + 2Cl_2$$

This reaction was operated in America by chlorination of methane at high temperature, so as to use the exothermic heat of chlorination to bring about the pyrolysis.[6] The normal route to tetrachloroethylene is by processes involving the chlorination of acetylene (Chapter 10, p. 157). The carbon tetrachloride route now appears to have been discontinued.

2. Chlorination of ethane

Under similar conditions, ethane has been chlorinated to give ethyl chloride, using a large excess of ethane and working in the temperature range 300–500° c.[7] The Ethyl Corporation have erected plant at Baton Rouge, La., to manufacture ethyl chloride from ethane,[8] so as to increase their supplies and ease the demand for ethylene and ethyl alcohol, then in short supply.

---

[5] B.I.O.S. 851; B.I.O.S. 1662.
[6] Dow, U.S.P. 2377669, 2442323, 2442324.
[7] Ellis, 'Chemistry of Petroleum Derivatives', *Reinhold*, Vol. 1, 1934, p. 712; Vol. 2, 1937, p. 741; Egloff, U.S.P. 1950720.
[8] *Chem. Ind.*, 1945, **56(5)**, 806.

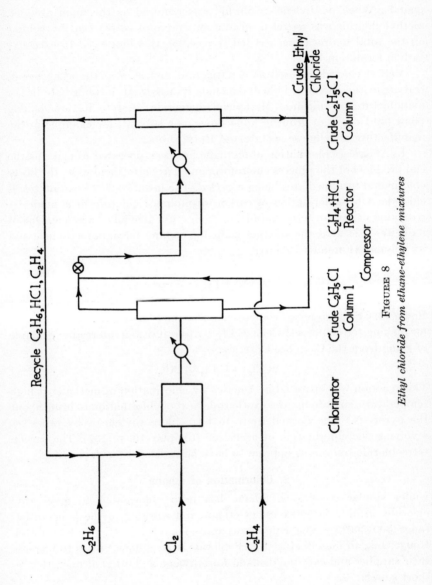

C₂H₆

Cl₂

C₂H₄

Recycle C_2H_6, HCl, C_2H_4

Crude Ethyl Chloride

Chlorinator

Crude C_2H_5Cl Column 1

Compressor

$C_2H_4 + HCl$ Reactor

Crude C_2H_5Cl Column 2

FIGURE 8

Ethyl chloride from ethane-ethylene mixtures

Monochlorination of ethane is favoured by the fact that ethyl chloride chlorinates at only one quarter the rate of ethane; the product of dichlorination is ethylidene chloride, CH_3CHCl_2, not ethylene dichloride.

In presence of ethylene, ethane chlorinates in the gas phase to give ethyl chloride without addition of chlorine to the ethylene.[9] This discovery has been used by Shell Development Co. as the basis of a process for complete conversion of a C_2 refinery cut containing ethane and ethylene (but no propylene) to ethyl chloride, which is operated at Stanlow in England.[10] Chlorine, ethane and recycle gas containing both ethane and ethylene are fed to the ethane chlorinator which operates at about 400° c. A little ethylene dichloride is formed, which loses hydrogen chloride to give vinyl chloride. A small excess of hydrogen chloride is formed compared with the ethane chlorinated. The gases are cooled, ethyl chloride and heavier products condensed, and inerts, hydrogen chloride unchanged ethane and ethylene and a little ethyl chloride pass overhead. The overhead stream is mixed with fresh ethylene, compressed, preheated and sent to the second reactor where ethylene and hydrogen chloride react in the gas phase over a catalyst to give more ethyl chloride. The gases are cooled to condense ethyl chloride, the ethane, unreacted ethylene and some hydrogen chloride being recycled to the first reactor. It is necessary to take a purge here to prevent build-up of inerts. The flowsheet is shown in Fig. 8.

The other processes to ethyl chloride from ethylene and from ethyl alcohol are dealt with in Chapter 10, p. 172.

3. Chlorination of propane

The chlorination of propane has been worked out in considerable detail by Hass and his school and gives a good illustration of the application of his chlorination rules. According to these rules, the relative rates of chlorination of primary, secondary and tertiary hydrogen atoms at 300° c. are 1·00 : 3·25 : 4·43. By chlorination of two mols of propane with one mol of chlorine at 300° c., with a reaction time to give complete utilisation of chlorine, a monochloride fraction was obtained containing 52·4 per cent 2-chloropropane and 47·6 per cent 1-chloropropane.

Propane contains six primary hydrogen atoms and two secondary atoms; therefore the ratio of 1-chloro to 2-chloropropane should be 6 × 1·00 : 2 × 3·25, or 48 per cent 1-chloro to 52 per cent 2-chloropropane. With the 2 : 1 ratio of propane to chlorine, about 15 per cent of polychlorides was formed; with an 8 : 1 ratio, polychloride formation was reduced to 5 per cent, but the ratio of 1-chloro to 2-chloropropane was unaffected.

---

[9] Shell Development, U.S.P. 2246082.
[10] Fleer, Johnson and Nelson, *Ind. Eng. Chem.*, 1955, **47**, 982.

Further chlorination of 1- and 2-chloropropanes will give a mixture of 1 : 1-, 1 : 2-, 1 : 3- and 2 : 2-dichloropropanes. 1 : 3-Dichloropropane is an intermediate for the anaesthetic, cyclopropane, previously made from trimethylene glycol, $HOCH_2CH_2CH_2OH$, a by-product of glycerol fermentation. Hass, McBee, Hinds and Gluesenkamp have described the conversion of propane to cyclopropane;[11] their process is operated in America.

A mixture of propane and monochloropropanes was chlorinated at 400° c., using ten mols of the mixture to one mol of chlorine. The monochlorides were chlorinated to dichlorides with a little trichloride and the propane to monochlorides with a little dichloride. The dichlorides and higher boiling material were completely condensed out, hydrochloric acid washed out with water and monochlorides and unchanged propane, together with added make-up propane, recycled to the chlorinator after drying with sulphuric acid. Chlorination proceeds as follows:

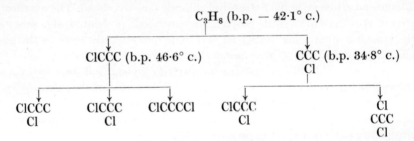

The boiling points of the dichloropropanes are:

Compound				b.p. ° c.
1 : 1-dichloro	.	.	.	87
1 : 2-dichloro	.	.	.	96·8
1 : 3-dichloro	.	.	.	120·4
2 : 2-dichloro	.	.	.	69·7

Separation of 1 : 3-dichloropropane from the other dichloropropanes and from monochloropropanes by fractional distillation is therefore easy. The 1 : 3-dichloropropane contains some 1 : 2 : 2-trichloropropane, b.p. 122° c., but this trichloropropane is removed in the subsequent processing. The composition of the dichloride fraction is:

Compound			%
1 : 1-dichloropropane	.	.	19·6
1 : 2-dichloropropane	.	.	35·6
1 : 3-dichloropropane	.	.	19·3
2 : 2-dichloropropane	.	.	22·0

The proportion of 1 : 3-dichloropropane is somewhat higher and of 1 : 2-dichloropropane somewhat lower than anticipated.

The yield of 1 : 3-dichloropropane on propane is therefore rather

---

[11] *Ind. Eng. Chem.*, 1936, **28**, 1178.

less than 20 per cent; nevertheless this is an economic route to cyclo-propane, and increasing the yield by separating the monochlorides and only chlorinating the 1-chloropropane does not appear to be worth while. The simplified flowsheet of preparation of 1 : 3-dichloropropane is as follows:

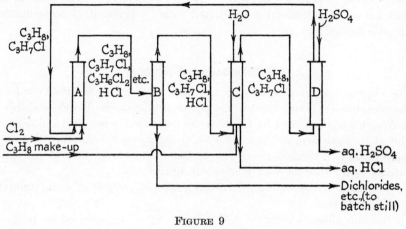

FIGURE 9
Chlorination of propane

1 : 3-Dichloropropane was converted to cyclopropane by refluxing in aqueous alcohol with a slight excess of zinc together with sodium carbonate and acetamide in presence of a catalytic quantity of sodium iodide. The bases were added to prevent formation of zinc iodide, which is catalytically inert.

$$\text{ClCH}_2\text{CH}_2\text{CH}_2\text{Cl} + \text{Zn} \rightarrow \overset{\text{CH}_2}{\underset{\text{CH}_2-\text{CH}_2}{\triangle}} + \text{ZnCl}_2$$

In this process, any 1 : 2 : 2-trichloropropane is converted to 2-chloro-propylene, $\text{CH}_3\text{CCl} : \text{CH}_2$, b.p. $+ 22.5°$ c., whereas cyclopropane boils at $- 32.9°$ c. The final step is fractional distillation of cyclopropane to free it both from 2-chloropropylene and from traces of propylene (b.p. $- 47.7°$ c.) and propane (b.p. $- 42.1°$ c.) formed during the ring closure.

4. Chlorination of the butanes

On monochlorination at 300° c., *n*-butane gives 1- and 2-chlorobutanes, 1 : 2- and 1 : 3-dichlorobutanes being by-products;[12] there is no rearrange-ment of the carbon skeleton. The chlorination of *n*-butane and of the monochloro-*n*-butanes has attracted interest since 1910 as possible routes to butadiene and to 2-chlorobutadiene (chloroprene). The chlorination of

---

[12] Hass, McBee and Weber, *Ind. Eng. Chem.*, 1936, **28**, 333.

n-butane to dichlorobutanes was operated in America in 1940 and for a few years afterwards with this objective[13] (Chapter 12, p. 209).

Isobutane chlorinates normally at 300° c. with two to eight mols of hydrocarbon per mol of chlorine; thus with five mols of isobutane, the monochloride fraction consists of 67 per cent isobutyl chloride and 33 per cent *tert*-butyl chloride, the calculated ratio; 6 per cent of polychlorides are also formed.

5. Chlorination of pentanes

The chlorination of pentanes is one of the early examples of a petroleum chemical process giving rise to a multiplicity of products. It was established in America in the 1920's by the Sharples Solvents Corporation and reached almost its final form in the early 1930's; the process is still operated on a scale of several thousand tons a year but has not expanded at the same rate as some other petroleum chemicals operations.

The usual feedstock is a mixture of *n*- and isopentane in approximately equal proportions.[14]

Gaseous chlorine is mixed with a large excess of vaporised pentanes at about 5–6 atma. pressure. The initial temperature is 120° c. and the final temperature at the end of the reactor, about 300° c. The crude product is fractionated to recycle the unchanged pentanes and to separate dichloropentanes from the mixed chloropentanes which were used for the series of derivatives shown below.[15, 16]

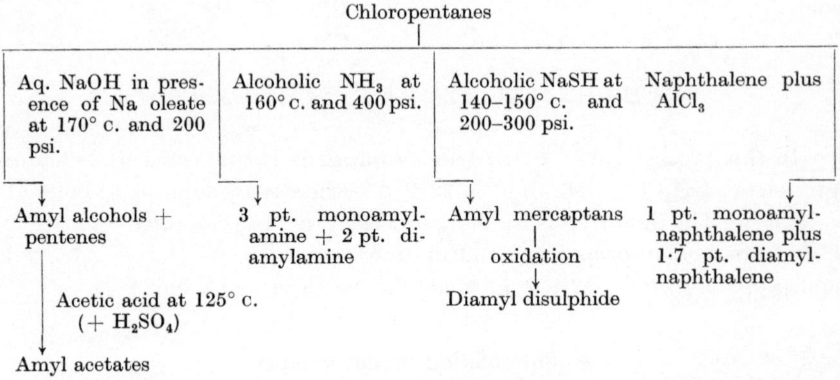

Chloropentanes

Aq. NaOH in presence of Na oleate at 170° c. and 200 psi.	Alcoholic NH₃ at 160° c. and 400 psi.	Alcoholic NaSH at 140–150° c. and 200–300 psi.	Naphthalene plus AlCl₃
Amyl alcohols + pentenes	3 pt. monoamylamine + 2 pt. diamylamine	Amyl mercaptans | oxidation | Diamyl disulphide	1 pt. monoamylnaphthalene plus 1·7 pt. diamylnaphthalene
Acetic acid at 125° c. (+ H₂SO₄)			
Amyl acetates			

The composition of the mixed chloropentanes (amyl chlorides), amyl alcohols (Pentasol), and amyl acetates (Pentacetate), is given by Hunt.[16]

[13] Hearne, *Oil Gas J.*, February 23, 1950, p. 163.
[14] Kenyon, Inskeep, Gillette and Price, *Ind. Eng. Chem.*, 1950, **42**, 2388.
[15] Clark, *Ind. Eng. Chem.*, 1930, **22**, 439.
[16] Hunt, *Ind. Eng. Chem.*, 1943, **35**, 1048.

Chloropentane	%	Pentasol	% *	Pentacetate	%
$CH_3CH_2CH_2CH_2CH_2Cl$	24	$CH_3CH_2CH_2CH_2CH_2OH$	26	$CH_3CH_2CH_2CH_2CH_2OCOCH_3$	17
$CH_3CH_2CH_2\overset{\textstyle \vert}{C}HCH_3$ Cl	8	$CH_3CH_2CH_2\overset{\textstyle \vert}{C}HCH_3$ OH	8	$CH_3CH_2CH_2\overset{\textstyle \vert}{C}HCH_3$ OCOCH$_3$	9
$CH_3CH_2\overset{\textstyle \vert}{C}HCH_2CH_3$ Cl	18	$CH_3CH_2\overset{\textstyle \vert}{C}HCH_2CH_3$ OH	18	$CH_3CH_2\overset{\textstyle \vert}{C}HCH_2CH_3$ OCOCH$_3$	19
$CH_3\overset{\textstyle \vert}{C}HCH_2CH_2Cl$ CH$_3$	15	$CH_3\overset{\textstyle \vert}{C}HCH_2CH_2OH$ CH$_3$	16	$CH_3\overset{\textstyle \vert}{C}HCH_2CH_2OCOCH_3$ CH$_3$	14
$CH_3CH_2\overset{\textstyle \vert}{C}HCH_2Cl$ CH$_3$	30	$CH_3CH_2\overset{\textstyle \vert}{C}HCH_2OH$ CH$_3$	32	$CH_3CH_2\overset{\textstyle \vert}{C}HCH_2OCOCH_3$ CH$_3$	26
$CH_3CH_2\overset{\textstyle \vert}{\underset{\textstyle \vert}{C}}CH_3$ Cl CH$_3$	5	$CH_3CH_2\overset{\textstyle \vert}{C}CH_3$ CH$_3$	—	mixed amyl alcohols	15
	100		100		100

The mixed amyl alcohols (Pentasol) and acetates (Pentacetate) are used as solvents. Mixed amyl mercaptan (Pentalarm) is a warning agent for natural gas or other odourless fuel gas. Monoamylnaphthalene is used as a heat transfer medium. The diamylnaphthalene is a plasticiser, rubber extender, and intermediate for wetting agents. Subsequently Sharples have established processes for alkylphenols from the by-product pentenes obtained in the hydrolysis of the crude chloropentanes.[14] These are referred to in Chapter 11, p. 192.

6. Chlorination of higher hydrocarbons

The most important outlet for chlorinated kerosene is for detergents. The feedstock consisted of a kerosene cut, boiling range 220–245° c. and corresponding to nC_{12} to C_{13} paraffins. The kerosene fraction is heavily solvent and sulphuric acid treated to remove aromatics. Chlorination is carried out at 60° c. to give a 50 per cent theoretical conversion to the monochloro-derivative (Keryl chloride).[17] This was used directly for alkylation of benzene to kerylbenzene as described in Chapter 14, p. 256.

Chlorination of paraffin wax is carried out in the liquid phase at 80–120° c. to give polychloroparaffins containing seven or more chlorine atoms. According to Scheer,[18] three main types of chlorinated paraffin wax are commercially available. The first contains about 43 per cent chlorine, corresponding to seven chlorine atoms introduced into a C_{25} paraffin; this is a mobile non-volatile liquid. With 60 per cent chlorine (15 Cl's per C_{25}), a soft resin is obtained, m.p. 50° c., and 70 per cent chlorine (22 Cl's per C_{25}) gives a hard brittle resin melting at about 80° c. These chlorinated paraffin waxes are used as extreme pressure lubricant bases, flame proofing agents and plasticisers. Less highly chlorinated paraffin waxes are used as chemical

---

* Reference (14) gives the composition of crude amyl alcohols as 25 per cent each of 1-rentanol and 2-rentanol, 17 per cent of 2-methyl-1-butanol, 12 per cent of 3-methyl-1-butanol, 10 per cent of 3-pentanol, 6 per cent of 2-methyl-2-butanol and traces of the other isomers.

[17] Birch, *J. Inst. Pet.*, 1952, **38**, 69.
[18] *Chem. Ind.*, 1944, **54(2)**, 203.

intermediates. Paraflow, a pour point depressant, is made by Friedel-Crafts condensation between naphthalene and chlorinated paraffin wax containing 10–12 per cent of chlorine.[19]

Chlorination of waxes is also carried out to give monochlorides as intermediates for long chain olefins. For example, the Germans made monochlorides from the paraffin waxes produced in the Fischer-Tropsch process (Chapter 3, p. 51) by chlorination at 50–80° c. in the dark.[20]

Except in the case of the two extremes, methane and paraffin wax, chlorination of saturated hydrocarbons is resorted to almost exclusively to make the monochloro derivatives. The technical polychlorohydrocarbons are obtained by addition of chlorine to acetylene, and to ethylene and other olefins, and subsequent dehydrochlorination and chlorination, etc. (see Chapter 10, p. 157).

7. Other reactions of monochlorides

The hydrolysis of monochlorides to alcohols, conversion to amines, mercaptans, xanthate esters and condensation with aromatics have already been touched on. Other reactions of potential interest are:

(a) Reaction with alkali sulphites to give sulphonates (Strecker reaction):

$$RCl + Na_2SO_3 \rightarrow RSO_2ONa + NaCl$$

(b) Reaction with alkali cyanides to give nitriles:

$$RCl + NaCN \rightarrow RCN + NaCl$$

(c) Reaction with alkali alkoxides or phenoxides to give ethers:

$$RCl + NaOR^1 \rightarrow ROR^1 + NaCl$$

Dehydrochlorination to olefins is more usually carried out with substituted chlorides but it has been used for synthetic purposes with the simple monochlorides. Volatile chlorides can conveniently be dehydrochlorinated in the vapour phase at temperatures up to about 400° c. over a variety of catalytic materials such as carbon, alumina, clay, or barium chloride. The high molecular weight chloroparaffins can be dehydrochlorinated in the liquid phase by treatment with alkalies or alkaline materials. The dehydrochlorination of these long chain chloroparaffins proceeds smoothly in the vapour phase at about 350° c. over aluminium silicate catalysts to give olefins of the same chain length as the initial waxes from which the chloroparaffins were prepared.[18]

8. Chlorinolysis

As a logical extension of their work on the chlorination of hydrocarbons with a deficiency of chlorine, Hass and his co-workers have examined the

---

[19] Standard Oil Development, U.S.P. 1815022.
[20] C.I.O.S. 27/69.

interaction of hydrocarbons and chlorohydrocarbons with a large excess of chlorine at high temperature and pressure.[21]

The main reaction is a breaking of the carbon skeleton of the original hydrocarbon into C_1 and C_2 fragments, yielding carbon tetrachloride and hexachloroethane; intermediate products of breakdown have been isolated. To this reaction Hass has applied the term chlorinolysis.

To give an example, one mol of polychloroheptanes of approximately the composition, $C_7H_{14}Cl_4$, reacted with seventeen mols of chlorine at 280° c. and 70 atm. pressure gave carbon tetrachloride and hexachloroethane with about 34 per cent of a highly chlorinated hydrocarbon now thought to be octachlorocyclopentene, C_5HCl_8, following Fruhwirth;[22] as the temperature was raised to 420° c., the yield of this compound decreased and the yield of CCl_4 and C_2Cl_6 reached a maximum of 76 per cent. Above this temperature, the yield again declined, perhaps because reaction could no longer take place in the liquid phase:

$$C_7H_{14}Cl_4 + 17Cl_2 \rightarrow 3CCl_4 + 2C_2Cl_6 + 14HCl$$

Chlorinolysis is operated commercially for the manufacture of hexachlorobutadiene, C_4Cl_6, from butanes and chlorine, and of hexachlorocyclopentadiene, C_5Cl_6, from pentane and chlorine.[23]

Hexachlorobutadiene is also made from trichlorethylene (Chapter 10, p. 156); it is used in transformer oils. Hexachlorocyclopentadiene is an intermediate for pest control chemicals.

9. Direct fluorination of paraffins

As mentioned at the beginning of this Chapter, the fluorine containing paraffins which were industrially important before 1939 were fluorochloroparaffins, made by partial replacement of some of the chlorine atoms in chloroparaffins by fluorinating agents such as antimony trifluoride or hydrofluoric acid.

The second world war led to a tremendous expansion of work on the organic chemistry of fluorine compounds.[24] The main objective in the paraffin series was the preparation of the so-called perfluoroparaffins C_nF_{2n+2}, in which all the hydrogen atoms of the paraffin were replaced by fluorine atoms; these were required on account of their outstanding inertness and stability.

The normal reaction of fluorine with paraffins is to give carbon tetrafluoride or carbon together with hydrogen fluoride, with explosive violence. By carrying out fluorination in the vapour phase in the presence of an inert gas over a solid catalyst, reaction could be moderated and controlled

[21] *Ind. Eng. Chem.*, 1941, **33**, 181; 1943, **35**, 317.
[22] *Ber.*, 1941, **74B**, 1700.
[23] Hooker, U.S.P. 2473162.
[24] *Ind. Eng. Chem.*, 1947, **39**, 236–434.

to give the desired products. The preferred method was to use nitrogen as the inert gas, silver fluoride deposited on copper as the catalyst, and to operate at about 200° c. using somewhat more fluorine than the theoretical requirements. Silver forms both silver fluoride, AgF, and silver perfluoride, AgF_2, which is probably the active fluorinating agent. Under these conditions, n-octane gives perfluorooctane (octadecylfluorooctane)

$$C_8H_{18} + 18F_2 \rightarrow C_8F_{18} + 18HF$$

This reaction has been carried out with lower and higher paraffins, such as hexadecane, $C_{16}H_{34}$, and with other hydrocarbon types, such as the naphthenes. Other metallic fluorides existing in two valency states could also be used as the catalyst, such as the fluorides of cobalt, which forms both cobalt fluoride, CoF_2, and cobalt trifluoride, CoF_3. Cobalt trifluoride could also be used as the sole fluorinating agent. n-Heptane mixed with nitrogen and passed in the vapour phase over cobalt trifluoride at 225–350° c. gave an 80% yield of perfluoroheptane

$$C_7H_{16} + 32CoF_3 \rightarrow C_7F_{16} + 32CoF_2 + 16HF$$

The cobalt fluoride was reconverted to the trifluoride with elementary fluorine.

A later method was the liquid phase fluorination of paraffins using silver perfluoride or cobalt trifluoride as the fluorinating agent. This reaction was carried out at about 100° c., frequently in presence of a perfluoroparaffin as an inert diluent.

All these methods consume large quantities of elementary fluorine, two fluorine atoms being required for each atom of hydrogen replaced. An economy in fluorine was effected by starting with a chloroparaffin and replacing the chlorine atoms with fluorine using hydrogen fluoride; the remaining hydrogen atoms in the molecule were then replaced using elementary fluorine. This method was developed mainly for the synthesis of perfluoronaphthenes.

Unlike the fully chlorinated paraffins, the perfluoroparaffins have physical properties similar to those of the parent hydrocarbons. The similarity in boiling points is shown in Table 20.

TABLE 20

Boiling points of some paraffins, perfluoroparaffins and perchloroparaffins

Paraffin	b.p., ° c./760 mm.	Perfluoro-paraffin	b.p., ° c./760 mm.	Perchloro-paraffin	b.p., ° c./760 mm.
CH_4	− 161	CF_4	− 128	CCl_4	76
C_2H_6	− 89	C_2F_6	− 78	C_2Cl_6	sublimes 187
C_3H_8	− 42	C_3F_8	− 38	C_3Cl_8	270
$n\text{-}C_4H_{10}$	0·5	$n\text{-}C_4F_{10}$	− 5		
$n\text{-}C_7H_{16}$	98	$n\text{-}C_7F_{16}$	82		
$n\text{-}C_{16}H_{34}$	287	$n\text{-}C_{16}F_{34}$	240		

The perfluoroparaffins are completely uninflammable. They have higher viscosities than the corresponding paraffins; their change of viscosity with temperature is steep, *i.e.*, they have very poor viscosity indices. They are stated to be valuable as inert solvents, heat transfer media, sealing liquids, lubricants, and dielectrics for use under high frequency and very high frequency conditions. Outlets will depend upon whether their unique properties more than compensate for their intrinsic high cost.[25]

---

[25] Goldstein, *Pet. Times*, 13 September, 1947, p. 892; Simons, *Chem. Eng.*, 1951, **57**(7), 129; Brice, Bryce and Scholberg, *Chem. Eng. News*, February 9, 1953, p. 510.

4

CHAPTER 6

NITRATION AND OTHER REACTIONS OF PARAFFINS

1. Nitration of paraffins

(a) Vapour phase nitration of the lower paraffins

This reaction of the paraffins was discovered by Hass, Hodge and Vanderbilt in 1934,[1] as an outcome of experiments on the liquid phase nitration of isobutane. The general reaction is:

$$RH + HNO_3 \rightarrow RNO_2 + H_2O$$

Reaction between excess of the paraffin in the vapour phase and the vapours of nitric acid was first examined at atmospheric pressure over the temperature range 250–600° c.; subsequently, nitration at superatmospheric pressure was shown to be equally successful and to give the same products in the same conversion at much greater speeds. Two main types of reaction occur, nitration and oxidation; oxidation is simultaneous with and does not merely follow nitration.

At least two mols of hydrocarbon are used per mol of nitric acid, to avoid explosive mixtures. The nitric acid which oxidises the hydrocarbon is reduced to nitric oxide, which is easily reconvertible to nitric acid so that the yield of nitrohydrocarbon on nitric acid consumed can be as high as 90 per cent. Most of the catalysts so far examined merely accelerate the oxidation reaction. Increase in temperature increases the velocity of nitration, the production of primary nitroparaffins at the expense of secondary and tertiary isomers, and the yield of fission products; the similarity to the effect of temperature on vapour phase chlorination of paraffins (Chapter 5) is noteworthy. At constant contact time, the conversion passes through a maximum with rising temperature. Temperatures below the optimum are too low for completion of the reaction whilst at excessive temperatures pyrolysis of nitroparaffin becomes serious; in the commercial nitration of paraffins, the temperature is controlled to $\pm 1°$ c., owing to the highly exothermic nature of the reaction, to prevent local hot-spots which might set off uncontrollable reactions.

Methane is the most difficult paraffin to nitrate.[2] At 475° c., with nine mols methane per mol of nitric acid and a contact time of 0·18 second, the conversion of nitric acid to nitromethane was 13 per cent per pass.

Ethane is somewhat easier to nitrate.[3] With ten mols hydrocarbon per

---

[1] U.S.P. 1967667.

[2] Landon, U.S.P. 2161475, 2164774; Boyd and Hass, *Ind. Eng. Chem.*, 1942, **34**, 300, 632.

[3] Hibshman, Pierson and Hass, *Ind. Eng. Chem.*, 1940, **32**, 427.

mol of nitric acid at 440–450° c. and 10 atma. pressure, contact time 0·2–0·3 second, in a salt film coated stainless steel reactor, 33% conversion of nitric acid was effected to give a mixture of 27 per cent nitromethane and 73 per cent nitroethane. Propane and the next higher homologues nitrate still more readily.

For technical reasons, propane was the first hydrocarbon which was nitrated on the commercial scale. Operating conditions were 375–450° c. at 8 atma. pressure, using a high ratio of paraffin to nitric acid in presence of oxygen, added as a source of free radicals. All the possible nitro-compounds, 1- and 2-nitropropane, nitroethane and nitromethane, were obtained. For many years, the capacity of this plant was in the range 1–2 tons per day; a new plant is being built with a capacity of 4,500 tons p.a.

Nitration of propane, in conjunction with work on nitration of higher hydrocarbons, has led to the following generalisation. When a paraffin is nitrated at high temperature in the vapour phase, all the mononitration substitution products are obtained which result if the nitro group behaves as if it could substitute any hydrogen atom or any alkyl radical present in the hydrocarbon. Thus, isopentane (2-methylbutane) yields 1-nitro-2-methylbutane, 2-nitro-2-methylbutane, 3-nitro-2-methylbutane and 4-nitro-2-methylbutane by substituting any of the hydrogen atoms, and nitromethane, nitroethane, 2-nitropropane, 2-nitrobutane and 1-nitro-2-methylpropane by substituting alkyl groups:

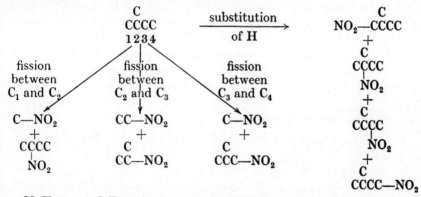

McCleary and Degering[4] suggested that the reaction proceeded by a free radical mechanism on much the same lines as vapour phase oxidation (Chapter 4) and chlorination (Chapter 5):

$$RH \rightarrow R^\times + H^\times$$
$$R^\times + HONO_2 \rightarrow RNO_2 + OH^\times$$
$$RH + OH^\times \rightarrow R^\times + H_2O$$

The initial radical formation could be started off by heat or by dissociation of nitric acid into OH and NO_2 radicals. This mechanism would explain

4 *Ind. Eng. Chem.*, 1938, **30**, 64.

the general course of the reaction, the inertness of water and catalysts and the effect of oxygen.

The main by-products in technical vapour phase nitration are volatile aldehydes and ketones, which amount to a considerable fraction of the total paraffin reacted. In processes in which unchanged paraffins are recycled, these aldehydes and ketones are removed after condensing out the nitroparaffins by scrubbing with water and then with sulphuric acid; the $> CO$ compounds cannot be recovered from these scrubbing liquors. Alternatively, they may be absorbed in concentrated aqueous hydroxylamine hydrochloride solutions to give the oximes. The aldehydes and ketones are regenerated by boiling these solutions, the hydroxylamine hydrochloride being simultaneously reformed and recycled.[5]

Vapour phase nitration with nitric acid does not give rise to di- or polynitro compounds. Urbanski and Slon[6] nitrated propane with nitrogen dioxide in the vapour phase at 200° c. and stated that the products included both nitropropanes and dinitropropanes. Vapour phase nitration with nitrogen dioxide instead of nitric acid has been examined.[7]

Later work by Imperial Chemical Industries confirms the statement of Urbanski and Slon that small amounts of dinitroparaffins are obtained in the vapour phase nitration of paraffins with nitrogen dioxide. This company considers that nitrogen dioxide has certain advantages over nitric acid for the vapour phase reaction. Lower temperatures, longer contact times and a higher proportion of nitrating agent can be used, permitting better temperature control. In one example, propane and nitrogen dioxide at 360° c. and 10 atma. pressure gave 20–25 per cent nitromethane, 5–10 per cent nitroethane, 45–55 per cent 2-nitropropane and 20 per cent 1-nitropropane. The overall yield was 75–80 per cent on propane reacted and over 90 per cent on the nitrogen dioxide.[8]

(b) LIQUID PHASE NITRATION

From the confused literature on the liquid phase nitration of paraffins, the following generalisations emerge:

(*i*) Tertiary hydrogen atoms are most readily replaced, secondary react more sluggishly and primary hydrogen atoms are relatively unreactive.

(*ii*) Reaction is slow but yields and conversions are increased with increase in temperature.

(*iii*) Nitration is accompanied by much oxidation and by formation of free nitrogen and not nitric oxide as with vapour phase nitration.

(*iv*) Large quantities of polynitro compounds are stated to accompany

---

[5] Commercial Solvents, U.S.P. 2213444.
[6] *Chem. Abs.*, 1937, **31**, 6190.
[7] Commercial Solvents, U.S.P. 2213444; I.C.I., B.P. 527031.
[8] Levy and Rose, *Quarterly Reviews of the Chemical Society*, 1947, **1**, 358.

the mononitro derivatives; this may be due to preferential solution of the mononitro compound initially formed in the nitric acid.

(v) The mechanism of liquid phase nitration is different from that of vapour phase nitration. This is indicated not only by formation of nitrogen and of polynitro compounds, neither of which are formed in vapour phase nitration, but by the observation that liquid phase nitration of *l*-3-methyloctane gives optically active 3-nitro-3-methyloctane, which, if confirmed, excludes a free radical mechanism.

(vi) In liquid phase nitration, fission of the carbon chain appears to occur as a secondary oxidative reaction and not during the initial nitration.

From these considerations, the easiest paraffins to nitrate are the isoparaffins. Thus isobutane readily yields 2-nitro-2-methylpropane by heating with fuming nitric acid under pressure at 150° c. for a few minutes.

Liquid phase nitration of the higher paraffins has been worked out by Grundman.[9] He passed the vapours of 95–100% nitric acid through the liquid paraffin at temperatures up to 190° c. Operating to give 50% unchanged paraffins, he obtained good yields of mono- and polynitroparaffins with some oxidation to fatty acids. High ratios of nitric acid to paraffin gave more oxidation and a high ratio of poly- to mononitroparaffin. The paraffins examined ranged from *n*-octane to *n*-octadecane; fractions of Fischer-Tropsch diesel oils boiling up to 340° c. were also successfully nitrated. As with vapour phase nitration, nitrogen dioxide could be used in place of nitric acid.

The interesting products of this reaction were the mononitro derivatives of the higher paraffins, on account of their potentialities as intermediates for surface active agents. The mononitro derivatives were isolated by vacuum distillation. No chain breaking was involved in the nitration, and no primary nitroparaffins were produced; the mononitroparaffins are now thought to consist of a mixture of all the possible isomeric secondary nitroparaffins.

2 : 2-Dinitropropane has been made by liquid phase nitration of 2-nitropropane at 60–80 atm. and at 204–232° c. using molar proportions of 2-nitropropane and nitric acid. The reaction conditions were chosen to give 11–14 per cent conversion per pass. The yield was 50 per cent overall. The 2 : 2-dinitropropane was of interest as a diesel fuel improver.[10]

(c) PROPERTIES OF NITROPARAFFINS

The nitroparaffins are liquids at ordinary temperatures, with boiling points from 102° c. (nitromethane) upwards. Some of the lower nitroparaffins (nitroethane and the nitropropanes) melt as low as − 100° c. They have densities from 1·14 (nitromethane) falling to 0·90 to 0·95 for

[9] *Die Chemie* (formerly *Angew. Chem.*), 1943, **56**, 159; see also B.I.O.S. 1151.
[10] Denton, Bishop, Nygaard and Noland, *Ind. Eng. Chem.*, 1948, **40**, 381.

the higher members. Nitromethane is appreciably soluble in water but solubility diminishes rapidly with increase of molecular weight.

(d) REACTIONS OF NITROPARAFFINS

The reactions of nitroparaffins have been fully examined[11, 12] but it should be mentioned that their technical outlets are so far limited. The principal commercial products are the nitropropanes, nitroethane, nitromethane and hydroxylamine salts.

(i) *Condensation with aldehydes and ketones*

Under the influence of basic catalysts, aldehydes and ketones undergo an aldol condensation with those nitroparaffins carrying a free hydrogen atom on the same carbon atom which bears the NO_2 group, *e.g.*,

$$\begin{array}{c} R \\ R \end{array}\!\!>\!\!C\!\!<\!\!\begin{array}{c} H \\ NO_2 \end{array} + R_1CHO \rightarrow \begin{array}{c} R \\ R \end{array}\!\!>\!\!C\!\!-\!\!CHR_1 \atop \quad\ \ NO_2\ \ OH$$

The ease of reaction and the number of hydrogen atoms displaced depend both on the nitroparaffin and on the aldehyde or ketone, decreasing with increase in molecular weight of either participant. With formaldehyde and nitromethane, it is almost impossible to stop the reaction before all three hydrogen atoms are replaced, giving trimethylolnitromethane, $NO_2C(CH_2OH)_3$.

This reaction gives rise to nitroalcohols, nitrodiols and nitrotriols, which can be esterified, and can be reduced to the corresponding aminoalcohols. A series of nitroalcohols and aminoalcohols are now commercially available.

The most important derivatives of the nitroalcohols are the trinitrate of $NO_2C(CH_2OH)_3$ and the dinitrate of 2-methyl-2-nitro-1 : 3-propanediol, $NO_2CCH_3(CH_2OH)_2$, both of which are explosives. The nitroalcohols have also been converted into the esters of phosphoric acid and of organic acids for plasticisers.

Those nitrohydroxy compounds with a hydrogen atom on the carbon atom carrying the NO_2 group can easily be converted to nitroolefins, either by direct dehydration or by splitting out acids from some of the esters, usually under the influence of catalysts.[13]

$$NO_2CHRCR_1R_2OH \text{ (or OAcyl)} \rightarrow NO_2CR : CR_1R_2 + H_2O \text{ (or HOAcyl)}$$

(ii) *Hydrolysis*

The free primary nitro compounds are hydrolysed by concentrated mineral acids to give the corresponding carboxylic acids and a salt of hydroxylamine:

$$RCH_2NO_2 + H_2SO_4 + H_2O \rightarrow RCOOH + NH_2OH \cdot H_2SO_4$$

---

[11] Gabriel, *Ind. Eng. Chem.*, 1940, **32**, 887.
[12] Schickh, *Angew. Chem.*, 1949, **62**, 547.
[13] See, for example, Nightingale and Janes, *J. Amer. Chem. Soc.*, 1944, **66**, 352.

This route is reported to be the principal commercial source of the hydroxyl-amine salts manufactured in the United States. As a process for manufacturing carboxylic acids from natural gas, it is of no importance.

Hydrolysis is usually carried out by dissolving the nitroparaffin in 95–100 per cent sulphuric acid at 50–100° c., followed by dilution with water.

(iii) Chlorination

In the presence of bases, chlorination of nitroparaffins higher than nitro-methane replaces each of the hydrogen atoms on the carbon atom carrying the NO_2 group in turn. Thus nitroethane gives first 1-chloro-1-nitroethane, then 1 : 1-dichloro-1-nitroethane (a fumigant for grain and other pests). From nitromethane, however, only trichloronitromethane (chloropicrin), CCl_3NO_2, the poison gas and insecticide, has been definitely isolated; presumably the mono and dichloronitromethanes react too readily with chlorine to permit isolation.

In the absence of bases and under the influence of intense illumination, chlorine reacts by substituting hydrogen atoms other than those on the carbon atom carrying the NO_2 group; nitroethane under these conditions gives 1-chloro-2-nitroethane. 1-Nitrobutane gives 2-, 3-, and 4-chloro-1-nitrobutanes.

The chloronitroparaffins prepared by either of these routes have been examined as new synthetic intermediates, and for incorporation into rubber cements.

2. Sulphonation of paraffins

The petroleum sulphonates obtained in the manufacture of 'white oils' from petroleum are referred to in Chapter 21, p. 387, and are probably mainly sulphonic acids of substituted aromatic or naphthenic hydrocarbons in which the sulphuric acid group has entered the ring. However, it is possible to sulphonate the paraffins directly. This has almost necessarily to be carried out in the liquid phase and as with other similar reactions, tertiary hydrogen is more reactive than secondary, and secondary than primary. This reaction has not been technically developed.

More important is the Reed reaction.[14] By reaction between sulphur dioxide and chlorine (or sulphuryl chloride) with the paraffin in the presence of light, sulphonyl chlorides are obtained in high yield:

$$RH + SO_2Cl_2 \rightarrow RSO_2Cl + HCl$$

The reaction is believed to proceed through a free radical mechanism:

$$Cl_2 \xrightarrow{\text{light}} 2Cl^\times$$
$$RH + Cl^\times \rightarrow R^\times + HCl$$
$$R^\times + SO_2 \rightarrow RSO_2^\times$$
$$RSO_2^\times + Cl_2 \rightarrow RSO_2Cl + Cl^\times$$

---

[14] U.S.P. 2046090 *et seq.* Lockwood, *Chem. Ind.*, 1948, **62(5)**, 760.

The scope of this type of reaction has been enlarged by the researches of Kharasch and his school.[15] Very little chlorine substitution takes place, which is surprising, as with other hydrocarbons sulphuryl chloride is a powerful chlorinating agent.

With the normal paraffins, the hydrogen atoms will probably be replaced by rules similar to Hass's rules for chlorination (Chapter 5), *i.e.*, tertiary > secondary > primary. With the paraffins which are reacted technically, the normal paraffins C_{10} to about C_{18}, the products will be almost exclusively secondary sulphonyl chlorides.

The reaction was developed both in America and in Germany to produce synthetic detergents by saponification of the sulphonyl chloride:

$$RSO_2Cl + 2NaOH \rightarrow RSO_2Na + NaCl + H_2O$$

In Germany, the source material was the diesel oil fraction, b.p. 220–330° c., from the Fischer-Tropsch synthesis (Chapter 3, p. 50). This consists of C_{10}–C_{18} normal paraffins (average C_{15}) with a small proportion of olefins. The oil was hydrogenated to give a completely saturated paraffin which was then reacted with sulphur dioxide and chlorine under exposure to ultraviolet light, at ordinary temperature and pressure; only 50–70% conversion was aimed at in order to reduce both chlorination and formation of disulphonyl chlorides, and to cause substitution as near the end of the chain as possible. Power consumption was very low, about 0·001 kWh/lb. product. The monosulphonyl chloride (Mersol) was separated from unchanged paraffin, which was recycled to the process. For detergents, the sulphonyl chloride was hydrolysed with caustic soda to give the sodium sulphonate (Mersolate). In the household field, Mersolate was mixed with sodium silicate or sodium cellulose glycollate, and used for making soap powders.

Owing to the shortage of natural fats in Germany, this reaction was carried out on a large scale during the second world war. The two plants at Leuna and Oppau manufactured 85,000 tons p.a. Mersolate.

The I.G. had examined alternative methods of sulphonating paraffins without use of chlorine.[16] Working on a hydrogenated Fischer-Tropsch fraction, b.p. 220–240° c., average molecular weight C_{13} to C_{14}, they examined three processes:

(i) Use of sulphur dioxide and oxygen, activated by light in presence of water

$$RH + 2SO_2 + H_2O + O_2 \rightarrow RSO_2OH + H_2SO_4$$

Reaction was carried out at 40–50° c. under strong illumination; only a relatively small excess of hydrocarbon was used. The diagrammatic flowsheet was as shown in Fig. 10.

---

[15] J. C. Smith, *Ann. Rep.*, 1939, **36**, 233; 1940, **37**, 209.
[16] C.I.O.S. 26/2; see also B.I.O.S. 478.

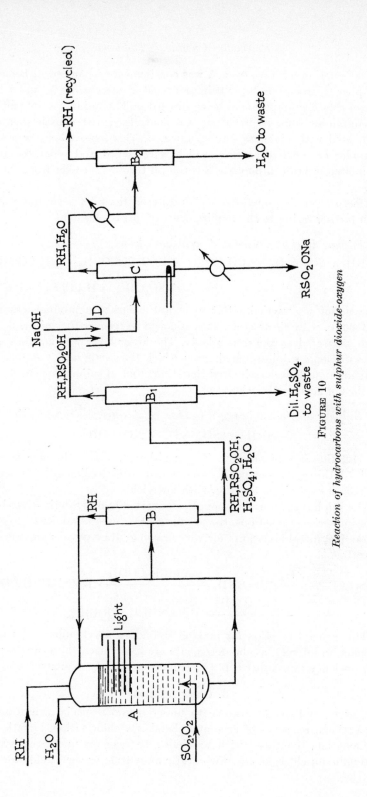

FIGURE 10

Reaction of hydrocarbons with sulphur dioxide-oxygen

The reaction mixture from A was continuously separated in B and B_1, the upper hydrocarbon layer being recycled to the reactor A, and a lower layer of dilute sulphuric acid being discarded. The product sulphonic acid still containing some hydrocarbon was neutralised with caustic soda in D, and heated with high pressure steam in C. This removed water and the remainder of the hydrocarbon which were cooled and separated in B_2. The molten sodium sulphonate was run off through a cooler from the base of C.

This process was operated successfully on the pilot scale but was not taken further owing to the requirements of ultraviolet light.

(ii) Sulphur dioxide, oxygen and acetic anhydride

$$RH + SO_2 + O_2 + (CH_3CO)_2O \rightarrow RSO_2OOCOCH_3 + CH_3COOH$$
$$\downarrow H_2O$$
$$RSO_2OH + CH_3COOH + \tfrac{1}{2}O_2$$

This reaction was carried out at 40° c. in the dark; the product was mixed at 55–60° c. with dilute aqueous acetic acid to recover the sulphonic acid, which separated as the upper layer. The lower layer was aqueous acetic acid with some sulphuric acid, from which the acetic acid was recovered by distillation. It was estimated that 1,000 tons of sulphonic acid required 215 tons of acetic anhydride.

(iii) Sulphur dioxide and oxygen in absence of water, activated by light

$$2RH + 2SO_2 + O_2 \rightarrow 2RSO_2OH$$

The equation is misleadingly simple; although some sulphonic acid was obtained, this route was quickly abandoned owing to difficulty of operation and risk of explosions, together with low yields.

The sulphonyl chlorides were also converted to other derivatives by the following series of reactions, the products being used as additives to engine oils, and to metal lubricants for wire drawing; they possess anti-corrosive properties.

$$RSO_2Cl \xrightarrow{+ NH_3} RSO_2NH_2 \xrightarrow{+ ClCH_2COOH} RSO_2NHCH_2COOH$$
$$\xrightarrow{+ C_7H_{15}OH} RSO_2NHCH_2COOC_7H_{15}$$

This general reaction for making secondary alkyl sulphonates is now declining in interest, as the detergents are less efficient in properties or in cost efficiency than other types which are now freely available.

3. Other reactions

Just as paraffins can be made to undergo under special conditions the conventional reactions of aromatic chemistry, chlorination, nitration and sulphonation, they react with Friedel-Crafts reagents under the influence of aluminium chloride, *e.g.*, with acetic anhydride or acetyl chloride, with formation of ketones, and with carbon monoxide and hydrogen chloride giving acid chlorides and aldehydes.[17]

However, the catalytic effect of the aluminium chloride is usually not limited to introduction of the reactant into the paraffin chain; isomerisation of the paraffin takes place (aluminium chloride is used industrially for isomerising the lower *n*-paraffins to isoparaffins—see Chapter 2), and further side reactions of the primary products also occur so that this reaction is not yet of much value as a new technical method of synthesis.

Methane and other paraffins can also be readily converted to hydrogen cyanide and to carbon disulphide. Routes to hydrogen cyanide are dealt with in Chapter 20, p. 363.

Methane has long been known to react with sulphur or with hydrogen sulphide at about 1,000° c. to give carbon disulphide.[18] The various possible reactions have been considered from the thermodynamic angle by Thacker and Miller.[19] The main reactions are:

$$CH_4 + 2S_2 \rightarrow CS_2 + 2H_2S \qquad . \qquad . \qquad . \qquad (1)$$
$$CH_4 + S_2 \rightarrow CS_2 + 2H_2 \qquad . \qquad . \qquad . \qquad (2)$$
$$CH_4 + 2H_2S \rightarrow CS_2 + 4H_2 \qquad . \qquad . \qquad . \qquad (3)$$

For the case where all reactants were gaseous, the calculated change in free energy and its variation with temperature are shown in Table 21.

TABLE 21

Carbon disulphide from methane; free energy change

	ΔG (g. cal./g. mol)		
° c.	Reaction 1	Reaction 2	Reaction 3
427	− 28,000	− 1,100	+ 25,000
527	− 28,000	− 4,000	+ 20,000
627	− 28,500	− 6,500	+ 15,000
727	− 29,000	− 10,000	+ 10,000

Reactions (1) and (2) will therefore proceed to completion at all temperatures above 400–500° c. The calculated equilibrium conversion to carbon disulphide in reaction (3) is as follows:

° c.	% conversion to CS_2
500	5
600	10
700	17
800	35

---

[17] Ellis, 'Chemistry of Petroleum Derivatives', *Reinhold*, Vol. 2, 1937, p. 1099.
[18] I.G., B.P. 293172; I.C.I., B.P. 331734.
[19] *Ind. Eng. Chem.*, 1944, **36**, 182.

Experimental work was carried out on reaction (1), passing methane and sulphur over catalysts, of which the most effective was alumina promoted with manganese dioxide or with vanadium pentoxide. Conversions approaching 100 per cent were obtained below 700° c.

This work is the basis of a technical process operated by the Barium Reduction Co., for making carbon disulphide and hydrogen sulphide from methane and sulphur.[20] The process is operated at about 600–650° c., using a silica gel catalyst; the conversion is over 90 per cent per pass. The hydrogen sulphide is used on site for the manufacture of lithopone. The standard manufacturing process for making carbon disulphide is from charcoal and sulphur. Its principal outlet is in the rayon industry but it is also used for manufacture of carbon tetrachloride and rubber chemicals.

Preparation of thiophene, $\begin{smallmatrix} CH—CH \\ \| \quad\quad \| \\ CH \quad CH \\ \diagdown S \diagup \end{smallmatrix}$, by reaction between butane and

sulphur in the vapour phase at 600–650° c. is described by Rasmussen, Hanford and Sachanen.[21] Best conditions were 0·07 second contact time at 650° c. using equal weights of hydrocarbon and sulphur, 50% conversion per pass and quick quenching. The reaction proceeds stepwise via n-butene and butadiene; by recycling these unsaturated hydrocarbons, a 50% overall yield of thiophene was obtained; side reactions include formation of tar and of carbon disulphide. The Socony-Vacuum Oil Co. have built a plant to operate this process with a capacity of 300 tons p.a. thiophene.[22] This plant is reported to be operated in the temperature range, 620–730° c.[23]

Thiophene is an intermediate for pharmaceuticals and pest control chemicals. At lower temperatures and higher pressures, thiophthenes are formed from C_8 and higher hydrocarbons and sulphur.[24]

---

[20] Folkins, Miller and Hennig, *Ind. Eng. Chem.*, 1950, **42**, 2202.
[21] *Ind. Eng. Chem.*, 1946, **38**, 376.
[22] Rasmussen and Ray, *Chem. Ind.*, 1947, **60**, 593.
[23] *Chem. Eng.*, Nov. 1955, p. 106.
[24] Friedman, *Ber.*, 1916, **49**, 1344.

CHAPTER 7

MANUFACTURE OF OLEFINS

1. Principles of cracking and pyrolysis

IN Chapter 2, it was pointed out that olefins do not occur in nature in crude petroleum. They are produced as by-products in the cracking of petroleum to petrol, one of the principal processes of the oil industry, or as main products of the cracking or pyrolysis of petroleum hydrocarbons. Cracking and pyrolysis imply the same type of chemical reaction but these terms are usually reserved for different temperature ranges; cracking is applied to the heat treatment of hydrocarbons in the temperature range 350–650° c.; pyrolysis relates to heat treatment above about 650° c.

Cracking is one of the major operations of the oil industry; it is carried out with the objective of converting fractions of crude petroleum into high octane petrol. The basic reactions are changes in the hydrocarbons of the paraffin series; two types of reaction can occur, dehydrogenation or chain rupture:

$$C_nH_{2n+2} \rightarrow C_nH_{2n} + H_2 \qquad . \qquad . \qquad . \qquad (1)$$

$$C_{m+n}H_{2(m+n)+2} \rightarrow C_mH_{2m} + C_nH_{2n+2} \qquad . \qquad . \qquad (2)$$

The olefins produced can then undergo further decomposition or condensation reactions. The products of cracking paraffins include olefins, diolefins, aromatics, naphthenes, and at the highest temperatures, acetylene. The thermodynamic possibilities of interchange amongst the various types of hydrocarbons are of vital importance both in this chapter, where olefins are the main consideration, and in subsequent chapters in which the manufacture of other types of hydrocarbons by heat treatment are considered.

We therefore introduce here data on the free energy of formation of the more important hydrocarbons and related compounds involved in cracking processes. The data in Table 22, based on A.P.I. Research Project No. 44,[1] show the free energy of formation of the gaseous hydrocarbon (unless otherwise stated) from graphite and hydrogen gas over the temperature range 700–1,000° K. This enables the free energy equations to be presented in the approximate form, $\Delta G = a + bT$.

The values of the free energies of formation per carbon atom against temperature for these hydrocarbons have been plotted in Fig. 11 to cover the temperature range 700–1,200° K.; although we shall use these equations later for exemplifying calculations of equilibrium at higher temperatures, their uncertainty outside the specified limits must be mentioned. This way

---

[1] 'Selected Values of Physical and Thermodynamic Properties of Hydrocarbons and Related Compounds', *Carnegie Press*, 1953.

of plotting free energies per carbon atom against temperature was introduced by Francis in 1928 and is most useful in getting a clear picture of the relative stabilities of the individual hydrocarbons.

TABLE 22

Hydrocarbons and related compounds.
Free energy of formation, 700–1,000°K.

Substance	Formula	Free energy of formation g. cal./g. mol. ΔG 700° K.–1,000° K.
Water (steam) . . .	$H_2O(g)$	$-58,973 + 12\cdot94T$
Carbon monoxide . .	CO	$-26,556 - 21\cdot39T$
Carbon dioxide . .	CO_2	$-94,230 - 0\cdot38T$
Methane	CH_4	$-20,920 + 25\cdot5T$
Ethane	C_2H_6	$-24,640 + 50\cdot8T$
Propane	C_3H_8	$-30,150 + 75\cdot8T$
n-Butane . . .	C_4H_{10}	$-36,530 + 101\cdot0T$
n-Hexane . . .	C_6H_{14}	$-48,400 - 152\cdot0T$
n-Octane . . .	C_8H_{18}	$-60,310 + 202\cdot9T$
Higher paraffins .	C_nH_{2n+2}	$-12,606 - 5,963n + 25\cdot3nT$
Ethylene . . .	C_2H_4	$-9,672 + 18\cdot6T$
Propylene . . .	C_3H_6	$630 + 42\cdot8T$
1-Butene . . .	C_4H_8	$-4,730 + 67\cdot8T$
trans-2-Butene . .	C_4H_8	$-8,040 + 70\cdot7T$
cis-2-Butene . .	C_4H_8	$-7,617 + 71\cdot0T$
Isobutene . . .	C_4H_8	$-9,113 + 70\cdot8T$
n-Hexene. . .	C_6H_{12}	$-16,720 + 118\cdot5T$
Higher olefins . .	C_nH_{2n}	$19,058 - 5,963n - 33\cdot6T + 25\cdot3nT$
Acetylene . . .	C_2H_2	$53,584 - 13\cdot0T$
1 : 3-Butadiene. .	C_4H_6	$23,160 + 39\cdot2T$
Cyclopentane . .	C_5H_{10}	$-26,150 + 109\cdot5T$
Cyclohexane . .	C_6H_{12}	$-37,200 + 141\cdot5T$
Methyl cyclopentane .	C_6H_{12}	$-33,770 + 132\cdot2T$
Methyl cyclohexane .	C_7H_{14}	$-45,070 + 164\cdot1T$
Benzene . . .	C_6H_6	$15,410 + 46\cdot86T$
Toluene . . .	C_7H_8	$6,273 + 70\cdot05T$
Ethyl benzene . .	C_8H_{10}	$696 + 94\cdot61T$
Styrene . . .	C_8H_8	$30,420 + 63\cdot5T$
Naphthalene . .	$C_{10}H_8$	$28,600 + 42\cdot6T$

So far as thermodynamic considerations are concerned, the tendency of a reaction to proceed at any given temperature is from a higher to a lower curve in the figure. Thus it is clear that methane is the most stable paraffin at all temperatures, and that the relative stability of paraffins decreases as we ascend the series. Methane itself becomes unstable with respect to its elements above 820° K. but the higher members, such as tetradecane, approach instability only a little above ordinary temperatures. The olefins are thermodynamically unstable at all temperatures, but their stability *vis-à-vis* the corresponding paraffin increases with rise in temperature; thus, ethylene is more stable than ethane above 1,066° K. In general, paraffins and naphthenes are relatively the more stable hydrocarbons at low temperatures, *i.e.*, below about 500° K., whilst the aromatics

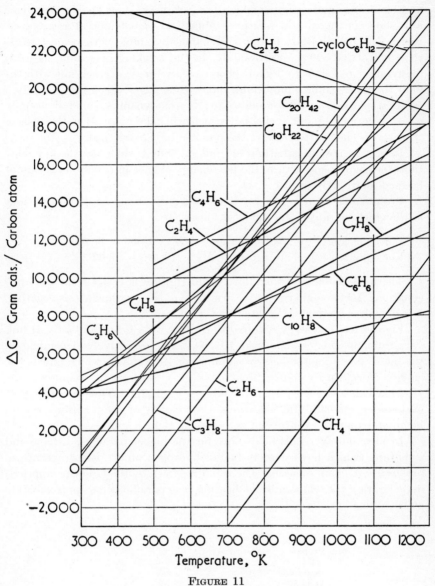

FIGURE 11

Free energy of formation of hydrocarbons

and olefins are more stable at high temperatures. Diolefins and acetylene also show an increase in relative stability at high temperatures. Nevertheless, no hydrocarbon is thermodynamically stable with respect to its elements above 820° K. Fortunately, in the cracking operation, as in so many other reactions in organic chemistry, we are concerned not with the final thermodynamic equilibrium, but with changes which involve only a small step towards true equilibrium; thermodynamics can tell us only which reactions cannot occur, not which will take place. It is the task of the process chemist to convert the possible to the practical.

Reverting now to equations (1) and (2) above, which are the key reactions for olefin manufacture, the free energy change in equation (2) cannot be read off directly from Fig. 11.

From Table 22, the general free energy equations for these reactions in the cracking range (700–1,000° K.) are:

For equation (1), dehydrogenation: $\Delta G = 31{,}600 - 33 \cdot 6T$.
For equation (2), chain rupture: $\Delta G = 19{,}100 - 33 \cdot 6T$.

Thermodynamically, therefore, chain rupture is easier than dehydrogenation; ΔG for chain rupture $= 0$ at 294° c., above which ΔG is negative. For dehydrogenation, $\Delta G = 0$ at 669° c.

Figures for the energy required to rupture a C—C link and a C—H link vary from 50–80 k. cal. and from 70–100 k. cal. respectively, depending on the figure taken for the heat of sublimation of graphite, which affects the energy of rupture equally; breaking a C—C link always requires some 18–20 k. cal. less energy than breaking a C—H link. This would suggest that under non-catalytic conditions, the velocity of chain rupture should be greater than the velocity of dehydrogenation.

In fact, however, this holds only for the higher paraffins. Ethane and isobutane (which has a loosely bound hydrogen atom) dehydrogenate in preference to chain breaking. The trend is shown by the following approximate figures,[2] the temperature of heating each paraffin being approximately 600–650° c. :

Paraffin	% reaction yielding hydrogen
Ethane	High
Propane	42
n-Butane . . .	16
Isobutane . . .	63
Isopentane . . .	2
n-Pentane and higher .	nil

The generalised equations of free energies of formation given in lines 10 and 18 of Table 22 are approximately true only for hydrocarbons with four or more carbon atoms. The lower paraffins and olefins are relatively more stable than their higher homologues. This means that dehydrogenation

---

[2] From Gruse and Stevens, 'Chemical Technology of Petroleum', *McGraw-Hill*, 1942.

is increasingly difficult as the number of carbon atoms in the paraffin decreases.

For the dehydrogenation of ethane to ethylene, on the equations in Table 22, $\Delta G = 0$ only at $1,066°$ K. (see Introduction, p. 7). A second deduction, based on the abnormal stability of methane, is that in chain rupture, demethanation, and to a lesser extent de-ethanation, producing as large an olefin as possible from the original molecule, is the type of rupture best favoured on thermodynamic grounds:

$$C_nH_{2n+2} \rightarrow C_{n-1}H_{2(n-1)} + CH_4$$

This conclusion finds some support from the presence of methane as one of the major constituents of cracking gases and is in agreement with Haber's cracking rule, advanced sixty years ago, which states that of two molecules formed in the cleavage of a paraffin, the smaller should be paraffinic and the larger olefinic. However, the differences in the free energy changes for the various possible rearrangements are relatively small, so that minor changes in conditions, *e.g.*, change in pressure, may alter the point of rupture.

Coming now to the changes in total heat content, both dehydrogenation and chain rupture are endothermic. The heats of reaction cannot be read off from equations (3) and (4), which have been rounded off.

The generalised heat of formation of paraffins of nC atoms is:

$$\Delta H = -10\cdot11 - 5\cdot467n - 0\cdot00304T - 0\cdot000553nT \text{ k. cal/mol}$$

Assuming that the heat of formation of olefins is of the same form as of paraffins, with the same increment per carbon atom, the heat of formation of olefins of nC atoms is:

$$\Delta H = 20\cdot16 - 5\cdot467n - 0\cdot00250T - 0\cdot000553nT \text{ k. cal./mol}$$

From these two equations, in the range $700–1,000°$ K.:

ΔH for equation (1), dehydrogenation, is $+31$ k. cal. (approx.)
ΔH for equation (2), chain rupture, is $+18$ k. cal. (approx.)

Of the possible secondary reactions which may take place, the polymerisation of olefins is independent of the size of olefin and can proceed up to about $300°$ c. at ordinary pressure:

$$2C_nH_{2n} \rightleftharpoons C_{2n}H_{4n}. \quad \Delta G = -19,100 + 33\cdot6T$$

Application of pressure will favour polymerisation and will retard the reverse reaction, depolymerisation.

Formation of diolefins is appreciable in practice above about $600°$ c.; this is dealt with in Chapter 12. Aromatics are also formed in much the same temperature range, *i.e.*, from $600°$ c. upwards. They seem to arise mainly through combination between olefins and diolefins, and their formation can be suppressed by working outside the temperature range of diolefin formation or by operation at short contact time, so that secondary reactions are prevented. Conditions for *ad hoc* synthesis of aromatics from simpler molecules and by breakdown of more complex molecules are discussed in Chapter 14, p. 242.

Several theories have been advanced in an attempt to visualise how the carbon-to-carbon rupture takes place and to account quantitatively for the products formed. Rice has suggested formation of free radicals which initiate chain reactions in which methyl and ethyl radicals and hydrogen atoms act as carriers. Although his original scheme is now thought to be kinetically untenable, there is evidence for the presence of free radicals in the thermal decomposition of paraffins. On the other hand, other types of hydrocarbons such as the naphthenes are known to decompose at cracking temperatures by a mechanism which does not involve intervention of free radicals.[3]

The major factors influencing the course of cracking are temperature, pressure and time of contact.

As has been indicated above, the temperature level at which cracking is carried out may alter the reactions which are thermodynamically possible. Increase in temperature also greatly increases the speed of cracking. At low percentage decomposition, *i.e.*, where secondary reactions do not occur to an appreciable extent, the velocity of cracking, k, is affected by temperature according to Arrhenius' equation:

$$\ln k = -\frac{E}{RT} + \text{Constant}$$

E, the energy of activation, varies from 50 to 70 k. cal./g. mol, being partly dependent upon whether chain rupture or dehydrogenation is the main reaction; chain rupture has the lower energy of activation. The last effect of temperature is on the stability of the products. According to Fig. 11, as the temperature rises, olefins and aromatics become the most stable hydrocarbons (or rather the least unstable), and above about 1,100° K., methane, ethylene and benzene are the most stable. These are therefore the likely products at high temperature and relatively long contact time (but not long enough to lead to coke formation).

Increase of pressure has two immediate effects; it tends to repress dehydrogenation, a reversible reaction in which two molecules of product are produced from one of reactant; chain rupture is irreversible, so it cannot be reversed by pressure. Secondly, pressure favours the secondary polymerisation and condensation reactions. Therefore increased pressure is desired when the maximum yield of liquid products is the objective; conversely, low pressure or low partial pressure of hydrocarbon vapour is

    [3] Kuchler, *Trans. Faraday Soc.*, 1939, **35**, 874.

indicated when the maximum yield of lower olefins is wanted. Variation of pressure has an effect on the chain rupture reaction. At higher pressure, the hydrocarbon chain tends to break more in the middle; at low pressure chain breaking occurs near the end.

Time of reaction also affects the secondary reactions; long contact time is in any case excluded in practice as it permits true thermodynamic equilibrium to be approached with decomposition of the primary and secondary products into carbon (coke) and hydrogen. For this reason, conversion per pass in any cracking or pyrolysis process has to be limited to a maximum of some 50–70 per cent per pass (an exception to this generalisation will be encountered later in the case of ethane). Temperature and time of contact are interdependent factors and their effect can be expressed as a composite variable.[4]

Summarising the theoretical position, production of the lower olefins will be favoured by thermal treatment of paraffins at high temperatures, low pressures and short contact time.

It has been pointed out earlier that on both thermodynamic and kinetic grounds, chain rupture is more likely than dehydrogenation. Nevertheless, by choice of catalysts favouring the dehydrogenation reaction, it can be made the major if not the sole reaction. However, the free energy change in this reaction does not permit complete conversion with any of the lower paraffins within the practicable range of operating temperatures. From the data in Table 22, the equilibrium proportion of the lower hydrocarbons converted to olefins of the same number of carbon atoms at 550° c. is:

TABLE 23

Equilibrium dehydrogenation of paraffins at 550°C

Paraffin	Olefin	Maximum conversion to olefin %	Maximum concentration of olefin in exit gas % by vol.
Ethane	Ethylene	9·2	8·4
Propane and higher paraffins	Propylene and higher olefins	28·2	22·0

This reaction is used as one way of making the C_4 olefins.

2. Cracking practice

The principal methods of thermal cracking are liquid-vapour phase and true vapour phase. The former is carried out at moderate temperature and high pressure; vapour phase cracking can be carried out at moderate or high temperature and at high or low pressure.

Cracking stocks vary from various crude petroleum fractions such as

---

[4] See, for example, Ellis, 'Chemistry of Petroleum Derivatives', *Reinhold*, Vol. 1, 1934, 102.

gas oil down to propane and ethane. Details of the various cracking processes can be found in Ellis and in 'Science of Petroleum'.[5] Here, it is possible to give only the broadest outline of the processes, attention being devoted to the composition of the gases produced.

In the liquid vapour process, the oil is pumped through heated coils or other vessels so that a mixture of liquid and vapour is subjected to temperatures of the order of 350–500° c. and at sufficiently high pressures (25–70 atma.) to keep the desired proportion of the hydrocarbon in the liquid phase. The liquid and normally gaseous products of cracking are then worked up by the usual methods, in much the same way as from vapour phase cracking.

In the vapour phase process, the hydrocarbon vapours, which may be obtained by evaporation of feedstocks as high boiling as gas oil, are passed through a series of tubes arranged in a furnace both to preheat the gases and to keep them at reaction temperature for the desired contact time (soaking time). Any inert diluent such as steam may be injected at the beginning of the furnace. The hot exit gases are partially cooled by injection of cold oil (quench oil) and separated into fuel oil, recycle oil, liquid products boiling in the petrol range, and gases, in a series of fractionating columns usually operating under pressure. A typical flowsheet of vapour phase cracking is shown in Fig. 12.

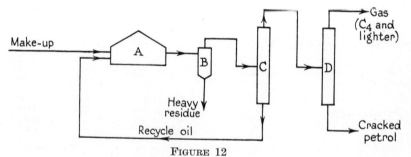

FIGURE 12

Vapour phase cracking and isolation of products

Besides thermal cracking, large quantities of olefins are available from catalytic cracking. This process was rapidly developed under the stimulus of war owing to the good yield of high octane petrol obtained, which served as the base stock for 100 octane petrol. The process consists of reacting oil in the vapour phase with a natural or artificial aluminium silicate catalyst at moderate temperature and low pressure, *e.g.*, 450° c. and 1–15 atma. There are three general ways of carrying out catalytic cracking; the oil vapours may be passed over the catalyst arranged in the usual fixed bed (Houdry process). The catalyst may flow as a very finely divided solid

---

[5] Ellis, 'Chemistry of Petroleum Derivatives', *Reinhold*, Vol. 1, 1934, 108; 'Science of Petroleum', *Oxford University Press*, Vol. 3, 1938, 2078 *et seq.*

co-current with the hot oil vapours (Fluid catalyst process), or in the form of granules, it may be moved mechanically through the reaction zone counter-current to the oil vapours (Thermofor process). In all cases carbon is deposited on the catalyst and has to be removed by burning off with oxygen containing gases, periodically in the Houdry process, continuously in the Fluid catalyst and Thermofor processes. The petrol obtained contains a high proportion of highly branched paraffins and it is to this that it owes its high octane number. As would be expected from the mild conditions of cracking, the gases contain little ethylene; they consist largely of C_3 and both normal and iso C_4 gases. These C_4 gases were used for manufacture of isooctane and for butadiene for the American synthetic rubber programme (see Chapter 12, p. 195).

One of the new catalytic cracking processes is the Catarole process. In this process, hydrocarbon vapours at 630–680° c. and atmospheric pressure are passed over a copper or copper-iron catalyst. A mixture of about equal parts by weight of C_4's and lighter and of liquid products is obtained. The gas is characterised by an unusually high methane content; a typical gas analysis is given in Table 24, col. 6. The liquid product is almost wholly aromatic in nature and is referred to in Chapter 14, p. 257. The process has been operated by Petrochemicals, Ltd., at Partington, near Manchester.

TABLE 24

Composition of gas from various cracking processes

PROCESS	Vapour-liquid	Vapour-liquid (tube and tank)	Catalytic			Vapour phase			
			Houdry	Fluid	Catarole	Gas oil	Naphtha	Ethane	Propane
Feed	Gas oil	Gas oil	Gas oil	Gas oil	Naphtha	Gas oil	Naphtha	Ethane	Propane
Temperature, ° C.	500	520	450	540	680	700	920	800	800
Pressure, atma.	27	51	2–10	2–4	1	2	3	2	3
GAS COMPOSITION, vol. %									
H_2	} 53	} 37	7	11	13	} 35	18	41	17
CH_4			12	20	43		30	3	41
C_2H_4	3	4	4	5	16	25	35	37	25
C_2H_6	16	22	5	5	10	12	4	17	10
C_3H_6	9	7	19	20	12	16	13	} 1	4
C_3H_8	10	18	15	12	2	5	nil		1
C_4H_8	} 8	4	11	12	} 4	4	—	} 1	} 2
C_4H_{10}		8	27	14		2	—		
References	6	6	6	7	8	2	9	10	11

References:

   6 Sachanen, 'Chemical Constituents of Petroleum', *Reinhold*, 1945.
   7 Walter, *J. Inst. Pet.*, 1946, **32**, 295.
   8 Weizmann, Bergmann *et al.*, *Ind. Eng. Chem.*, 1951, **43**, 2322.
   9 King and Warburton, *Pet. Proc.*, 1952, **7**, 1644.
   10 Schutt, *Chem. Eng. Prog.*, 1947, **43**, 103.
   11 Buell and Weber, *Pet. Proc.*, 1950, **5**, 266.

Typical gas compositions from various feeds and cracking processes are shown in Table 24. The figures are only approximate and the table is incomplete as comprehensive data covering all the information required are not always published. The gas compositions have been calculated in all cases on a C_5 free basis.

Sachanen[6] gives gas yields as follows:

Process	Gas yield, ft.³/bbl.†
Vapour-liquid phase . .	500
Vapour phase	1,000–1,500
Catalytic (Houdry) . . .	200–300

Brooks[12] points out that gas yields on vapour phase cracking increase with temperature of cracking; his figures are 1,300 ft.³/bbl. oil at 580° c., 2,000–2,500 ft.³ at 650–700° c., and about 3,000 ft.³ at 750–850° c.; the increased gas volume is due both to an increased weight yield and to an increased proportion of lighter gases. In catalytic cracking, the fluid process gives considerably higher gas yields than the Houdry (fixed bed) process.

Acetylene is present in traces in high temperature pyrolysis; it is reported as becoming appreciable above 800° c.

In considering the gas compositions in Table 24, the points to note are the percentage of ethylene, and the ratios of ethylene-ethane and propylene-propane, since these two factors vitally affect the problem of gas separation. It will be seen that, as anticipated from Section 1, low temperature cracking gives little ethylene; maximum ethylene is obtained at the highest cracking temperatures, and then the concentration is only about 30 per cent by volume.

However cracking is carried out, the products are usually segregated into four main fractions, (*i*) gas, which includes all products lighter than C_5; (*ii*) petrol, the fraction boiling from about 10° c. to about 200° c.; (*iii*) kerosene and gas oil boiling from about 200° c. upwards; and (*iv*) fuel oil. In this chapter, we are concerned primarily with the fate of the gas. The petrol and higher fractions contain considerable proportions of olefins but, as will be explained later, the large number of isomers present make these fractions unsuitable sources of individual olefins. These fractions may be sold directly, or may be recycled for further cracking to gas. The fuel oil cannot be recycled; it is used for fuel purposes on the cracker or elsewhere.

It has been pointed out in Section 1 that the cracking process is highly endothermic; even the chain rupture reaction requires about 18 k. cal. per mol of paraffin split. Since contact time is usually short, especially in high temperature cracking, we are faced with the problem of rapid transfer of a large amount of heat at a high temperature from one gas, flue gas, to

---

† 1 ft.³/bbl. equals 0·0285 ft.³/Imp. gal. or 6·3 ft.³/m.³
[12] Brooks, *Ind. Eng. Chem.*, 1935, **27**, 278.

another gas, oil vapours. This is a design problem encountered frequently in the petroleum chemicals industry. Most cracking furnaces consist of narrow tubes, through which the oil vapours pass at high speed, heated by radiation from burning fuel gas. Pressure cracking has two operating advantages – reduction in size of cracker for a given throughput, and increase in overall heat transfer; unfortunately it does not give maximum yield. A second problem is the material of construction of the reactor. This must have the required mechanical strength for the operating conditions and must not catalyse decomposition of the oil vapours; in particular, it must not accelerate coke or carbon formation. At the highest temperatures, both iron and nickel lead to coke formation; high chrome steels such as 25/18 chrome-nickel steel are usually used for the most extreme conditions; for more moderate conditions, a range of alloy steels such as the austenitic steels and molybdenum steels is available. Two newer methods of avoiding the problems of heat transfer and of materials of construction will be met with later in the dehydrogenation of ethane which needs a temperature of nearly 900° c. to obtain high conversions (p. 107).

3. Separation of gases

By whatever methods the olefin gases are obtained, certain preliminary operations are necessary before the olefins are isolated. The first step is to purify the gases after they have been separated from the liquid products. If sulphur is present in the original feedstock, some or all of it will appear as hydrogen sulphide and has to be removed; depending on the amounts present, stripping with a regenerative solvent such as one of the ethanolamines, scrubbing with caustic soda solution or passing over a sulphur active catalyst is chosen. If cracking at high temperature has been adopted, acetylene will be present in appreciable proportion; it has to be removed by solvent scrubbing or by selective hydrogenation to ethylene. Finally the gases have to be dried, using regeneratable solid adsorbents such as active alumina or silica gel; a preliminary dehydration with a liquid absorbent such as diethylene glycol is sometimes used.

The two main methods of separation of olefins are by fractional distillation and by absorption in petroleum solvents. Adsorption on solid adsorbents and chemical combination are used but only in special circumstances.

Fractional distillation depends upon the difference in vapour pressure (strictly speaking the difference in fugacity; this distinction becomes important when distilling at high pressures) of the various components.

The fundamental physical properties of the gases produced in cracking, on which separation by fractionation depends, are set out in Table 25.

Inspection of this table shows that the separation of the C_2 fraction from methane and hydrogen, of the C_3 fraction from the C_2 fraction and of the C_4 fraction from the C_3 fraction will be relatively easy. Separation of ethylene from ethane and of propylene from propane is much more difficult, but these separations are technically feasible.

TABLE 25

Physical properties of gases which may be present in cracked gas

Gas	b.p. 760 mm. ° c.	Critical temperature ° c.	Critical pressure atm.
Hydrogen	− 252·7	− 239·9	12·8
Methane	− 161·5	− 82·5	45·8
Ethylene	− 103·7	9·9	50·5
Ethane	− 88·6	32·3	48·2
Acetylene	− 84	36·3	61·6
Propylene	− 47·7	91·9	45·4
Propane	− 42·1	96·8	42·0
Isobutane	− 11·7	135	36·0
Isobutene	− 6·9	144·7	39·5
1-Butene	− 6·3	146	39·7
1 : 3-Butadiene	− 4·4	152	42·7
n-Butane	− 0·5	152	37·5
trans-2-Butene	+ 0·9	155	41
cis-2-Butene	+ 3·7	155	41

The major factors in the cost of separation are the amount of refrigeration and the depth of refrigeration (*i.e.*, the lowest temperature required). To reduce the refrigeration load, it is usual to carry out the fractional distillation of cracked gases under pressure, but this is not an invariable practice. Pressure fractionation permits the separation of the C_3 and C_4 fractions with water cooling. Separation of ethylene from methane will, however, require deep refrigeration as it is necessary to supply a liquid methane reflux, and the highest temperature at which methane is liquid is − 82·5° c. A drawback of pressure distillation is that the relative volatilities of the hydrocarbons, the difference of which is the driving force of separation, are appreciably narrowed with rise in pressure; the effect may be quite considerable.

Absorption and adsorption would be expected to be more suitable for separation of hydrocarbons of similar chemical constitution than of similar boiling point, and hence to be used for separating olefins from paraffins rather than the C_2 fraction from the C_3 fraction. This does not hold in practice.

The principal method of absorption is by dissolving in a low boiling hydrocarbon such as the C_4 and higher hydrocarbons obtained as part of the olefin-making process. The main use of this process is to separate the hydrogen and methane from the C_2 and higher gases; it avoids the very low temperature required to separate ethylene from methane in the distillation process. As described by Curtiss,[13] the absorption step is carried

---

[13] *Chem. and Ind.*, August 10, 1953, p. 818.

out at about 35 atma., using a butane-rich lean oil as absorbent, with a top temperature of 0–20° c. and a base temperature of about 120° c. Hydrogen and methane are taken overhead with only 2–4 per cent of the ethylene in the feed. No hydrogen and about 4 per cent of methane go through to the stripper, which is operated at about 25 atma. and a base temperature of about 200° c. The C_2 and C_3 gases from the top of the stripper then require separation by conventional fractional distillation methods.

The higher olefins are more soluble than ethylene in organic solvents, but ethylene is the more soluble in cuprous salt solutions, and these salt solutions have been examined fully as specific absorbents for ethylene only. Compounds claimed include ammoniacal cuprous formate,[14] cuprous ethanolamine hydrochloride[15] and cuprous pyridine acetate.[16] Ammoniacal cuprous monoethanolamine nitrate was used in Germany during the second world war for concentration of ethylene from gases from the high temperature dehydrogenation of ethane[17] but this method is not now used.

Turning to adsorption, although silica gel has been mentioned in the literature, the solid adsorbent most widely examined is active charcoal. As explained in Chapter 2, p. 30, this method has now been made continuous in the Hypersorption process. This process is used industrially to recover the ethylene content from the methane overhead obtained from the ethylene tower of a conventional fractional distillation system.[18] The methane overhead contained 5·8 per cent of ethylene; Hypersorption gave a concentrate of 93% pure ethylene which could either be used as such or recycled to the distillation circuit. The Hypersorber was operated at about 6 atma. pressure with a base temperature of 260° c. Carbon was circulated at the rate of about 8 tons/hr. The ethylene recovery was of the order of 3 tons-hr., the recovery efficiency being over 95 per cent. No separation of the C_2 gases was achieved, the ethylene containing all the ethane and acetylene in the feed gas.

Coming to the chemical methods of separation, these differ from the physical methods dealt with above in that the olefin is separated not as such but as a chemical derivative from which the original olefin may not be regeneratable by economic processes.

The most general method of chemical separation is absorption in sulphuric acid, giving sulphuric esters from which the corresponding alcohol can easily be made by hydrolysis:

$$RCH:CH_2 + H_2SO_4 \rightarrow \underset{\underset{OSO_3H}{|}}{RCHCH_3} \rightarrow \underset{\underset{OH}{|}}{RCHCH_3} + H_2SO_4$$

---

[14] I.C.I., B.P. 304345.
[15] Distillers, B.P. 428106.
[16] Standard Oil Development, B.P. 540209.
[17] C.I.O.S. 27/85.
[18] Berg, Fairfield, Imhoff and Multer, *Pet. Refiner*, 1949, **28(11)**, 113.

Not only can this reaction be used to separate olefins from paraffins, it also serves to separate olefins from one another owing to their differential reactivity to sulphuric acid. Thus from a gas mixture containing ethylene, propylene, n-butenes, isobutene and paraffins, the isobutene is absorbed by cold 50–65% sulphuric acid, the n-butenes by cold 75% acid, the propylene by cold 90% acid, the ethylene by hot 90–96% acid, and the paraffins are unabsorbed. Details of this process, as applied to the absorption of the individual olefin and hydrolysis of the sulphuric acid ester to the corresponding alcohols, are dealt with in Chapter 8. The method is of wide applicability, and can be used with gas mixtures containing anything from 2 per cent to 100 per cent olefin. It was employed during the 1914–18 war in England for the absorption of the small concentration of ethylene from coke oven gas; however, this route to alcohols is not as good as preliminary separation and concentration of the olefins, followed by hydration. The process is still used in cases where physical separation is difficult, *e.g.*, in the separation of isobutene from the n-butenes and other gases in the C_4 fraction.

Another method of olefin segregation is addition of chlorine to give the dichloride:

$$RCH : CHR^1 + Cl_2 \rightarrow RCHClCHClR^1$$

This reaction may be carried out in the vapour phase using metal chloride catalysts. It leaves the problem of isolation of the dichloride from large volumes of inert gas and is attractive only where special circumstances operate.

4. Individual olefins

(a) ETHYLENE

(i) *Petroleum raw materials*

For lowest costs of separation of pure ethylene, the gas to be separated must have as high a concentration of ethylene and as high a ratio of ethylene to ethane as possible. Gases from low temperature cracking of oil are therefore not suitable sources; they contain only a few per cent of ethylene, and the ethylene-ethane ratio is low. The most suitable gas mixtures are those from the high temperature low pressure cracking of naphtha or of the light paraffin gases such as propane and ethane.

The effect of temperature on gas composition in the atmospheric pressure pyrolysis of propane has been investigated by Frolich and Wiezevich.[19] Fig. 13, which is based on this paper, summarises the results of their laboratory experiments. Similar curves were obtained by pyrolysis of n-butane.

---

[19] *Ind. Eng. Chem.*, 1935, **27**, 1055.

The effect of conversion in the cracking of ethane and of propane at about 800° c. and about 1 second contact time is shown in Figs. 14 and 15, based on Schutt.[10]

Ethane cracks almost entirely to ethylene and hydrogen, but even under

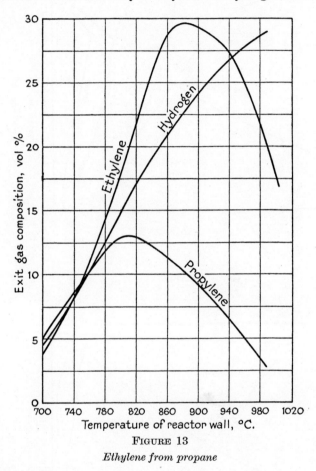

FIGURE 13

Ethylene from propane

conditions of almost complete conversion, the ethylene in the off gases does not rise above 37 per cent. Propane cracks both to ethylene and methane and to propylene and hydrogen; according to Schutt, 63·5 per cent goes to ethylene, 30 per cent to propylene, and the remaining 6·5 per cent decomposes as follows:

$$2C_3H_8 \rightarrow 2C_2H_6 + C_2H_4$$

Present American practice favours the pyrolysis of propane, ethane, or propane-ethane mixtures; these feedstocks are available from natural gas separation, either directly or as the stabiliser overhead from the isolation

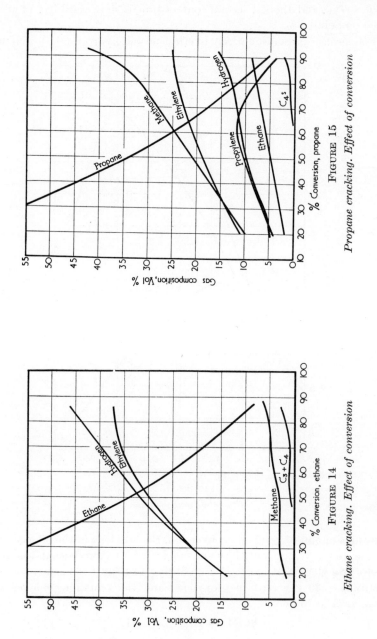

FIGURE 15

Propane cracking. Effect of conversion

FIGURE 14

Ethane cracking. Effect of conversion

of propane-butane mixtures, and from the debutanised fraction of refinery cracked gases. The gases are purified and fed into the separation system where their ethylene content augments that given in the cracking step and the ethane and propane fractions are separated and recycled to the cracking stage. A typical refinery gas suitable for augmenting ethylene production is given as:

Gas composition		% by vol.
H_2	. . .	19·2
CH_4	. . .	25·1
C_2H_4	. . .	6·5
C_2H_6	. . .	14·8
C_3H_6	. . .	6·1
C_3H_8	. . .	11·5
C_4's	. . .	1·4
N_2, CO, etc.	. .	15·4
		100·0

Under American conditions the natural gas sources of propane and ethane have economic advantages over liquid feedstocks. Debutanised refinery cracked gases can be used for increasing ethylene production where they are available near ethylene cracking units, whatever the chosen feedstock.

In America, it was estimated that in 1954, 10 per cent of the ethylene made was present in refinery gases used as feedstock, 40 per cent was made from ethane isolated from natural gas or from refinery gases, and 50 per cent was made from propane.[19a] In Europe, the position is different; it has been estimated that in 1955, 60 per cent of European ethylene from petroleum sources was made by pyrolysis of liquid hydrocarbon feedstocks. The proportion from liquid hydrocarbons in Great Britain was even higher.

Pyrolysis is normally carried out in gas-fired tube stills of the type developed in the petroleum industry. The necessary high temperature for pyrolysis of ethane has been achieved by two other methods, internal combustion and pebble heating. In one German plant, operated during the war,[20] 1 vol. of ethane and 0·33 vol. of oxygen, both preheated, were mixed at high velocity and passed up a ceramic packed tower, where the main reaction of partial combustion and dehydrogenation took place, the maximum temperature being 880° c. About half the oxygen was converted to water, the remainder appearing as carbon dioxide and carbon monoxide. Plans to modify this partial combustion process by use of air instead of oxygen have been devised in America.[21]

An alternative way of achieving the high temperature and heat input necessary is to use refractory inert solid materials. These are heated to a high temperature, up to 1,200–1,300° c., by burning flue gases. The solids

---

[19a] *Chem. Week*, 12 June, 1954, p. 89.
[20] C.I.O.S. 32/107.
[21] Deanesley and Watkins, *Chem. Eng. Prog.*, 1951, **47**, 134.

are transferred by gravity to the reaction zone where they contact the feed stock, either paraffin gases or vaporised liquids, and pyrolysis takes place. Having given up their heat, the solid materials are gas-lifted to the heating zone for reheating. This process has been used in the Thermofor pyrolytic process[22] and in the Phillips pebble heater.[23]

Coming back to conventional methods of pyrolysis of ethane and propane, the theoretical and practical background has been reviewed by Schutt[10] and by Buell and Weber.[11] Two main factors control the selection of conditions of operation. Firstly, whilst the chief reaction in the pyrolysis of propane is demethanation, the pyrolysis of ethane involves the more difficult process of dehydrogenation, in which a higher temperature is required for the same proportion of ethylene from each unit of ethane or propane, and which is more endothermic. From the empirical equations covering the percentage of propane or ethane cracked at varying reaction times and temperatures given by Buell and Weber, the variation of pyrolysis velocity constant with feedstock and temperature is given in Table 26.

TABLE 26

Velocity constants of pyrolysis of propane and ethane

Temperature ° c.	Pyrolysis velocity constant (reciprocal seconds)	
	Propane	Ethane
760	0·72	0·19
825	3·41	1·07
875	12·6	4·4
925	38·9	15·9

Secondly, whilst ethane and propane give a small proportion of liquid products under actual conditions of pyrolysis, propylene and the butenes give high proportions. Schutt points out that at 760–800° c. with 50% conversion, ethane and propane give 0·5–1·5 per cent of liquid products, whilst propylene and the butenes give 20–25 per cent.

With ethane, therefore, one has to use higher temperatures than with propane; with ethane-propane mixtures one must choose conditions to pyrolyse sufficient ethane at least to prevent any build-up of ethane when recycling the unchanged saturated gases. Finally, separation of olefins from product gases should be as complete as possible; recycling olefins leads to their loss as low grade liquid products and to an increase in coking in the pyrolysis coils.

The operating conditions given by Schutt for cracking propane-ethane mixtures were: coil exit temperature, about 770° c., coil outlet pressure,

---

[22] Eastwood and Potas, *Pet. Times*, Oct. 22, 1948, p. 941.
[23] Dean, Hall and Seed, *Pet. Proc.*, 1954, **9**, 903.

3 atma., contact time about 1 second, and use of two to four mols of steam per mol of feed gas. The main purpose of the steam was to lower the partial pressure of the hydrocarbons, but its presence also reduced corrosion due to sulphur compounds in the feed. Similar conditions have been cited for another American plant.[24]

There is a tendency now to move from propane towards ethane, where these gases are freely available, as the right feedstock for ethylene. The reason is the higher weight yield which can be obtained; as a first approximation, propane will give in practice only some 50 per cent by weight of ethylene, whilst ethane will give 75 to 80 per cent. Against this, propane gives a higher conversion, and separation of ethylene from propane cracking is easier than from ethane cracking.

TABLE 27

Ethylene Manufacture

Comparison of gas compositions from pyrolysis of gas oil, naphtha, ethane and propane

FEED	Gas oil	Naphtha	Propane	Propane-ethane (with re-cycle)	Ethane	Ethane (pyrolysis with O_2)
TEMPERATURE, °c.	700	920	750	780	800	880
PRESSURE, atma.	1	3	2	3	2	0·5
GAS COMPOSITION, vol. %						
H_2	11	18	11	11	36	27
CH_4	25	30	26	33	4	8
C_2H_4	25	35	24	25	33	31
C_2H_6	11	4	4	11	26	17
C_3H_6	} 22	13	15	12	} 1	} 3
C_3H_8		nil	17	4		
C_4's	6	—	3	4		—
CO	—	—	—	—	—	10
N_2, CO_2, O_2	—	—	—	—	—	4
References	25	9	24	10	10	20

In countries where natural gas paraffins are not readily available, one is forced to use suitable transportable liquid feedstocks. The general conditions of cracking are milder than with propane and ethane; temperatures are normally 700–725° c., but the weight yield of ethylene on liquid feedstock is as low as 15 per cent. To improve this yield and to give a gas with as high an ethylene to ethane ratio as possible, a high temperature steam cracking process has been devised which was first established in I.C.I.'s Wilton plant. The principal feature of this process[9] is cracking at 920° c. in the presence of excess steam, the steam being superheated to supply the final preheat of the feedstock vapours and the heat of pyrolysis. As an indication, naphtha vapours are preheated to 680° c. and mixed with

---

[24] Kniel and Slager, *Chem. Eng. Prog.*, 1947, **43**, 335.
[25] du Pont, U.S.P. 2346642.

excess superheated steam at about 930° c. The recovered yield of ethylene on naphtha is 22·5 per cent. The gas composition is given in Table 24, column 8. It is characterised by a high ethylene concentration, a high ratio of ethylene to ethane and ethylene to propylene, and an extremely high ratio of propylene to propane. The composition of the C_4 fraction is not known but the butadiene content is 20–50 per cent.

Gas compositions on a C_5 or C_4 free basis from different methods and feedstocks are given in Table 27.

(ii) Separation of ethylene

Although these gas mixtures are very complex, methods of separation of pure ethylene have been worked out and operated in several countries. The most general method is fractional distillation but, as explained in Section 3, absorption in oil is employed for the separation of methane and hydrogen from ethylene and the other higher boiling gases, and adsorption on charcoal is adopted in one special case. Pure ethylene is always finally isolated by fractional distillation.

Concentrating attention on distillation, from first principles and from the physical properties of the gases given in Table 25, several columns will be required; in theory, to separate n components of a multicomponent mixture, we require (n — 1) columns; to separate the C_3 and C_4 gases with water cooling, distillation must be carried out under pressure; separation of ethylene requires provision of temperatures at least as low as — 100° c., to provide a liquid methane reflux; here also, pressure operation will reduce the depth of refrigeration required.

The various processes which have been devised have all these points in common, but differ in the type of fraction produced, and in the method of refrigeration employed. However, as the lowest temperature required is considerably higher than the temperatures for liquefaction of air or hydrogen, it is usually obtained by 'cascade refrigeration', *i.e.*, use of a series of refrigerants of progressively lower boiling points, and not by employment of the Joule-Thomson effect or of expansion engines.

The main feature distinguishing the different distillation processes is the operating pressure, especially of the first column where methane and hydrogen are separated from ethylene and higher boiling gases. Pratt and Foskett[26] describe one plant in which the methane column was operated at 40 atma. and — 90° c. head temperature; the ethylene column was worked at 27 atma., the ethane column at 24 atma. and the propylene column at 15 atma. Only in this fourth column could water cooling be used for the condenser. At the other extreme is the German plant for the separation of ethylene from the pyrolysis of ethane by partial internal combustion.[20] The methane column was at 15 atma. and — 140° c. head temperature;

---

[26] *Trans. Amer. Inst. Chem. Eng.*, 1946, **42**, 149.

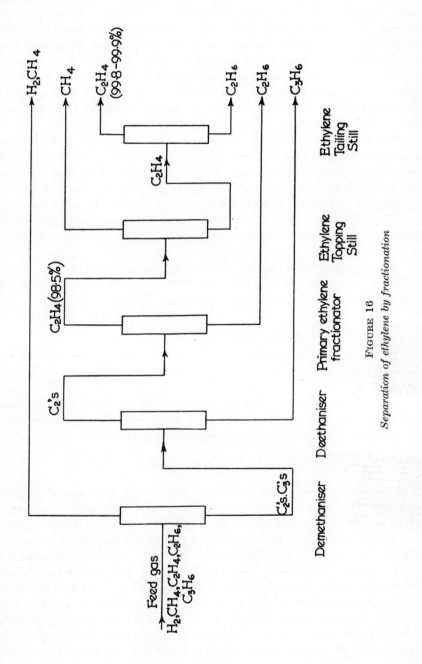

FIGURE 16

Separation of ethylene by fractionation

5

C_2's were separated from C_3's and heavier in the second column at 1·5 atma. and — 95° c.; in the third column, ethylene was separated from ethane at 1 atma. and — 102° c. This arrangement was adopted because of the small proportion of C_3's and heavier obtained. The ethane from the base of the third column was recycled and had to be as free as possible from olefins.

The I.C.I. plant at Wilton is more recent, and uses an intermediate process.[9] The gases from the cracking process are freed of hydrogen sulphide, dried, and acetylene removed by partial hydrogenation at about 200° c. The scheme of gas separation is shown in Fig. 16.

The demethaniser is operated at 7–10 atma., and — 133° c. head temperature. The reflux ratio is only 0·24 : 1. The ethylene from the head of the primary ethylene fractioner, col. 3, is 98·5% pure. Two final columns are required for "topping and tailing" to give ethylene of 99·8–99·9% purity. It is a feature of the cracking process used in this plant that the propylene from the base of column 2 is 93–97% pure, with very little propane. The cascade refrigeration system used comprised propylene-ethylene-methane.

Of the various methods for isolating ethylene, about 75 per cent of the ethylene manufactured in the United States in 1954 was separated by low temperature, high pressure, fractional distillation.

(iii) Other routes to ethylene

The importance of ethylene as a key material for the petroleum chemicals warrants a brief reference to its production from non-petroleum sources.

One of the most convenient routes to ethylene is by vapour phase dehydration of ethyl alcohol, carried out at 300–400° c., over conventional dehydration catalysts such as phosphoric acid or alumina:

$$C_2H_5OH(g) \rightarrow C_2H_4 + H_2O(g). \quad \Delta H = + 9\cdot6 \text{ k. cal.}$$

The reaction is simple, can be carried out on any scale and gives pure ethylene. It will be economically attractive where the scale of cracking is very low, or where ethyl alcohol from agricultural sources is very cheap.

Ethylene is present to the extent of some 2 per cent in coke oven gas and in coal gas. Owing to the enormous weight of coal carbonised, the total tonnage of ethylene produced from coal in highly industrialised countries such as America and Gt. Britain is very considerable. However, the low concentration of ethylene and the fact that about one hundred tons of coal have to be processed for each ton of ethylene produced, meaning that ethylene is in every sense of the word a by-product dependent on the prices realised from the main products of coal carbonisation, are deterrent factors. Nevertheless, under at least one set of conditions, extraction of ethylene from coke oven gas is a profitable operation. This is when the coke oven gas is worked up for manufacture of pure hydrogen or of hydrogen-nitrogen mixtures for synthetic ammonia. In this process[27] the coke oven gas is cooled in three stages to about − 200° c., using liquid ammonia and liquid nitrogen in external circuits in the Linde-Bronn system, or by expansion of gas from the final cooler in an expansion engine when using the Claude system. The first stage cooler collects only a small proportion of higher hydrocarbons; the second stage cooler collects a liquid fraction containing all the ethylene in about 30% concentration. Ruhemann gives for the analysis of this fraction, C_2H_6 31 per cent, C_2H_4 31 per cent, CH_4 30 per cent, C_3H_6 6 per cent, CO 2 per cent. The third stage cooler collects methane with some carbon monoxide and nitrogen. The liquid from the second stage cooler is therefore somewhat similar to gases from high temperature cracking in ethylene concentration and is a convenient source of this olefin. As this preliminary concentration has to be carried out in any case, since pure hydrogen is the objective of the process, the cost of making pure ethylene may be little more than the value of the ethylene present in the raw gas plus the cost of the final concentration from 30 per cent. This process is obviously limited to those localities where large volumes of coke oven gas are worked up for pure hydrogen. It has been operated for many years on the continent of Europe where it was for long a source of ethylene for chemicals. The ethylene content of coke oven gas has not, except in one or two cases, been used so far in this way in America or in Great Britain.

Direct extraction of ethylene from coke oven gas by fractionation methods is regarded as unattractive owing to the low initial concentration. Mention may be made of an interesting process,[28] in which partial liquefaction is effected at low pressures (2–3 atma.), the higher boiling impurities being removed by a system of periodical alternating generators.

Finally, reference must be made to the partial hydrogenation of acetylene to ethylene, which was operated on a very large scale in Germany at Huls and Gendorf during the war.[29] Acetylene, freed from traces of hydrogen sulphide and phosphine by treatment with dilute chlorine water, was reduced with 50 per cent excess hydrogen at 270° c. and atmospheric pressure over a special palladium catalyst (0·01 per cent Pd on silica gel). The inlet gas was diluted with steam and the temperature of the reaction was controlled by injection of water at points along the catalyst bed. The exit gases contained about 65 per cent ethylene and required purification by liquefaction and fractionation in a Linde-Bronn system; the yield of ethylene on acetylene was 85 per cent. By-products included ethane and unsaturated C_4 and C_6 hydrocarbons.

This route is not now used; its adoption during the war is an example

[27] Ruhemann, 'Separation of Gases', *Oxford University Press*, 1940.
[28] Brit. Oxygen, B.P. 526652–4. Schuftan, *Ind. Chem.*, 1947, **23,** 787.
[29] B.I.O.S. 1411.

of the effect of raw materials shortages in distorting the normal choice of sources of organic chemicals.

(iv) Uses of ethylene

The uses for ethylene in the petroleum chemicals industry are indicated by the estimated outlets in America in 1954[30] and 1956[31] on total estimated usages of 900,000 tons and 1,430,000 tons p.a. respectively.

Outlets	1954 % by wt.	1956 % by wt.
Ethyl alcohol	30	25
Ethylene oxide . . .	25	29
Ethylbenzene . . .	11	11
Ethyl chloride . . .	10	9
Polyethylene	10	17
Ethylene dichloride . .	7	⎫
Ethylene dibromide . .	2	⎬ 9
Others	5	⎭
	100	100

In the United Kingdom, it is estimated that in 1952 some 85,000 tons of ethylene were used for chemicals; as in America, ethyl alcohol and ethylene oxide each consumed about 30 per cent of the total. Polyethylene was the most important of the other outlets.

(b) PROPYLENE

Propylene is present in the gases from all cracking processes. Conditions of cracking do not have a major effect on the propylene concentration, which is usually in the range 10–30 per cent. As with ethylene, the propylene-propane ratio is improved by cracking at higher temperatures.

A convenient source of propylene is the 'stabiliser overhead' obtained in separating the petrol fraction obtained on cracking heavier oils from undesirable volatile constituents; the following is a typical average analysis:

Hydrocarbon	% by vol.
Ethylene	2– 3
Ethane	6–12
Propylene	21–30
Propane	38–50
Butenes	4–13
Butanes	4–17

Separation of the C_3 gases by distillation from the C_2 gases on one side and from the C_4 gases on the other is easy and presents no practical difficulty. Making a propylene-propane concentrate from these stabiliser gases or from the total gases from almost any cracking operation is therefore equally facile. Such a concentrate is suitable for the main chemical outlet

---

[30] Matthew, Messing and James, *Chem. Eng.*, Oct. 1955, 280.
[31] Kuhn and Hutcheson, *Pet. Proc.*, Sept. 1956, p. 107.

for propylene, hydration to isopropyl alcohol (Chapter 8, p. 135); however, pure propylene is required for an increasing number of chemical operations and this involves separation from propane. By straight fractional distillation this is not an easy operation, since the relative volatility of propylene to propane at 3 atma. pressure and − 20° c. is only about 1·15, and this ratio will decrease slightly with increase in pressure; in order to avoid refrigeration, and to use cooling water for condensation, it is necessary to distil propylene-propane mixtures at at least 15 atma. However, there is no practical difficulty in obtaining 98% pure propylene on the large scale.[13, 32] The separation can be improved by azeotropic distillation in presence of ammonia;[33] the ammonia alters the relative vapour pressures of propylene and propane, increasing the relative volatility of the propane.

In countries where cracking operations are conducted, propylene is the most readily available olefin. Unlike ethylene, it is produced at reasonable concentration from most cracking processes; again, unlike ethylene, it can be separated from cracker gas without provision of deep refrigeration. It has a lower value than the butenes as an intermediate for aviation petrol, and is not a starting point for the synthesis of butadiene.

Propylene usage for chemicals in America was about 550,000 tons in 1953, of which about 70 per cent was used for making isopropyl alcohol, 15 per cent for detergents and 15 per cent for other outlets.[34]

(c) BUTENES

The C_4 fraction of all cracker gases contains the normal butenes (1-butene and *cis*- and *trans*-2-butene), isobutene, the butanes, and from high temperature cracking, butadiene. The proportions of the individual C_4 hydrocarbons vary both with the feed and with the conditions of cracking. Catalytic cracking increases the ratio of isoparaffin and isoolefin; high temperature cracking increases the proportion of total olefins and the proportion of diolefin.

The variation of equilibrium with temperature between the butanes, the butenes and butadiene is indicated by Fig. 11, p. 93. Although this figure and Table 22 suggest that the free energies of formation of all four butenes are the same at all temperatures, this is not so. More refined equations, from Table 22, are shown in Table 28. These free energy equations have been used to calculate K_p and equilibrium conversions for two typical isomerisations at normal and higher temperatures. These are given in Table 29, where x is % of product (*trans*-2-butene in col. 2; isobutene in col. 3) at equilibrium.

Analyses of the C_4 fraction from various cracking processes are given in Table 30.

---

[32] Williams, *Trans. Amer. Inst. Chem. Eng.*, 1941, **37**, 157.
[33] Shell Development, U.S.P. 1866800.
[34] *Chem. Week*, June 12, 1954, p. 89.

TABLE 28

Free energy of formation of the butenes

Butene	Heat of formation 298° K. k. cal./g. mol	Simplified free energy equation $\Delta G = $ g. cal./g. mol
1-Butene	—	$- 4{,}700 + 67 \cdot 8T$
trans-2-Butene	$- 2 \cdot 7$	$- 8{,}000 + 70 \cdot 7T$
cis-2-Butene	$- 1 \cdot 7$	$- 7{,}600 + 71 \cdot 0T$
Isobutene	$- 4 \cdot 0$	$- 9{,}100 + 70 \cdot 8T$

TABLE 29

Equilibrium in isomerisation of butenes

		Reaction	
		1-butene $\Updownarrow$ *trans*-2-butene	*trans*-2-butene isobutene
Free energy change		$- 3{,}300 + 2 \cdot 9T$	$- 1{,}100 + 0 \cdot 1T$
25° c. K_p		61·9	5·8
x		98%	85%
250° c. K_p		5·6	2·7
x		85%	73%
500° c. K_p		2·0	1·9
x		67%	66%

TABLE 30

Composition of C_4 fraction from cracking processes

Hydrocarbon	Process			
	Vapour phase cracking of gas oil[6] % by vol.	From stabiliser overhead of vapour phase cracking[34a] % by vol.	Mixed-phase cracking[35] % by vol.	Catalytic cracking (Houdry)[6] % by vol.
n-Butane . .	} 10–12	} 24	49	12
Isobutane . .			11	53
Isobutene . .	20–24	21	10	6
1-Butene . .	} 50–55	} 44	11	} 25
2-Butene . .			18	
Butadiene . .	12–14	11	1	—
C_3 and C_5 . .	2	—	—	4

[34a] Birch and Tait, 'Science of Petroleum', *Oxford University Press*, Vol. 4, 1938, 2830.

[35] Snow, U.S.P. 2128971.

The percentage of butadiene may rise to 50 per cent when cracking at the highest temperatures used, above 900° c.

Preparation of mixed *n*-butenes from the C_4 fraction of refinery gases is relatively easy. Butadiene, when present, has to be removed, usually after separation of isobutene. The separation method selected depends on the proportion present; if small, it is polymerised over clay or selectively hydrogenated to *n*-butenes using nickel sulphide or copper as catalyst;[36] if large, it is removed by any of the methods discussed in Chapter 12, p. 199, for example by selective absorption in ammoniacal cuprous acetate. Isobutene may be removed by absorption in 50–65% sulphuric acid; this leaves only the *n*-butenes and saturated hydrocarbons, a mixture suitable for hydration to *sec*-butyl alcohol (see Chapter 8, p. 138).

The *n*-butenes are best separated from the butanes by extractive distillation. One method uses a mixture of 85 per cent acetone and 15 per cent water. In an example, the feed gas had the following composition:

Components					% by vol.
Isobutene .	.	.	.	.	1·7
Isobutane .	.	.	.	.	42·8
1-Butene .	.	.	.	.	12·6
2-Butene .	.	.	.	.	27·1
n-Butane .	.	.	.	.	15·8
					100

The 1- and 2-butenes were recovered at 85–95% purity from the stripping column. It was necessary to scrub all product streams with water to recover traces of acetone and to rework these dilute aqueous acetone streams to reduce solvent losses. Acetonitrile is now replacing aqueous acetone as the extractive solvent.

It is possible to separate 1-butene from the two 2-butenes and a brief description of the separation of the C_4 fraction (B-B fraction) of refinery gases to give 1-butene and 2-butene for dehydrogenation to butadiene at Port Neches will illustrate the scope of fractional distillation combined with extractive distillation.[37] The extractive solvent used was furfural, which was also employed for purification of butadiene from the dehydrogenation stage (see Chapter 12, p. 200).

From Table 25, straight fractional distillation will separate isobutane, isobutene and 1-butene from *n*-butane and the 2-butenes.

The effect of extractive distillation was to enhance the relative volatilities of *n*- and isobutane compared with 1-butene and 2-butene.

The flowsheet of the separation is given in Fig. 17. The feed gases contained isobutane, isobutene, *n*-butane and the three *n*-butenes, but no butadiene.

Extractive distillation was therefore used to separate isobutane from

---

[36] Borrows and Seddon, *Chem. and Ind.*, Aug. 10, 1953, p. S57.
[37] Happel *et al.*, *Trans. Amer. Inst. Chem. Eng.*, 1946, **42**, 189.

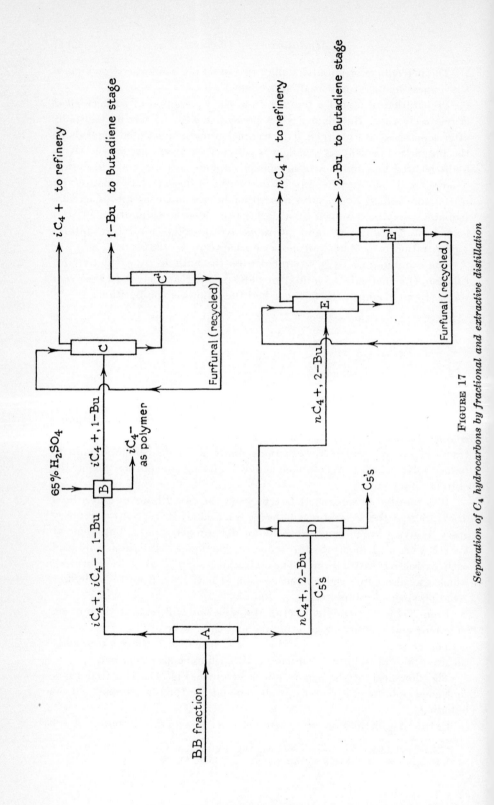

FIGURE 17

Separation of C₄ hydrocarbons by fractional and extractive distillation

1-butene, boiling 5·2° c. apart, and *n*-butane from *cis*- and *trans*-2-butene which boil 0·8° c. and 4·2° c. respectively higher than *n*-butane. The extractive distillation towers were operated at about 4–5 atma. pressure, so as to be able to use water cooling, with a high ratio of furfural to hydrocarbon to ensure complete miscibility on every tray of the towers. The separation effected by these "solvent towers" is shown in Table 31.

TABLE 31

Separation of n-butenes by extractive distillation

Fraction	Isobutane solvent column % unsaturateds	n-Butane solvent column % unsaturateds
Feed . . .	38·1	50·7
Overhead . .	5·3	3·0
Bottoms . .	93·7	94·8

The 2-butenes are more stable than 1-butene and are usually produced as the major product in high temperature reactions. 1-Butene can be isomerised to the equilibrium mixture containing the two 2-butenes under the influence of acidic catalysts such as acid phosphates, sulphuric acid on silica gel,[38] or even by short contact with 70% sulphuric acid at about 75° c.[39] This isomerisation step has been claimed as a method of improving the separation of the butenes.[40]

It is also possible to isomerise the *n*-butenes to the equilibrium mixture of isobutene and the *n*-butenes under relatively mild conditions, *e.g.*, in the vapour phase over aluminium silicate catalyst. This isomerisation received some attention from the oil companies when isobutene was wanted for isooctane, but has fallen into the background with the development of alkylation and the isomerisation of *n*-butane to isobutane. Nevertheless, methods exist for the inter-conversion of the C_4 olefins, and for their separation, if new chemical discoveries call for the manufacture of any individual member in very large quantities.

The amounts of *n*- and isobutenes produced as by-products of cracking by the American oil industry were inadequate for the combined war-time requirements for aviation petrol and for synthetic rubber. This led to the rapid large scale application of the dehydrogenation of the butanes to the butenes, a reaction discovered and taken on to the pilot scale only immediately prior to the outbreak of hostilities. Simultaneously, it was established on the plant scale in Great Britain, and we shall limit ourselves here to a brief résumé of the British plant for making butenes from mixed *n*- and isobutane.[41]

---

[38] Phillips Pet., U.S.P. 2348931.
[39] Standard Oil Development, B.P. 553297.
[40] U.O.P., B.P. 570692.
[41] Beesley and Whipp, *Chem. and Ind.*, Aug. 10, 1953, p. 850.

It has been pointed out in Section 1 of this chapter that dehydrogenation of paraffins is less favoured thermodynamically and is kinetically slower than chain rupture. It can therefore be achieved in practice only by the discovery of highly selective catalysts which greatly increase the speed of the dehydrogenation reaction without affecting the chain rupture reaction; chain rupture cannot be suppressed by catalytic means, but the relative velocities of the two reactions can be so altered that chain rupture becomes unimportant.

A very wide range of catalysts has been examined and described in the patent literature but final choice appears to have settled on chromic oxide-alumina stabilised with alkali compounds.

The equilibrium for the reaction:

$$C_4H_{10} \rightleftharpoons C_4H_8 + H_2 \qquad . \qquad . \qquad . \qquad (3)$$

is given by the approximate equation (Table 22) $\Delta G = 31,600 - 33 \cdot 6T$. The reaction is highly endothermic, ΔH being about 30 k. cal./mol.

Assuming no secondary reactions take place, such as butadiene formation, the equilibrium concentration of the butenes at various temperatures is given in Table 32.

TABLE 32

Equilibrium in dehydrogenation of butane to butenes

T ° c.	K_p	Equilibrium conversion %	Butenes in gases % by vol.
400	0·00085	2·9	2·8
500	0·0185	13·5	11·9
600	0·198	40·6	28·9
700	1·300	75·2	42·9

The reaction is favoured by reduced pressure, the conversion being proportional to the reciprocal of the square root of the absolute pressure at low conversions. In practice, it is better to operate at atmospheric pressure but at partial conversion, the excess butane acting more or less as an inert diluent.

The process is carried out at 550–575° c. and at 3–10 atma., the space velocity being chosen to give about 22% conversion per pass. The catalyst is contained in a multitubular reactor, heated with recirculating flue gas. Carbon is deposited rapidly on the catalyst, and it is necessary to operate two reactors in pairs, one on make and one being reactivated. Reactivation is carried out by burning off the carbon with air. The make and reactivating periods are one hour each. The process imposes very severe metallurgical problems, resolved by the use of high chrome-nickel steels (27% Cr., 8% Ni.). The nett yield of butenes on butanes converted was 85 per cent; losses were about equally divided between lighter hydrocarbons and carbon.

The butane-butene mixture is usually isolated from the reactor gases by absorption in a petroleum solvent. The butenes may be further separated by the methods indicated in this chapter.

Coming to isobutene, its separation from the C_4 fraction of cracked gas by absorption in weak sulphuric acid has been mentioned earlier and is dealt with in greater detail on p. 125. Absorption in 50–65% sulphuric acid at 10–30° c. converts the isobutene to *tert*-butyl alcohol; on heating the solution to 80–100° c., diisobutene and higher polymers are formed. The isobutene can be recovered from the solution by dilution to 40–50% acid, desorption of any dissolved butenes followed by heating, when the *tert*-butyl alcohol dehydrates smoothly.

Isobutene can also be made by catalytic dehydrogenation of isobutane. The isobutane may be isolated from natural gas or may be synthesised by catalytic isomerisation of *n*-butane using catalysts such as aluminium chloride (Chapter 2).

In America, the principal chemical outlet for *n*-butenes is for butadiene for synthetic rubber. A few per cent of chemical *n*-butenes is hydrated to *sec*-butyl alcohol.

Isobutene has more varied outlets. The principal use is for making Butyl rubber, by copolymerisation with about 2 per cent isoprene in methyl chloride solution. Isobutene has a second outlet in the high polymer field, straight polymerisation with boron trifluoride at very low temperature to give a series of polyisobutenes of molecular weight from 3,000 to 200,000. About 15,000 tons polyisobutenes were made in America in 1955. Other chemical outlets include diisobutene, for detergents and plasticisers, tert-butylated phenols as antioxidants and for resin intermediates, and *tert*-butyl alcohol.

The American consumption of isobutene in 1955 for chemicals is estimated at more than 80,000 tons, of which the major share was required for Butyl rubber and the polyisobutenes.

(d) PENTENES

There are six isomeric pentenes – three *n*-pentenes, 1-pentene and two geometrical isomers of 2-pentene, and three branch chain pentenes, trimethylethylene, $(CH_3)_2C : CHCH_3$, methylethylethylene, $CH_3CH : CHC_2H_5$, and isopropylethylene, $(CH_3)_2CHCH : CH_2$.

The *n*-pentenes can easily be separated from the branch chain pentenes, which are readily absorbed by weak sulphuric acid. The mixed *n*-pentenes are converted to *sec*-pentanols on hydration (Chapter 8).

The 1- and 2-pentenes can be made by catalytic dehydrogenation of *n*-pentane.[42] 1-Pentene, which boils at 30·1° c., can be separated by straight fractional distillation from 2-pentene, which boils at 36·4° c., and from *n*-pentane, which boils at 36·1° c.; this is one step in the synthesis of

---

[42] Phillips Pet., U.S.P. 2381693.

piperylene from n-pentane (Chapter 12, p. 210). 2-Pentene could no doubt be separated from n-pentane by processes indicated earlier in this chapter, such as by azeotropic distillation with ammonia.

The most stable branch chain pentene is trimethylethylene; the other two branch chain pentenes isomerise to trimethylethylene under mild conditions. Isopropylethylene gives trimethylethylene on contact with 84% sulphuric acid at 35° c.

(e) HIGHER OLEFINS

The higher olefins are present in all fractions of the petrol range of thermally and catalytically cracked oils, but the rapidly increasing number of isomers makes isolation of any individual olefin a practically impossible task with the technical weapons at present at the disposal of industry. Thirteen isomeric hexenes boil over the range 41·2–73·3° c. At the lower level, they approach the highest boiling pentene, trimethylethylene, b.p. 38·6° c.; at the upper, they overlap with the lower boiling heptenes. And five paraffins, four diolefins, and two naphthenes boil within this range of 41·2–73·3° c.

The proportion of olefins in a low boiling debutanised cracked petrol (boiling range 21–135° c.) is given in Table 33.[43] 'Saturateds' include paraffins, naphthenes and aromatics.

TABLE 33

Olefin content of fractions of cracked petrol

Temperature range ° c.	Fraction	% hydrocarbon in total petrol (by vol.)	% olefin in fraction (by vol.)
21 – 29·5	Isopentane	15·5	29
	Isopentenes	6·4	
29·5– 38·5	n-Pentane	24·4	32
	Pentenes	11·5	
38·5– 54	Saturateds (cyclopentane fraction)	1·6	50
	Olefins	1·6	
54 – 66	Saturateds (isohexane fraction)	5·3	27
	Olefins	2·0	
66 – 71	Saturateds (n-hexane fraction)	6·1	22
	Olefins	1·7	
71 – 93·5	Saturateds (isoheptane fraction)	7·6	19
	Olefins	1·8	
93·5–101	Saturateds (n-heptane fraction)	3·9	15
	Olefins	0·7	
above 101	Saturateds (residue)	8·4	15
	Olefins	1·5	

Note–the total proportion of olefins in this particular cracked petrol was 27·2 per cent.

[43] Morrell and Egloff, 'Science of Petroleum', *Oxford University Press*, Vol. 2, 1938, 996.

The average composition of cracked petrol (b.p. up to 200° c.) is roughly :

Hydrocarbon type	%
Olefins	15–30
Aromatics	15–30
Naphthenes	10–20
Paraffins	25–50

Specific higher olefins or relatively simple mixtures are available by the following methods. The cracking of paraffin wax under mild thermal conditions gives *n*-olefins in which the double bond is at the end of the chain. A whole range of molecular weights is produced, and the olefins are mixed up with paraffins of the same boiling range also produced in the cracking. However, the higher molecular weight olefins tend to predominate in accordance with Haber's rule :

$$C_{n+m}H_{2(n+m)+2} \rightarrow C_nH_{2n} + C_mH_{2m+2}$$

The cracking is carried out in the temperature range 400–500° c., at atmospheric or superatmospheric pressure, and is assisted by the presence of steam.

In one process operated in Germany,[44] petroleum wax of average molecular weight 500 and containing less than 5 per cent oil, was cracked at 540° c. and 3–4 atma. pressure in presence of steam with between six and seven seconds contact time; the products obtained were :

Product	% by wt.
Gas and loss	30
Cracked distillate (b.p. 40–300° c.) .	60
Heavy residue	10
	100

The boiling range of the distillate corresponds to a range of straight chain paraffins and olefins from C_5 to C_{17}.

Another route to olefins from paraffin wax is by monochlorination (Chapter 5) followed by removal of hydrogen chloride :

$$C_nH_{2n+2} \xrightarrow{Cl_2} C_nH_{2n+1}Cl \xrightarrow{- HCl} C_nH_{2n}$$

It appears that catalytic dehydrochlorination gives little or no alteration in chain length or structure, whereas use of alkalies may lead to side reactions, including oxidation at the double bond. Catalytic vapour phase removal of hydrogen chloride is effected at 350° c. over aluminium silicate.[45] The position of the double bond will depend upon the point of entry of the chlorine atom into the paraffin wax molecule; there is some indication that low temperature chlorination favours substitution near the end of the molecule, which would give an olefin in which the double bond was also near the end of the molecule.

---

[44] F.I.A.T. 423.
[45] C.I.O.S. 27/69.

A similar series of *n*-olefins, in which the double bond is in the 1- or the 2-position, is produced by the Fischer-Tropsch process, particularly when the ratio of carbon monoxide to hydrogen is greater than 1 : 2 (Chapter 3, p. 50). Here also both olefins and paraffins are present together. From the direct Fischer-Tropsch process, the limit of chain length of the olefins is about C_{18} but longer chain olefins may be made from the very high molecular weight Fischer-Tropsch waxes (for example, those made with iron or with ruthenium as catalyst) by thermal cracking or by chlorination and dehydrochlorination.

A different method of making higher olefins is by the controlled polymerisation of the lower olefins.

Ethylene is the most difficult olefin to polymerise. At high temperatures, over 600° c., it gives *n*-butene; this reaction was at one time considered as a route to butadiene. On polymerisation with aluminium chloride at 120–150° c. and about 60 atm. pressure, it gives lubricating oils possessing a branch chain structure;[21] under mild conditions, aluminium chloride gives polymers containing butenes, hexenes and octenes, probably of branch chain structure. Its most important polymerisation reaction is the formation of polyethylene at pressures of about 1,200 atm. and at 200° c. in presence of catalytic amounts of oxygen.[46] The commercial polymers, which are partly branch chain in structure, have molecular weights from 15,000 to about 50,000.[47]

New types of polyethylenes are now being produced commercially by different methods of polymerisation. These are more linear in structure and are characterised by a higher density, a higher melting point and higher tensile strength or lower elasticity than high pressure polyethylene. I.C.I. have modified their own high pressure process to give these high density polyethylenes, but the alternative processes operate at low or moderate pressure. In the Ziegler process, the polymerisation is carried out at temperatures up to about 150° c. and pressures from atmospheric to 50 atm. using an aluminium trialkyl such as aluminium triethyl with titanium tetrachloride as the activator, *e.g.*, at 60–70° c. in diesel oil as solvent.[48] The active catalyst is thought to be a titanium subchloride, functioning as a solid heterogeneous catalyst. The Phillips process also uses a solid heterogeneous catalyst, 2–3 per cent chromium oxide on silica–alumina. 0·6 per cent by weight of the catalyst is suspended in a hydrocarbon solvent and pure ethylene fed in at 132–150° c. and about 30 atms.[49] Standard Oil of Indiana use supported molybdenum and nickel catalysts for the same purpose.

[46] Freeth, *Brit. Plastics*, 1946, **18**, 444.
[47] Oakes and Raine, *Chem. and Ind.*, Aug. 10, 1953, p. 843.
[48] *Chem. Trade J.*, Dec. 16, 1955, p. 1638; Ziegler, B.P. 713081.
[49] Clark, Hogan, Banks and Lanning, *Ind. Eng. Chem.*, 1956, **48**, 1152. Phillips Pet., Belg. Pat. 530617.

The polymerisation of propylene leads to polymers used as intermediates in the petroleum chemicals industry. Polymerised over a supported phosphoric acid catalyst at about 200° c. and 15 atma. pressure, a mixture of nonenes (propylene trimer) and dodecenes (propylene tetramer) is obtained. These are highly branch chain in structure, used mainly in the detergent industry. Dimers can also be made. Propylene tetramer is part of the molecule of the most widely used type of synthetic detergent, the alkylaryl sulphonates. Propylene trimer is used for alkylation of phenols which are subsequently converted to detergents. Propylene can also be polymerised with sulphuric acid or by thermal treatment at 350–550° c. and 100–150 atm. pressure.

High molecular weight linear polypropylenes (isotactic polymers) melting at 150° c. or higher have now been obtained by Natta in Italy, using solid catalysts thought to be crystalline titanium subchlorides, developed from Ziegler's work, and by Phillips Petroleum using their polyethylene granular catalyst.[50]

Isobutene polymerises much more readily to dimers and trimers. The reaction is brought about by absorbing the isobutene in 60–65% sulphuric acid at 10–20° c. and then heating to 80–100° c. for about half an hour. The polymers separate as an upper layer which is separated, washed and distilled. The yield of polymers is about 90 per cent on isobutene; of the polymers, about 80 per cent is dimer and 20 per cent trimer.

The dimer itself is a mixture of 2 : 4 : 4-trimethyl-1-pentene and 2 : 4 : 4-trimethyl-2-pentene in the ratio of about 4 : 1. The trimer contains pentamethyl-heptenes and dineopentylethylene. The polymerisation is believed to proceed by a carbonium ion mechanism.[51]

The principal outlets of diisobutene are as an intermediate for detergents and for the manufacture of the branch chain primary alcohol, 3 : 5 : 5-trimethylhexanol, by the Oxo reaction (Chapter 11, p. 184).

The *n*-butenes are not polymerised to olefins used in the chemical industry. The outlets of the lower *n*-butene polymers is in the petroleum industry; similarly, the 'codimer' obtained from an *n*-butene-isobutene mixture by absorption in 63–70% sulphuric acid at 75–100° c., is, or was, a raw material for aviation stock. It has to be hydrogenated before use. The initial octene obtained in the codimer process is 2 : 2 : 3-trimethyl-2-pentene, but isomerisation then takes place with wandering of the double bond and of one of the methyl groups.

On the other hand, the mixed selective polymerisation of propylene and *n*-butenes using solid phosphoric acid under pressure gives a mixture of branch chain heptenes used both for motor spirit and for conversion to 'isooctyl alcohol' by the Oxo reaction (Chapter 11, p. 184); higher members have been used for dodecyl mercaptan (Chapter 11, p. 182).

---

[50] *Chem. Week*, February 2, 1956, p. 62; June 16, 1956, pp. 64, 79.
[51] Whitmore, *Ind. Eng. Chem.*, 1934, **26**, 94.

CHAPTER 8

THE HYDRATION OF OLEFINS

FROM the standpoint of scale of operation, the hydration of olefins to alcohols is one of the most important in the petroleum chemicals industry.

Except in the case of ethylene, the hydration of olefins invariably gives secondary or tertiary alcohols, for example:

$$RCH : CH_2 \xrightarrow{H_2O} \underset{\underset{OH}{|}}{R}CHCH_3$$

$$RR_1C : CH_2 \xrightarrow{H_2O} \underset{\underset{OH}{|}}{R}R_1CCH_3$$

Primary alcohols other than ethyl alcohol are never obtained by this reaction; if wanted, they have to be built up by synthetic methods, *e.g.*, by the synthesis of *n*-butyl alcohol from acetaldehyde (Chapter 16, p. 291) and of straight and branch chain primary alcohols from olefins by the Oxo reaction (Chapter 11, p. 183). Branch chain primary alcohols are also manufactured from carbon monoxide-hydrogen mixtures by the 'Higher Alcohols' synthesis (Chapter 3, p. 45).

There are two general methods of hydration of olefins:

(1) absorption in sulphuric acid to give the alkyl hydrogen sulphate, followed by dilution and hydrolysis (concentration-dilution process).

(2) catalytic hydration, using either a liquid phase catalyst or a solid contact catalyst.

The choice between these routes depends upon the relative tendency of the olefin to hydrate or to polymerise under reaction conditions. Compared with hydration, the tendency to polymerise increases rapidly with increasing molecular weight of the olefin. Thus, whilst the world's production of synthetic ethyl alcohol is split approximately equally between these two methods, only a small proportion of isopropyl alcohol is made by direct hydration and this method is not used at all for the C_4 and higher olefins.

1. Absorption in sulphuric acid

The main reaction is:

$$RCH : CH_2 + H_2SO_4 \rightarrow \underset{\underset{OSO_3H}{|}}{R}CHCH_3 \xrightarrow{+ H_2O} \underset{\underset{OH}{|}}{R}CHCH_3 + H_2SO_4$$

Absorption is carried out in sulphuric acid of from 50% to 98% strength, depending on the olefin to be absorbed. Ease of absorption increases in the order ethylene < propylene < *n*-butenes < isobutene and other tertiary olefins. Indeed, as was pointed out in the previous chapter, this differential ease of absorption is used as a method of separation of mixtures of olefins.

The speed of absorption increases with rise in temperature but this also increases polymerisation and side reactions; increase in concentration of sulphuric acid produces similar effects. One therefore has to balance reaction conditions to obtain a practicable reaction velocity with minimum losses. Where possible, absorption is carried out in the liquid phase, which involves the use of pressure with the lower olefins.

Side reactions occurring are formation of ethers, of polymers, and of dialkyl sulphates:

$$2RCH : CH_2 + H_2SO_4 \rightarrow SO_2 \left(OCH \Big\langle {}^{CH_3}_{R} \right)_2$$

Ease of polymer formation increases in the order ethylene < propylene < *n*-butenes < isobutene and other tertiary olefins, *i.e.*, the same order as the ease of formation of the alkyl hydrogen sulphates. Polymer formation is favoured by concentration of acid and temperature of absorption, and for each particular olefin there is a limit in these reaction conditions, imposed both by increase in polymer formation, and by the tendency to carbonisation and formation of sulphur dioxide under the more extreme conditions. The general conditions chosen, shown in Table 34, bring out the variation in these limits with the different olefins. These can be further varied by adjustment of the contact time.

TABLE 34

Conditions of olefin/sulphuric acid reaction

Olefin	Usual range of acid strength %	Usual range of temperature ° c.
Ethylene	90–98	up to 75°
Propylene	70–85	35–75°
n-Butenes	70–85	about 15–30°
Isobutene	50–65	below 30°

Formation of dialkyl sulphates is favoured by pressure, by concentration of acid and by a high olefin-acid ratio. Although diethyl sulphate is a commercial product, its outlets are small, and the other dialkyl sulphates are technically useless. In the manufacture of alcohols from olefins, formation of dialkyl sulphates is a nuisance; they are much more difficult to hydrolyse than the alkyl hydrogen sulphates, and they are believed to be the main source of the ethers which are also a by-product of this method of hydration:

$$R_2SO_4 + 2ROH \rightarrow 2ROR + H_2SO_4$$

For these reasons, the dialkyl sulphates are sometimes separated from the alkyl hydrogen sulphates and hydrolysed separately.

The alkyl hydrogen sulphates are hydrolysed by dilution with water and heating:

$$ROSO_2OH + H_2O \rightarrow ROH + H_2SO_4$$

Under certain conditions of sulphation, particularly with the C_4 and higher olefins, some alcohol is obtained directly. On dilution, any dialkyl sulphate formed may separate as a non-aqueous phase; the diester can be removed at this stage and will then not interfere in the hydrolysis.

The degree of dilution is controlled by two factors; firstly, it is necessary to dilute to a sufficient extent to prevent the reverse reaction, dehydration of the alcohol back to the olefin, on heating. Secondly, dilution is limited economically by the cost of reconcentration of the acid.

There are special problems in concentrating sulphuric acid which has been used for hydrating olefins, due toe th presence of tars and organic sulphonates. These have to be removed by oxidation and the only convenient agent is sulphuric acid itself, and this step requires acid of at least 85% strength. It is fairly easy to concentrate dilute sulphuric acid to 70–75% strength in simple equipment, above which trouble due to sulphur trioxide aerosol fumes becomes serious. Further concentration requires vacuum evaporation as in the Mantius unit, or the use of the pot concentrator or the Chemico drum unit, which require, for their feed, acid of at least 70% strength. The high cost and trouble of concentrating sulphuric acid, especially to over 90% strength, has made it attractive to use the dilute sulphuric acid for other purposes where the impurities do not matter, for example in making superphosphate fertiliser. This is only possible where the two manufacturing facilities adjoin.

The alcohols are usually distilled out of the sulphuric acid solution; they are concentrated by fractionation, being obtained in all cases as water azeotropes. To obtain the anhydrous alcohols, these azeotropes have to be dried, usually by addition of third components which either form still lower boiling binary azeotropes with water or give ternary azeotropes containing a small proportion of the alcohol. Originally, chemical drying was used, and various ingenious chemical methods of water removal have been described but they are not now employed.

2. Catalytic hydration

Formally, catalytic hydration involves the direct addition of a molecule of water to an olefin:

$$RCH : CH_2 + H_2O \rightarrow \underset{\underset{\displaystyle OH}{|}}{RCHCH_3}$$

However, it seems likely that in most catalytic processes, hydration proceeds via an intermediate compound of the alkyl hydrogen sulphate type, which is hydrolysed at the same rate as it is formed.

In the early catalytic processes, the olefin and water were introduced in the vapour phase, and the alcohol also removed in the vapour phase. The conversion to alcohol is therefore limited by the thermodynamic equilibrium of the reaction:

$$\text{Olefin (gas)} + \text{Steam} \rightleftharpoons \text{Alcohol (gas)}$$

This equilibrium has been determined experimentally by several workers. The results of Stanley, Youell and Dymock[1] for the equilibrium constant, $K_p = \dfrac{\text{(Alcohol)}}{\text{(Olefin) (Steam)}}$, for the vapour phase hydration of the simpler olefins are given in Table 35; the variation of K_p with temperature is shown in Fig. 18.

From Table 35, the equilibrium concentrations of the alcohols are very low at atmospheric pressure, even at 150° c. From equimolar proportions of olefin and steam, the equilibrium concentration of the alcohol (at 150° c. and 1 atma. pressure) is 0·4% ethyl alcohol, 0·2% isopropyl alcohol and 0·03% sec-butyl alcohol.

TABLE 35

Equilibrium constant in hydration of olefins

Olefin	Alcohol	Log K_p	ΔH (g. cal./g. mol.)
Ethylene	Ethyl alcohol	$\dfrac{2,100}{T} - 6\cdot195$	$- 9,600$
Propylene	Isopropyl alcohol	$\dfrac{1,950}{T} - 6\cdot060$	$- 9,000$
n-Butenes	sec-Butyl alcohol	$\dfrac{1,845}{T} - 6\cdot395$	$- 8,450$
Isobutene	tert-Butyl alcohol	(as for isopropyl alcohol)	(as for isopropyl alcohol)

The features of vapour phase hydration are (i) equilibrium conversion decreases with increasing temperature, but is favoured by operation at high pressure, (ii) reaction is very slow, compared with the concentration-dilution process. Hydration therefore has to be carried out at as high a temperature as possible to get a practicable reaction velocity, (iii) the reaction velocity is lower with solid contact catalysts than with liquid catalysts; solid catalysts therefore have to be operated at higher temperatures than liquid catalysts and give lower conversions, (iv) under comparable conditions, reaction velocity increases in the order ethylene < propylene < n-butenes < isobutene, (v) there is an increasing tendency to

---

[1] *J. Soc. Chem. Ind.*, 1934, **53**, 205T.

polymer formation with increase in temperature in the order ethylene < propylene < *n*-butenes < isobutene, (*vi*) owing to the low conversions, there is the problem of removal of the alcohol from the reacter gases with minimum loss of heat and pressure.

The usual range of operating conditions is 150–300° c. at pressures from 10–300 atm. Liquid catalysts are usually dilute aqueous sulphuric or phosphoric acids. Solid catalysts include the usual dehydrating catalysts, for

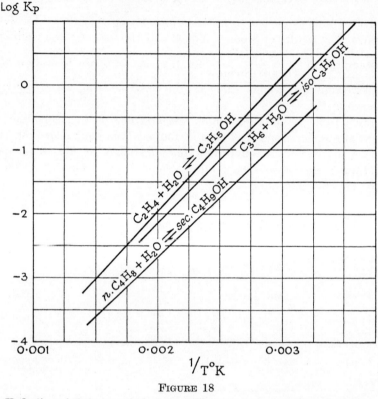

FIGURE 18

Hydration of olefins: variation of equilibrium constants with temperature

example phosphoric acid and simple and complex phosphates, and unpromoted and promoted active alumina. The application of these different methods to the individual olefins is dealt with below.

3. Ethyl alcohol

(*a*) MANUFACTURE

In America, synthetic ethyl alcohol is manufactured by both the concentration-dilution process and the direct hydration process.

The concentration-dilution process involves the following steps: (*i*) absorption of ethylene is concentrated sulphuric acid, (*ii*) dilution, hydrolysis and distillation of the ethyl alcohol formed, (*iii*) reconcentration of the sulphuric acid.

The gases used must be free of higher olefins which react more readily than ethylene with sulphuric acid. Ethylene reacts so slowly with the most concentrated acid which can be used that temperatures above its critical point are necessary and the ethylene has to be in the gas phase. Nevertheless, it is advantageous to operate at considerable pressure to improve the reaction rate by physical means. The temperature of absorption must not exceed 80° c., to keep down carbonisation and polymerisation. Acid strength should not exceed 98 per cent to avoid formation of carbyl sulphate, ethionic acid, and isethionic acid:

$$
\begin{array}{cccc}
\underset{\parallel}{CH_2} & CH_2-O-SO_2 & CH_2OSO_3H & CH_2OH \\
\overset{\mid}{CH_2} & \overset{\mid}{CH_2-SO_2-O} & \overset{\mid}{CH_2SO_2OH} & \overset{\mid}{CH_2SO_2OH} \\
& \text{Carbyl Sulphate} & \text{Ethionic Acid} & \text{Isethionic Acid}
\end{array}
$$

The American method of carrying out this process has been described by Aries.[2] Gases containing 40–95 per cent (by volume) of ethylene, and free from higher olefins were absorbed at 85° c. under 12–30 atma. total pressure in 95% sulphuric acid; the working pressure was chosen with reference to the partial pressure of the ethylene. A portion of the liquor from the base of the absorber was recirculated and introduced half way up the absorber, to increase the proportion of sulphuric esters, which facilitates the absorption of the ethylene. The absorbed liquors were diluted with sufficient water so that, after hydrolysis, 50% aqueous sulphuric acid was obtained. Hydrolysis was carried out with steam heating and the mixture of alcohol, ether, sulphuric acid and water passed to the stripping column. From the base of this column, the dilute aqueous sulphuric acid was drawn off; it was concentrated in two stages to 95% strength. The alcohol and ether vapours from the top of the column were washed with water or dilute caustic soda to remove traces of acid, condensed, and rectified in two columns. Ether was taken off in the first column and alcohol from the second, rectifying, column. Oily impurities were also drawn off as a side-stream from the second column. The ethyl alcohol was obtained as the azeotrope with water, containing 95·6 per cent by weight of water. The azeotrope boils at 78·15° c., compared with 78·38° c. for pure ethyl alcohol. The yield of alcohol on ethylene was about 90 per cent, and 4–7 per cent ether was recovered as a by-product. The ether can be returned to process with fresh ethylene as it is readily converted to ethyl hydrogen sulphate under process conditions.

When anhydrous ethyl alcohol is wanted, it is obtained by distilling the azeotrope with an 'entraining agent' such as benzene. Benzene forms a ternary azeotrope with water and alcohol, boiling at 69·7° c., containing

---

[2] *Pet. Refiner*, April 1948, p. 124; *Chem. Trade J.*, 25 July, 1948, p. 88.

64 per cent by weight benzene, 31 per cent alcohol, and 5 per cent water. It also forms a binary azeotrope with alcohol, boiling at 72·5° c. and containing 52·6 per cent by weight of benzene and 47·4 per cent of alcohol.

Coming to the catalytic processes, the approximate equilibrium for the vapour phase reaction was given in Table 35. Subsequent publications do not give markedly different figures. Gilliland[3] suggested as an average equation for the free energy change in the reaction:

$$C_2H_4(g) + H_2O(g) \rightleftharpoons C_2H_5OH(g)$$

$\Delta G = -8,300 + 26·9T$. This gives values for ΔG close to those derivable from the equilibrium measurements of Stanley, Youell, and Dymock,[1] $\Delta G = -9,600 + 28·3T$.

Liquid phase processes involving passing ethylene through dilute sulphuric or phosphoric acids at temperatures of the order of 200–300° c. and pressures of about 25–100 atm.,[4, 5] have been examined but are not operated commercially, presumably because of corrosion troubles. The present process for synthetic ethyl alcohol by the direct hydration process, which is operated both in the United States and Great Britain, uses a solid phosphoric acid on silica catalyst. The basic operating conditions are:[6]

Reaction temperature	300° c.
Reaction pressure	68 atm.
Water to ethylene ratio (mol.)	0·6 : 1
Fresh ethylene make-up	97%
Ethylene in reactor feed (water free basis) . . .	85%
Space velocity (vol. of gas at S.T.P./min./vol. catalyst) .	30
Ethylene conversion per pass	4·2%

These conditions were chosen for economic reasons. The equilibrium concentration of ethyl alcohol decreases rapidly with rise in temperature (Fig. 18) but the reaction rate increases, from which the optimum economic conditions have to be worked out.

The process flow sheet is shown in Fig. 19. There is only partial conversion, so that unchanged ethylene has to be recycled. The ethylene water mixture is vaporised and brought to reaction temperature in the heater and then passes downwards through the catalyst bed. The gases are scrubbed with dilute caustic soda to neutralise traces of phosphoric acid, most of the ethyl alcohol condensed, and the remainder scrubbed out with water from the recycle gas stream. A purge has to be taken from the recycle gas to prevent accumulation of methane and ethane.

The dilute ethyl alcohol is concentrated by fractional distillation; the product alcohol from this column is taken off as a vapour and purified from traces of acetaldehyde and higher aldehydes by hydrogenation over a

---

[3] Gilliland, Gunness, and Bowles, *Ind. Eng. Chem.*, 1936, **28**, 370.
[4] Air Reduction, U.S.P. 2021564, 2044414, 2044417, 2050442–3.
[5] Standard Oil Development, B.P. 446781.
[6] Johnson and Nelson, *Chem. and Ind.*, Aug. 10, 1953, p. S. 28.

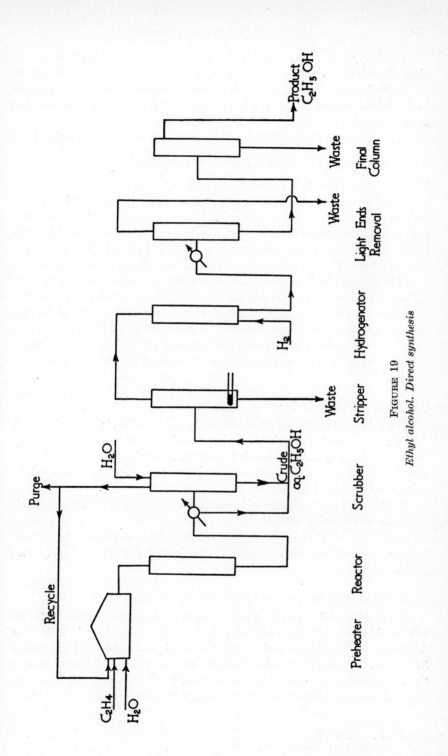

FIGURE 19

Ethyl alcohol. Direct synthesis

nickel catalyst. The treated alcohol is purified by further distillation; any diethyl ether is removed at this stage and either recycled to process or sold.

The principal advantage of this process compared with the concentration-dilution process is stated to be the elimination of the problems involved in the sulphuric acid cycle.

A modification of the solid catalyst process in which the reaction is:

$$C_2H_4(g) + H_2O(l) \rightleftharpoons C_2H_5OH(l)$$

has been developed in Germany.[7] A catalyst of reduced tungsten oxides promoted with zinc oxide and supported on silica gel, containing 20 per cent by weight of tungsten, was used. Conditions of working were 250–300° c. and 300 atm. pressure. Ethylene and water were introduced into the top of the reactor and a 20% aqueous ethyl alcohol solution withdrawn from the base. The output was 1 l. ethyl alcohol/day/l. catalyst space.

It is not operated, probably because of the low space time yield.

An improvement on this process involves the use of solid blue tungsten oxide as catalyst; water and ethylene, with some liquid water present, are passed downward over this catalyst at 300–345° c. and 300 atma.[8] The process being part liquid phase, part vapour phase, the equilibrium in favour of ethyl alcohol is more favourable than in the true vapour phase process.

(b) Outlets for ethyl alcohol

The principal outlet for ethyl alcohol in the chemical industry is acetaldehyde. It is used for a variety of other chemicals and in a very wide range of solvent outlets. In America, it is used as an anti-freeze and during the war years and occasionally subsequently, has been used for making butadiene for synthetic rubber.

Of the total consumption of industrial alcohol in the United States in 1956, about 1,250,000 tons, 50 per cent was used for aldehydes, 19 per cent for acetic acid, ethyl chloride and other chemicals, 21 per cent in the solvent industry, 4 per cent for synthetic rubber and 6 per cent for drugs and pharmaceuticals.[9]

(c) Alternative routes to ethyl alcohol

Ethyl alcohol is produced on so large a scale that reference to the relationship between the petroleum route and other routes is called for. Although in certain countries, ethyl alcohol has actually been manufactured from carbide via acetaldehyde, the main source has always been the fermentation of waste vegetable matter. The usual materials fermented are molasses, a by-product of the sugar industry, grain, starch from

[7] F.I.A.T. 968.
[8] I.C.I., B.P. 691360.
[9] *Chem. Week*, 11 August, 1956, p. 78.

surplus foodstuffs such as potato and maize, and sulphate waste liquor from the paper industry.

In America, the petroleum route, which was started in the 1920's, overhauled fermentation ethyl alcohol in 1949; in 1956, of their total output of 1,250,000 tons of industrial alcohol, about 75 per cent was made from petroleum ethylene. There has been a similar development in the United Kingdom; the first ethyl alcohol from petroleum ethylene went into operation in 1952 with a capacity of about one-third of the total British market for industrial alcohol. This plant has now been doubled. In these two countries, the route from petroleum ethylene is cheaper than any of the fermentation processes. Alterations in economic conditions from country to country and the scope for improvements in processes do not make this conclusion necessarily valid for all countries and for all time.

It must be added that hydration of ethylene is not the only possible petroleum route to ethyl alcohol. Ethyl alcohol could be an important by-product from the 'Hydrocol' process of making high octane petrol from mixtures of carbon monoxide and hydrogen. The cost of making ethyl alcohol by this route is bound up with the realisations obtained both from the major products of the synthesis and from the other by-products, and with the problem of purification to the necessary high quality.

4. Isopropyl alcohol

Although attempts to make ethyl alcohol from ethylene from coal have been undertaken since the pioneering work of Fritsche in 1897, the first alcohol manufactured from petroleum olefins was isopropyl alcohol, made by Standard Oil Co. of New Jersey (subsequently operated by the Standard Alcohol Co.) at Bayway, N.J., in 1920 and by Carbide and Carbon Chemicals Corporation at Charleston, W.Va., about the same time. As with ethyl alcohol, which was manufactured subsequently, both companies used the concentration-dilution process.

Propylene hydrates more readily than ethylene by this process but polymerises more readily. The gas mixture usually used is a propylene-propane mixture, freed from the C_2 and C_4 fractions, and obtained in working up the gases from thermal or catalytic cracking; this mixture may contain anything from 30 per cent to 85 per cent propylene. Sulphuric acid concentration varies from 70% to 93%; the usual range is probably 75–80%. The process is always carried out in the liquid phase which necessitates the use of pressure, but this simplifies the problem of efficient contact and of control of temperature. The temperature should be below 40° c., and pressure and efficient agitation are important factors. Production of isopropyl alcohol may be as high as 0·6 kg./kg. sulphuric acid used.

Formation of carbyl sulphate when ethylene was absorbed in sulphuric acid of too high a concentration has been referred to; this type of reaction occurs to some extent with propylene and the higher olefins, but in addition with strong sulphuric acid they form sultones presumably by attack on the methyl or methylene group next to the double bond:

$$\begin{array}{ccc} CH_3 & CH_2SO_3H & CH_2{-}SO_2 \\ | & | & | \qquad | \\ CH + 2H_2SO_4 \longrightarrow CH_2 & \rightarrow CH_2 \qquad | + H_2SO_4 \\ \| & | & | \qquad | \\ CH_2 & CH_2OSO_3H & CH_2{-}\!O \end{array}$$

As in the ethyl alcohol process, the acid liquors containing isopropyl hydrogen sulphate require dilution and heating to effect hydrolysis. The liquors must be diluted below 50% acid strength; the usual figure is 35–40%. On fractionating the aqueous isopropyl alcohol, the azeotrope with water is obtained, containing 87·7 per cent isopropyl alcohol, 12·3 per cent water, and boiling at 80·35° c. Pure isopropyl alcohol boils at 82·4° c. The azeotrope is dried by distillation with entraining agents such as toluene, ethylene dichloride or xylene.

In Germany, only one plant was operated for the hydration of propylene and the *n*-butenes, at Moers. The feed was the mixture of C_3 and C_4 hydrocarbons obtained as a by-product of the atmospheric pressure Fischer-Tropsch process. The hydrocarbon mixture, containing 25–45 per cent olefins, was reacted with 75% sulphuric acid at 60° c. and 20 atma. pressure, the hydrocarbons being maintained in the liquid phase. 0·66 mol of olefin was absorbed per mol of sulphuric acid; only small proportions of dialkyl sulphates and of ethers were formed. The alkyl hydrogen sulphates were hydrolysed by dilution to 30% acid concentration and steam distillation; the alcohols were subsequently dried azeotropically and separated by distillation. The yield of isopropyl alcohol was over 90 per cent on propylene; the yield of *sec*-butyl alcohol was lower owing to formation of much butene dimer in the sulphuric acid reactor.[10]

Propylene can also be hydrated catalytically in the liquid phase or in the vapour phase in the same way as ethylene.[11]

A variant of the liquid phase process is the Usines de Melle method.[12] This depends upon production of free isopropyl alcohol in the sulphation step; the alcohol is extracted with a selective solvent, and the acid liquors containing some isopropyl hydrogen sulphate recycled to the absorption stage. In an example, propylene was absorbed at 50° c. and 1 atma. pressure in 75% sulphuric acid containing 0·5 per cent copper oxide as catalyst; the isopropyl alcohol was extracted with butyl cresol, an acid resistant solvent, and the acid layer returned to the absorber. The solvent layer was distilled to recover the isopropyl alcohol and the solvent recycled to the extraction stage.

One solid contact process uses reduced tungsten oxide promoted with

[10] B.I.O.S. 131.
[11] Air Reduction, U.S.P. 2050443.
[12] F.P. 799704.

zinc oxide on a silica gel support. The process involved hydration of propylene with water. Ten mols of water and one mol of propylene were passed cocurrent down a tower reactor packed with the catalyst at 200–240° c. and 200 atm. pressure. Isopropyl alcohol as a 12–15% aqueous solution was withdrawn from the base of the tower. The best yields were obtained operating at 50% conversion of propylene per pass, when the yield of isopropyl alcohol on propylene reacted was 95 per cent. The make of isopropyl alcohol was 15–30 g./l. catalyst space/hr. This is a partial liquid phase process; the equilibrium conversion is more favourable than in the true vapour phase process. An improvement in this method involves using unsupported blue tungsten oxide, operating at 250–290° c. and 150–300 atm.[13]

OUTLETS FOR ISOPROPYL ALCOHOL

The main outlet for isopropyl alcohol is for the manufacture of acetone (see Chapter 17, p. 303), but considerable quantities are used as a solvent. Hydration of propylene is the only technically economic route to isopropyl alcohol.

In 1955, American production of isopropyl alcohol was estimated at 410,000 tons with the following end-use pattern.[14]

Outlet	*% offtake*
Acetone	57
Solvent	12
Chemical manufacture, other than acetone	11
Petrol additive (antistalling, deicing)	10
Rubbing alcohol, drugs, and cosmetics	6
Miscellaneous	3
Export	1
	100

Isopropyl alcohol is no longer used as an anti-freeze but a new chemical outlet is now emerging, as a route to hydrogen peroxide to be used in a new synthesis of glycerol from propylene not involving chlorine (Chapter 10, p. 169; Chapter 16, p. 300).

On partial oxidation with oxygen at about 105–110° c. and 25 atma. pressure, isopropyl alcohol gives one mol of acetone and one mol of hydrogen peroxide in yields of 90 per cent or over.[15]

$$(CH_3)_2CHOH + O_2 \rightarrow (CH_3)_2CO + H_2O_2$$

The reaction mixture is diluted with water and distilled to remove acetone and unchanged isopropyl alcohol. The hydrogen peroxide, obtained as a 6–10 per cent aqueous solution, is contaminated with organic impurities, and requires purification, for example, via calcium peroxide.[16]

---

[13] I.C.I., B.P. 671971.
[14] *Chem. Week*, June 11, 1955, p. 95.
[15] B.P.M., B.P. 708339.
[16] Shell Development, U.S.P. 2695217.

5. sec-Butyl alcohol

On hydration, both 1-butene and 2-butene give the same alcohol, *sec*-butyl alcohol:

$$CH_3CH_2CH : CH_2 \underset{CH_3CH : CHCH_3}{\overset{}{\Bigg]}} \xrightarrow{H_2O} CH_3CH_2\underset{\underset{OH}{|}}{C}HCH_3$$

Isobutene gives the tertiary alcohol, *tert*-butyl alcohol:

$$\begin{array}{c} CH_3 \\ CH_3 \end{array}\!\!\!>\!C : CH_2 \xrightarrow{H_2O} \begin{array}{c} CH_3 \\ CH_3 \end{array}\!\!\!>\!\underset{\underset{OH}{|}}{C}CH_3$$

Isobutyl alcohol, $(CH_3)_2CHCH_2OH$, a primary alcohol, is not directly derivable by hydration of an olefin. It is manufactured as the principal constituent of the higher alcohols synthesis from carbon monoxide and hydrogen (Chapter 3, p. 45), or as a by-product of making *n*-butyl alcohol from propylene by the Oxo reaction (Chapter 11, p. 184).

The C_4 fraction of cracked gases contains *n*-butenes, butanes, isobutene, and when cracking at high temperatures, butadiene (Chapter 7, Table 30). Before the *n*-butenes can be hydrated to *sec*-butyl alcohol, both the isobutene and the butadiene have to be removed. The isobutene polymerises under the conditions necessary for hydration of the *n*-butenes; butadiene forms tars under these conditions, allegedly by interpolymerisation with the *n*-butenes.

As was shown in Chapter 7, p. 102, the physical properties of isobutene are too close to those of the *n*-butenes to make separation by physical methods easy, although it is not impossible. However, isobutene is almost invariably removed by prior absorption in 50–65% sulphuric acid which does not affect the *n*-butenes under mild conditions. The action of sulphuric acid on isobutene is dealt with below (*tert*-butyl alcohol). Butadiene is not attacked by cold 50–65% sulphuric acid; it can therefore be removed before or after the isobutene by any of the methods mentioned in Chapter 7, p. 117, and Chapter 12, p. 199, depending on how much is present.

The direct hydration process is not used with the *n*-butenes because of formation of too much polymer. In the concentration-dilution method, reaction is easier than with ethylene or propylene and the higher boiling point of the C_4 hydrocarbons makes the complete liquid phase process relatively easy. The usual conditions are use of 70–85% acid at about 20–35° c. Mild conditions are desirable to avoid polymer formation. In the German process for hydration of mixtures of propylene and butenes at 60° c., using 75% sulphuric acid, much polymer was obtained from the butenes but not from the propylene.[10] In the complete liquid phase process, the exothermic heat of the reaction can be controlled by boiling off some of the hydrocarbons, the vapours being condensed and returned. Sulphation is carried out to give butyl hydrogen sulphate, avoiding dibutyl sulphate formation as far as possible.

sec-Butyl alcohol is isolated from the acid liquors in the usual way, by dilution with water to about 20–30% acid concentration, heating and distillation. On dilution, the liquor usually separates into a butane layer containing some free *sec*-butyl alcohol and a lower acid layer containing the butyl hydrogen sulphate. The upper layer can be separated and the butyl alcohol recovered from it by distillation. *sec*-Butyl alcohol boils at 99·5° c.; it forms an azeotrope with water, boiling at 88° c. and containing 68 per cent by weight of the alcohol.

The Usines de Melle process[12] takes advantage of the formation of free *sec*-butyl alcohol on sulphation. *n*-Butene is absorbed in 72% sulphuric acid containing 0·5 per cent copper oxide at 50° c. and 1 atma. pressure, the acid solution extracted with tricresyl phosphate (an acid resistant solvent), which is neutralised and distilled to recover the *sec*-butyl alcohol.

sec-Butyl alcohol is used as a solvent and as an intermediate for the manufacture of methyl ethyl ketone (Chapter 17, p. 320) and of *sec*-butyl esters (Chapter 18).

6. tert-Butyl alcohol

Isobutene, like all tertiary olefins, is much more reactive to sulphuric acid than the other olefins. It was shown thirty years ago that it was absorbed by sulphuric acid some 200–400 times as fast as 1-butene or 2-butene.

Two reactions may take place, (*i*) direct hydration to *tert*-butyl alcohol,

$$\begin{array}{c} CH_3 \\ CH_3 \end{array}\!\!\!>\!C:CH_2 + H_2O \rightarrow \begin{array}{c} CH_3 \\ CH_3 \end{array}\!\!\!>\!\!\!\begin{array}{c} CCH_3 \\ | \\ OH \end{array}$$

(*ii*) polymerisation to dimers and higher polymers (see Chapter 7, p. 125),

$$\begin{array}{ccc} CH_3 & CH_3 & CH_3 & CH_3 \\ | & | & | & | \\ CH_3C + CH_3C:CH_2 \rightarrow CH_3C\!-\!CH_2C:CH_2 \\ \| & & | \\ CH_2 & & CH_3 \end{array}$$

Hydration is favoured by mild conditions—low acid strength and low temperatures. The usual range of conditions is 50–65% sulphuric acid at 10–30° c. Reaction is carried out in the liquid phase under slight pressure.

The usual product under these conditions is *tert*-butyl alcohol. *tert*-Butyl hydrogen sulphate has been described.[17] *tert*-Butyl alcohol is much more easily dehydrated than *sec*-butyl alcohol or isopropyl alcohol; it is therefore isolated from the acid liquors either by considerable dilution with

[17] Carbide and Carbon, Can. P. 350409.

water, or even by neutralisation,[18] or by extraction with a solvent such as cresol.[19] It forms an azeotrope with water containing 88 per cent alcohol and boiling at 79·9° c. The pure alcohol boils at 82·4° c. The azeotrope can be dried by the usual methods.

tert-Butyl alcohol is not a particularly valuable solvent; it has been used as an intermediate for introducing the *tert*-butyl group into the aromatic ring, *e.g.*, with phenol it gives *tert*-butylphenol, an intermediate for oil soluble phenol formaldehyde resins. *tert*-Butylphenol can also be obtained from phenol and either isobutene or diisobutene under appropriate conditions (see Chapter 11, p. 191).

7. Higher alcohols

The straight chain pentenes and hexenes are hydrated to *sec*-amyl alcohols and *sec*-hexyl alcohols by the concentration-dilution process using the same process as for *sec*-butyl alcohol. Brooks[20] cites 82–90% acid and 15–20° c. as reaction conditions. According to him, technical *sec*-amyl alcohol consists of a mixture of 80 per cent 2-pentanol and 20 per cent 3-pentanol. On hydration, 1-pentene gives exclusively 2-pentanol; 2-pentene gives a mixture of 65 per cent 2-pentanol and 35 per cent 3-pentanol:

$$CH_3CH_2CH_2CH : CH_2 + H_2O \longrightarrow CH_3CH_2CH_2\underset{\underset{OH}{|}}{C}HCH_3 \quad \text{2-Pentanol}$$

$$CH_3CH_2CH : CHCH_3 + H_2O \longrightarrow \begin{cases} CH_3CH_2CH_2\underset{\underset{OH}{|}}{C}HCH_3 & \text{2-Pentanol} \\ & (65\%) \\ CH_3CH_2\underset{\underset{OH}{|}}{C}HCH_2CH_3 & \text{3-Pentanol} \\ & (35\%) \end{cases}$$

Long chain olefins have been converted to the *sec*-alcohols but the reaction is usually stopped at the alkyl hydrogen sulphate stage (see Chapter 11, p. 181).

The higher branch chain olefins react like isobutene with sulphuric acid, but show an even greater tendency to give polymers, rather than to give the tertiary alcohol.

8. Dialkyl sulphates

Passing reference has been made to the di-esters. They are conveniently prepared by interaction between excess olefin and concentrated sulphuric acid at moderate temperatures, if necessary under pressure. For example, diethyl sulphate is obtained in 80 per cent yield from excess ethylene and 98% sulphuric acid at 80° c. and 30 atma. pressure; similarly, excess 2-pentene with 90% sulphuric acid at 15–20° c. gives a 75 per cent yield of

---

[18] Shell Development, U.S.P. 2019762.
[19] Shell Development, U.S.P. 2042212.
[20] *Ind. Eng. Chem.*, 1935, **27**, 278, 282.

mixed diamyl sulphates. The academic route is by distillation *in vacuo* of the mono-esters:

$$2ROSO_3H \rightarrow R_2SO_4 + H_2SO_4$$

The simplest member of the series, dimethyl sulphate, cannot be made by sulphation of an olefin. It is usually made from dimethyl ether and fuming sulphuric acid.

The lower dialkyl sulphates have limited outlets as alkylating agents; they are less active than the alkyl halides, and the dialkyl sulphates above C_3 have no technical value.

9. Ethers

Formation of ethers during hydrolysis by interaction between dialkyl sulphate and alcohol has been mentioned on p. 127:

$$R_2SO_4 + ROH \rightarrow R_2O + ROSO_3H$$

This is believed to be the mechanism of the Erlenmeyer synthesis of ethers.

If diethyl ether is wanted, it is made by passing the vapour of ethyl alcohol into a mixture of 1 mol concentrated sulphuric acid and 1·2 mols of ethyl alcohol at 140° c.

TABLE 36

Boiling points of simpler ethers

Name	Formula	b.p., ° c./760 mm.
Dimethyl ether	$(CH_3)_2O$	− 23·6
Methyl ethyl ether	$CH_3OC_2H_5$	7·9
Diethyl ether	$(C_2H_5)_2O$	34·6
Di-*n*-propyl ether	$(CH_3CH_2CH_2)_2O$	91
Diisopropyl ether	$\left(\dfrac{CH_3}{CH_3}\!\!>\!\!CH\right)_2 O$	67·5
Di-*n*-butyl ether	$(CH_3CH_2CH_2CH_2)_2O$	142
Di-*sec*-butyl ether	$\left(\begin{array}{c}CH_3CH_2CH \\ | \\ CH_3\end{array}\right)_2 O$	121
Diisobutyl ether	$\left(\dfrac{CH_3}{CH_3}\!\!>\!\!CHCH_2\right)_2 O$	122·5
Di-*tert*-butyl ether	$((CH_3)_3C)_2O$	107
Methyl *tert*-butyl ether	$CH_3OC(CH_3)_3$	55–56
Ethyl *tert*-butyl ether	$C_2H_5OC(CH_3)_3$	73
Di-*n*-amyl ether	$(CH_3CH_2CH_2CH_2CH_2)_2O$	190
Diisoamyl ether	$((CH_3)_2CHCH_2)_2O$	172·5

Ethers may also be made by vapour phase dehydration of alcohols at 190–250° c. over catalysts such as alum or active alumina.

Dimethyl ether is made by vapour phase catalytic dehydration of methyl alcohol; a process for making mixed *tert*-alkyl ethers by addition of alcohols to *tert*-olefins in the presence of sulphuric acid is described in Chapter 11, p. 190.

The lower ethers are available as by-products from the manufacture of synthetic alcohols. As a surplus is produced, the excess is returned to process, for reconversion to the alcohol.

The most important ether is diethyl ether, used as a solvent in a wide variety of industries, and as an anaesthetic. Production in America reached the figure of 34,000 tons p.a. in 1944, but declined to 25,000 tons p.a. by 1954. Diisopropyl ether has also been used as a solvent and as a component of high octane fuels; it has a greater tendency to peroxide formation than diethyl ether. The boiling points of the simpler ethers are given in Table 36.

CHAPTER 9

OXIDATION OF OLEFINS

THIS chapter deals with the oxidation of olefins to oxygen containing organic chemicals, and not with the oxidation of olefins to other hydrocarbons.

1. Gas phase oxidation of olefins with oxygen

Reaction between excess of olefin and a limited amount of oxygen has led to the identification of breakdown products which can be formulated as arising by one or all of the following routes, the exact mechanism followed in each particular case not yet being certain.

(*i*) *Formation of a hydroperoxide on a methylene group next to the double bond*

This hydroperoxide can then break down to give an alcohol, or a ketone or aldehyde which can then further oxidise to acids:

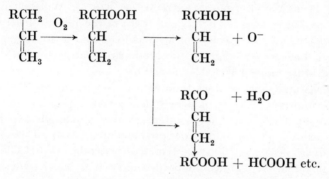

(*ii*) *Formation of a* 1 : 2-*oxide*

This can then hydrate to a 1 : 2-diol in the presence of water or isomerise to an aldehyde or ketone, which can undergo further oxidation:

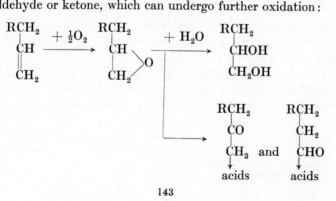

(iii) Oxidation of a methylene group attached to the double bond, to a CO group:

$$\begin{array}{c} RCH \\ \| \\ CH_2 \end{array} \rightarrow \begin{array}{c} RCH_2 \\ | \\ CHO \end{array} \rightarrow \text{acids}$$

(iv) Fission of the double bond to give ketones and aldehydes

This may be done via a cyclic peroxide (an old formulation revived by E. H. Farmer):

$$\begin{array}{c} RCH \\ \| \\ CH_2 \end{array} + O_2 \longrightarrow \begin{array}{c} RCH-O \\ | \quad \ | \\ CH_2-O \end{array} \rightarrow \begin{array}{l} RCHO \rightarrow \text{acids} \\ + \\ CH_2O \rightarrow \text{formic acid, CO, CO}_2 \end{array}$$

Examples of all these products by the non-catalytic vapour phase interaction of olefins and oxygen will now be quoted. Their industrial significance is that it should be possible by suitable choice of highly selective catalysts to make one or other of these various methods of oxygen attack and breakdown preponderate, and so to give technically valuable intermediates.

Direct conversion of ethylene to formaldehyde by heating with oxygen has long been known from Schutzenberger (1875), Willstatter, Bone, Wheeler and their schools; best yields were in the region of 550–600° c. with short contact time; traces of acetaldehyde and of formic acid were also noted. Lenher[1] investigated the products of interaction in detail in the temperature range 300–500° c., using both long contact times in single pass systems and short contact time with recirculation. The condensable products comprised ethylene oxide, ethylene glycol, glyoxal, acetaldehyde, formaldehyde, formic acid and water; in the circulation experiments, ethylene oxide and formaldehyde predominated. With a larger unit, formaldehyde peroxide, di(hydroxymethyl)peroxide, $O_2(CH_2OH)_2$, was isolated in quantity. This could be decomposed to yield hydrogen and formic acid, both present in the oxidation products:

$$O_2 \begin{array}{c} \diagup CH_2OH \\ \diagdown CH_2OH \end{array} \rightarrow 2HCOOH + H_2$$

Similarly, Newitt and Mene[2] with ethylene-air mixtures at 30–100 atm. and 210–270° c. isolated formaldehyde, acetaldehyde, ethylene glycol and formic and acetic acids.

In his work on propylene-oxygen mixtures, Lenher[1] isolated only acetaldehyde, formaldehyde and formic acid, whereas Newitt and Mene[2] at 12–18 atma. and 215–280° c. using excess propylene, obtained propylene oxide, propylene glycol and glycerol, together with mixed acids and aldehydes. Allyl alcohol and propionaldehyde were stated to be formed in the

---

[1] *J. Amer. Chem. Soc.*, 1931, **53**, 3737, 3752.
[2] *J. Chem. Soc.*, 1946, 97.

early stages of oxidation. Allyl alcohol and glycerol almost certainly arise by initial attack on the methyl group.

Oxidation of 2-butene has been examined by Lucas *et al.*[3] using oxygen at 350–500° c. The main products were acetaldehyde and butadiene. Other products identified were glyoxal, an olefin oxide, an acid and peroxides. No methyl ethyl ketone was detected. The butadiene was supposed to arise by dehydration of 2 : 3-butane diol or oxide and to give glyoxal by oxidation at the double bonds:

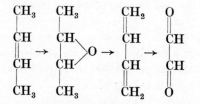

So much for a broad picture of the results. The mechanism of vapour phase oxidation of olefins has not yet been fully worked out. Bone's hydroxylation theory is not now accepted; oxidation is considered to proceed by a chain mechanism in which either peroxide radicals or olefin radicals are the propagating mechanism, but it is not easy to account for all the products obtained.

The complicated nature of the products makes the industrial application of these reactions relatively unattractive. The main line of improvement has been the discovery of selective catalysts. For example, Riley and Friend[4] have shown that selenium dioxide oxidises the double bonded methylene group to a $> CO$ group, *e.g.*, ethylene at 220–240° c. gives over 80 per cent glyoxal, and propylene gives some methylglyoxal (pyruvic aldehyde):

$$
\begin{array}{ccc}
CH_2 & \to & CHO \\
\| & & | \\
CH_2 & & CHO
\end{array}
$$

$$
\begin{array}{ccc}
CH_3 & & CH_3 \\
| & & | \\
CH & \to & CO \\
\| & & | \\
CH_2 & & CHO
\end{array}
$$

This reaction is not of technical value.

Technically the most important application of selective catalysts is the use of silver to bring about conversion of ethylene and oxygen to ethylene oxide,

$$
\begin{array}{ccc}
CH_2 & & CH_2 \\
\| & + \tfrac{1}{2}O_2 \to & | \!\!\!\diagdown \\
CH_2 & & CH_2 \!\!\!\diagup O
\end{array}
$$

[3] *J. Amer. Chem. Soc.*, 1935, **57**, 723.
[4] *J. Chem. Soc.*, 1932, 2342.

This reaction was discovered in France in 1930 by the Société Française Catalyse Généralisée[5] and has been actively developed, particularly in America. The importance of this process resides in the great versatility of ethylene oxide, the reactions of which are made the principal subject of Chapter 19, and in its advantages over the chlorhydrin route to ethylene oxide (Chapter 10, p. 177).

Only an approximate idea of the present position on the catalytic ethylene oxide process can be given owing to the mass of information from patents issued over the last twenty years and from the literature appraisals published since the war.

The general method is to pass a mixture of ethylene and oxygen containing gases over a catalyst consisting of silver on a support at temperatures usually in the range 200–300° c. Partial oxidation of the ethylene occurs, two main reactions taking place:

$$C_2H_4 + \tfrac{1}{2}O_2 \rightarrow CH_2\!\!-\!\!CH_2(g). \quad \Delta H = -35 \text{ k. cal.} \qquad (1)$$
$$\diagdown\!O\!\diagup$$

$$C_2H_4 + 3O_2 \rightarrow 2CO_2 + 2H_2O(g). \quad \Delta H = -316 \text{ k. cal.} \qquad (2)$$

Most attention has been devoted to improvements in catalysts. Although alternatives to silver have been disclosed, silver is the basis of all the industrial catalysts. A wide variety of methods of preparation and activation of the catalyst, and of promoters and supports has been disclosed and it is difficult to select the favoured method. A novel suggestion is the use of traces of organic vapours introduced continuously with the reactor gases, to act as suppressors of the total combustion reaction. Compounds such as ethylene dichloride[6] and lead tetraethyl and other suppressors of detonation[7] have been claimed.

The general conditions of the process comprise the following:

The gas mixture must be outside the explosive range for ethylene-air which means that the ethylene concentration must be less than 3 per cent by volume. In some processes, oxygen is used instead of air. The ethylene should be pure, as paraffin gases such as propane and ethane may exert a harmful effect on conversion and catalyst life. With pure ethylene, it is reported that suppressors of total combustion are disadvantageous.

The catalyst is always silver on an inert fused support; it may be promoted with alkali or alkaline earth compounds such as barium peroxide or calcium oxide.

The usual operating range of temperature is 260–290° c. with ethylene-air mixtures; with ethylene-oxygen, temperatures as low as 230° c. can be used.[8]

---

[5] F.P. 739562.
[6] Carbide and Carbon, B.P. 518823.
[7] Berl, B.P. 490123.
[8] *Pet. Refiner*, Sept. 1953, p. 154.

The process is usually operated at atmospheric pressure. Increased pressure favours heat transfer and may simplify the isolation problem but is otherwise said to be without effect on the process; pressures of the order of 5–10 atma. are used in at least one process.

The conversion of ethylene per pass is 40–50 per cent, and the final yield of ethylene oxide on ethylene may vary from 50 per cent to as high as 65 per cent.

The ethylene oxide is isolated by scrubbing with water at atmospheric or increased pressure, and the aqueous solution distilled to recover high purity ethylene oxide. Adsorption on active charcoal has been claimed but is not used. Similarly, direct conversion of the ethylene oxide in the reactor gases to ethylene glycol by scrubbing with hot dilute sulphuric acid has been operated in some semi-commercial plants; this method is believed to have been discontinued.

Because of the relatively low conversion per pass, it is necessary either to recycle the scrubbed gases, taking a purge to prevent accumulation of inerts, or to pass through a second converter in series. Both methods are available for use.

Accurate temperature control is essential to retard subsequent decomposition of the ethylene oxide. Although the ethylene oxide reaction itself is very exothermic, the total combustion reaction contributes the bulk of the heat unless high yields are obtained. The reaction appears as sensitive as the Fischer-Tropsch process (Chapter 3, p. 47) to small temperature changes. For large scale working, patents disclose the use of long narrow tubes through which the gases pass at high velocity to increase heat transfer. The tube material must not catalyse decomposition of ethylene oxide or the total combustion of ethylene; silver, austenitic steels and galvanised iron have been mentioned as suitable. Tube dimensions may be 1 in. to 3 in. diameter, 10 to 30 ft. long, and reaction heat may be conveniently removed by cooling with boiling liquids such as Dowtherm.

The use of the silver catalyst in a fluidised form has been proposed, to improve the precision of temperature control. It has, however, some drawbacks, of which the most serious is back-mixing.[9] In one commercial process, the effect of back-mixing was reduced by using the fluidised catalyst in a multi-tubular reactor.[10]

Probably the best attainable overall yield to be expected is about 55–60 per cent. The ethylene consumption per pound of ethylene oxide produced is usually reckoned at about 1·1 lb.; this includes an allowance of about 5 per cent for losses of ethylene oxide in the recovery system. Where oxygen is used instead of air, the oxygen usage is about 1·8 lb./lb. ethylene oxide.[8] Compared with the chlorhydrin route (Chapter 10, p. 177) the usage of ethylene is considerably higher and a higher purity is required. The capital

---

[9] Landau, *Pet. Refiner*, Sept. 1953, p. 146.
[10] Corrigan, *Pet. Refiner*, Feb. 1953, p. 87.

cost of the plant is much higher but chlorine and lime are not required although oxygen may be wanted. The choice between the two processes probably depends to-day upon the relative cost and availability of ethylene and of chlorine on site. The current trend is definitely in favour of the direct oxidation process.

The mechanism of the reaction has been investigated by Twigg.[11] Of the reactant gases, the oxygen was firmly chemisorbed on the silver catalyst; the rate of the ethylene oxide reaction (1) was proportional to the first power of the oxygen concentration and the rate of total combustion (2) to the square of the oxygen concentration. Twigg suggested that where an ethylene molecule approached two oxygen atoms close together on the silver surface, carbon dioxide was formed via formaldehyde; where the oxygen atoms were widely spaced, ethylene oxide was formed.

In addition, some ethylene oxide was lost by isomerisation to acetaldehyde which was immediately oxidised in the gas phase to carbon dioxide:

$$CH_2-CH_2 \diagdown O \diagup \rightarrow CH_3CHO \rightarrow 2CO_2 + 2H_2O$$

Whilst some patents disclose the extension of this reaction to propylene and the butylenes, it is difficult to obtain good yields of epoxides. Instead, the methyl group next to the double bond is the point of attack. With propylene, acrolein is the product:

$$\begin{matrix} CH_3 \\ | \\ CH \\ || \\ CH_2 \end{matrix} + O_2 \rightarrow \begin{matrix} CHO \\ | \\ CH \\ || \\ CH_2 \end{matrix}$$

This vapour phase reaction was first achieved using a silver selenite catalyst.[12] With 90 per cent air —10 per cent propylene, at 230–300° c., the conversion to acrolein was 30 per cent per pass; unfortunately, the catalyst was short lived. The process has now been put on a commercial basis by the discovery of the use of supported cuprous oxide as catalyst,[13] by which yields of over 80 per cent were obtained.

Favourable conditions involve use of $1·4\%$ Cu_2O on silicon carbide with a propylene-air-steam mixture at 348° c. and 2 atma. pressure with 0·8 sec. contact time; the process is operated to give rather low conversions per pass.

A further modification is the use of a combination of selenium, introduced in the gas phase, and copper oxide as the solid catalyst.[14] Other routes to acrolein, and its reactions, are dealt with in Chapter 16, p. 299.

---

[11] *Trans. Faraday Soc.*, 1946, **42**, 284.
[12] Battelle Mem., U.S.P. 2383711.
[13] Shell Development, U.S.P. 2451485.
[14] Distillers, B.P. 723003.

With the development of a new major synthesis of glycerol from propylene via acrolein and the possibility of making acrylonitrile from acrolein (Chapter 20, p. 371), the catalytic oxidation of propylene will become a good second in industrial importance to the catalytic oxidation of ethylene.

In the same way, isobutene gives methacrolein, not isobutene oxide:

$$CH_3—\underset{\underset{CH_2}{\|}}{C}—CH_3 \rightarrow CH_3—\underset{\underset{CH_2}{\|}}{C}—CHO$$

n-Butenes on vapour phase oxidation with excess air at 350° c. using a supported vanadium pentoxide catalyst give maleic anhydride:

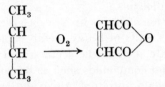

The yields are indifferent but the process was operated commercially for a time in America. It has now been displaced by the usual route from benzene (Chapter 18, p. 335).

2. Liquid phase oxidation of olefins

Considerable advances have been made in the last few years in our understanding of the mechanism of the liquid phase oxidation of mono-olefins with oxygen.[15] The reaction proceeds by a radical propagated chain mechanism. The first identifiable product is a peroxide attached to a methylene group next to the double bond:

$$—CH_2CH : CH— + O_2 \longrightarrow \underset{\underset{OOH}{|}}{—CHCH} : CH—$$

This peroxide can then undergo decomposition in any of the ways discussed in Chapter 4 in dealing with the paraffin peroxides, *i.e.*, to give ketones or alcohols or to undergo ring scission. In addition, these olefin peroxides are sufficiently stable to be decomposed in acid or alkaline solution; in acid media, triols are frequent products, whilst alkalies cause mainly ring scission:

(acid) —CHOOHCH : CH— → —CH(OH)CH—CH— → —CHCHCH—

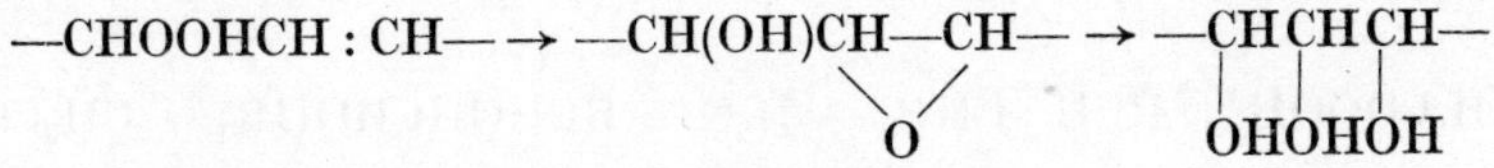

(alkali) —CH—CH—CH— → —CHO + CHO—CH₂—

+ OH—H

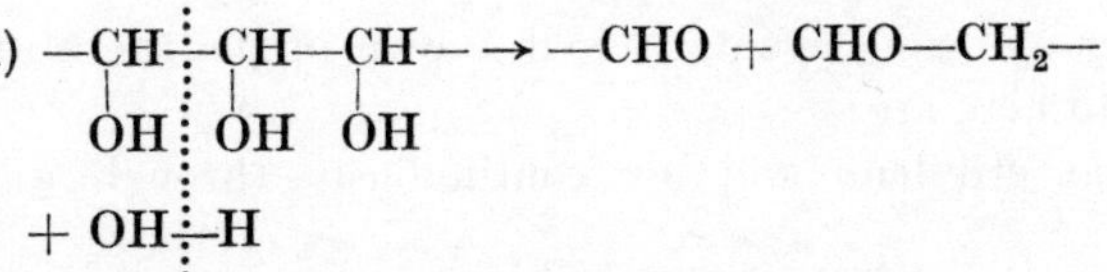

[15] Farmer, *Trans. Faraday Soc.*, 1946, **42**, 228; Gee and Bolland, *ibid.*, 236, 244.

Besides forming olefin peroxides, it is also believed that a small proportion of oxygen adds on to the double bond to give Engler's cyclic moloxide, which then undergoes scission at the —C—C— bond to give two molecules of an aldehyde or ketone, *e.g.*,

$$-CH:CH- + O_2 \rightarrow \underset{\underset{O-O}{|\quad|}}{-CH-CH-} \rightarrow \underset{\underset{O^{\times}\ O^{\times}}{|\quad|}}{-CH-CH-} \rightarrow -CHO + OHC-$$

Formation of polymeric peroxides is relatively unimportant with most mono-olefins; polymers are, however, important products in the peroxidation of 1 : 3- and 1 : 4-diolefins.

Liquid phase oxidation of olefins with oxygen is accelerated by the usual two classes of catalysts, salts of heavy metals capable of existing in more than one oxidation state such as the acetates and naphthenates of manganese, copper, etc., and compounds such as benzoyl peroxide giving free radicals which act as chain initiators. Air oxidation is usually carried out in the temperature range 50–150° c., if necessary under pressure.

The air oxidation of the isomeric pentenes has been investigated so far as peroxide formation occurs by Hyman and Wagner.[16] Working at 0–5° c. with cobalt stearate as catalyst, they found that pentenes with a terminal double bond formed no peroxide in 250 hours, whereas trimethylethylene and *sym*-methylethylethylene formed peroxides rapidly. Isopropylethylene was anomalous in forming peroxides after an induction period; it perhaps rearranged to trimethylethylene before taking up oxygen. The breakdown products of these peroxides were not investigated.

Liquid phase oxidation of olefins and other olefinic compounds is now being developed commercially to make epoxides (substituted ethylene oxides) or glycols. Either hydrogen peroxide in acetic acid solution (which gives peracetic acid and water) or peracetic acid itself is used; for epoxides, the conditions required are low temperature, short contact time and low hydrogen ion concentration. For making glycols, the reaction is carried out in presence of a mineral acid catalyst in formic or acetic acid solution :[17]

$$CH_3COOH + H_2O_2 \rightarrow CH_3COOOH + H_2O$$
$$CH_3COOOH + RCH:CHR_1 \rightarrow RCH\underset{O}{\overset{\diagdown\diagup}{C}HR_1} + CH_3COOH$$
$$CH_3COOOH + RCH:CHR_1 + H_2O \rightarrow RCHOHCHOHR_1 + CH_3COOH$$

The use of other oxidising agents is well known in the literature. All that we may refer to here are:

Skarblom passed ethylene and air continuously through a dilute

[16] *J. Amer. Chem. Soc.*, 1930, **52**, 4345; 1931, **53**, 3019.
[17] Hatch, *Pet. Refiner*, March 1956, p. 197.

sulphuric acid solution containing iodine at 100–120° c. and obtained ethylene glycol;[18] the reaction probably proceeds as follows:

$$\begin{matrix} CH_2 \\ \| \\ CH_2 \end{matrix} + I_2 \rightarrow \begin{matrix} CH_2I \\ | \\ CH_2I \end{matrix} \xrightarrow{2H_2O} \begin{matrix} CH_2OH \\ | \\ CH_2OH \end{matrix} + 2HI$$

followed by: $2HI + \tfrac{1}{2}O_2 \rightarrow I_2 + H_2O$.

The methyl group next to the double bond can be oxidised directly to a > CO group by acid mercuric sulphate,[19] *e.g.*, on passing propylene into acid mercuric sulphate at 50–60° c., about 20 per cent of the propylene reacts to give a high yield of acrolein, which is liberated on heating above 100° c.:

$$\begin{matrix} CH_3 \\ | \\ CH \\ \| \\ CH_2 \end{matrix} + 4HgSO_4 + H_2O \rightarrow \begin{matrix} CHO \\ | \\ CH \\ \| \\ CH_2 \end{matrix} + 2Hg_2SO_4 + 2H_2SO_4$$

The mercurous sulphate can be oxidised electrochemically back to mercuric sulphate so that this process can be used as a semi-continuous method of electrochemical oxidation of propylene to acrolein.

The long chain olefins have been oxidised by sodium dichromate-sulphuric acid to long chain acids; the dichromate is reduced to chromic sulphate from which dichromate is regenerated by electrochemical oxidation. Here also oxidation can be regarded as electrochemical.

---

[18] B.P. 369141.
[19] du Pont, U.S.P. 2197258.

CHAPTER 10

REACTIONS OF OLEFINS WITH COMPOUNDS OF CHLORINE AND BROMINE

1. Reactions with chlorine

(a) ETHYLENE

THE normal reaction between ethylene and chlorine is addition, to give ethylene dichloride:

$$CH_2 : CH_2 + Cl_2 \rightarrow CH_2ClCH_2Cl$$

This reaction proceeds either in the vapour phase or the liquid phase.

In the vapour phase, there is no reaction at moderate temperatures in the absence of catalysts or active surfaces. The vapour phase reaction has been used for the recovery of ethylene from coke oven gas, containing 2 per cent ethylene, using metal chlorides on inert supports as catalysts.

Where concentrated ethylene is available, for example from petroleum sources, it is preferable to operate a liquid phase process, passing ethylene and chlorine simultaneously into a common solvent, most conveniently ethylene dichloride itself.

Addition of chlorine to ethylene is highly exothermic:

$$C_2H_4 + Cl_2(g) \rightarrow C_2H_4Cl_2(l). \quad \Delta H_{298} = -48 \text{ k. cal.}$$

It is advantageous to limit the temperature of the liquid phase reaction to about 50° c. to prevent substitution to give more highly chlorinated products. Metal chlorides are catalysts for this reaction and the use of $0·1-0·5\%$ ferric chloride, preferably at 25° c. and atmospheric pressure, has been claimed. In one industrial process ethylene and chlorine are reacted in ethylene dichloride solution at 50° c. and 6 atma. using ferric chloride as catalyst.[1] The product is water washed to remove catalyst, dried and distilled. Conversion of ethylene is 98 per cent and the yield of ethylene dichloride is over 95 per cent. Reaction of 99% ethylene with chlorine in ethylene dichloride by circulation of the solvent in a long narrow water cooled tube has also been described.[2]

Under more drastic conditions, substitution takes place; Shell Development have studied the high temperature substitutive chlorination, on the lines of their well-known work on the chlorination of propylene (p. 160). By interaction of five mols of ethylene with one mol of chlorine at 436° c., high yields of vinyl chloride were obtained:[3]

$$CH_2 : CH_2 + Cl_2 \rightarrow CH_2 : CHCl + HCl$$

---

[1] Sherwood, *Pet. Proc.*, 1952, **7**, 1809.
[2] Distillers, B.P. 557720.
[3] Groll and Hearne, *Ind. Eng. Chem.*, 1939, **31**, 1530.

Reaction was regarded as proceeding by direct substitution, and not by addition to give ethylene dichloride followed by pyrolysis, since vinyl chloride was obtained under conditions when ethylene dichloride was stable. Other manufacturing routes to vinyl chloride, from ethylene dichloride and from acetylene, are discussed later.

With excess of chlorine at about 400° c. over an active charcoal catalyst, a complex mixture of chlorinated ethylenes is obtained;[4] by recycling the lower and more highly chlorinated ethylenes, trichloroethylene and perchloroethylene are the main products. Similar results were obtained using ethylene dichloride instead of ethylene but altering the chlorine ratio. With ethylene, 3·5–4 mols of chlorine per mol of ethylene were used; with ethylene dichloride, only 2·5–3 mols of chlorine were needed.

Combined reaction between ethylene, chlorine or hydrogen chloride, and oxygen at high temperatures gives a similar mixture of the more highly chlorinated ethylenes; the oxygen serves to oxidise hydrogen chloride present in the original mixture or liberated in the initial stages of chlorination to chlorine, thereby ensuring high efficiency in chlorine utilisation. du Pont claim the use of an oxidation catalyst for facilitating this reaction.[5] In a typical example, a mixture of ethylene, chlorine and oxygen in the molar ratio 1 : 2 : 1 were passed over a supported copper oxide catalyst at 375–425° c.; the principal products were trichloroethylene and perchloroethylene, $CCl_2 : CCl_2$. By recycling the lower chlorinated ethylenes, a yield of 75–80 per cent of perchloroethylene on ethylene could be obtained.

Ethylene dichloride

Ethylene dichloride is obtained industrially both by the addition of chlorine to ethylene and as a by-product from the manufacture of ethylene chlorhydrin (see p. 174).

It boils at 83·8° c. and is a useful solvent in many industries, although it is not used on a scale approaching that of the polychloroethylenes. Despite its high chlorine content (72 per cent), it will burn in air. It is reasonably resistant to hydrolysis. Due to its reactivity, availability and low cost, it has found more outlets in chemical synthesis than as a solvent.

It readily loses the elements of hydrogen chloride to give vinyl chloride, for example by pyrolysis at 600° c. or above;[6] high temperatures and presence of inert diluents favour loss of a second molecule of hydrogen chloride to give acetylene:

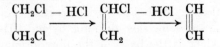

---

[4] Diamond Alkali, B.P. 673565.
[5] B.P. 553950.
[6] I.C.I., B.P. 363009.

One technical process operates the dehydrochlorination of ethylene dichloride at 480–500° c. and 3 atma. over a catalyst of pumice or kaolin. Conversion is limited to 70 per cent or less; the exit gases are chilled, detarred, and the vinyl chloride absorbed in ethylene dichloride.[1] The absorbate is distilled at 5 atma. pressure and the vinyl chloride redistilled. The yield on ethylene dichloride is 90 per cent.

A second method of making vinyl chloride from ethylene dichloride is by treatment with alkalies in solution at moderate temperature. Use of caustic soda in methyl alcohol solution has been claimed for this process.[7]

The other major route to vinyl chloride is by addition of hydrogen chloride to acetylene:

$$\begin{matrix} CH \\ \| \\ CH \end{matrix} + HCl \to CH_2 : CHCl$$

This is carried out in the vapour phase by passing the pure dry reagents with a slight excess of hydrochloric acid over a mercury chloride on charcoal catalyst at 100–180° c. and atmospheric pressure. The process can be operated at very high conversion and yields of about 85 per cent or at moderate conversion and yields of over 90 per cent. The vinyl chloride is condensed out or absorbed in non-reactive solvents, such as ethylene dichloride, at low temperature; it is then purified by distillation.

The principal outlets of vinyl chloride are in the high polymer field for making polyvinyl chloride, one of the "big three" of the thermoplastic field (polyvinyl chloride, polystyrene and polyethylene), and for copolymers such as vinyl chloride-vinyl acetate. In 1955, American production of vinyl chloride was 240,000 tons, most of which was used for polyvinyl chloride and copolymers. The outlets of vinyl chloride as an intermediate are small compared with these figures. The principal use is in making *as*-dichloroethylene, another intermediate for high polymers.

In the liquid phase, vinyl chloride adds chlorine to give 1 : 1 : 2-trichloroethane in 95–96% yield.[8] Trichloroethane is also obtained by liquid phase chlorination of ethylene dichloride in presence of aluminium chloride or other metal chloride:

$$\begin{matrix} CHCl \\ \| \\ CH_2 \end{matrix} + Cl_2 \to \begin{matrix} CHCl_2 \\ | \\ CH_2Cl \end{matrix} \overset{+ \ Cl_2}{\underset{- \ HCl}{\longleftarrow}} \begin{matrix} CH_2Cl \\ | \\ CH_2Cl \end{matrix}$$

On treatment with caustic soda, 1 : 1 : 2-trichloroethane gives *as*-dichloroethylene (vinylidene chloride), $CCl_2 : CH_2$, which polymerises readily to polyvinylidene chloride. With lime, trichloroethane gives a mixture of *as*-dichloroethylene and some *sym*-dichloroethylene, CHCl : CHCl.

as-Dichloroethylene is the basis of the fibre-forming polymers, Saran

---

[7] I.G., F.P. 694575.
[8] I.C.I., B.P. 577876.

and Velon, which are interpolymers with a small percentage of vinyl chloride.

as-Dichloroethylene adds the elements of hydrogen chloride to give not 1 : 1 : 2-trichloroethane, but 1 : 1 : 1-trichloroethane (methyl chloroform):

$$\begin{array}{c} CCl_2 \\ \parallel \\ CH_2 \end{array} + HCl \rightarrow \begin{array}{c} CCl_3 \\ \mid \\ CH_3 \end{array}$$

On further chlorination in the liquid phase, 1 : 1 : 2-trichloroethane gives first 1 : 1 : 1 : 2-tetrachloroethane (*as*-tetrachloroethane), then pentachloroethane and hexachloroethane:

$$\begin{array}{c} CHCl_2 \\ \mid \\ CH_2Cl \end{array} \xrightarrow[-HCl]{+Cl_2} \begin{array}{c} CCl_3 \\ \mid \\ CH_2Cl \end{array} \xrightarrow[-HCl]{+Cl_2} \begin{array}{c} CCl_3 \\ \mid \\ CHCl_2 \end{array} \xrightarrow[-HCl]{+Cl_2} \begin{array}{c} CCl_3 \\ \mid \\ CCl_3 \end{array}$$

1 : 1 : 1 : 2-Tetrachloroethane is resistant to the action of alkalies, but on pyrolysis at 550–650° c., it gives the important industrial solvent, trichloroethylene:

$$\begin{array}{c} CCl_3 \\ \mid \\ CH_2Cl \end{array} \xrightarrow{-HCl} \begin{array}{c} CCl_2 \\ \parallel \\ CHCl \end{array}$$

The standard route to trichloroethylene is from acetylene via 1 : 1 : 2 : 2-tetrachloroethane. Acetylene is chlorinated in tetrachloroethane solution at about 80° c. using antimony chloride or ferric chloride as catalyst, the reaction being carried out with very efficient mixing and good temperature control, to avoid high local concentrations of chlorine and acetylene. 1 : 1 : 2 : 2-Tetrachloroethane loses one mol of hydrogen chloride by treatment with a slurry of lime at the boil. Removal of hydrogen chloride may also be brought about by pyrolysis at 600° c., or at lower temperatures, 230–320° c., over a barium chloride catalyst.[9, 10]

$$\begin{array}{c} CH \\ \parallel \\ CH \end{array} + 2Cl_2 \rightarrow \begin{array}{c} CHCl_2 \\ \mid \\ CHCl_2 \end{array} \xrightarrow{-HCl} \begin{array}{c} CCl_2 \\ \parallel \\ CHCl \end{array}$$

Comparing this route to trichloroethylene with synthesis from ethylene via ethylene dichloride, the acetylene route uses four atoms of chlorine per mol of trichloroethylene, whilst the ethylene route uses six atoms, the extra chlorine being required to remove two atoms of hydrogen from the ethylene:

$$\begin{array}{c} CH \\ \parallel \\ CH \end{array} \xrightarrow[-1HCl]{+2Cl_2} \begin{array}{c} CCl_2 \\ \parallel \\ CHCl \end{array} \xleftarrow[-3HCl]{+3Cl_2} \begin{array}{c} CH_2 \\ \parallel \\ CH_2 \end{array}$$

Trichloroethylene is hydrolysed by sulphuric acid to chloroacetic acid,

---

[9] du Pont, B.P. 575559.
[10] B.I.O.S. 1056.

a process which has been operated as an alternative to the older method of chlorination of acetic acid :[11]

$$CHCl : CCl_2 + 2H_2O \xrightarrow{(H_2SO_4)} CH_2ClCOOH + 2HCl$$

Trichloroethylene also undergoes a number of interesting condensation reactions. With formaldehyde in sulphuric acid, it gives derivatives of 1-chlorohydracrylic acid:

$$CHCl : CCl_2 + CH_2O + H_2SO_4 \rightarrow (HOCH_2CHClCCl_2 \cdot HSO_4) \rightarrow$$
$$O(CH_2CHClCOOH)_2$$

By heating trichloroethylene with formaldehyde in 80% sulphuric acid in presence of alcohols, esters of 1-chloroacrylic acid have been obtained in good yield; in absence of alcohols, the product was the free acid :[12]

$$(HOCH_2CHClCCl_2 \cdot HSO_4) + ROH \rightarrow CH_2 : CClCOOR + H_2SO_4 + 2HCl$$

Other chloroethylenes react with formaldehyde similarly. Thus vinyl chloride with formaldehyde and hydrogen chloride gives a mixture of glycerol-1 : 2-dichlorohydrin and 3 : 3-dichloro-*n*-propyl alcohol, the latter predominating.[13]

$$CH_2 : CHCl + CH_2O + HCl \begin{cases} \rightarrow CH_2OHCHClCH_2Cl \\ \rightarrow CH_2OHCH_2CHCl_2 \end{cases}$$

Trichloroethylene reacts with carbon tetrachloride and chloroform in the presence of aluminium chloride to give highly chlorinated propanes; here also other chlorinated ethylenes behave similarly. Trichloroethylene will also condense with itself, either on heating to 210° c. under 40 atma. pressure, or under moderate conditions under the catalytic influence of aluminium chloride-hydrogen chloride, to give a hexachlorobutene, used as an intermediate for hexachlorobutadiene, an additive for transformer oils.[10]

$$CCl_2 : CHCl + CHCl : CCl_2 \rightarrow CCl_2 : CHCHClCCl_3 \xrightarrow[- HCl(FeCl_3)]{100-125° c.}$$

$$\underset{\substack{\text{pentachlorobuta-} \\ \text{diene}}}{CCl_2 : CHCCl : CCl_2} \xrightarrow{+ Cl_2} CCl_3CHClCCl : CCl_2 \xrightarrow[\text{boil (Fe)}]{- HCl}$$

$$\underset{\text{hexachlorobutadiene}}{CCl_2 : CClCCl : CCl_2}$$

---

[11] B.I.O.S. 1154.
[12] I.C.I., B.P. 528761.
[13] I.G., B.P. 465467.

The other technical chlorinated ethylenes are obtained as follows. *sym*-Dichloroethylene, $CHCl:CHCl$, is made by reduction of $1:1:2:2$-tetrachloroethane with iron or zinc and water at 100–200° c. Tetrachloroethylene, $CCl_2:CCl_2$, is made by removal of one mol of hydrogen chloride from pentachloroethane by treatment with alkali. As pointed out in Chapter 5, p. 69, it has also been made by pyrolysis of carbon tetrachloride. It adds chlorine to give hexachloroethane, C_2Cl_6.

The complete series of chlorinated ethanes and ethylenes, and their syntheses from ethylene and acetylene is shown in Fig. 20.

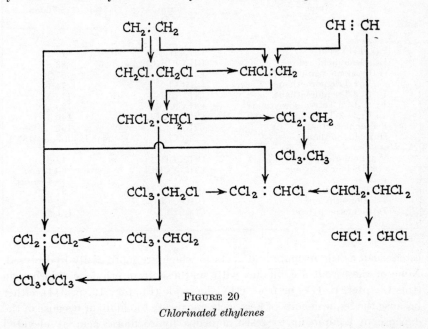

FIGURE 20
Chlorinated ethylenes

The main outlets of the chlorinated solvents are in metal degreasing and in dry cleaning. In the United States in 1954, 150,000 tons of trichloroethylene were made, of which 90–93 per cent was used in metal degreasing; production of perchloroethylene was 75,000 tons, 80 per cent going to dry cleaning and 15 per cent to metal degreasing.[14] Perchloroethylene is not so widely used in Europe.

The boiling points of the chlorinated derivatives of ethane and ethylene are given in Table 37.

Ethylene dichloride can be hydrolysed to ethylene glycol in several ways. Water alone will bring about the hydrolysis, but the reaction conditions are severe; a patented method uses 15 vol. of water per vol. of ethylene dichloride in a silver lined autoclave at 160–175° c. under 15 atma.

---

[14] *Chem. Week*, March 19, 1955, p. 101.

pressure. The water should be slightly acid with hydrochloric acid to start the hydrolysis, and of course produces more hydrochloric acid during the reaction. Alternatively, it is hydrolysed at 140–250° c. and up to 40 atma. pressure, with continuous addition of caustic soda at a pH controlled at 2–4 by a phosphate buffer.[15] Finally, the dichloride can be converted to

TABLE 37

Boiling points of chlorinated C_2 compounds

Name	Formula	b.p., ° c./760 mm.
1. *Saturated*—		
Ethyl chloride	CH_3CH_2Cl	12·2
Ethylene dichloride	CH_2ClCH_2Cl	83·8
(Ethylidene dichloride .	CH_3CHCl_2	57·3)
1 : 1 : 1-Trichloroethane	CH_3CCl_3	74·1
1 : 1 : 2-Trichloroethane	$CH_2ClCHCl_2$	113·5
1 : 1 : 1 : 2-Tetrachloroethane	CH_2ClCCl_3	130·5
1 : 1 : 2 : 2-Tetrachloroethane	$CHCl_2CHCl_2$	146·3
Pentachloroethane	$CHCl_2CCl_3$	162
Hexachloroethane	CCl_3CCl_3	(solid, sublimes 187°)
2. *Unsaturated*—		
Vinyl chloride	$CH_2 : CHCl$	− 13·9
sym-Dichloroethylene	$CHCl : CHCl$	60·1 (*cis*)
		48·4 (*trans*)
as-Dichloroethylene	$CH_2 : CCl_2$	37
Trichloroethylene	$CHCl : CCl_2$	87
Tetrachloroethylene	$CCl_2 : CCl_2$	121·2

esters such as the formate and acetate, which are more easily hydrolysed. None of these routes competes with synthesis from ethylene chlorhydrin (this Chapter, p. 177) or from ethylene oxide (Chapter 19, p. 344), either because the requirements of heavy chemicals are too high, or because of the expense of equipment to resist aqueous hydrochloric acid at elevated temperatures and pressures.

On reaction with excess of ammonia under pressure at about 120° c., preferably in presence of an emulsifying agent such as sodium oleate, ethylene diamine is obtained;[16] it is isolated from the reaction mixture by basification with caustic soda, removal of ammonia, and distillation of the ethylene diamine hydrate, $C_2H_4(NH_2)_2H_2O$:

$$\begin{array}{l} CH_2Cl \\ | \\ CH_2Cl \end{array} + 4NH_3 \rightarrow \begin{array}{l} CH_2NH_2 \\ | \\ CH_2NH_2 \end{array} + 2NH_4Cl$$

Usually more than five mols of ammonia per mol of ethylene dichloride are used. If the proportion is cut down, the products are the polyethylene

---

[15] Shell Development, U.S.P. 2148304.
[16] Carbide and Carbon, U.S.P. 1832534.

polyamines, such as diethylene triamine, $NH_2C_2H_4NHC_2H_4NH_2$, triethylene tetramine, $NH_2(C_2H_4NH)_2C_2H_4NH_2$, etc. The properties and reactions of these amines are described in Chapter 20, p. 380.

Reaction with sodium cyanide gives succindinitrile, which can also be obtained from acetylene via acrylonitrile (see Chapter 20, p. 373).

$$\begin{array}{c} CH_2Cl \\ | \\ CH_2Cl \end{array} + 2NaCN \rightarrow \begin{array}{c} CH_2CN \\ | \\ CH_2CN \end{array} \xleftarrow{+ HCN} \begin{array}{c} CH_2 \\ \| \\ CHCN \end{array} \xleftarrow{+ HCN} \begin{array}{c} CH \\ \| \| \| \\ CH \end{array}$$

Ethylene dichloride reacts with alkali polysulphides to give rubber-like polymers, which can be vulcanised and have unique solvent resistant properties. The products are now being used in the pest control industry. The reaction, first discovered in 1839, was improved by the Thiokol Corporation by carrying out the condensation in aqueous solution in presence of solid dispersing agents to give an emulsion or latex, which was subsequently coagulated. Thiokol A is polyethylene tetrasulphide:

$$n \begin{array}{c} CH_2Cl \\ | \\ CH_2Cl \end{array} + nNa_2S_4 \rightarrow [-CH_2CH_2S_4-]_n + 2nNaCl$$

The reaction is general for organic compounds containing two reactive terminal halogen atoms.

Ethylene dichloride also undergoes a number of reactions in which only one of the chlorine atoms is replaced at a time; for example, with sulphur trioxide in the form of oleum, it gives chloroethyl sulphuryl chloride, and with sodium sulphite, it gives chloroethanesulphonic acid:

$$\begin{array}{c} CH_2Cl \\ | \\ CH_2Cl \end{array} + SO_3 \rightarrow \begin{array}{c} CH_2OSO_2Cl \\ | \\ CH_2Cl \end{array}$$

$$\begin{array}{c} CH_2Cl \\ | \\ CH_2Cl \end{array} + Na_2SO_3 \rightarrow \begin{array}{c} CH_2SO_2ONa \\ | \\ CH_2Cl \end{array} + NaCl$$

(b) PROPYLENE

Propylene adds chlorine more readily than ethylene, to give propylene dichloride, $CH_3CHClCH_2Cl$ (b.p. 95·9° c.). Like ethylene dichloride, it can be made either by a liquid phase or by a vapour phase reaction. It has been used in cleaning and scouring compounds and as a selective solvent. Its general reactions are similar to those of ethylene dichloride.

Removal of one mol of hydrogen chloride from propylene dichloride has been examined as a possible route to allyl chloride. Over calcium chloride at 340° c., a poor yield of allyl chloride was obtained, the main products being 1- and 2-chloropropylenes. On pyrolysis at 600–700° c., decomposing 30 per cent of the dichloride per pass, the yield of allyl chloride was 50 per cent with 35 per cent 1-chloropropylene and less than

5 per cent 2-chloropropylene.[17] Alcoholic caustic potash gave a mixture of 1- and 2-chloropropylenes :

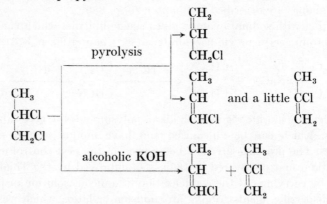

A new chapter in industrial chemistry was opened in 1936, when Shell Development Co. discovered that interaction of propylene and chlorine at high temperatures led not to addition but to direct substitution of chlorine on the methyl group next to the double bond, giving allyl chloride:

$$CH_2 : CHCH_3 + Cl_2 \rightarrow CH_2 : CHCH_2Cl + HCl$$

This reaction, and its extension to the synthesis of glycerol, has now been established.

Propylene adds chlorine very readily at all temperatures up to about 300° c. giving propylene dichloride, but the Shell workers discovered that at higher temperatures the reaction could be changed over to substitution; at a sufficiently high temperature addition could be effectively suppressed, allyl chloride being the main product.

Considerable experimental difficulties were faced and solved in the translation of the process to the large scale. Rapid reaction was essential; if the reactants were mixed cold, on heating up, addition occurred before the temperature of substitution was reached. If mixed hot, inflammation and carbon formation were liable to take place. There was an upper limit to reaction temperature occasioned by the liability of allyl chloride to undergo pyrolytic decomposition.

These troubles were overcome in ways recalling Hass's work on the vapour phase chlorination of the paraffin gases (Chapter 5). Excess of propylene was employed; pure propylene had to be used as propane would give 1- and 2-chloropropanes, both of which boil close to allyl chloride. Reaction was conducted to give complete utilisation of chlorine and efficient mixing was employed to avoid any local concentration of chlorine.

On the full scale plant,[18] the propylene-chlorine mol ratio was about

---

[17] Williams, *Trans. Amer. Inst. Chem. Eng.*, 1941, **37**, 157.
[18] Fairbairn, Cheney and Cherniavsky, *Chem. Eng. Prog.*, 1947, **43**, 280.

4 : 1. The reaction temperature was maintained at 500–510° c., the control being achieved by regulating the preheat of the propylene to about 200° c.; the chlorine was introduced cold. The exothermic heat of chlorination, about 26·7 k. cal./g. mol, was adequate to maintain the optimum reaction temperature. With a residence time of 1·8 secs., conversion of chlorine was 99·95 per cent. Carbon formation led to shut-down every two weeks, so that pairs of reactors and coolers were installed to maintain continuous operation. Pressure has little effect on the process; as a matter of convenience, the process was operated at 2 atma.

The following yields were obtained: boiling points are shown to indicate some of the isolation problems.

TABLE 38

Allyl chloride from propylene.
Composition and boiling points of products

Halide	Formula	Yield %	Boiling point, ° c./760 mm.
2-Chloropropylene . . .	$CH_2 : CClCH_3$	2·3	22·5
Isopropyl chloride . . .	$CH_3CHClCH_3$	0·2	36·5
Allyl chloride	$CH_2 : CHCH_2Cl$	85	44·9
2 : 3-Dichloropropylene .	$CH_2 : CClCH_2Cl$	0·8	93·8
Propylene dichloride . .	$CH_3CHClCH_2Cl$	2·6	96·8
cis-1 : 3-Dichloropropylene .	$CHCl : CHCH_2Cl$	} 6·5	103·8
trans-1 : 3-Dichloropropylene .	$CHCl : CHCH_2Cl$		112·1
Trichlorides, etc.. . . .	—	2·6	—

The problems of isolation of pure allyl chloride include the isolation of a low boiling liquid from a large excess of inert gas, and the separation of close boiling isomers.

In their pilot plant, the Shell workers washed out the hydrochloric acid with water and separated allyl chloride and higher boiling halides from the excess of propylene by absorption in kerosene.[17] On the full scale plant[18] propylene was separated from the allyl chloride by fractional distillation at about 2 atma. pressure with a head temperature of − 40° c., to provide liquid propylene reflux. Hydrochloric acid was washed out with water, the propylene scrubbed with dilute caustic soda, and returned to wet propylene storage.

The mixed chlorides from the recovery plant were purified in two fractionating columns, 2-chloropropylene and other light ends being removed as the overhead in the first, using a high reflux ratio, and pure allyl chloride being obtained as the overhead product in the second column, di- and polychlorides being rejected as bottoms. Allyl chloride so prepared analysed 99·5% pure with only traces of 1- and 2-chloropropylenes. Removal of 2-chloropropylene is not necessary for most purposes as allyl chloride is normally hydrolysed to allyl alcohol, and the chlorine in 2-chloropropylene is relatively unreactive; it is therefore readily removed at the

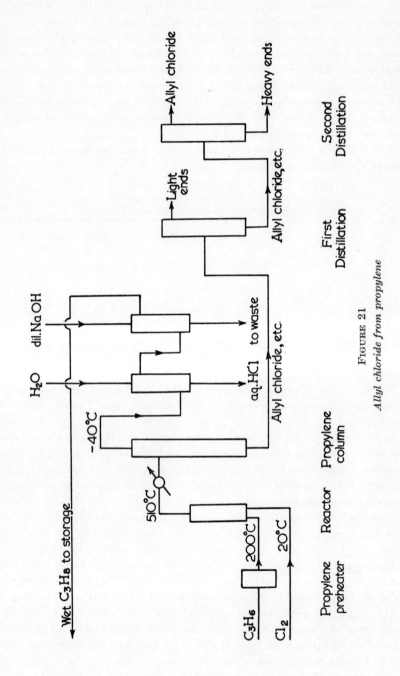

FIGURE 21

Allyl chloride from propylene

next stage by separation from the higher boiling allyl alcohol. Separation of 2-chloropropylene from allyl chloride has now been discarded.

The flowsheet of the chlorination and recovery operations is shown in Fig. 21.

The Shell workers regard the high temperature chlorination of propylene as proceeding by direct substitution and not by addition of a molecule of chlorine followed by removal of hydrogen chloride. The monochloride fraction obtained consists of 96 per cent allyl chloride, 3 per cent 2-chloropropylene and 1 per cent 1-chloropropylene. Pyrolysis of propylene dichloride under similar conditions gives about 50 per cent allyl chloride, 35 per cent 1-chloropropylene and less than 5 per cent 2-chloropropylene. The reactivity of methyl or methylene groups next to a double bond has been encountered in oxidation reactions (Chapter 9) but under quite different physical conditions.

The principal industrial outlets of allyl chloride, besides its use for making glycerol, are allyl alcohol and epichlorhydrin, both of which are used mainly in the plastics industry. Allyl chloride is also used for allyl bromide and cyclopropane, used in pharmaceuticals, for glycerol dichlorhydrin,[18] and for allyl ethers such as allyl starch.

Allyl chloride is one of the most reactive of the alkyl halides; it undergoes readily all the usual metathetic reactions in which the chlorine atom is replaced by another atom or group; the most important of these is hydrolysis to allyl alcohol. Conditions for the full scale hydrolysis have been described. 5–10% Aqueous caustic soda was used and the pH was kept at 8–10, to restrict formation of diallyl ether. Allyl chloride and the caustic soda solution were charged continuously in the molar ratio 1 : 1·05 to a mild steel reactor. The temperature was kept at 150–160° c. and the working pressure was about 14 atma. Reaction was complete in about ten minutes. The alcohol was isolated from the saline solution by continuous distillation and purified by batch distillation. It forms an azeotrope with water (73% allyl alcohol, boiling at 88·2° c.), which can be dried by distillation with diallyl ether or with any of the usual water entraining agents. Anhydrous allyl alcohol boils at 97° c. The yield of allyl alcohol on allyl chloride was 88 per cent, the main by-product being 9 per cent of diallyl ether.

Allyl alcohol was formerly of no technical interest, as it was available only by the indifferent process of heating glycerol with formic or oxalic acid to 200° c. in presence of a trace of mineral acid:

$$CH_2OHCHOHCH_2OH + (COOH)_2 \rightarrow CH_2 : CHCH_2OH + 2H_2O + 2CO_2$$

It can also be made by isomerisation of propylene oxide (Chapter 19, p. 362), and by partial hydrogenation of acrolein or of propargyl alcohol. The propylene oxide route was operated in the United States for a time in the late 1940's but at present allyl alcohol is manufactured only from allyl chloride made by propylene chlorination.

However, it would appear that the new Shell route to glycerol from propylene, referred to later in this Chapter (p. 169) will involve making allyl alcohol as a stage in the synthesis. This route involves the air oxidation of propylene to acrolein (Chapter 9, p. 148) followed by reduction of the acrolein to allyl alcohol with isopropyl alcohol, one mol of acetone being obtained as a co-product.[19]

$$CH_2 : CHCH_3 \xrightarrow{\ O_2\ } CH_2 : CHCHO$$

$$CH_2 : CHCHO + CH_3CHOHCH_3 \rightarrow CH_2 : CHCH_2OH + CH_3COCH_3$$

The possible technical routes to allyl alcohol are displayed as follows:

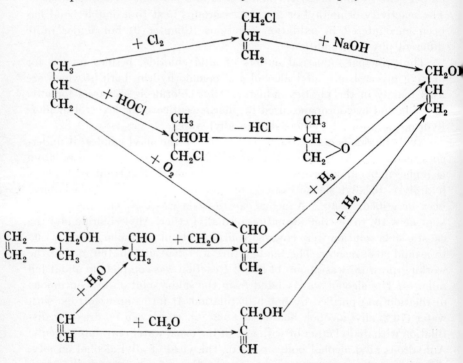

The principal outlet for allyl alcohol is for making esters used in the high polymer field, for example, for polyesters. The most important ester is diallyl phthalate (Shell Development Co.) but allyl alcohol is also used for the diallyl ester of diethylene glycol dicarbonate $CH_2 : CHCH_2OCOOCH_2$-$CH_2OCH_2CH_2OCOOCH_2CH : CH_2$ and diallyl phenyl phosphonate, $(CH_2 : CHCH_2O)_2(C_6H_5)P : O$. Polyallyl alcohol itself is best made by polymerisation of an allyl ester, such as the acetate, and hydrolysis of the polyallyl ester.[20]

[19] Shell Development, B.P. 619014; Hatch, *Pet. Refiner*, March 1956, p. 197.
[20] Shell Development, B.P. 565719.

Allyl alcohol is used to a limited extent for making pharmaceuticals such as glycerol-1 : 2-dithiohydrin, $CH_2OHCHSHCH_2SH$ (BAL, British Anti-Lewisite).

Allyl alcohol undergoes an unusual reaction with cuprous cyanide; in aqueous solution in presence of hydrochloric acid, allyl cyanide is obtained in high yield.[21]

$$CH_2 : CHCH_2OH + CuCN + HCl \rightarrow CH_2 : CHCH_2CN + CuCl + H_2O$$

Allyl cyanide can also be obtained from allyl chloride or bromide by reaction with cuprous cyanide; with the alkali cyanides, crotonic acid nitrile is obtained, the alkaline condensation conditions leading to rearrangement of the double bond:

$$CH_2 : CHCH_2Cl \begin{cases} \xrightarrow{(CuCN)} CH_2 : CHCH_2CN \\ \xrightarrow{(NaCN)} CH_3CH : CHCN \end{cases}$$

Besides its metathetic reactions, allyl chloride also undergoes the usual reactions of the double bond. It adds chlorine to give glycerol trichlorhydrin (1 : 2 : 3-trichloropropane), hydrates with concentrated sulphuric acid to 1-chloro-2-hydroxypropane (α-propylene chlorhydrin), and adds hypochlorous acid to give glycerol-1 : 3-dichlorhydrin:

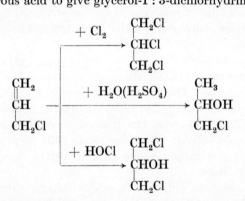

Addition of hypochlorous acid to allyl chloride has been used as a way of making synthetic glycerol from propylene. The usual method of making glycerol is by isolation from the mother liquors obtained in the manufacture of soap by hydrolysis of fats; a second method is by controlled fermentation of sugar. Both these methods involve use of foodstuffs as the starting material; the Shell route is based upon crude petroleum.

The dichlorhydrin is best made by the reaction between preformed hypochlorous acid and allyl chloride, and not by a method analogous to

---

[21] Breckpot, *Bull. Soc. Chim. Belg.*, 1930, **39**, 466.

the ethylene chlorhydrin process (this Chapter, p. 174). The reaction should proceed in the aqueous phase, and contact between free chlorine and allyl chloride must be avoided to prevent direct addition. Sodium hypochlorite was used as the source of hypochlorous acid, by the reaction:

$$NaOCl + Cl_2 + H_2O \rightarrow NaCl + 2HOCl$$

The process was operated continuously, the dilute aqueous hypochlorous acid being mixed with allyl chloride, the lower layer separated and worked up and the upper aqueous layer recirculated; the temperature was kept at 28° c. The product obtained contained 91·4 per cent dichlorhydrin, of which 70 per cent was 1 : 3-dichlorhydrin and 30 per cent 1 : 2-dichlorhydrin, 5·2 per cent trichloropropane, and 2·5 per cent high boiling material.

The dichlorhydrin can be hydrolysed to glycerol in steps:

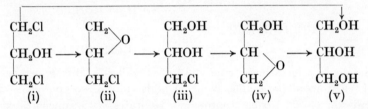

Removal of hydrogen chloride to give epichlorhydrin, (ii), and glycidol, (iv), was carried out with cold dilute aqueous alkali, the epoxides being isolated by vacuum distillation. The hydration steps, (ii) to (iii) and (iv) to (v), were effected by heating with water to 90–100° c. in presence of a trace of sulphuric acid.

Alternatively, dichlorhydrin can be hydrolysed to glycerol in one step by continuous addition to lime or dilute aqueous caustic soda at controlled pH in a stirred reactor.[22] The 5% aqueous glycerol is concentrated to 80% strength by vacuum evaporation, desalted, further concentrated to 98% and the remaining salt removed. The desalted concentrate is then extracted with a hydrocarbon solvent to remove colour; the final purification step is vacuum steam distillation, giving glycerol better than 99% pure and passing all U.S.P. tests.

Glycerol can also be obtained from allyl alcohol; direct addition of chlorine to allyl alcohol to give glycerol 1 : 2-dichlorhydrin is apparently not practicable, but the alcohol adds hypochlorous acid smoothly in dilute aqueous solution to give glycerol monochlorhydrin, $CH_2OHCHOHCH_2Cl$, which can be hydrolysed to glycerol either directly, or via glycidol:

$$
\begin{array}{ccccc}
CH_2OH & & CH_2OH & CH_2OH & CH_2OH \\
| & +\,HOCl & | & | & | \\
CH & \longrightarrow & CHOH \longrightarrow & CH & \longrightarrow CHOH \\
\| & & | & |\!\!>\!\!O & | \\
CH_2 & & CH_2Cl & CH_2 & CH_2OH
\end{array}
$$

---

[22] Shell Development, U.S.P. 2177419.

The monochlorhydrin is best made by passing chlorine into a 4·5% aqueous solution of allyl alcohol at 14° c.; on hydrolysis with sodium bicarbonate at 150° c. under pressure, an overall yield of 93·5 per cent glycerol on allyl alcohol is obtained. This route is an alternative to the allyl chloride route to glycerol. A second alternative, part of the new Shell route to glycerol from propylene (this Chapter, p. 169), is direct addition of hydrogen peroxide (from isopropyl alcohol, Chapter 8, p. 137) to allyl alcohol; the reaction can be carried out at 90–98° c. in presence of a mineral acid catalyst or a catalyst of similar acidity:[23]

$$CH_2 : CHCH_2OH + H_2O_2 \rightarrow CH_2OHCHOHCH_2OH$$

Epichlorhydrin, $CH_2ClCHCH_2$, a stage in the glycerol synthesis, has
$$\diagdown O \diagup$$
recently achieved significance in its own right as an intermediate in the new polycondensation resins, the epoxy or ethoxyline resins. The basic material for these compounds is made by reaction between 2 mols of epichlorhydrin and 1 mol of diphenylolpropane, di-2-(*p*-hydroxyphenyl)-propane, from phenol and acetone:

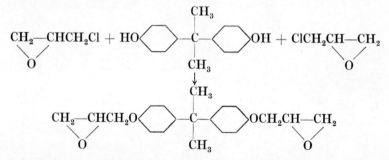

The synthesis of glycerol from propylene via allyl chloride is a masterly example of the versatility of the organic chemist and of the ubiquity of petroleum as a source of organic chemicals.

After having a pilot plant in operation for several years, the Shell Chemical Corporation erected in 1948 a plant at Houston, Texas, for the manufacture of 16,000 tons p.a. of glycerol from propylene via allyl chloride. This has been extended by 50%, and a second synthetic glycerol plant is now in operation by another company (Dow Chemical Co.). The delay between discovery of the process and commercial exploitation permitted the demand for glycerol for chemical outlets to expand; at the same time, it could be seen that in the post-war years, the great increase in synthetic detergents would reduce soap production and hence would reduce the amount of by-product glycerol available for industry.

In 1956 the total production of glycerol in U.S.A. was 110,000 tons, of

---

[23] Shell Development, U.S.P. 2741502.

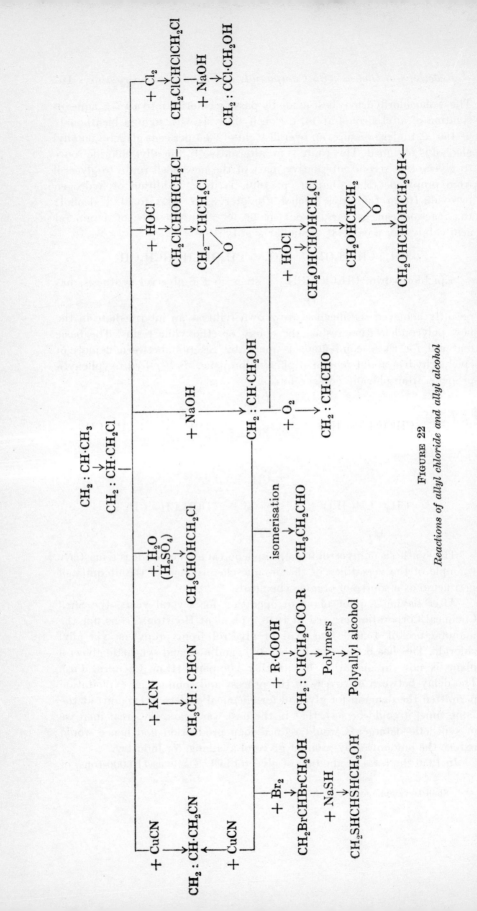

FIGURE 22

Reactions of allyl chloride and allyl alcohol

which 45,000 tons, or over 40 per cent, was synthetic, from propylene by the allyl chloride route.[24]

The further expansion of this synthetic route to glycerol must now face competition from the synthesis from propylene, via acrolein (pp. 148, 300), which requires only propylene and air, avoiding having to rely on chlorine as one of the reagents. A plant for this process, also discovered by Shell Development Co., is being planned in the United States.[25] The process appears to involve the following steps:

$$CH_3CH : CH_2 \xrightarrow{\text{air}} CH_2 : CHCHO$$

$$2CH_3CH : CH_2 + 2H_2O \xrightarrow{(H_2SO_4)} 2CH_3CHOHCH_3$$

$$CH_3CHOHCH_3 \xrightarrow{\text{air or } O_2} CH_3COCH_3 + H_2O_2$$

$$CH_2 : CHCHO + CH_3CHOHCH_3 \rightarrow CH_2 : CHCH_2OH + CH_3COCH_3$$

$$CH_2 : CHCH_2OH + H_2O_2 \rightarrow CH_2OHCHOHCH_2OH$$

Therefore, in theory, three mols of propylene give one mol of glycerol and two mols of acetone. No other chemical reagent is consumed; only air and water are used.

The important reactions of allyl chloride and allyl alcohol are summarised in Fig. 22.

(c) THE BUTENES

The 1- and 2-butenes add chlorine readily in the usual way to give the expected dichlorides. These lose one and two mols of hydrogen chloride on treatment with alkali or on catalytic or thermal pyrolysis to give chlorobutenes and butadiene; 2 : 3-dichlorobutane on further chlorination gives 2 : 2 : 3-trichlorobutane which is a possible route to 2-chlorobutadiene (see Chapter 12, p. 212):

$$CH_3CH_2CH : CH_2 \xrightarrow{+ Cl_2} CH_3CH_2CHClCH_2Cl \xrightarrow{- 2HCl} CH_2 : CHCH : CH_2$$

$$\downarrow - HCl$$

$$CH_3CH : CHCH_3 \xrightarrow{+ Cl_2} CH_3CHClCHClCH_3 \xrightarrow{- HCl} CH_3CCl : CHCH_3$$

$$\downarrow \begin{matrix} + Cl_2 \\ - 2HCl \end{matrix}$$

$$CH_2 : CClCH : CH_2$$
$$\text{(2-chloro-1 : 3-butadiene)}$$

At high temperatures, the Shell workers found that 2-butene substituted rather more readily than propylene, the product being crotyl chloride:

$$CH_3CH : CHCH_3 + Cl_2 \rightarrow CH_3CH : CHCH_2Cl + HCl$$

---

[24] *Chem. Eng. News*, February 4, 1957, p. 104.
[25] *Chem. Week*, April 23, 1955, p. 30.

Crotyl chloride boils at 77° c. It is a very reactive halide, but no technical use has so far been made of it; it readily loses hydrogen chloride to give butadiene:

$$CH_3CH : CHCH_2Cl \xrightarrow{\;- \; HCl\;} CH_2 : CHCH : CH_2$$

The reaction of chlorine with isobutene (and with other tertiary olefins) is quite unexpected, the main product being methallyl chloride even at temperatures as low as − 50° c.:

$$\underset{\displaystyle CH_2 : CCH_3}{\overset{\displaystyle CH_3}{|}} + Cl_2 \rightarrow \underset{\displaystyle CH_2 : CCH_2Cl}{\overset{\displaystyle CH_3}{|}} + HCl$$

This reaction was discovered in 1884 by Sheshukov, but was left virtually untouched for fifty years, when workers in the Shell Development laboratories reexamined it.[26] They originally suggested that the reaction involved direct substitution, and not addition of a molecule of chlorine followed by loss of hydrogen chloride, as the equilibrium of the reaction:

$$\underset{\displaystyle CH_2 : CCH_2Cl}{\overset{\displaystyle CH_3}{|}} + HCl \rightarrow CH_3 - \underset{\displaystyle Cl}{\overset{\displaystyle CH_3}{\underset{|}{\overset{|}{C}}}} - CH_2Cl$$

is far on the right hand side at ordinary temperature.

The current view of the mechanism of this reaction is that it involves attack of a chlorine ion on the methylene group, giving a carbonium ion, the methallyl chloride arising by shift of the double bond.[17]

$$\underset{\displaystyle CH_3}{\overset{\displaystyle CH_2 : CCH_3}{|}} + Cl_2 \longrightarrow \underset{\displaystyle CH_3}{\overset{\displaystyle CH_2Cl\overset{+}{C}CH_3}{|}} + Cl^-$$

$$\underset{\displaystyle CH_3}{\overset{\displaystyle CH_2Cl\overset{+}{C}CH_3}{|}} \begin{cases} \longrightarrow \underset{\displaystyle CH_3}{\overset{\displaystyle CH_2ClC : CH_2}{|}} + H^+ \\ \qquad \text{methallyl chloride} \\ \longrightarrow \underset{\displaystyle CH_3}{\overset{\displaystyle CHCl : CCH_3}{|}} + H^+ \end{cases}$$

isocrotyl chloride

In the methallyl chloride process, the early workers bubbled chlorine into liquid isobutene; this gave much *tert*-butyl chloride as by-product by addition to free isobutene of the hydrogen chloride liberated in the substitution reaction. The difficulty was overcome by operating the process continuously, removing the hydrogen chloride as quickly as possible from contact with free isobutene.[26] In the preferred process, liquid isobutene

---

[26] Burgin, Groll and Hearne, *Ind. Eng. Chem.*, 1939, **31**, 1413.

and chlorine in the molar ratio 1·5 : 1 were mixed at an efficient jet, passed through a short water-cooled reactor (contact time, at 0° c., 0·0057 sec.) into a tower in which hydrogen chloride was scrubbed out with warm water. The methallyl chloride and other chlorinated products were condensed out, and the methallyl chloride isolated by fractional distillation.

The chlorination is hardly affected by temperature or by the presence of oxygen; it goes rapidly in the liquid phase, or in the vapour phase in presence of surfaces such as glass. Pressure favours addition of hydrogen chloride to isobutene to give *tert*-butyl chloride. Analysis of the crude chlorination product made as described above is:

Halides	Formula	Yield %	b.p., ° c./760 mm.
Methallyl chloride	$CH_2 : CCH_2Cl$ $\|$ CH_3	87	72·2
Isocrotyl chloride	$(CH_3)_2C : CHCl$	3	68·1
tert-Butyl chloride	$(CH_3)_3CCl$	1	50·8
1 : 2-Dichloroisobutane	$(CH_3)_2CClCH_2Cl$	6	108·0
Unsaturated dichlorides	—	2	130–135
Trichlorides	—	1	—

Separation of methallyl chloride and isocrotyl chloride by fractionation is virtually impossible but, as in the case of allyl chloride and 2-chloropropylene, this is unimportant as the chlorine atom in isocrotyl chloride is unreactive. Commercial methallyl chloride contains 4 per cent isocrotyl chloride.

Methallyl chloride undergoes the same types of metathetic and addition reactions as allyl chloride, but it has not yet reached the same level of technical importance. A range of its derivatives has already been marketed. Its reactions and the properties of its derivatives have been described in a series of papers from the laboratories of the Shell Development Co.[27] These are summarised in Fig. 23.

(d) HIGHER OLEFINS

Higher straight chain and tertiary olefins react like the corresponding butenes. 2-Pentene adds chlorine in the cold in the liquid phase to give 2 : 3-dichloropentane; it undergoes substitutive chlorination in the vapour phase somewhat more readily than 2-butene. Trimethylethylene with chlorine at ordinary temperature gives a high yield of an equilibrium mixture of 3-chloro-2-methyl-1-butene and 1-chloro-2-methyl-2-butene:

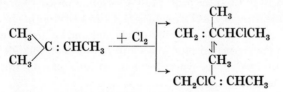

[27] *Ind. Eng. Chem.*, 1941, **33**, 115, 385, 805, 940.

2. Reactions with hydrogen chloride

Ethylene combines with hydrogen chloride in the vapour phase over catalysts such as aluminium chloride, bismuth chloride or silica gel, to give ethyl chloride:

$$C_2H_4(g) + HCl(g) \rightarrow C_2H_5Cl(g). \quad \Delta H = -13 \cdot 4 \text{ k. cal.}$$

The reaction is reversible; the equilibrium $K_p = \dfrac{p_{C_2H_5Cl}}{p_{C_2H_4}p_{HCl}}$ is given by the equation, $\log K_p = \dfrac{2{,}925}{T} - 4 \cdot 96$.

The usual reaction temperature is 130–250° c.; the equilibrium conversion falls off between 200° c. and 250° c. but the higher temperature levels are used to obtain rapid reaction. A side reaction is polymerisation of the ethylene, and this leads in time to deactivation of the catalyst.

Isolation of ethyl chloride from the gaseous reaction product is not too easy as it boils at + 12·2° c.; the usual methods are adsorption on charcoal, or refrigeration and scrubbing with an absorbent liquid such as kerosene.

The vapour phase process can be used both with dilute ethylene containing gases and with concentrated ethylene. This process has been developed in conjunction with direct chlorination of ethane in presence of ethylene, the hydrogen chloride liberated from the ethane being combined with the ethylene in a second operation (Chapter 5, p. 71). The process is operated by the Shell organisation at Stanlow.

Liquid phase processes have been developed which require concentrated ethylene. For example,[28] ethylene and hydrochloric acid are reacted in a solvent such as ethyl chloride or 1 : 1 : 2-trichloroethane using aluminium chloride as catalyst. Operating conditions involve temperatures between − 5° c. and 55° c. at pressures from atmospheric to 9 atma. An alternative way is to react ethylene and hydrogen chloride in a molar ratio of 1·07 to 1 at 10 atma. pressure and 55° c. in ethyl chloride solution with ferric chloride as catalyst; periodic addition of catalyst is necessary to maintain the reaction.[29]

One of the problems of this process is to keep down both polymerisation of ethylene and its interaction with ethyl chloride under the influence of the catalyst.

The synthesis of ethyl chloride by direct chlorination of ethane has been referred to in Chapter 5, p. 71. The original process for ethyl chloride was by esterification of ethyl alcohol with hydrogen chloride in presence of a metal halide catalyst. The vapours of alcohol and hydrogen chloride were passed into a concentrated aqueous solution of a metal halide such as zinc chloride at 110–140° c., the water formed distilling off from the salt solution

[28] Dow, U.S.P. 2140927.
[29] B.P.M., B.P. 691500.

together with the ethyl chloride. There are therefore three routes to ethyl chloride; choice of the most economical depends upon the relative costs of ethane, ethylene, and ethyl alcohol at the site of manufacture. In 1955, 88 per cent of America's ethyl chloride is reported as made from ethylene and hydrogen chloride.[30]

Ethyl chloride is required mainly for the manufacture of lead tetraethyl (from ethyl chloride and sodium lead alloy)[31] for other ethylations such as for ethyl cellulose use relatively small quantities. In 1954, American production of ethyl chloride was 245,000 tons. Almost the whole of this was consumed in manufacture of lead tetraethyl, annual requirements of which exceeded 100,000 tons.

A new process for lead ethyl, of potential interest, has been disclosed.[32] This involves the electrolysis of aluminium triethyl-sodium fluoride complex using a lead anode giving lead ethyl and pure aluminium at the cathode. The aluminium alkyl is made from aluminium and ethylene. so that, in effect, compared with the present route, the manufacture of sodium and of ethyl chloride from ethylene are replaced by the electrolysis of the complex and making the aluminium alkyl. This route does not seem likely to displace the present one.

$$Al + 3C_2H_4 + 1\tfrac{1}{2}H_2 \rightarrow Al(C_2H_5)_3$$

$$2\{NaF{\cdot}2Al(C_2H_5)_3\} + 3Pb \rightarrow 3Pb(C_2H_5)_4 + 4Al + 2NaF$$

The use of lead ethyl requires the use of two other reaction products of olefins and halogens. In aviation petrol, ethylene dibromide is employed in stoichiometric proportions. In motor petrol, a mixture of ethylene dichloride and ethylene dibromide are used, so that for each atom of lead there are two atoms of chlorine and one atom of bromine present. The function of these additions is as a lead scavenger, to prevent lead deposition on the plugs and elsewhere.

Addition of hydrogen chloride to other olefins proceeds more readily than with ethylene. The direction of addition to unsymmetrical olefins follows Markownikoff's Rule, the chlorine tending to attach itself to the carbon atom which is combined with the fewest hydrogen atoms. Thus, propylene gives 2-chloropropane:

$$
\begin{array}{ccc}
CH_3 & & CH_3 \\
| & & | \\
CH & + \ HCl \rightarrow & CHCl \\
\| & & | \\
CH_2 & & CH_3
\end{array}
$$

---

[30] Kuhn and Hutcheson, *Pet. Proc.*, September 1956, p. 107.
[31] *Pet. Times*, 1954, **58**, 217.
[32] *Chem. Eng. News*, Aug. 22, 1955, p. 3486; *Chem. Week*, June 2, 1956, p. 70.

Similarly, isobutene gives *tert*-butyl chloride:

$$CH_3C : CH_2 + HCl \rightarrow CH_3\overset{\overset{\displaystyle Cl}{|}}{\underset{\underset{\displaystyle CH_3}{|}}{C}}CH_3$$
$$\underset{\displaystyle CH_3}{|}$$

Reaction is usually carried out in the liquid phase; addition of hydrogen chloride to isobutene is particularly easy and proceeds smoothly under such different conditions as − 80° c. with dry hydrogen chloride, or + 100° c. with aqueous hydrochloric acid. *tert*-Butyl chloride rearranges to isobutyl chloride at high temperatures, 400–500° c., in the presence of catalysts:

$$(CH_3)_3CCl \rightarrow (CH_3)_2CHCH_2Cl$$

The hydrochlorination of the higher olefins is not yet of any technical importance.

3. Reactions with hypochlorous acid

Addition of hypochlorous acid to ethylene gives the important intermediate ethylene chlorhydrin:

$$CH_2 : CH_2 + HOCl \rightarrow CH_2OHCH_2Cl$$

The only technical method employed is to pass ethylene and chlorine simultaneously into water at about 10–50° c. The general conditions for reaction were described by Gomberg in 1919,[33] and have not been modified in any important respect.

In the system:

$$Cl_2 + H_2O \rightleftharpoons HOCl + HCl$$

the actual proportions of hypochlorous acid and hydrochloric acid are very small; however, the velocity of addition of hypochlorous acid to ethylene is much faster than the competing reaction, direct addition of chlorine to ethylene. Provided a slight excess of ethylene is maintained, a concentration of 6–8 per cent chlorhydrin can be reached before an appreciable amount of ethylene dichloride is formed. Efficient agitation is essential to accelerate reaction and to avoid local concentrations of chlorine. If the concentration of chlorhydrin is taken above 8 per cent, dichloride formation increases.

The overall reaction is:

$$\underset{\displaystyle CH_2}{\overset{\displaystyle CH_2}{\|}} + Cl_2 + H_2O \rightarrow \underset{\displaystyle CH_2Cl}{\overset{\displaystyle CH_2OH}{|}} + HCl$$

one mol of hydrochloric acid being produced for each mol of chlorhydrin made. The reaction mixture is therefore corrosive, and much work has been carried out on the most economical constructional materials.

---

[33] *J. Amer. Chem. Soc.*, 1919, **41**, 1414.

In the German process,[34] ethylene chlorhydrin was made continuously by passing excess of ethylene and chlorine simultaneously into water in a tile-lined rubber-lined tower. The unreacted ethylene was recirculated after removal of acid vapours by scrubbing with caustic soda solution and of organic chloride vapours by adsorption on charcoal. The heat of reaction was sufficient to maintain the product from the tower at about 45° c. The process was operated to give ethylene chlorhydrin as a 4–5% solution, which was converted directly to ethylene oxide without concentration or purification (this Chapter, p. 177). In the continuous process, conversion must be held to a lower figure than in the batch reaction for a given ethylene dichloride production.

Ethylene chlorhydrin boils at 132° c.; it forms an azeotrope with water, containing 42·5 per cent chlorhydrin and boiling at 97·8° c. The isolation of the anhydrous chlorhydrin from the 4–8% solutions obtained in technical processes therefore calls for special methods. This dilute solution can easily be concentrated by distillation to 25–30% strength. Addition of sodium chloride causes separation into two phases, the oil layer containing 70 per cent chlorhydrin; on fractionating this layer, the azeotrope is obtained as an overhead and anhydrous chlorhydrin as a bottoms product. Other methods include drying by distillation with benzene. A synthetic method of making anhydrous chlorhydrin is by addition of hydrogen chloride to ethylene oxide:

$$
\begin{array}{c}
CH_2 \\
| \quad\diagdown O + HCl \rightarrow \\
CH_2 \diagup
\end{array}
\qquad
\begin{array}{c}
CH_2OH \\
| \\
CH_2Cl
\end{array}
$$

Ethylene chlorhydrin is completely miscible with water, by which it is readily hydrolysed. It is extremely reactive, but for most of its industrial applications, the dilute aqueous solution or the azeotrope is quite satisfactory.

By-products always obtained in the chlorhydrin process include ethylene dichloride and di-2-chloroethyl ether, $(ClC_2H_4)_2O$. Manufacture of ethylene dichloride from ethylene and chlorine has been dealt with at the beginning of this chapter. Di-2-chloroethyl ether is synthesised from ethylene chlorhydrin and concentrated sulphuric acid at 90–100° c., or by passing excess of ethylene and chlorine simultaneously into ethylene chlorhydrin at 80° c.[35]

$$
\begin{array}{c}
CH_2OH \\
| \\
CH_2Cl
\end{array}
+ CH_2 : CH_2 + Cl_2 \rightarrow
\begin{array}{c}
CH_2OCH_2CH_2Cl \\
| \\
CH_2Cl
\end{array}
+ HCl
$$

This ether is used as a solvent, for example in the refining of lubricating oil (Chlorex process), in the purification of butadiene and in the textile

---

[34] B.I.O.S. 1059.
[35] Carbide and Carbon, B.P. 438271.

industry. It is also employed as a soil fumigant and as an inter-mediate for other chemicals. With ammonia and amines, it gives morpho-line (Chapter 19, p. 354) and substituted morpholines:

$$O \Big\langle {}^{CH_2CH_2Cl}_{CH_2CH_2Cl} + 3NH_3 \rightarrow O \Big\langle {}^{CH_2CH_2}_{CH_2CH_2} \Big\rangle NH + 2NH_4Cl$$

Morpholine can also be made from diethanolamine, $NH(C_2H_4OH)_2$ (Chapter 19).

With sodium polysulphides, di-2-chloroethyl ether gives polysulphide plastics analogous to Thiokol A, but with better rubber-like properties. With fused alkalies, the anaesthetic, divinyl ether (Vinethene), is obtained:

$$ClCH_2CH_2OCH_2CH_2Cl + 2KOH \rightarrow CH_2 : CHOCH : CH_2 + 2KCl + 2H_2O$$

There are other variants of the chlorhydrin synthesis, some of which have already been taken to the manufacturing scale. Ethylene and chlorine passed into ethyl alcohol give 2-chloroethyl ethyl ether:[36]

$$\begin{matrix} CH_2OH \\ | \\ CH_3 \end{matrix} + CH_2 : CH_2 + Cl_2 \rightarrow \begin{matrix} CH_2OCH_2CH_2Cl \\ | \\ CH_3 \end{matrix} + HCl$$

If the di-2-chloroethyl ether synthesis from ethylene chlorhydrin, ethylene and chlorine is carried out between 20° c. and 100° c. using aqueous chlor-hydrin, the main product is 2-chloroethoxyethyl-2-chloroethyl ether (tri-glycol dichloride), $ClCH_2CH_2OCH_2CH_2OCH_2CH_2Cl$.[37] This is a chlorinated solvent and extractant with higher water solubility than di-2-chloroethyl ether. If olefins other than ethylene are used, the product is a 2-chloroalkyl-2-chloroethyl ether, *e.g.*, ethylene chlorhydrin, propylene and chlorine give 2-chloroisopropyl-2-chlorethyl ether, $ClCH_2CH(CH_3)OCH_2CH_2Cl$.

$$\begin{matrix} CH_2OH \\ | \\ CH_2Cl \end{matrix} \xrightarrow{(H_2O)} \begin{matrix} CH_2OH + CH_2 : CH_2 + Cl_2 \\ | \\ CH_2OH + CH_2 : CH_2 + Cl_2 \end{matrix} \rightarrow \begin{matrix} CH_2OCH_2CH_2Cl \\ | \\ CH_2OCH_2CH_2Cl \end{matrix} + 2HCl$$

Triglycol dichloride

$$\begin{matrix} CH_2OH \\ | \\ CH_2Cl \end{matrix} + CH_2 : \overset{CH_3}{\underset{|}{CH}} + Cl_2 \rightarrow \begin{matrix} CH_3 \\ | \\ CH_2OCH_2CHCl \\ | \\ CH_2Cl \end{matrix} + HCl$$

2-chloroisopropyl-2-
chloroethyl ether

The boiling points of these chloroalkyl ethers are given in Table 39.

---

[36] Wacker, D.R.P. 537696.
[37] Carbide and Carbon, U.S.P. 2017811.

Reverting to ethylene chlorhydrin, its main peace-time outlets are for the manufacture of ethylene oxide and ethylene glycol.

TABLE 39

Boiling points of chloroalkyl ethers

Name	Formula	b.p. at 760 mm. ° c.
Di-2-chloroethyl ether . .	$ClCH_2CH_2OCH_2CH_2Cl$	178
2-Chloroethyl ethyl ether .	$ClCH_2CH_2OCH_2CH_3$	107–8
2-Chloroethyl-2-chloroethoxy-ethyl ether . . .	$ClCH_2CH_2OCH_2CH_2OCH_2CH_2Cl$	230
2-Chloroisopropyl-2-chloro-ethyl ether . . .	$ClCH_2CH(CH_3)OCH_2CH_2Cl$	65/8 mm.

Ethylene oxide is obtained from the chlorhydrin by reaction with alkalies under such conditions that the ethylene oxide is immediately removed from the solution, to avoid hydration to ethylene glycol:

$$\begin{array}{c} CH_2Cl \\ | \\ CH_2OH \end{array} + NaOH \rightarrow \begin{array}{c} CH_2 \\ | \hspace{0.4em} \diagdown \\ CH_2 \diagup \end{array}\hspace{-0.5em}O + NaCl + H_2O$$

In one process, caustic soda is added to boiling 10% aqueous chlorhydrin in equipment fitted with a fractionating column, which condenses the steam, allowing the more volatile ethylene oxide to pass overhead. Lime, however, is usually used as the alkali. The reaction is carried out continuously, using a reactor divided into several compartments by baffles to promote good mixing. In the German process,[38] weak aqueous ethylene chlorhydrin of 4–5% strength, containing some ethylene dichloride, from the reaction between ethylene, chlorine, and water (this Chapter, p. 175), was mixed with a 10–20 per cent excess of a hot slurry of slaked lime and introduced into the head of a tower reactor down which it followed a serpentine course. The temperature at the head was maintained at the boil by blowing live steam into the base of the tower. The vapours liberated contained ethylene oxide, ethylene dichloride and steam. Most of the steam was condensed and returned; the ethylene oxide was separated from the ethylene dichloride and from the remainder of the steam by fractional distillation at atmospheric pressure in two continuous columns. Loss of ethylene oxide by hydration to ethylene glycol was stated to be negligible.

The yield of ethylene oxide on ethylene by the chlorhydrin route is about 75–80 per cent. One ton of ethylene oxide requires 0·9 tons of ethylene, 2·1 tons of chlorine and 2 tons of quicklime. This route is now faced with competition from the direct oxidation of ethylene (Chapter 9, p. 147); although the yield on ethylene is considerably higher, the large requirements of chlorine and lime for the chlorhydrin process are weighing the scales increasingly in favour of the direct route.

---

[38] B.I.O.S. 776; see also B.I.O.S. 1059.

The properties and reactions of ethylene oxide are discussed in Chapter 19.

In the formation of ethylene oxide from chlorhydrin and alkalies, the ethylene oxide must be removed from the reaction zone as fast as it is formed; in the alkaline hydrolysis of chlorhydrin to ethylene glycol:

$$\begin{matrix} CH_2Cl \\ | \\ CH_2OH \end{matrix} + NaOH \rightarrow \begin{matrix} CH_2OH \\ | \\ CH_2OH \end{matrix} + NaCl$$

any ethylene oxide formed must be retained in the reactor to complete its hydration. Aqueous chlorhydrin may be hydrolysed with sodium bicarbonate in an autoclave at 105–110° c. to give a 90 per cent yield of ethylene glycol. Continuous hydrolysis with caustic soda in a closed vessel has been described; chalk and calcium bicarbonate have also been suggested. By these processes, ethylene glycol is obtained as a dilute aqueous solution containing much dissolved inorganic salts; it is isolated by concentration in a desalting type evaporator, followed by fractional distillation. Ethylene glycol may also be manufactured from formaldehyde and carbon monoxide (Chapter 16, p. 285) or by hydration of ethylene oxide (Chapter 19, p. 343), which is the principal route. Its properties and reactions are described in Chapter 19.

Other reactions of ethylene chlorhydrin also depend upon the smooth replacement of the mobile chlorine atom. With sodium sulphide, di 2 hydroxyethyl sulphide (thiodiglycol), the intermediate for mustard gas, is obtained in high yield (Chapter 19, p. 356):

$$2ClCH_2CH_2OH + Na_2S \rightarrow S(CH_2CH_2OH)_2 + 2NaCl$$

With sodium cyanide, ethylene cyanhydrin is obtained; this product is an intermediate in one of the technical routes to acrylonitrile and the acrylates (Chapter 19, p. 357):

$$ClCH_2CH_2OH + NaCN \rightarrow CNCH_2CH_2OH + NaCl$$

As with glycol, it is better to make all these compounds from ethylene oxide and discussion is therefore deferred to Chapter 19.

Propylene chlorhydrin is made in the same way as ethylene chlorhydrin, from propylene, chlorine and water.[39] Commercial propylene chlorhydrin consists of 90 per cent 1-chloro-2-propanol and 10 per cent 2-chloro-1-propanol. The higher olefins are stated to react more readily than ethylene with hypochlorous acid; nevertheless there is a tendency to increasing proportions of di- and polychlorides. The relative rates of addition of hypochlorous acid and of chlorine to the higher olefins are less favourable than with ethylene.

The manufacture of a mixture of ethylene and propylene chlorhydrins

---

[39] Soc. Carbochimique, U.S.P. 2103813.

by the ethylene chlorhydrin process from gases, such as cracked gases, containing both ethylene and propylene has been described[40] and is operated in the United States by Wyandotte Chemicals Corp. The higher chlorhydrins are not technically important. If wanted, they are made by reaction between the olefin and hypochlorous acid free of chlorine, for example in the same way as in the addition of hypochlorous acid to allyl chloride (this Chapter, p. 165). In special cases, one can use N-chlorourea (Detoeuf) or an alkyl hypochlorite.[41] *tert*-Butyl hypochlorite, $(CH_3)_3COCl$, which is relatively stable and can be made by passing chlorine into a solution of caustic soda in *tert*-butyl alcohol at 0° c., is probably the most convenient alkyl hypochlorite to use; it is a yellow oil, b.p. 79° c., stable in absence of light.

Propylene chlorhydrin resembles ethylene chlorhydrin in its properties and reactions; its most important industrial outlet is for the manufacture of propylene oxide and of propylene glycol, dealt with in Chapter 19. It can also be dehydrated smoothly by refluxing with concentrated sulphuric acid to give di-2-chloroisopropyl ether,[42] a liquid boiling at 187° c. with the physical and chemical properties of di-2-chloroethyl ether, and now commercially available:

$$2 \underset{\overset{|}{CH_2Cl}}{\overset{\overset{|}{CH_3}}{CHOH}} \xrightarrow{-H_2O} \underset{CH_2Cl}{\overset{CH_3}{\diagdown}}CHOCH\underset{CH_2Cl}{\overset{CH_3}{\diagup}}$$

Propylene chlorhydrin reacts twenty times as rapidly as ethylene chlorhydrin with alkalies to give the olefin oxide, a method that has been used to separate propylene oxide when working up the products from hypochlorinating a mixture of ethylene and propylene.[43]

The butene chlorhydrins do not appear to have any technical importance. With hypochlorous acid, 1-butene gives mainly 1-chloro-2-hydroxybutane; 2-butene gives 2-chloro-3-hydroxybutane and isobutene gives 1-chloro-2-hydroxy-2-methylpropane (α-isobutene chlorhydrin):

$$CH_3CH_2CH : CH_2 \xrightarrow{(HOCl)} CH_3CH_2CHOHCH_2Cl$$

$$CH_3CH : CHCH_3 \xrightarrow{(HOCl)} CH_3CHClCHOHCH_3$$

$$(CH_3)_2C : CH_2 \xrightarrow{(HOCl)} (CH_3)_2C(OH)CH_2Cl$$

Chlorhydrins can be prepared synthetically by reaction of hydrogen chloride with olefin oxides or with diols; these methods give mixtures with the higher unsymmetrical olefin derivatives. They can also be prepared

[40] Ellis, 'Chemistry of Petroleum Derivatives', *Reinhold*, Vol. 1, 1934, p. 491.
[41] B.P.M., B.P. 402880, U.S.P. 2046469.
[42] Carbide and Carbon, U.S.P. 2052264.
[43] Wyandotte, U.S.P. 2417685.

by the hydration of allyl chloride and its homologues with concentrated sulphuric acid at low temperatures (this Chapter, p. 165).

The boiling points of the olefin chlorhydrins are given in Table 40.

TABLE 40
Boiling points of olefin chlorhydrins

Name	Formula	b.p., ° c./760 mm.
Ethylene chlorhydrin . . .	CH_2ClCH_2OH	132
α-Propylene chlorhydrin . . .	$CH_2ClCHOHCH_3$	133–4
β-Propylene chlorhydrin . . .	$CH_2OHCHClCH_3$	126–7
α-1-Butene chlorhydrin . . .	$CH_2ClCHOHCH_2CH_3$	141
β-1-Butene chlorhydrin . . .	$CH_2OHCHClCH_2CH_3$	75/25 mm.
2-Butene chlorhydrin . . .	$CH_3CHClCHOHCH_3$	138–9
α-Isobutene chlorhydrin . . .	$(CH_3)_2C(OH)CH_2Cl$	128

4. Reactions with bromine compounds

The most important compound prepared by reaction between any olefin and bromine is ethylene dibromide, used in conjunction with lead tetraethyl in high octane petrols. It is manufactured by direct addition of bromine to ethylene, using any of the methods developed for manufacture of ethylene dichloride from ethylene and chlorine; the bromine is made by chlorination of sea water.[44]

Addition of hydrogen bromide to olefins gives alkyl bromides. Although not industrially important, the reaction is interesting because with substituted olefins, addition may be made to follow an abnormal course. Normal addition follows Markownikoff's Rule, the bromine attaching itself to the carbon atom poorest in hydrogen; in presence of peroxides, however, the order of addition may be reversed:

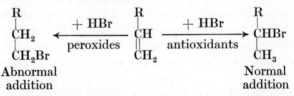

| Abnormal addition | | Normal addition |

With unsymmetrical olefins containing non-terminal double bonds, a 50 : 50 mixture of the two possible isomers is always obtained, whatever the conditions.

The abnormal addition is considered to depend upon attack of bromine atoms, formed in the presence of peroxides, on the carbon atom richest in hydrogen. The reaction has been extended to addition of bromine and of other reagents to substituted olefins containing both hydrocarbon and non-hydrocarbon substituents.

The abnormal addition does not take place with reactions involving addition of chlorine to a double bond.

---

[44] *Pet. Times*, 1954, **58**, 238.

CHAPTER 11

OTHER REACTIONS OF OLEFINS

PREVIOUS chapters have dealt with the principal industrial reactions of the olefins. In this chapter, it is not intended to deal with all the other chemical reactions of the olefins, which can be found in the standard text-books of organic chemistry, but only with a selected number, in which industrial application has already taken place on some scale or appears to be possible.

1. Reactions with compounds of sulphur

The formation of mono- and di-esters of sulphuric acid was discussed in Chapter 8 from the standpoint of processes for the manufacture of alcohols. It was remarked that one of the competing reactions, polymerisation, became increasingly serious as the molecular weight of the olefin increased. However, by reaction with concentrated sulphuric acid at low temperature, e.g., $0°$ c., the long chain olefins, particularly the normal olefins from cracking of paraffin wax or from the Fischer-Tropsch process which have the double bond at or near the end of the chain, give good yields of the long chain alkyl hydrogen sulphate. The sodium salts of these sulphates are good detergents. They are manufactured by the Shell Petroleum Co. on a large scale at Stanlow in England and elsewhere, the olefins being obtained by the vapour phase cracking of paraffin wax.

Sulphation of the C_{12} to C_{18} olefin fraction is carried out at 10–$15°$ c. with 90% sulphuric acid and an acid to olefin molar ratio of $2:1$. Efficient mixing and short contact time is essential. The main reaction is monosulphation but some dialkyl sulphate is also formed:

$$RCH : CH_2 + H_2SO_4 \rightarrow RCHCH_3$$
$$\underset{OSO_3H}{|}$$

$$2RCH : CH_2 + H_2SO_4 \rightarrow \left[\underset{CH_3}{\overset{R}{\diagdown}} CH \right]_2 SO_4$$

Controlled dilution with water precipitates olefin polymers which are separated. The acid layer is neutralised and hydrolysed; aqueous isopropyl alcohol is added and the solution extracted with a light petroleum hydrocarbon to remove unchanged olefin and any remaining dialkyl sulphate; a lower alcohol such as isopropyl alcohol is added to prevent formation of intractable emulsions. The dialkyl sulphate in the extract is hydrolysed with aqueous caustic soda at $80°$ c. to monoalkyl sulphates which are combined with the main product.[1]

---

[1] B.P.M., B.P. 459017, 459078, 459081, 480490; *Ind. Eng. Chem.*, 1955, **47**, 2.

Similar detergents are made in the U.K. by sulphation of the olefins in the fraction of shale oil distillates boiling at 180–330° c.;[2] this contains 42 per cent of olefins and diolefins. After removal of phenols and nitrogen compounds, sulphation is carried out with 96–98% sulphuric acid at 10–20° c.; the further steps are essentially the same as those outlined above.

Sulphation of olefins gives only secondary alkyl sulphates which have certain limitations as detergents. Primary alkyl sulphates can be made from olefins via the primary alcohols obtained by the Oxo reaction described later in this chapter (p. 183).

Addition of hydrogen sulphide to olefins giving mercaptans proceeds much more readily than direct hydration of olefins. Branch chain olefins such as isobutene, diisobutene and triisobutene, react particularly readily. This reaction is used for making dodecyl mercaptan from the C_{11}–C_{13} branch chain olefin, b.p. 166–190° c. The process is carried out at about 110° c. and 25 atma. pressure in presence of a silica-alumina catalyst containing only a few per cent of alumina. About 1·5 mols of hydrogen sulphide are used per mol of olefin; by operating to about 50 per cent conversion, ultimate yields of dodecyl mercaptan are about 90 per cent.[3]

In this reaction the double bond migrates, the SH group being in the middle of the molecule. The principal outlets of commercial dodecyl mercaptan are as a polymerisation modifier in synthetic rubber manufacture, and as an intermediate for detergents, by condensation with ethylene oxide.

The simple mercaptans are usually made from the corresponding alcohol and hydrogen sulphide (Chapter 21, p. 384); amyl mercaptan is made via chlorination of pentane (Chapter 5, p. 74).

Reaction of olefins with sulphur dioxide or with bisulphites leads to direct addition of sulphur to carbon, giving sulphonates, *e.g.*,

$$RCH : CH_2 + NaHSO_3 \rightarrow \underset{\underset{SO_2ONa}{|}}{RCHCH_3}$$

The long chain sulphonates obtained by this reaction do not appear to be industrially important. Olefins and sulphur dioxide also react in presence of traces of oxygen or peroxides to give high polymers, the so-called sulphone resins, *e.g.*, *n*-butene forms $(C_4H_8SO_2)_n$. Even ethylene and propylene form high polymers quite readily, propylene sulphone resin being assigned a molecular weight of 390,000. These resins are stable substances in which the sulphur is directly bound to two carbon atoms in a linear chain. Their structure is unusual in that the sulphur dioxide adds on to

---

[2] Stewart and McNeill, *Chem. Trade J.*, July 14, 1950, p. 95.
[3] Schulze, Lyon and Short, *Ind. Eng. Chem.*, 1948, **40**, 4308.

unsymmetrical olefins not head to tail, but head to head and tail to tail, *e.g.*, propylene sulphone has the structure:

$$\underset{\begin{subarray}{c} | \\ -\text{CHCH}_2\text{SO}_2\text{CH}_2 \end{subarray}}{\text{CH}_3} \quad \underset{\begin{subarray}{c} | \\ \text{CHSO}_2 \end{subarray}}{\text{CH}_3} \quad \underset{\begin{subarray}{c} | \\ \text{CHCH}_2\text{SO}_2- \end{subarray}}{\text{CH}_3}$$

The polysulphone resins do not appear to have attained commercial importance.

The only important reaction of olefins with sulphur chloride is the one in which ethylene is reacted with sulphur monochloride at about 50–60° c. to give di-2-chloroethyl sulphide (mustard gas):

$$2\text{CH}_2 : \text{CH}_2 + \text{S}_2\text{Cl}_2 \rightarrow \text{ClCH}_2\text{CH}_2\text{SCH}_2\text{CH}_2\text{Cl} + \text{S}$$

The sulphur liberated reacts with the di-2-chloroethyl sulphide to give di-2-chloroethyl polysulphides. This route was used by the Allies during the first world war. The Germans used the alternative synthesis from di-2-hydroxyethyl sulphide (thiodiglycol) referred to in Chapter 19, p. 356.

2. Carbon monoxide reactions

Reactions of carbon monoxide with olefins is a field developed only within the last twenty years. Industrially, the most important reaction is the direct addition of carbon monoxide and hydrogen to give aldehydes, the so-called Oxo synthesis,[4] *e.g.*,

$$\text{CH}_2 : \text{CH}_2 + \text{CO} + \text{H}_2 \rightarrow \text{CH}_3\text{CH}_2\text{CHO}$$

The reaction goes well with most olefins and with many olefinic compounds. It is carried out in the temperature range 110–180° c., preferably at the lower range, at 100–200 atm. pressure in presence of a cobalt catalyst, the active catalyst being cobalt carbonyl; unsymmetrical olefins usually give a mixture of the two possible aldehydes. In a complete investigation of a variety of olefins up to eight carbon atoms, Keulemans and his colleagues found that the following rules held:[5]

(*i*) Straight chain olefins gave a mixture of aldehydes containing 60 to 40 per cent of normal C_{n+1} aldehydes and 40 to 60 per cent of 1-alkyl branched chain aldehydes, regardless of the position of the double bond in the original olefin.

(*ii*) Shifting of the double bond generally but not necessarily accompanies reaction.

(*iii*) Addition to a tertiary carbon atom, or to a carbon atom adjacent to a quaternary carbon atom, does not occur.

(*iv*) Addition to a carbon atom adjacent to a tertiary carbon atom is hindered but does occur.

---

[4] Roelen and Ruhrchemie A-G., U.S.P. 2327066; C.I.O.S. 27/69; B.I.O.S. 447.
[5] Keulemans, Kwantes and van Bavel, *Rec. Trav. Chim.*, 1948, **67**, 298.

The reaction is usually carried out in the liquid phase using purified water gas as the source of CO $+$ H$_2$. The crude product may be directly hydrogenated at a somewhat higher temperature than the Oxo reaction itself, or the aldehydes may be isolated and hydrogenated separately. The two stage operation for conversion of olefins to alcohols is preferred to a one-stage process using a CO—H$_2$ ratio of 1 : 2 for a number of technological reasons.[6]

One typical process, manufacture of isooctyl alcohol from the branch chain heptene mixture obtained by copolymerisation of propylene and isobutene, is carried out as follows.[7] The olefin and synthesis gas are passed over a cobalt catalyst at 200 atm. and 175° c. with continuous addition of cobalt naphthenate to the feed to avoid depletion of the cobalt catalyst. To control the temperature, the bulk of the product is recycled, the ratio of recycle to feed being 5 : 1. Cobalt is removed from the product stream which is taken off, by heating at 150° c. and 6 atma. Hydrogenation is carried out at 200° c. and 200 atma., using a nickel chromite on tungsten sulphide catalyst. The yield of octyl alcohols on heptene is over 75 per cent. With diisobutene, reaction proceeds even more readily.[8] In 30 minutes at 125° c., a yield of over 95 per cent of nonanal (3 : 5 : 5-trimethylhexyl aldehyde) is obtained.

Industrially, the reaction is used for making propionaldehyde from ethylene, n- and isobutyl alcohols from propylene, branch chain octyl alcohols from the heptene fraction obtained either by non-selective polymerisation of propylene and n-butenes, or from cracking of slack wax for olefins for detergents (p. 182), 3 : 5 : 5-trimethylhexanol from technical diisobutene, and branched chain C$_{10}$, C$_{12}$ and C$_{15}$ primary alcohols from the olefins of one carbon atom less.

n-Butyl alcohol was hitherto made either by fermentation or from acetaldehyde; its outlets are discussed in Chapter 16, p. 292. Isobutyl alcohol as a co-product of the Oxo synthesis has or will displace manufacture by the 'higher alcohols' synthesis (Chapter 3, p. 45). The C$_8$ and C$_9$ primary alcohols are used as intermediates for plasticisers; the formation of only 3 : 5 : 5-trimethylhexanol is interesting, as technical diisobutene is a mixture of 80 per cent of 2 : 4 : 4-trimethyl-1-pentene and 20 per cent of 2 : 4 : 4-trimethyl-2-pentene. Its reactions are described by Bruner.[9]

The Germans planned to use the Oxo reaction to make long chain primary alcohols for sulphation to detergents. They were to start with the C$_{11}$ to C$_{17}$ olefins from the Fischer-Tropsch synthesis, carry out the Oxo reaction at 130–140° c. and 150 atm. followed immediately by hydrogenation with the same catalyst at 180° c. and 150 atm. using pure hydrogen.

[6] C.I.O.S. 32/107.
[7] Standard Oil Development, U.S.P. 2595096.
[8] du Pont, U.S.P. 2437600.
[9] Bruner, *Ind. Eng. Chem.*, 1949, **41**, 2860.

These plans have not been implemented either in Western Germany or elsewhere.

The Oxo reaction is exothermic, about 35 k. cal. being liberated per g. mol olefin reacted. The final yield of alcohol is usually about 75–85 per cent, some 10–15 per cent more highly condensed products being obtained.

Where two products are obtained, as with propylene, the ratio can be altered slightly by selection of the reaction conditions.

The Oxo synthesis is a way of making an aldehyde containing one more carbon atom than the initial olefin by an industrially feasible process. Aldehydes are not important as such but are wanted as intermediates for acids, alcohols and more highly condensed products (see Chapter 16). There is little point in using the Oxo synthesis for making acids which can be obtained from olefins, carbon monoxide and water in one step (this Chapter, below) but, on reduction, aldehydes give the industrially important primary alcohols, which are not readily accessible from other petroleum sources. The usual processes of petroleum chemistry give secondary alcohols (see Chapter 8), and primary alcohols other than ethyl alcohol can be obtained only by rather complex synthetic operations (see, *e.g.*, Chapter 16, p. 292).

Another synthesis based on carbon monoxide is the direct production of acids by interaction between olefins, water and carbon monoxide, a reaction developed by du Pont.[10] This is also a high pressure reaction but is operated at a considerably higher temperature than the Oxo synthesis. The usual conditions are 200–1,000 atm. at 300–400° c.; an acidic catalyst is required which involves problems of provision of materials of construction resistant to high pressure and to corrosion. In fact, silver and silver alloys have been patented for this purpose. Among the catalysts suggested are phosphoric, hydrochloric, and sulphuric acids and boron trifluoride, etc. Ethylene reacts readily to give propionic acid; propylene gives isobutyric acid. 2-Butene undergoes rearrangement of the carbon skeleton to give trimethylacetic acid (pivalic acid):

$$CH_2 : CH_2 + CO + H_2O \rightarrow CH_3CH_2COOH$$
$$CH_3CH : CH_2 + CO + H_2O \rightarrow CH_3\underset{|}{C}HCH_3$$
$$COOH$$
$$CH_3CH : CHCH_3 + CO + H_2O \rightarrow (CH_3)_3CCOOH$$

The reaction proceeds with methyl alcohol to give acetic acid (Chapter 18, p. 324), and with the higher alcohols to give the same acids as are obtained from the corresponding olefins.

The process has been improved by reacting the olefin with carbon monoxide in the presence of 96% sulphuric acid or of anhydrous hydrofluoric acid at temperatures below 100° c. and at pressures of 20–50 atma., followed by addition of water to free the acid.[11] In a modification of this

---

[10] U.S.P. 1924766 and many later patents.
[11] Studien und Verwertungs G.m.b.H., B.P. 743597.

process, it has been found that carbon monoxide could be added on to olefins in the presence of water, alcohols and amines, etc., to give acids, esters and amides, using either stoichiometric quantities of metal carbonyls in the presence of acids or, catalytically, using a salt of a metal capable of forming a metal carbonyl under reaction conditions.[12] Most attention was paid to the acid synthesis; using nickel carbonyl, reaction conditions were 200–300° c. and 150 atm. Ethylene could be made to give either propionic acid or propionic anhydride.

The reaction could be extended to organic compounds containing the olefinic double bond; allyl alcohol gave methacrylic acid via 2-hydroxy-isobutyric acid:

$$\begin{array}{ccc}
CH_2 & CH_3 & CH_3 \\
\| & | & | \\
CH + CO + H_2O \rightarrow & CHCOOH \rightarrow & CCOOH \\
| & | & \| \\
CH_2OH & CH_2OH & CH_2
\end{array}$$

Another carbon monoxide reaction is the direct synthesis of n-propyl alcohol from ethylene by reaction with the metal hydrocarbonyls obtained by the action of alkalies on the metal carbonyls.[13] Thus with $Fe(CO)_4H_2$ from iron pentacarbonyl, ethylene and water react as follows:

$$Fe(CO)_4H_2 + 2C_2H_4 + 4H_2O \rightarrow 2CH_3CH_2CH_2OH + Fe(HCO_3)_2$$

Reaction is carried out in presence of tertiary bases, the sodium salt of dimethylglycine, $(CH_3)_2NCH_2COONa$, being preferred.

Formaldehyde, CH_2O, may be regarded as a CO-H_2 mixture, but it does not react with olefins to give aldehydes; under acid conditions of condensation, the products are 1 : 3-diols or their esters or the derived unsaturated alcohols, as shown by Prins thirty years ago. Addition of formaldehyde to chloroolefins follows a similar course (Chapter 10, p. 156). The reaction of formaldehyde with olefins is not of technical importance.

3. Reactions with nitrogen compounds

With fuming nitric acid, olefins give nitroalkyl nitrates, *e.g.*, with ethylene:

$$CH_2 : CH_2 + 2HNO_3 \rightarrow NO_2CH_2CH_2ONO_2 + H_2O$$

This reaction has not been developed technically.

Direct addition of nitrogen tetroxide to olefins gives dinitroparaffins as the main product. The olefin was reacted in the liquid phase with excess nitrogen tetroxide, alone or diluted with a suitable solvent, at about 0° c.

---

[12] B.I.O.S. 266.
[13] B.I.O.S. 355.

Addition of nitrogen tetroxide always took place in two ways, giving the dinitroparaffin and a nitroalkyl nitrite; *e.g.*, with ethylene:

$$\begin{array}{c} CH_2 \\ \| \\ CH_2 \end{array} + \begin{array}{c} NO_2 \\ | \\ NO_2 \end{array} \longrightarrow \begin{array}{c} CH_2NO_2 \\ | \\ CH_2NO_2 \end{array}$$

$$\begin{array}{c} CH_2 \\ \| \\ CH_2 \end{array} + \begin{array}{c} NO_2 \\ | \\ NO_2 \end{array} \longrightarrow \begin{array}{c} CH_2NO_2 \\ | \\ CH_2ONO \end{array}$$

The nitroalkyl nitrites were never isolated; they were partly oxidised by excess nitrogen tetroxide to the nitroalkyl nitrates and partly hydrolysed during the isolation steps to the nitroalkyl alcohol:

$$\begin{array}{c} CH_2NO_2 \\ | \\ CH_2ONO \end{array} \left\{ \begin{array}{c} \xrightarrow{+ N_2O_4} \begin{array}{c} CH_2NO_2 \\ | \\ CH_2ONO_2 \end{array} + N_2O_3 \\ \\ \xrightarrow{+ H_2O} \begin{array}{c} CH_2NO_2 \\ | \\ CH_2OH \end{array} + HNO_2 \end{array} \right.$$

The three principal products isolated by this method are the dinitroparaffin, the nitroalkyl nitrate and the nitroalcohol; overall yields on olefin reacted may be as high as 75–80 per cent. Reaction of nitrogen tetroxide with ethylene, propylene, the butenes and some of the higher olefins has been described.[14]

Dinitroethane is a solid, m.p. 40° c., b.p. 135° c./5 mm. On acid hydrolysis, it gives two molecules of hydroxylamine. By rapid distillation with alcohol and rapid chilling, nitroethylene and ethyl nitrite are obtained:[15]

$$NO_2CH_2CH_2NO_2 + C_2H_5OH \rightarrow CH_2 : CHNO_2 + C_2H_5ONO + H_2O$$

Nitroethylene may also be obtained by dehydration of 2-nitroethyl alcohol or by elimination of acids from nitroethyl esters (see also Chapter 6, p. 84, and Hass and Riley[16]):

$$NO_2CH_2CH_2OH \rightarrow CH_2 : CHNO_2 + H_2O$$
$$NO_2CH_2CH_2OCOR \rightarrow CH_2 : CHNO_2 + RCOOH$$

Other nitroolefins may be obtained in these ways; the higher members are accessible by the condensation of aldehydes or ketones with nitroparaffins (see Chapter 6, p. 84).

Nitroethylene boils at 98° c./760 mm. It is an extremely reactive substance, possessing in a high degree the addition reactions of an activated double bond. With alcohols, it gives 2-nitroethyl ethers:

$$CH_2 : CHNO_2 + ROH \rightarrow NO_2CH_2CH_2OR$$

---

[14] Levy and Scaife, *J. Chem. Soc.*, 1946, p. 1093, 1100; Levy, Scaife and Wilder Smith, *J. Chem. Soc.*, 1946, p. 1096; Levy and Rose, *Quarterly Reviews of the Chemical Society*, 1947, **1**, 358. See also I.C.I., B.P. 572949; B.P. 575604; B.P. 575618; U.S.P. 2384050.

[15] I.C.I., B.P. 572803.

[16] *Chem. Rev.*, 1943, **32**, 373.

These ethers can be obtained directly from dinitroethane and the alcohol with elimination of the alkyl nitrite.[17] With sulphites or bisulphites, it gives nitroethyl sulphonates :[18]

$$CH_2 : CHNO_2 + NaHSO_3 \rightarrow NO_2CH_2CH_2SO_2ONa$$

It readily adds to 1 : 3-dienes by the Diels-Alder reaction :

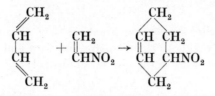

With traces of alkali, it gives a high polymer with great ease; this poly-nitroethylene can also be obtained from nitroethylene precursors such as dinitroethane or nitroethyl nitrate.[19] The higher nitroolefins with the NO_2 group directly attached to the unsaturated carbon atom react similarly.

Industrial outlets for these nitroolefins have not yet been developed.

Long chain olefins have been reacted with nitrosyl chloride followed by treatment with alkali sulphites to give long chain amino-alkyl sulphonates, used for a time as synthetic detergents.

The interaction of olefins and ammonia has been examined from time to time. With ethylene at 450° c. and 20 atma. pressure, over reduced ammonium molybdate catalyst, mixtures of the ethylamines are obtained;[20] these reaction conditions are similar to those required for the synthesis of the ethylamines from ethyl alcohol and ammonia (Chapter 20, p. 374).

With zinc sulphate on silica gel at 450° c., ethylene and ammonia are stated to give acetonitrile :[21]

$$CH_2 : CH_2 + NH_3 \rightarrow CH_3CN + 2H_2$$

The general reaction has been further examined since the war in America. In the Sinclair Refining Company's work,[22] reaction between the olefins and ammonia was carried out at high pressure and at about 350° c. in the presence of hydrogenation catalysts such as cobalt. Products from ethylene, propylene and the *n*-butenes included the straight chain amines and nitriles; from propylene, acrylonitrile was obtained :

$$CH_3CH : CH_2 + NH_3 \rightarrow CH_2 : CHCN + 3H_2$$

The yields appear to be too low for development of this process.

Socony-Vacuum Oil Co. operated at higher temperatures and lower

[17] I.C.I., B.P. 573872.
[18] I.C.I., B.P. 571157.
[19] I.C.I., B.P. 572891.
[20] I.G., D.R.P. 479079.
[21] Ellis, 'Chemistry of Petroleum Derivatives', *Reinhold*, Vol. 1, 1934, 571.
[22] Sinclair Ref., U.S.P. 2381470–3; 2381709; 2417892–3; 2419420; 2429855.

pressures with a less active hydrogenation catalyst and obtained acetonitrile as the main product from most olefins.[23] The general conditions involved reaction between the olefin, or an olefin-paraffin mixture, and ammonia at 470–500° c. and 1–6 atma. pressure over a molybdenum oxide-active alumina catalyst. The yield of acetonitrile on ammonia was moderate; conversion per pass was low and was best with ethylene. In one example, 40 mol per cent of ammonia with 60 mol per cent of propane—propylene fraction containing about 35 per cent of propylene at 470° c., 6 atma pressure and 20 seconds contact time, over a catalyst containing 10 per cent molybdenum oxide on active alumina gave 20 per cent conversion per pass to acetonitrile. The ultimate yield on ammonia was 42 per cent and on C_3 hydrocarbon, 94 per cent.

4. Reactions with derivatives of acids, etc.

Another set of olefin addition reactions is with carbon dioxide, acids, acid anhydrides and acid chlorides.

Carbon dioxide is stated to react with ethylene at high pressure and moderate temperature over acidic catalysts to give acrylic acid in poor yield.[24]

$$CH_2 : CH_2 + CO_2 \rightarrow CH_2 : CHCOOH$$

With acids, olefins form esters by direct addition:

$$\underset{R}{\overset{R}{>}}C = C\underset{R}{\overset{R}{<}} + R^1COOH \rightarrow \underset{R}{\overset{R}{>}}\underset{OCOR^1}{C}\!\!-\!\!CH\underset{R}{\overset{R}{<}}$$

The usual order of reactivity holds. Ethylene reacts with considerable difficulty; propylene and the higher *n*-olefins are moderately reactive. Isobutene and *tert*-olefins add acids relatively easily. Reaction has been most studied with acetic acid; it is carried out in presence of sulphuric acid as catalyst at slightly elevated temperature and, in the case of the lower olefins, under increased pressure. Boron trifluoride has also been claimed as a catalyst for this reaction.

According to Brooks,[25] the yields are not good enough for this route to compete with the usual method for making esters from olefins by hydration to the alcohol and esterification with acetic acid in the standard way (Chapter 18, p. 335). Another defect is the very considerable proportion of sulphuric acid required to act as a 'catalyst,' usually about 10–20 per cent by weight on the reactants. Isobutene acetylates much more readily than the *n*-butenes, but tertiary esters as a rule have little commercial value as solvents owing to their ease of hydrolysis.

---

[23] Denton and Bishop, *Ind. Eng. Chem.*, 1953, **45**, 282. Socony-Vacuum, U.S.P. 2450636–2450642; 2450 675–8.

[24] Rohm und Haas A-G., D.R.P. 553179.

[25] *Ind. Eng. Chem.*, 1935, **27**, 282.

Acid chlorides add on to olefins in inert solvents in presence of aluminium chloride, or, with the more reactive olefins, with zinc chloride, etc., to give unstable chloroketones which easily lose hydrogen chloride forming unsaturated ketones. The chloroketones can be isolated by working at low temperatures; carbon disulphide seems one of the most suitable solvents to use, at any rate for laboratory preparations. Ethylene reactions are illustrated:

$$CH_2 : CH_2 + CH_3COCl \rightarrow CH_2ClCH_2COCH_3 \rightarrow CH_2 : CHCOCH_3$$
$$CH_2 : CH_2 + C_6H_5COCl \rightarrow CH_2ClCH_2COC_6H_5 \rightarrow CH_2 : CHCOC_6H_5$$

Propylene and phosgene give 2-chloroisobutyryl chloride, which gives esters of methacrylic acid on reacting with alcohol.[26]

$$CH_3CH : CH_2 + COCl_2 \rightarrow CH_2ClCHCOCl + ROH \rightarrow CH_2 : \overset{\overset{\textstyle CH_3}{\textstyle |}}{C}COOR + 2HCl$$

Acid anhydrides add on to branch chain olefins to give unsaturated ketones directly, as was shown by Kondakoff in 1895. In later American work,[27] technical diisobutene, mainly 2 : 4 : 4-trimethyl-1-pentene, was condensed with acetic anhydride in presence of zinc chloride at 45° c. to give moderate yields of 4 : 6 : 6-trimethyl-3-heptene-2-one together with smaller quantities of the diketone from one mol of the olefin and two of the anhydride:

$$(CH_3)_3CCH_2\overset{\overset{\textstyle CH_3}{\textstyle |}}{C} : CH_2 + (CH_3CO)_2O \rightarrow (CH_3)_3CCH_2\overset{\overset{\textstyle CH_3}{\textstyle |}}{C} : CHCOCH_3 + CH_3COOH$$

$$+ \left| (CH_3CO)_2O \right.$$

$$\downarrow$$

$$(CH_3)_3CCH_2\overset{\overset{\textstyle CH_3}{\textstyle |}}{C} : C(COCH_3)_2$$

Somewhat related to these reactions is the addition of tertiary olefins to alcohols to give tertiary alkyl ethers. Reaction is carried out at 60° c. under pressure in presence of sulphuric acid as catalyst; as in the direct esterification of olefins, an equilibrium mixture is obtained which separates into two phases, the upper hydrocarbon layer containing the ether. The *tert*-alkyl ethers are readily hydrolysed by mineral acids but are stable under neutral or alkaline conditions; they are distinguished from the usual normal or secondary ethers by a very low tendency to form peroxides. The simplest member, methyl *tert*-butyl ether, $CH_3OC(CH_3)_3$, boils at 55° c.; a whole range of these *tert*-alkyl ethers have been prepared, and the method has even been extended to the preparation of *tert*-butyl phenyl ether,

---

[26] du Pont, U.S.P. 2028012.
[27] Byrns and Doumani, *Ind. Eng. Chem.*, 1943, **35**, 349.

$(CH_3)_3COC_6H_5$, b.p. 185–6° c., which rearranges to *p-tert*-butylphenol with aluminium chloride under mild conditions.[28]

5. Reactions with aromatic compounds

Alkylation of aromatic hydrocarbons with olefins to give alkyl substituted aromatic hydrocarbons is dealt with in Chapter 14, p. 248. Nuclear alkylation of phenols proceeds more readily and is operated industrially on a considerable scale. The reaction is catalysed by mineral acids, anhydrous metal chlorides, boron trifluoride and related compounds. The olefin usually but not invariably substitutes in the para position to the OH group if free.

The industrially important alkyl phenols made by this route are derived largely from isobutene, methylethylethylene, and diisobutene, condensed with phenol or with the methyl substituted phenols occurring in coal tar or in certain petroleum fractions (Chapter 21, p. 385). *tert*-Butylphenol is manufactured from phenol and isobutene in the presence of sulphuric acid, using for example the butane-butene fraction obtained from many cracking processes (Chapter 7, p. 115), only the isobutene reacting. It can also be made from phenol and diisobutene at high temperature, or from phenol and *tert*-butyl alcohol or *tert*-butyl chloride. At moderate temperatures, phenol and diisobutene give 1 : 1 : 3 : 3-tetramethylbutylphenol (*tert*-octylphenol):

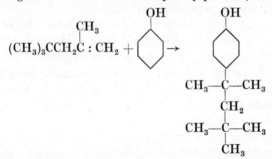

This *tert*-octylphenol can be made in over 90% yield from excess of phenol and diisobutene with a trace of sulphuric acid at 120° c.; above 140° c., the main product is *tert*-butylphenol, the diisobutene molecule splitting into two fragments. At low temperatures, *e.g.*, 50° c., *tert*-olefins give considerable proportions of the ortho-substituted phenols; these rearrange to the corresponding para-substituted phenol on heating to 150° c. with a trace of sulphuric acid:

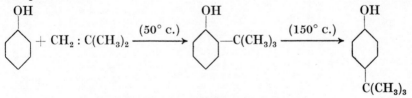

[28] Evans and Edlund, *Ind. Eng. Chem.*, 1936, **28**, 1186.

Di-substituted *tert*-alkyl phenols can be obtained from the mono *tert*-alkyl phenol and a second mol of the olefin under the conditions indicated above:[29]

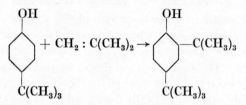

p-tert-Amylphenol is made from phenol and the isopentenes arising as a by-product in the manufacture of technical amyl alcohols from chloro-pentanes (Chapter 5, p. 74) by reaction with sulphuric acid at 50° c. The normal pentenes do not react under these conditions but give *sec*-amyl-phenols and di-*sec*-amylphenols with phenol in presence of sulphuric acid above 100° c. and at 10 atma pressure.[30]

p-tert-Butylphenol and *p-tert*-amylphenol are intermediates for oil soluble phenol-formaldehyde resins and bactericides. *tert*-Octylphenol has been claimed as a bactericide and fungicide. Diamylphenol is a soil fumigant. The *tert*-butyl xylenols, such as 2 : 4 dimethyl-6-*tert*-butylphenol, are gum inhibitors for petrol and anti-oxidants.

A range of alkyl phenols is manufactured from phenol, cresol or β-naphthol and various medium chain length olefins for subsequent condensation with ethylene oxide to give detergents. The alkylation is usually carried out by reaction between equimolar proportions of the reactants at 50° c. using boron trifluoride as catalyst. At completion, the catalyst is washed out with water and any unchanged phenol and olefin removed by steam distillation.[31]

Another method uses a mixture of active clay and zinc chloride as the catalyst; phenol was alkylated with dodecene (propylene tetramer) using this catalyst at 165–170° c., to give isododecylphenol which was employed as a plasticiser for nylon and an intermediate for detergents.[32]

---

[29] Monsanto, U.S.P. 2189805.
[30] Kenyon, Inskeep, Gillette and Price, *Ind. Eng. Chem.*, 1950, **42**, 2388.
[31] C.I.O.S. 26/2.
[32] F.I.A.T. 1039.

CHAPTER 12

DIOLEFINS

THE only diolefins of technical importance are the conjugated 1 : 3-diolefins which yield synthetic rubbers on polymerisation, either by themselves or in conjunction with other polymerisable monomers. Synthetic rubber was of such vital importance to the warring nations that tremendous efforts were devoted to the synthesis of the necessary starting materials; the methods worked out and employed were conditioned by the availability of raw materials and, in some cases, even of constructional materials in the various countries.

The best route to make the various dienes required and the relative importance of the different synthetic rubbers is slowly emerging under the conditions of freer economy operating since the end of the war.

1. Butadiene

This is the most important diene, being the basis of GR–S (America) and the Bunas (Germany).

In America, the routes employed were (i) from oil sources, (ii) from ethyl alcohol by a two-stage process. Russia employed a one-stage process from ethyl alcohol. The two German routes both started from acetylene. The main route was from acetaldehyde via 1 : 3-butane diol; the second proceeded via butyne diol and 1 : 4-butane diol. Work had also been carried out in America on one-stage processes from n-butane and from ethyl alcohol, and on a process from 2 : 3-butane diol.

In America, the ethyl alcohol route appears to have been abandoned. Western Germany is adopting a one-stage process from n-butane. In Great Britain, butadiene will initially be obtained from the C_4 fraction obtained in the high temperature steam cracking of naphtha to ethylene, $i.e.$, as a by-product, and subsequently from n-butenes.

(a) OIL ROUTES TO BUTADIENE

On high temperature cracking of normally liquid hydrocarbons, some butadiene is always formed and is isolated in the C_4 fraction (see Chapter 7). The ease of formation of butadiene from the various types of hydrocarbons increases in the order aromatics < paraffins < olefins < naphthenes < unsaturated naphthenes; butadiene is formed above about 650° c. and with short contact time (less than one second). At longer contact time, secondary reactions take place involving both the breakdown of butadiene and its participation in the building up of aromatic molecules (see Chapter 14, p. 242).

In a review of hydrocarbon routes to butadiene, Egloff and Hulla[1] noticed the particular tendency of C_2, C_4, and C_6 hydrocarbons to give butadiene. This diene is therefore likely to arise during thermal cracking in any one of three ways, (*i*) by polymerisation of ethylene, one of the primary products of cracking, (*ii*) by dehydrogenation of straight chain C_4 hydrocarbons, (*iii*) by chain or ring fission of and dehydrogenation of C_6 hydrocarbons:

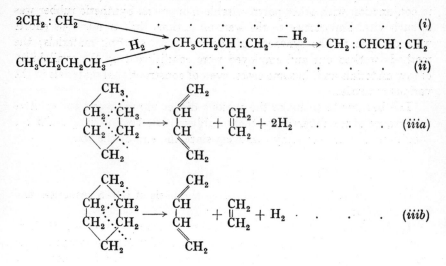

All these reactions can in fact be realised independently. It will be noticed that with the exception of the first half of route (*i*), they all involve increase in the number of molecules in the product. Butadiene formation is therefore favoured by cracking at ordinary or reduced pressure.

An illustration of the cracking of naphtha to butadiene is given by Berg, Sumner and Montgomery.[2] On the grounds that cyclohexane was the most suitable liquid hydrocarbon normally available for cracking to butadiene they chose a low boiling fraction of a highly naphthenic oil, containing about 50 per cent naphthenes (including methylcyclopentane). Best yields were obtained on pyrolising at 850° c. with added steam; contact time was 0·2–0·3 seconds, and the yield of butadiene was 27 per cent by weight on the naphtha feed.

Normal high temperature cracking of liquid hydrocarbons does not of course give this high yield of butadiene; in fact, the yield is at best only a few per cent. The butadiene is segregated in the C_4 fraction (see Chapter 7). Typical analyses of butadiene containing C_4 gases are given in Table 41 (from Chapter 7); the conditions of cracking are not stated.

---

[1] *Chem. Rev.*, 1944, **35**, 279.
[2] *Ind. Eng. Chem.*, 1945, **37**, 352.

TABLE 41

Analyses of C_4 fraction from conventional high temperature cracking processes

Hydrocarbon	%	%	%
Butanes	10–12	24	27
n-Butenes . . .	50–55	44	41
Isobutene . . .	20–24	21	11
Butadiene . . .	12–14	11	21
References	3	4	5

The butadiene can be isolated from this type of mixture by the methods described in Section 2 below. This source of butadiene was used in America at the beginning of their synthetic rubber programme and is being adopted in the United Kingdom.

The main petroleum route was, however, the catalytic dehydrogenation of the n-butenes, *e.g.*,

$$CH_3CH_2CH : CH_2 \rightarrow CH_2 : CHCH : CH_2 + H_2 \quad . \quad . \quad (1)$$

As described in Chapter 7, the n-butenes were available as by-products of cracking processes or were manufactured by catalytic dehydrogenation of n-butane. The catalytic dehydrogenation of the n-butenes to butadiene is very similar to the dehydrogenation of butane. It gives an equilibrium mixture at somewhat higher temperatures and will proceed over a similar type of catalyst. It is also endothermic and originally had to be operated semi-continuously owing to carbon deposition, the catalyst requiring periodical regeneration by burning with air.[6]

Information on the dehydrogenation step is given in a paper describing the process which supplied the bulk of the petroleum butadiene for the American synthetic rubber programme.[7]

For the reaction:

$$n\text{-}C_4H_8 \rightleftharpoons C_4H_6 + H_2 \quad . \quad . \quad (2)$$

the approximate free energy change over the range 700–1,000° K. is, from Table 22, p. 92, $\Delta G = 27,900 - 28 \cdot 6T$. The graph of equilibrium constant versus temperature is shown in Fig. 24.

From the equation for the change in free energy with temperature for

[3] Brooks, *Ind. Eng. Chem.*, 1935, **27**, 278.

[4] Birch and Tait, 'Science of Petroleum', *Oxford University Press*, 1938, Vol. 4, p. 2830.

[5] Standard Oil Development, B.P. 547730.

[6] Grosse, Mavity and Morrell, *Ind. Eng. Chem.*, 1940, **32**, 309. These workers employed an alumina base catalyst and worked at 600–650° c. and low pressure.

[7] Russell, Murphree and Asbury, *Trans. Amer. Inst. Chem. Eng.*, 1946, **42**, 1.

reaction (2), the equilibrium conversion has been calculated at 1 atma. and at 0·1 atma.; the calculated conversions and per cent butadiene at

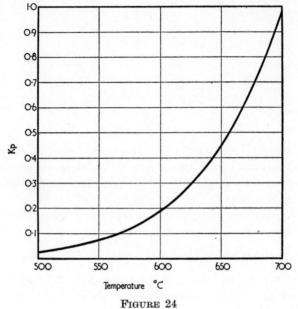

FIGURE 24

Butadiene from n-*butenes. Variation of equilibrium constant with temperature*

equilibrium are given in Table 42. The equilibrium is favoured by reduced pressure.

TABLE 42

Equilibrium in reaction, $n\text{-}C_4H_8 \rightleftharpoons C_4H_6 + H_2$

Temperature °C.	ΔG	K_p	1 atmosphere		0·1 atmosphere	
			Conversion n-butene %	Butadiene in exit gases %	Conversion n-butene %	Butadiene in exit gases %
500	5,776	0·023	15·1	13·1	43·4	30·3
600	2,916	0·186	39·6	28·3	80·6	44·6
700	56	0·970	70·2	41·2	95·2	48·8

In practice, there is an upper limit to temperature of about 700° c. to avoid cracking of the *n*-butenes and polymerisation and coking of the butadiene; an operating temperature range of 625–675° c. and a contact time of 0·2 second was chosen. Low partial pressure was selected both because of the more favourable equilibrium and to reduce polymerisation of butadiene.

Under the best conditions, thermal dehydrogenation of *n*-butenes gave an overall yield of butadiene of only 40 per cent; catalytic dehydrogenation was therefore selected.

The low partial pressure of n-butenes required was achieved by operating in presence of steam as diluent; this avoided periodical cycles of air burning to remove carbon deposited on the catalyst, as the carbon was removed by the steam by the water gas reaction:

$$C + H_2O \rightarrow CO + H_2$$

Employment of steam also solved many engineering and design problems, such as provision of preheat and of the endothermic heat of the reaction. A large excess of superheated steam was mixed with the preheated feedstock, before the reactor. The use of steam, however, introduces the serious difficulty that the conventional dehydrogenation catalysts such as chromic oxide on alumina were unsuitable for use in its presence.

The war-time and post war development work on catalysts has been described by Kearby.[8] The war-time catalyst used was known as catalyst 1707; it had the composition 72·4% (by wt.) magnesium oxide, 18·4% ferric oxide, 4·6% cupric oxide, 4·6% potassium oxide. This catalyst still gave some carbon deposition resulting in shorter operating cycles or longer regeneration periods, during which steam containing no butene was passed over the catalyst. With a 7 : 1 steam to butene ratio at 650° c., regeneration steaming was required for 10 minutes each one or two hours. At these high temperatures, the potassium carbonate, which is essential to maintain long life and to repress carbon deposition, is sufficiently volatile to be gradually stripped from the catalyst, and it had to be continually replenished.

This catalyst has now been replaced by an unsupported ferric oxide-chromic oxide-potassium oxide catalyst (Catalyst No. 105) because of much longer life (1 week as against 1 hour) and ability to operate at high steam to butene ratios without intermittent regeneration. A further modification is the calcination of these potassium promoted iron oxide catalysts at 800–950° c.[9]

Finally, the Dow Chemical Co.'s Catalyst Type B, calcium nickel phosphate containing a little chromic oxide, has attracted great attention because it gives a 90% selectivity† at 35% conversion compared with 70% selectivity at the same conversion from Catalyst No. 105; it requires hourly regeneration and a steam/butene ratio of at least 20 : 1.[10] This catalyst has been proved at Sarnia. Since the war, the target has moved

---

[8] *Ind. Eng. Chem.*, 1950, **42**, 295.

[9] Shell Development, U.S.P. 2408139, 2408140, 2461147.

† Selectivity $= \dfrac{\text{Yield butadiene per pass}}{\text{Conversion butenes per pass}} =$ ultimate yield.

[10] Britton, Dietzler and Noddings, *Ind. Eng. Chem.*, 1951, **43**, 2871; Noddings, Heath and Covey, *Ind. Eng. Chem.*, 1955, **47**, 1373.

from maximum butadiene production to maximum yield and minimum steam utilisation.

The I.G. have also described catalysts suitable for continuous operation for the dehydrogenation of n-butenes to butadiene in presence of steam.[11] These were based on zinc oxide promoted with calcium chromate and alumina. n-Butenes and steam in the mol ratio 1 : 6 gave, at 580° c. and 20% conversion per pass, overall yields of about 70 per cent butadiene. The catalyst used was similar to one developed by them for the reaction of dehydrogenation of ethylbenzene to styrene in presence of steam.[12]

The American process was operated in large reactors, 16 ft. diameter with 1·5–6 ft. catalyst bed. A cyclic process was adopted in which the carbon deposited on the catalyst was removed with steam every two hours; this eliminated wasteful periods of purging when using air burning for catalyst regeneration. The steam-butene ratio was about 15–20 : 1. The conversion per pass was 30 per cent with a selectivity of 65 per cent so that the butadiene content of the reactor gases was about 20 per cent. The products from the reactor were quenched immediately. The overall yield of isolated butadiene on butene consumed was about 0·55–0·6 lb./lb. Yields of 70 per cent and even higher are now being obtained in the United States on the full scale, using the new catalysts described by Kearby.[13] The butadiene was isolated by the copper liquor method (Section 1, b, iii).

The so-called one-stage process to butadiene gives similar gas mixtures; this has been briefly described.[14] n-Butane was dehydrogenated at 565° c. and 5–10 mm. pressure in A; butadiene was removed in B and the mixture of butane and the n-butenes dehydrogenated at 600° c. and 0·2 atma. over chromia-alumina catalyst in fixed bed reactors, the on-stream time being only 10 minutes before regeneration was necessary. The exit gases were combined with gases from treatment of n-butane, compressed, and butadiene extracted with a solvent. The flow of gases is given in Fig. 25.

This process has been operated at one plant in the United States and has now been selected for making butadiene on a scale of 45,000 tons p.a. in West Germany; the weight yield of butadiene on n-butane is expected to be about 50 per cent; about 25 per cent of n-butenes is also obtained.

(b) SEPARATION OF BUTADIENE

The reactor gases from pyrolysis of butenes or n-butane consist of butenes, which have to be recovered and recycled, butadiene and hydrogen, Some C_1, C_2 and C_3 hydrocarbons, due to unavoidable chain rupture reactions, and traces of highly unsaturated C_3, C_4 and C_5 hydrocarbons are

[11] B.P. 524918.
[12] C.I.O.S. 27/6 and 22/21.
[13] Chem. Week, Feb. 20, 1954, p. 15.
[14] Chem. Eng., Sept. 1955, p. 108.

also present. As in cracking processes, separation of the C_4 fraction is easy; the next problem is the isolation of butadiene from these C_4 hydrocarbons.

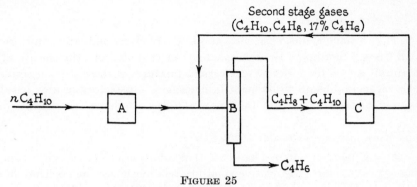

FIGURE 25

Butadiene. One-stage process

The boiling points of the C_4 hydrocarbons are (Table 43):

TABLE 43

Boiling points of C_4 hydrocarbons

Hydrocarbon	Formula	b.p., ° c./760 mm.
Isobutane	$\frac{CH_3}{CH_3}{>}CHCH_3$	$-$ 11·7
Isobutene	$\frac{CH_3}{CH_3}{>}C : CH_2$	$-$ 6·9
1-Butene	$CH_3CH_2CH : CH_2$	$-$ 6·3
Butadiene	$CH_2 : CHCH : CH_2$	$-$ 4·4
n-Butane	$CH_3CH_2CH_2CH_3$	$-$ 0·5
trans-2-Butene . . .	$\begin{array}{c}CH_3CH\\ \|\|\\ HCCH_3\end{array}$	$+$ 0·9
cis-2-Butene	$\begin{array}{c}CH_3CH\\ \|\|\\ CH_3CH\end{array}$	$+$ 3·7

Only a partial separation can be effected by fractional distillation owing to the closeness of the boiling points and the formation of mixtures with abnormal vapour pressures; for example, *n*-butane and butadiene form an azeotrope. However, separation and isolation of pure butadiene can be effected by physical methods which alter the relative volatilities of the C_4 hydrocarbons, and by chemical methods based on the greater reactivity of butadiene. These methods are:

(*i*) Solvent extraction

(*ii*) Azeotropic and extractive distillation

(*iii*) Absorption in solvents to form chemical complexes

(*iv*) Formation of chemical compounds which are separated and decomposed to regenerate the pure diene.

The two most widely used methods are extractive distillation with furfural and absorption in aqueous copper ammonium acetate.

(i) Solvent extraction

The solvents claimed include various glycol esters and ethers, furfural and bases.[15] Smith and Braun[16] examined methyl alcohol, ethylene glycol, furfural and triethanolamine and various mixtures of these; they describe the various problems to be faced in devising a satisfactory process based on solvent extraction. No suitable process appears to have been developed.

(ii) Azeotropic and extractive distillation

It was pointed out in Chapter 2 that addition of certain third components would alter the relative volatility relationships of monoolefins and diolefins of the same boiling point. This is therefore a possible method of purification and these improved distillation methods are in fact widely used. Azeotropic distillation is illustrated by the use of ammonia as entrainer.[17] This was employed by the Dow Chemical Co. on a scale of over 1,000 tons per month at the beginning of the American synthetic rubber drive. They had available a C_4 fraction containing 50 per cent of butadiene from a plant producing ethylene from oil under very severe cracking conditions. The principal other constituents were 1-butene (35–40 per cent), isobutene (5–10 per cent), and smaller amounts of 2-butenes, monovinylacetylene and methyl- and ethylacetylenes. Distillation was carried out in presence of ammonia at 16 atma. pressure; a curious feature of the system is that at this pressure, not only do most of the C_4 hydrocarbons form azeotropes with ammonia, but these azeotropes all boil at the same temperature, $39 \pm 1°$ c. Separation depends upon the fact that butadiene has the lowest volatility; the relative volatility for $C_4H_8 : C_4H_6$ is 1·3, and for $C_4H_{10} : C_4H_6$, 1·6. This process was considered to be cheaper than the alternative technical processes with a feed-stock containing more than 45 per cent butadiene; below 35 per cent butadiene, the copper liquor or furfural processes dealt with later were superior.

Sulphur dioxide has also been claimed as entrainer; a rather complex method of working up involving isomerisation of 1-butene to 2-butene, and addition of *n*-butane to assist the desired separation has been described.[18]

Turning to extractive distillation, furfural is used at the Port Neches butadiene plants, which produced 100,000 tons p.a. butadiene from refinery C_4 gases and is being adopted by I.C.I. in the United Kingdom. Extractive

[15] I.G., B.P. 319025.
[16] *Ind. Eng. Chem.*, 1945, **37**, 1047.
[17] Dow, B.P. 526387; Poffenberger, Horsley, Nutting and Britton, *Trans. Amer. Inst. Chem. Eng.*, 1946, **42**, 815.
[18] Phillips Pet, U.S.P. 2382473.

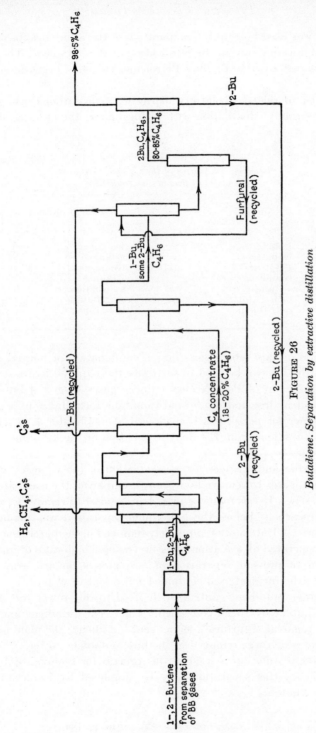

FIGURE 26

Butadiene. Separation by extractive distillation

distillation was used both in the preparation of the *n*-butenes for dehydrogenation, and as one step in the purification of the butadiene. The process used (developed by the Phillips Petroleum Co.) has been described in detail.[19]

The order of relative volatility of the C_4 hydrocarbons was given in Table 43; extractive distillation with furfural alters the order as shown in Table 44.

TABLE 44

Relative volatilities of the C_4 hydrocarbons
(in order of decreasing volatility)

Normal	In the presence of furfural
Isobutane	Isobutane
Isobutene	*n*-Butane
1-Butene	Isobutene
Butadiene	1-Butene
n-Butane	*trans*-2-Butene
trans-2-Butene	*cis*-2-Butene
cis-2-Butene	Butadiene

Inspection of this table shows how a combination of normal and extractive distillation can be used to segregate the required hydrocarbons.

The working up of Port Neches refinery gases to give 1-butene and 2-butene for dehydrogenation, *n*- and isobutane for refinery uses and isobutene polymer for petrol has been described in Chapter 7, p. 117. The isolation of butadiene from the dehydrogenation of the *n*-butenes is illustrated in Fig. 26.

The absorber and stripper for concentration of the C_4 gases after the dehydrogenator was to remove hydrogen; it employed the usual absorbent (? light kerosene). It was followed by a depropaniser to remove C_3 and any lighter hydrocarbons before the first rough separation was made in the 2-butene tower. 1-Butene was completely removed in the butadiene solvent tower. This operated at 4–5 atma. pressure, using a high ratio of furfural to hydrocarbon to prevent separation of two phases on any tray in the fractionator; the furfural used contained 4 per cent of water.

The average butadiene content of the feed to this tower was 27·6 per cent; the 1-butene overhead contained 1·4 per cent butadiene and the C_4 gases (after removal of furfural), 85 per cent butadiene; the main impurity was 2-butene which was removed in the final butadiene tower.

Extractive distillation is used in this process for removal of 1-butene from butadiene; this separation may be simplified by isomerisation of 1-butene to 2-butene.

---

[19] Happel *et al.*, *Trans. Amer. Inst. Chem. Eng.*, 1946, **42**, 189.

(iii) Complex formation with metallic solutions

Butadiene forms complexes with cuprous salts which can be used to separate it from the other C_4 hydrocarbons. Ammoniacal cuprous chloride was described in 1935 as a good method of removing butadiene quantitatively from admixture with *n*-butenes. The method is selective and nearly quantitative. The improved copper liquors developed for ethylene absorption (Chapter 7, p. 103) have also been claimed for butadiene, *e.g.* pyridine acetate and ethanolamine solutions of cuprous chloride.[20, 21, 22] The solubility of butadiene in cuprous ethanolamine hydrochloride at 18° c. and 1 atma. pressure is 11 vol./vol. solvent, whilst the solubility of the *n*-butenes is only 1 vol./vol.

These copper ethanolamine liquors are not employed in practice.

On the alkaline side, the ethanolamine tended to reduce the cuprous salts to metallic copper. In neutral or acid solution, all copper liquors gave insoluble precipitates with butadiene. Therefore copper ammonium acetate was finally chosen and the method developed[23] by Standard Oil Development Co. was used for manufacture of 55 per cent of the butadiene from petroleum sources made in America in 1943–44. The solubility of the hydrocarbons present in quantity or in traces in the butadiene containing gases is shown in Table 45.

TABLE 45

Solubility of hydrocarbons in cuprous ammonium acetate containing 3 mols/litre cuprous ion, at 0° C. and 0·5 atma. hydrocarbon partial pressure

Hydrocarbon	Formula	Solubility
Allene (b.p. − 34·3° c.) . . .	$CH_2 : C : CH_2$	1·35
Isobutene	$(CH_3)_2C : CH_2$	0·02
1-Butene	$CH_3CH_2CH : CH_2$	0·07
1 : 3-Butadiene	$CH_2 : CHCH : CH_2$	0·7
trans-2-Butene	CH_3CH $\parallel$ $CHCH_3$	0·013
cis-2-Butene	CH_3CH $\parallel$ CH_3CH	0·028
1 : 2-Butadiene . . . . (methylallene, b.p. 10·3° c.)	$CH_3CH : C : CH_2$	1·15

Methyl-, ethyl- and vinylacetylenes, also present in traces, formed stable compounds with the cuprous salt; these acetylenes were removed by continuous polymerisation of a portion of the stripped copper liquor.

[20] Standard Oil Development, B.P. 568818.
[21] Distillers, B.P. 428106.
[22] Distillers, B.P. 573046.
[23] Morrell, Paltz, Packie, Asbury, and Brown, *Trans. Amer. Inst. Chem. Eng.*, 1946, **42**, 471.

The simplified flowsheet of the process is shown in Fig. 27, based on the paper by Morrell *et al.*[23]

Three operations were involved. Firstly, absorption of butadiene and some of the other hydrocarbons which was carried out in A. Secondly, the butadiene solution was enriched in B by removal of the less soluble components by recycling concentrated butadiene from the top of Column C

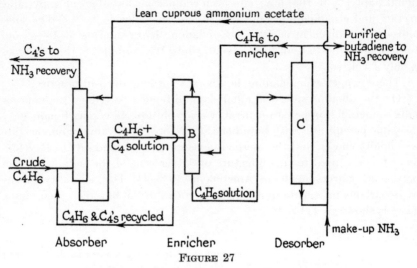

FIGURE 27

Butadiene separation by the copper liquor process

to the base of Column B. The gases given off from the enricher were recycled to the absorber. Thirdly, the purified butadiene was desorbed in C, from the base of which lean cuprous ammonium acetate was recycled to the head of the absorber, A.

Butadiene made by pyrolysis of *n*-butenes and purified with copper ammonium acetate is at least 98% pure, the main impurity being *n*-butene; C_3 hydrocarbons and more highly unsaturated C_4 hydrocarbons are present in barely detectable amounts.[24]

(iv) Compound formation

Formation of a solid compound between solid cuprous chloride and gaseous butadiene has been claimed as a method of separation.[25] Some attention has been paid to the formation of the cyclic monomeric sulphones with sulphur dioxide. These are obtained by heating the two components

[24] Starr and Ratcliff, *Ind. Eng. Chem.*, 1946, **38**, 1020.
[25] An example is Phillips Pet., U.S.P. 2401114.

under pressure; the reaction is reversible and at a higher temperature, the sulphone splits up again into its generators, *e.g.*,

$$CH_2 : CHCH : CH_2 + SO_2 \rightleftharpoons \underset{\underset{SO_2}{\diagdown \diagup}}{\overset{\overset{CH = CH}{\mid \quad \mid}}{CH_2 \quad CH_2}}$$

Butadiene sulphone is a solid, m.p. 65° c. On heating to about 125° c., it decomposes into butadiene and sulphur dioxide. The general method is to combine the generators at moderate temperature and elevated pressure, separate the non-diene hydrocarbons, and decompose the sulphone by further heating at ordinary pressure. Sulphur dioxide is usually removed from the butadiene by water scrubbing; one recent method decomposes the sulphone in presence of a non-hydroxylic solvent for one of the components, *e.g.*, light kerosene, which dissolves butadiene but is immiscible with sulphur dioxide. This is claimed to avoid corrosion troubles.[26] The process is not used for butadiene.

(c) ROUTES FROM ETHYL ALCOHOL

Since in several countries ethyl alcohol from petroleum is cheaper than from fermentation processes (Chapter 8), ethyl alcohol processes can be claimed as petroleum routes to butadiene. During the war, however, the butadiene made from ethyl alcohol in Russia and in America was derived almost wholly from fermentation ethyl alcohol.

The Russian process is a one-stage catalytic vapour phase reaction, using a mixture of alumina and zinc oxide, which act to bring about simultaneous dehydrogenation and dehydration. Reaction conditions are 400° c. and reduced pressure, *e.g.*, 0·25 atma.[27]

$$2C_2H_5OH \rightarrow C_4H_6 + 2H_2O + H_2$$

Catalyst life was about 12 hours when carbon deposition compelled interruption of production and regeneration by burning in air. The yield was believed to be about 50 per cent.

This process was examined both in Germany and in the United States but was not taken to the full scale. The Germans developed a supported magnesia catalyst promoted with a small percentage of cobalt or chromium oxides. They reported 60 per cent yields at 270–300° c. (this seems unusually low) and atmospheric pressure.[28]

The Americans developed a similar catalyst containing 59 per cent magnesia, 2 per cent chromic oxide and 39 per cent silica gel. This gave

---

[26] Dow, U.S.P. 2384376.
[27] Lebedev, B.P. 331482.
[28] B.I.O.S. 1060.

overall yields of 56 per cent at 38% conversion per pass, the optimum temperature being 400–425° c.[29]

The mechanism of the reaction appears to follow the same course as the Ostromisslenski or Carbide and Carbon Chemicals Corporation's synthesis.

At the beginning of the first world war, Ostromisslenski showed that ethyl alcohol and acetaldehyde gave some butadiene when passed over catalysts in the vapour phase:

$$C_2H_5OH + CH_3CHO \rightarrow C_4H_6 + 2H_2O$$

This discovery formed the basis of the Carbide and Carbon Chemicals Corporation's process, which supplied the major proportion of America's synthetic butadiene in 1943–44. Owing to the intrinsic high cost of ethyl alcohol, this process is now more expensive than the butene route.

In the American process, a mixture of 69 per cent by weight ethyl alcohol, 24 per cent acetaldehyde and 7 per cent water, obtained by partial dehydrogenation of the ethyl alcohol over a standard copper catalyst, was passed at atmospheric pressure over a 2% tantalum oxide 98% silica gel catalyst at 325–350° c. at a space velocity of 0·4 to 0·6 l.hr.$^{-1}$. The catalyst required regeneration every 4 to 5 days.[29]

A very complex mixture was obtained. The products, expressed as a per cent theory of ethyl alcohol consumed, were:

Product	% of theory
CH_4	0·1
C_2H_4	3·9
C_2H_6	0·1
C_3H_6	1·7
C_3H_8	0·1
C_4H_6	63·9
C_4H_8	1·4
C_5 hydrocarbons	0·9
C_6 hydrocarbons	4·0
C_8 hydrocarbons	0·2
Methyl ethyl ether	0·3
Diethyl ether	8·0
Ethyl vinyl ether	0·2
Butyraldehyde and methyl ethyl ketone	0·3
Ethyl acetate	1·2
Diethylacetal	1·2
Crotonaldehyde	0·1
Butyl and crotyl alcohols	1·2
Butyl acetate	0·1
Acetic acid	1·4
C_6 oxygen containing compounds	0·7
Unidentified	3·8
Loss	5·2
	100·0

The ethylene, butenes, diethyl ether and butyl alcohol, representing about 15 per cent of the ethyl alcohol consumed, could be usefully employed

[29] Corson, Jones, Welling, Hinckly and Stahly, *Ind. Eng. Chem.*, 1950, **42**, 359.

either by recycling or in other directions. The overall yield of butadiene on ethyl alcohol was 63 per cent at a conversion per pass of 30–35 per cent.

The American workers considered that their synthesis proceeded through the intermediate formation of crotonaldehyde and that the Lebedev synthesis proceeded by the same mechanism, the acetaldehyde required being provided in this case by dehydrogenation *in situ* of the ethyl alcohol. The steps they suggest are:

$$C_2H_5OH \rightarrow CH_3CHO + H_2$$
$$2CH_3CHO \rightarrow CH_3CH : CHCHO + H_2O$$
$$CH_3CH_2OH + CH_3CH : CHCHO \rightarrow CH_2 : CHCH : CH_2 + CH_3CHO + H_2O$$

The impurities obtained in the Carbide and Carbon process are very similar to those reported in the direct ethyl alcohol process.

In the Carbide and Carbon process, the silica gel in the catalyst is believed to catalyse the dehydration to crotonaldehyde, and the tantalum oxide the 'deoxygenation' of crotonaldehyde to butadiene.

(d) ROUTES FROM ACETYLENE

All the butadiene required for synthetic rubber in Germany was manufactured from acetylene, another example of how almost all the German aliphatic chemical industry was based on carbide and acetylene up to and during the second world war.

The main process proceeded in four steps from acetylene:

$$CH : CH + H_2O \rightarrow CH_3CHO$$
$$2CH_3CHO \rightarrow CH_3CHOHCH_2CHO$$
$$CH_3CHOHCH_2CHO + H_2 \rightarrow CH_3CHOHCH_2CH_2OH$$
$$CH_3CHOHCH_2CH_2OH \rightarrow CH_2 : CHCH : CH_2 + 2H_2O$$

Manufacture of acetaldehyde and aldol is dealt with in Chapter 16, pp. 287, 289. The hydrogenation of aldol to 1 : 3-butane diol was carried out in the liquid phase at 300 atm. and 50–150° c., using as a catalyst copper promoted with chromic oxide on silica. To remove the heat of hydrogenation, a high ratio of recycle to make-up hydrogen was used; the aldol and hydrogen were passed co-current down the reactor.

Crude aldol was used for the hydrogenation and the butane diol contained the hydrogenated impurities such as ethyl and *n*-butyl alcohols derived from traces of acetaldehyde and crotonaldehyde; it was purified by fractionation and dehydrated in the vapour phase to butadiene at 280° c. and 1 atma. pressure using sodium phosphate on coke as catalyst. This catalyst was prepared from sodium phosphate, butylamine phosphate and phosphoric acid; on heating it gave a mixture of $NaPO_3$ and $Na_2P_2O_7$. The metaphosphate was inactive, dehydration depending on the pyrophosphate content. The butane diol was vaporised and preheated to 210° c.,

8

when it was mixed with steam at 400° c. to give the desired reaction temperature. The dehydration is endothermic, ΔH_{298} for the vapour phase reaction being about $+$ 30–35 k. cal., and the reactor had a large number of flat pancake heating coils arranged at short intervals along its length to supply this heat whilst keeping within the required temperature range; each reactor was about 5 m. high and 3·5 m. diameter, and was provided with about twenty of the pancake heating coils. The products contained, besides butadiene, about 10 per cent of allyl carbinol, $CH_2 : CHCH_2CH_2OH$, and small percentages of butyraldehyde, ethylhexenal, propylene and n-butenes. The butadiene was worked up by compression and water scrubbing, followed by distillation at normal pressure; the butadiene was 99·5% pure and was substantially free of active oxygen and of acetaldehyde. The yield of butadiene on 1 : 3-butane diol was 81 per cent, and the overall yield of butadiene on acetylene was 60 per cent.[30]

The second acetylene route was based upon Reppe's discovery of the synthesis of 1 : 4-butyne diol from acetylene and formaldehyde:

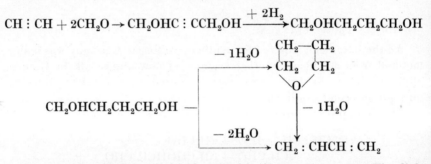

Preparation of butyne diol is described in Chapter 15, p. 275. The diol, as a 35–40% aqueous solution, was reduced to 1 : 4-butane diol at 200–300 atm. and 40–130° c. with a large excess of hydrogen using a nickel-copper-manganese silica catalyst.[31] ΔH for the hydrogenation is $-$ 65 k. cal./g.mol. Dehydration of the butane diol was carried out by a rather complex method. The diol mixed with excess of steam and with tetrahydrofuran was dehydrated at 280° c. and at atmospheric pressure over the same sodium phosphate catalyst used for 1 : 3-butane diol dehydration. The exit products contained butadiene and as much tetrahydrofuran as was present in the feed; in effect, but probably not actually, only the 1 : 4-butane diol was dehydrated, the tetrahydrofuran passing through unchanged.[32] Tetrahydrofuran itself was made by liquid phase dehydration of aqueous 1 : 4-butane diol (35–40% concentration) at 280° c. and 100 atm. pressure, using 0·3% phosphoric acid as catalyst.[31]

[30] C.I.O.S. 22/21.
[31] B.I.O.S. 367.
[32] C.I.O.S. 22/7.

The overall yield of butadiene on acetylene was about 70–75 per cent. It is not clear whether it is a more economic route than the aldol route, but it probably had attractions for operation under war conditions in Germany as it required only half the carbide and acetylene, the other half of the carbon skeleton being supplied from carbon monoxide via methyl alcohol and formaldehyde.

These acetylene routes are no longer attractive in Western Germany, which is setting up its post-war synthetic rubber programme on the basis of butadiene made by the one-stage dehydrogenation of *n*-butane (this Chapter, p. 198).

(*e*) OTHER ROUTES TO BUTADIENE

Routes to butadiene from chlorinated butanes have attracted attention since the earliest days of interest in synthetic rubber. The pyrolysis of the mixture of dichlorobutanes obtained on chlorination of 1- and 2-butenes was operated on the large scale during the early 1940's in America.[33] Pyrolysis was conducted at 500–550° c., and yields were probably of the order of 80 per cent. It seems unlikely that this route can now compete with processes not involving heavy chemicals.

2 : 3-Butane diol, which is obtained by a special fermentation process from molasses, has also been investigated on the semi-large scale as a route to butadiene. The diol itself dehydrates to methyl ethyl ketone, but its diacetate is pyrolised smoothly and in high yield on heating to 475–600° c. to butadiene and acetic acid, which is recycled :[34]

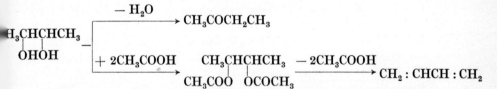

There are many other methods of making butadiene but none of them has so far been developed on any considerable scale; they are catalogued in Egloff and Hulla's two reviews of routes to butadiene from hydrocarbons,[1] and from oxygen containing compounds.[35]

2. Other diolefins

Although it is stated in German reports that only 2- and 2 : 3-substituted butadienes are valuable monomers for synthetic rubbers, the terminal substituted butadienes giving inferior products, the synthesis of the simplest substituted butadienes is included here since outlets for dienes are not necessarily restricted to synthetic rubbers.

---

[33] Hearne, *Oil and Gas J.*, Feb. 23, 1950, p. 163.
[34] I.C.I., B.P. 483989.
[35] *Chem. Rev.*, 1945, **36**, 63.

Piperylene, isoprene, and sometimes cyclopentadiene, are present in petrols made by high temperature cracking. Their separation from the saturated and monoolefinic hydrocarbons can be carried out by some of the methods outlined in Section 1 (*b*). They still have to be separated from one another; their boiling points are:

Piperylene	$CH_3CH : CHCH : CH_2$	b.p. $+ 43°$ c.
Isoprene	$CH_2 : C(CH_3)CH : CH_2$	b.p. $+ 34°$ c.
Cyclopentadiene	$\begin{array}{c} CH=\!\!=CH \\ \Big| \qquad \Big\rangle CH_2 \\ CH=\!\!=CH \end{array}$	b.p. $+ 42.5°$ c.

The most important C_5 dienes are cyclopentadiene and isoprene. They can be isolated from the C_5 fraction obtained in vapour phase cracking of naphtha at 650–750° c., which contains some 15–25 per cent of isoprene. The piperylene and cyclopentadiene are separated from the isoprene containing fraction by distillation, and the isoprene separated from the other C_5 hydrocarbons by extractive distillation with aqueous acetone; the copper ammonium acetate method is unsuitable.

From the higher boiling fraction, cyclopentadiene is separated by formation of its dimer, a solid melting at 32.9° c. and boiling at 170° c. (with decomposition) which can readily be depolymerised. The piperylene is then finally isolated by extractive distillation, once more with aqueous acetone.

The differential ease of formation of sulphones has also been suggested as a method of separating the C_5 dienes.[36, 37]

Pyrolysis of 1- and 2-pentene gives butadiene, not piperylene; trimethylethylene, however, gives isoprene on pyrolysis. Piperylene can be made from 1-pentene by catalytic dehydrogenation, for example at 585° c. over a bauxite catalyst in presence of excess inert gases; the overall yield of piperylene on 1-pentene was 40 per cent.[38]

Piperylene exists in two forms, boiling at 44.1° c./760 mm. and 42.0° c./760 mm. The higher boiling has been assigned the *cis* structure, and the lower boiling, the *trans* structure.[39]

cis-Piperylene does not form a crystalline Diels-Alder adduct with maleic anhydride but slowly gives a polymer. *trans*-Piperylene forms an adduct rapidly and quantitatively with maleic anhydride. Both piperylenes form the same cyclic sulphone, $\begin{array}{c} CH=\!\!=CH \\ \Big| \qquad \Big| \\ CH_2 \quad CHCH_3 \\ \diagdown \quad \diagup \\ SO_2 \end{array}$; on heating this regenerates only *trans*-piperylene.

[36] Phillips Pet., U.S.P. 2380831.
[37] Dow, U.S.P. 2381409.
[38] Phillips Pet., U.S.P. 2381693.
[39] Craig, *J. Amer. Chem. Soc.*, 1943, **65**, 1006.

Piperylene can also be synthesised from acetylene, acetaldehyde and formaldehyde:

$$CH : CH + CH_3CHO \rightarrow CH_3CHOHC : CH + CH_2O$$

$$\rightarrow CH_3CHOHC : CCH_2OH \xrightarrow{\ +\ 2H_2\ } CH_3CHOHCH_2CH_2CH_2OH$$

$$\xrightarrow{\ -\ 1H_2O\ } CH_3\underset{\diagdown O \diagup}{\overset{CH_2—CH_2}{CH \quad CH_2}} \xrightarrow{\ -\ 1H_2O\ } CH_3CH : CHCH : CH_2$$

The synthesis of isoprene from isopentene by catalytic dehydrogenation over an alumina base catalyst was described in 1940.[6] Details of this iso-pentene process are given by Mavity and Zetterholm.[40] The feed was isopentene or an isopentene-isopentane mixture. Dehydrogenation was carried out at 615–660° c. Products were separated into gas, isoprene, other C_5 hydrocarbons, which were recycled to the dehydrogenation, and heavier hydrocarbons. With isopentene at 0·1 atma. and 630° c., the C_5 cut contained 48 per cent isoprene. Yields of 80 per cent starting with iso-pentene and using a recycle process were indicated.

Isoprene can also be synthesised from acetylene and acetone by the following series of reactions:

$$\underset{CH_3}{\overset{CH_3}{>}}CO + CH : CH \rightarrow \underset{CH_3}{\overset{CH_3}{>}}C\underset{C : CH}{\overset{OH}{<}} \xrightarrow{\ +\ H_2\ } \underset{CH_3}{\overset{CH_3}{>}}C\underset{CH : CH_2}{\overset{OH}{<}}$$

$$\xrightarrow{\ -\ H_2O\ } CH_2 : \overset{CH_3}{\underset{|}{C}}CH : CH_2$$

At present, the isoprene wanted for making Butyl rubber is isolated from the C_5 fraction from high temperature cracking of naphtha. When wanted in larger quantities than are available from this by-product source, it will be made by catalytic dehydrogenation of isopentene.

2 : 3-Dimethyl-1 : 3-butadiene was made from acetone via pinacol in Germany during the 1914–18 war (see also Chapter 17, p. 319):

$$2\ \underset{CH_3}{\overset{CH_2}{>}}CO \xrightarrow{\ +\ H_2\ } CH_3—\overset{CH_3}{\underset{OH}{\overset{|}{C}}}—\overset{CH_3}{\underset{OH}{\overset{|}{C}}}—CH_3 \xrightarrow{\ -\ 2H_2O\ } CH_2 : \overset{CH_3}{\underset{|}{C}}—\overset{CH_3}{\underset{|}{C}} : CH_2$$

Two other dimethylbutadienes are accessible by catalytic liquid phase dehydration of 2-methyl-2 : 4-pentane diol with hydrochloric acid at 120–130° c.[41] The methylpentane diol was made from acetone via diacetone

---

[40] *Trans. Amer. Inst. Chem. Eng.*, 1944, **40,** 473.
[41] Shell Development, B.P. 572602.

alcohol (Chapter 17, p. 307). On dehydration, it gave both 1 : 3-dimethyl-1 : 3-butadiene (2-methyl-1 : 3-pentadiene) and 1 : 1-dimethyl-1 : 3-buta-diene (4-methyl-1 : 3-pentadiene):

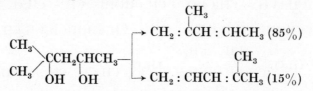

The semi-commercial product contains 85 per cent of the 1 : 3-dimethyl-butadiene and 15 per cent of the 1 : 1-dimethylbutadiene.[42]

The other important monosubstituted butadiene, 2-chlorobutadiene (chloroprene), $CH_2 : CClCH : CH_2$, the monomer of neoprene, is manufactured from acetylene via monovinylacetylene. Dimerisation of acetylene was brought about with cuprous ammonium chloride as catalyst (see Chapter 15, p. 279); monovinylacetylene adds a molecule of hydrogen chloride in presence of aqueous cuprous chloride to give momentarily 4-chloro-1 : 2-butadiene, by 1 : 4 addition, which immediately rearranges in the presence of cuprous chloride to 2-chloro-1 : 3-butadiene :

$$2CH \vdots CH \rightarrow CH \vdots CCH : CH_2 + HCl \rightarrow [CH_2 : C : CHCH_2Cl]$$

$$\xrightarrow{\text{(CuCl)}} CH_2 : CClCH : CH_2$$

The process can be carried out by introducing monovinylacetylene and hydrogen chloride simultaneously into a 5–25% aqueous solution of cuprous chloride containing 20–38% hydrochloric acid at 30–60° c. The chloroprene is carried off by unreacted gases, condensed and recovered. The process may be operated batchwise or continuously.[43]

Chloroprene can also be made from 2-butene by the following series of reactions :[44]

$$CH_3CH : CHCH_3 + Cl_2 \rightarrow CH_3CHClCHClCH_3 \xrightarrow[\substack{\text{(over BaCl}_2 \text{ at} \\ 215\text{–}235° \text{ c.)}}]{- HCl}$$

$$CH_3CCl : CHCH_3 + Cl_2 \xrightarrow[\substack{(35\text{–}40° \text{ c. in pres-} \\ \text{ence of FeCl}_3)}]{} CH_3CCl_2CHClCH_3$$

$$\xrightarrow[(470\text{–}520° \text{ c.)}]{- 2HCl} CH_2 : CClCH : CH_2$$

The last stage is carried out in the absence of catalysts and gives a yield of 60 per cent on the trichlorobutane.

---

[42] McMillan, Bishop, Marple and Evans, *I.R.W.*, 1946, **113**(5), 663.
[43] du Pont, B.P. 387325.
[44] du Pont, B.P. 535585–6; B.P. 564473.

Other routes to chloroprene include removal of hydrogen chloride catalytically or non-catalytically from other dichlorobutenes such as those made by addition of one molecule of chlorine to butadiene (see p. 214), and by pyrolysis of chlorinated cyclohexanes.

The boiling points of the dienes referred to are given in Table 46.

TABLE 46

Boiling points of 1 : 3-dienes

Butadiene	Formula	b.p. ° c./760 mm.
Butadiene	$CH_2 : CHCH : CH_2$	− 4·4
cis-Piperylene	$CH_3CH : CHCH : CH_2$	+ 44·1
trans-Piperylene . . .	$CH_3CH : CHCH : CH_2$	+ 42·0
Isoprene	$CH_2 : C(CH_3)CH : CH_2$	+ 34·1
Cyclopentadiene . .	$CH_2 \underset{CH : CH}{\overset{CH : CH}{\Big\langle}}$	+ 42·5
1 : 1-Dimethylbutadiene .	$CH_2 : CHCH : C(CH_3)_2$	+ 76·8
1 : 3-Dimethylbutadiene .	$CH_2 : C(CH_3)CH : CH(CH_3)$	+ 75·8
2 : 3-Dimethylbutadiene .	$CH_2 : C(CH_3)C(CH_3) : CH_2$	+ 69·6
2-Chlorobutadiene . .	$CH_2 : CClCH : CH_2$	+ 59·4

3. Uses and reactions of diolefins

The major outlet for diolefins is in the synthetic rubber field. Butadiene is used in butadiene-styrene (GR–S or Buna S) and butadiene-acrylonitrile (GR–N or Buna N) synthetic rubbers. In 1954, about 350,000 tons of butadiene were made; 89 per cent was used for GR–S rubbers, 4 per cent for nitrile rubbers and 7 per cent for nylon, emulsion paints and other resins.

The scope for the most important synthetic rubber, GR–S, has been enlarged in recent years by the development of low temperature polymerisation systems giving 'cold rubber', which possesses better properties, and by oil extension; in this process, up to 25 per cent of low cost petroleum oils can be incorporated into GR–S without loss of properties but with a considerable lowering of cost. By 1955, 70 per cent of all GR-S was made by the cold rubber process. The oil-extended rubbers were made using a tougher than normal cold rubber. A *cis*-1 : 4-polybutadiene, resembling natural rubber, has been prepared by a process similar to those used for *cis*-polyisoprene, referred to below. *trans*-1 : 4-Polybutadiene is a high softening paint resin.[45] By polymerisation in presence of sodium, a liquid polybutadiene resin has been obtained.[46] The interesting method of polymerising to very high molecular weight rubbers using sodium allyl and sodium isopropoxide catalysts – Alfin rubber – has not yet been established commercially.[47]

Butadiene is also used in other branches of the high polymer field,

[45] Weil, *Pet. Proc.*, September 1956, p. 100.
[46] Phillips Pet., U.S.P. 2577677; 2636910: 2638460.
[47] Morton, *Ind. Eng. Chem.*, 1950, **42**, 1488.

principally in high styrene butadiene polymers used in emulsion water paints and in synthetic shoe soling material. A butadiene-sodium polymer is used as a source of mixed sebacic acids (Chapter 18, p. 333).

Isoprene is used as the minor constituent of butyl rubber (98% iso-butylene – 2% isoprene). It has now been successfully polymerised to *cis*-1 : 4-polyisoprene, which closely resembles natural rubber and therefore now permits the manufacture of all types of rubbers independent of plantations. The polymerisation is carried out either with 0·1 per cent of lithium at 30–40° c.[48] or with metal alkyl catalysts of the Ziegler type (Chapter 7, p. 124) under conditions which have not yet been published.[49] 2-Chloroprene is the source of neoprene; the other diolefins are not yet used for synthetic rubbers.

The dienes undergo most of the usual olefin reactions; the ones of technical interest are chlorination, the Diels Alder reaction and addition of sulphur dioxide.

Reaction of butadiene with 1 mol of chlorine gives both 1 : 2- and 1 : 4-addition:

$$CH_2 : CH \cdot CH : CH_2 + Cl_2 \longrightarrow \begin{cases} CH_2 : CHCHClCH_2Cl \\ CH_2ClCH : CHCH_2Cl \end{cases}$$

The two dichlorobutenes can be readily isomerised so that either can be made the main product of addition.

3 : 4-Dichloro-1-butene boils at 45° c., 1 : 4-dichloro-2-butene at 76° c. Both dichlorobutenes on heating with caustic potash give chloroprene.

This reaction is not believed to be operated technically. More important is the reaction of these dichlorobutenes with sodium cyanide in presence of cuprous chloride to give 1 : 4-dicyanobutene. On hydrogenation, this gives adiponitrile and then hexamethylene diamine, which is the amine half of the nylon molecule:

$$CH_2ClCH : CHCH_2Cl + 2NaCN \rightarrow CNCH_2CH : CHCH_2CN \xrightarrow{H_2}$$

$$CNCH_2CH_2CH_2CH_2CN \xrightarrow{4H_2} NH_2(CH_2)_6NH_2$$

This process is operated on a scale of over 10,000 tons p.a. as one of the routes by which du Pont manufacture nylon.

Most, but not all, dienes form crystalline monomeric sulphones on heating under pressure with sulphur dioxide. Reaction is reversible, and at higher temperatures, the sulphones dissociate into their generators:

$$CH_2 : CHCH : CH_2 + SO_2 \rightleftharpoons \begin{array}{c} CH=CH \\ | \quad\quad | \\ CH_2 \quad CH_2 \\ \diagdown \quad\diagup \\ SO_2 \end{array}$$

---

[48] Stavely *et al.*, *Ind. Eng. Chem.*, 1956, **48**, 778.
[49] Horne *et al.*, *Ind. Eng. Chem.*, 1956, **48**, 784.

This process has been suggested for isolation of dienes from less unsaturated hydrocarbons, and for separation of individual dienes from one another.

Properties of sulphones from some 1 : 3-dienes are given in Table 47.

TABLE 47

Properties of sulphones of 1 : 3-dienes

Diene	m.p. of sulphone ° c.	Decomposition temperature ° c.
1 : 3-Butadiene	65	125
Piperylene (trans)	oil	100
Isoprene	63	125
1 : 3-Dimethylbutadiene . . .	39·5–40	100
2 : 3-Dimethylbutadiene . . .	135	140

The hydrogenated sulphones of butadienes are marketed under the generic name 'Sulfolane.' They are made by hydrogenation of the corresponding butadiene sulphone, the 'Sulfolene.' The product derived from butadiene itself, tetramethylene sulphone or 'Sulfolane,'

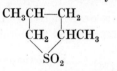

melts at 28° c. and boils at 285° c.; it is completely miscible with water. 'Dimethylsulfolane,' derived from 1 : 3-dimethylbutadiene, *i.e.*,

$$CH_3CH—CH_2$$
$$CH_2 \quad CHCH_3$$
$$SO_2$$

melts at − 3° c. and boils at 281° c.; it is soluble to the extent of 24 per cent by weight in water at 20° c. The main scope for these new compounds is as selective solvents for extractive distillation and solvent extraction processes. They are non-corrosive, chemically inert, and possess very high selective solvent properties for aromatics. On the other hand, they are stable only up to about 240° c.[50]

The 1 : 4 addition of 1 mol of an olefin or acetylene to 1 mol of a 1 : 3-diene is known as the Diels-Alder reaction. The reaction, discovered in 1928, was first developed with maleic anhydride, which reacts with butadiene to give tetrahydrophthalic anhydride:

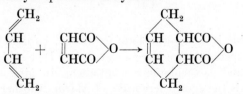

[50] Staaterman, Morris, Stager and Pierotti, *Chem. Eng. Prog.*, 1947, **43**, 148.

The reaction proceeds with compounds containing an activated ethylene bond or with acetylenic compounds, in general:

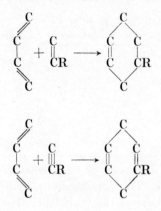

The second component is called the dienophile, and the product is termed the adduct.

R is usually a $> C : O$ group directly attached to the ethylenic or acetylenic carbon atom, *e.g.*, acids, anhydrides, esters, acid chlorides, ketones, quinones, etc.; but it may also be groups such as nitro, sulphonyl, cyano, vinyl, or even hydrogen.

Dienes vary in their reactivity towards a given dienophile. Increasing substitution generally decreases reactivity. 1-Chlorobutadiene and 2 : 3-dichlorobutadiene do not react whilst 2-chlorobutadiene behaves normally. Cyclopentadiene, $\begin{matrix} CH{=}CH \\ | \\ CH{=}CH \end{matrix} \rangle CH_2$, is particularly reactive and will add on vinyl chloride, allyl chloride, allyl alcohol, etc. With maleic anhydride, it gives carbic anhydride (endomethylenetetrahydrophthalic anhydride):

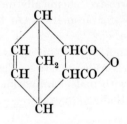

This anhydride is an intermediate for resins; its dimethyl ester is an insecticide. Cyclopentadiene undergoes a complex Diels-Alder reaction with vinyl chloride and hexachlorocyclopentadiene to give the insecticide, Aldrin. Dieldrin is the epoxy derivative of Aldrin. Another example is the condensation of butadiene with acrylonitrile to give tetrahydrobenzonitrile, an intermediate for the synthesis of pimelic acid (see Chapter 18, p. 333).

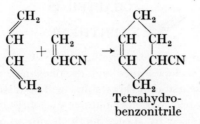

Tetrahydro-
benzonitrile

Finally, the diene content of cracked petrol fractions is one of the components of petroleum resins which are used in the paint and plastics industries. These resins are made by polymerising the diene and olefin content of the fractions with ionic catalysts such as aluminium chloride (Chapter 21, p. 389).

CHAPTER 13

NAPHTHENES

THE naphthenes are saturated cycloparaffins, C_nH_{2n}. Only the C_5 and C_6 ring compounds, cyclopentanes and cyclohexanes, are present in crude petroleum, and discussion in this chapter will be restricted to these hydrocarbons. The cyclopropane, cyclobutane, cycloheptane, etc., ring systems have to be synthesised by special methods, for which reference must be made to the usual text-books of organic chemistry.

In the petroleum chemicals field, the main interest of the naphthenes is as a source of aromatic hydrocarbons, aside from cyclohexane which has some important outlets as a raw material for chemicals.

1. Routes to naphthenes

The main source of the naphthenes we are considering is the crude petroleum itself, and what is known of the problems of isolation will be discussed below. Before we come to this, however, other possible methods of making naphthenes will be considered.

These are:

(i) Hydrogenation of the corresponding aromatic hydrocarbon

This gives only a cyclohexane hydrocarbon:

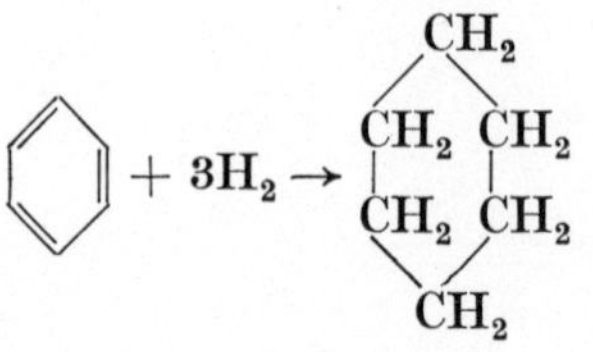

$$\bigcirc + 3H_2 \rightarrow \begin{matrix} CH_2 \\ CH_2 \quad CH_2 \\ CH_2 \quad CH_2 \\ CH_2 \end{matrix} \quad \Delta H = -49 \cdot 2 \text{ k. cal.} \qquad . \quad (1)$$

Usually, aromatics are more valuable than naphthenes, and therefore the reverse reaction, dehydrogenation of cyclohexanes to substituted benzenes, is more important. This is dealt with in Chapter 14, p. 230.

The hydrogenation of aromatics is a relatively simple operation. It is carried out below about 200° c., preferably under increased pressure in the liquid phase in the presence of conventional hydrogenation catalysts. For the free energy change in reaction (1), the data in Chapter 7, Table 22, give:

$$\Delta G = -52,610 + 94 \cdot 6T$$

from which $\Delta G = 0$ at about 282° c. This is for the hydrogenation of benzene vapour to cyclohexane vapour, but there will be little difference in free energy change for these hydrocarbons in the liquid phase.

(ii) Ring closure of paraffins

This reaction may take place during the conversion of paraffins to aromatics; however, the dehydrogenation of the naphthenes which may be initially formed is much more facile both thermodynamically and kinetically than ring closure of the paraffin.

$$\text{For } n\text{-}C_6H_{14} \rightarrow \begin{array}{c} CH_2 \\ CH_2 \quad CH_2 \\ CH_2 \quad CH_2 \\ CH_2 \end{array} + H_2. \qquad \Delta H = +\ 10{\cdot}5 \text{ k. cal.} \qquad (2)$$

$$\Delta G = 11{,}200 - 10{\cdot}5T$$

and $\Delta G = 0$ only at 793° c.; this reaction will also be favoured by low or moderate pressures. Previously it was shown that ΔG for the dehydrogenation of cyclohexane to benzene would be 0 at 282° c., above which temperature dehydrogenation would proceed to completion with an increasingly great driving force. As the present known catalysts for cyclisation are also efficient catalysts for aromatisation, practical methods of stopping the reaction at the cyclohexane stage are not obvious.

A second alternative route is dehydrogenation of the paraffin to an olefin and ring closure of the olefin to the cyclohexane:

$$CH_3CH_2CH_2CH_2CH_2CH_3 \rightleftharpoons CH_3CH_2CH_2CH_2CH : CH_2 + H_2.$$
$$\Delta H = +\ 30{\cdot}0 \text{ k. cal.} \qquad (3)$$

$$\begin{array}{c} CH_3 \\ CH_2 \quad CH_2 \\ CH_2 \quad CH \\ CH_2 \end{array} \rightarrow \begin{array}{c} CH_2 \\ CH_2 \quad CH_2 \\ CH_2 \quad CH_2 \\ CH_2 \end{array} \qquad \Delta H = -\ 19{\cdot}5 \text{ k. cal.} \qquad (4)$$

For equation (3), $\Delta G = 31{,}670 - 33{\cdot}5T$.

$\Delta G = 0$ at 672° c., *i.e.*, this reaction requires temperatures of at least 672° c. at atmospheric pressure to go to 70% conversion.

For reaction (4), $\Delta G = -\ 20{,}480 + 23{\cdot}0T$.

$\Delta G = 0$ at 617° c., below which temperature cyclohexane could be formed. That is to say, only in a comparatively narrow temperature band, say 550–700° c., can these two consecutive reactions overlap. At these temperatures, benzene is the stable end hydrocarbon and the same problem of finding a catalyst effective for making and ring closing olefins, yet at the same time not leading to any aromatisation, faces us. Similar calculations apply to the alkylcyclohexanes, and it seems safe to say that at present there is no practical direct route from paraffins to cyclohexanes. Indeed, in considering the actual mechanism by which aromatics are formed from paraffins, it has been suggested that cyclohexanes, though formed, are continuously chemisorbed on to the catalyst surface, and are never liberated in the free state.[1]

Cyclopentanes do not dehydrogenate as easily as cyclohexanes as they cannot give rise to aromatics. The main thermal reaction of cyclopentanes is to split into two olefin fragments; cyclopentane itself gives ethylene and propylene, and methylcyclopentane gives two molecules of propylene, together with some ethylene plus C_4 olefins:[2]

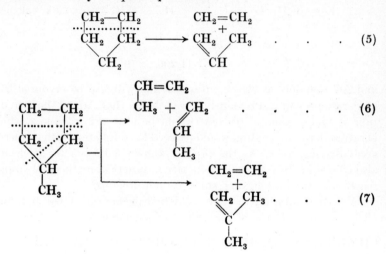

The free energy change in reaction (5) is $\Delta G = 36{,}450 - 48{\cdot}1T$, from which $\Delta G = 0$ at 485° c. In reaction (6), $\Delta G = 35{,}030 - 46{\cdot}6T$, giving $\Delta G = 0$ at 479° c., whilst in reaction (7) $\Delta G = 34{,}330 - 42{\cdot}8T$, and $\Delta G = 0$ at 527° c.

For these three reactions, $\Delta G = 0$ only at or above 480° c., a temperature some 200° c. above that at which the free energy change for aromatisation of cyclohexane, reaction (1) reversed, becomes 0.

(iii) *Ring enlargement and contraction between cyclopentane and cyclohexane rings*

This is the next possibility in the synthesis of naphthenes. Nenitzescu and Cantuniari[3] found that cyclohexane and methylcyclopentane on boiling with aluminium chloride both gave the same equilibrium mixture containing about 23 per cent methylcyclopentane. The equilibrium has been investigated in more detail by Glasebrook and Lovell.[4] Their results for the reaction are given in Table 48.

---

[1] Twigg, *Trans. Faraday Soc.*, 1939, **35**, 1006.
[2] Berg, Sumner and Montgomery, *Ind. Eng. Chem.*, 1945, **37**, 352.
[3] *Ber.*, 1933, **66**, 1097.
[4] *J. Amer. Chem. Soc.*, 1939, **61**, 1717.

From the equilibrium data, the free energy change may be expressed by the approximate linear equation:

$$\Delta G = 3,400 - 7 \cdot 5T$$

TABLE 48

Equilibrium in the reaction : cyclohexane (l) $\rightleftharpoons$ methylcyclopentane (l)

° c.	K_p	ΔG (g. cal./g. mol)	Mol % methylcyclopentane at equilibrium
25	0·143	1,150	12·5
35	0·170	1,085	14·5
45	0·193	1,040	16·2
55	0·238	936	19·2
65	0·272	875	21·4
77·4	0·344	743	25·6

The heat change in the reaction at 25° c. has been calculated by Parks and Moore[5] to be approximately + 4 k. cal.

From the free energy equation, cyclohexane is the more stable form at room temperature, but its stability decreases with increase in temperature. This is for the liquid phase equilibrium; the closeness of the boiling points means that there will be little difference in the equilibrium for isomerisation in the vapour phase.

The interchange of the two types of naphthenes at low and at high temperatures is therefore available as a method of making one or the other. Isomerisation will usually be used for conversion of cyclopentanes to the more valuable cyclohexanes. This process has been used as the first step in one of the routes to make synthetic benzene and, during the war, synthetic toluene from petroleum.

When benzene was wanted, a naphthene cut containing methylcyclopentane and cyclohexane, boiling at 65–85° c., was isomerised with an aluminium chloride complex activated with a trace of hydrochloric acid for 20–30 minutes at 80° c.[6] The fraction boiling from 76–85° c. contained 88 per cent of cyclohexane.

For toluene, a C_7 cut boiling at 87–99° c. and containing 47 per cent of naphthenes, mainly dimethylcyclopentanes, was contacted with an aluminium chloride-kerosene complex at 80° c. and about 4 atma. In about 15 minutes, 83 per cent of the C_5 naphthenes present were converted to methylcyclohexane. The subsequent processing to toluene is outlined in Chapter 14, p. 230.

Rearrangement of dimethylcyclopentanes and ethylcyclopentane to

---

[5] *J. Amer. Chem. Soc.*, 1939, **61**, 2561.
[6] Shell Development, U.S.P. 2415065.

methylcyclohexane is more facile than the isomerisation of methylcyclopentane to cyclohexane. According to Parks,[7] the free energy change at 26° c. for the reaction:

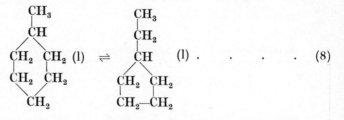

$$ \text{(8)} $$

is $+ 3\cdot7$ k. cal.; K_p at 25° c. is 0·002, giving 0·2 mol per cent ethylcyclopentane at equilibrium; from Table 49, the corresponding figures for methylcyclopentane were $\Delta G = + 1\cdot1$ k. cal., $K_p = 0\cdot145$, and 12·5 mol per cent methylcyclopentane at equilibrium. The heat change in reaction (8) is also greater than in the isomerisation of cyclohexane, ΔH_{298} being $+ 6\cdot0$ k. cal. At elevated temperatures, there will therefore be a greater tendency for the higher alkyl cyclopentanes to isomerise to alkyl cyclohexanes than for methylcyclopentane to isomerise to cyclohexane. Evidence of this is given in Chapter 14.

The simultaneous isomerisation of cyclopentanes to cyclohexanes and their dehydrogenation to aromatics is one of the important reactions brought about by the newer catalytic reforming processes such as Platforming, Houdriforming, etc. In the case of the Platforming process, the catalyst is a fluoride activated clay which is the isomerisation catalyst plus platinum, which is the dehydrogenation catalyst. This reaction is dealt with more fully in Chapter 14, p. 231, but these processes are further examples of the difficulty of making C_6 naphthenes by catalytic processes without dehydrogenating the naphthene to the aromatic.

2. Occurrence of naphthenes

Coming to the main source of naphthenes, crude petroleum, the naphthenes definitely identified include cyclopentane, methylcyclopentane, di- and trimethylcyclopentanes, ethylcyclopentane, cyclohexane, methylcyclohexane, di- and trimethylcyclohexanes, ethylcyclohexane and methylethylcyclohexanes. Examination has usually been limited to petrol fractions with end points of 150–180° c., and it is not surprising that the heaviest naphthene identified, 1 : 2 : 4-trimethylcyclohexane, has a boiling point of only 144° c.

The average proportions of naphthenes in paraffinic and naphthenic straight run petrols is shown in Table 49; the data relate mainly to American and Russian petrols.

---

[7] *Chem. Rev.*, 1940, **27,** 75.

TABLE 49

Content of simpler naphthenes in straight run petrols (end point, 150–180° C.)

Naphthene	Petrol from paraffinic crude % by wt.	Petrol from naphthenic crude % by wt.
Cyclopentane	0·1–0·4	0·2–1·0
Methylcyclopentane . . .	2–5	3– 5
Cyclohexane	2–3	3– 7
Methylcyclohexane	4–6	7–10

Cyclopentane is usually present only in traces; the proportion of cyclohexane is about half that of methylcyclohexane.

Some petrols are very rich in naphthenes; a straight run petrol from Saxet, U.S.A., boiling range 35–117° c., is reported to contain 5 per cent (by vol.) methylcyclopentane, 15 per cent cyclohexane, and 37 per cent of methylcyclohexane.[8]

In connection with the toluene problem (see Chapter 14), determination of the methylcyclohexane content of various American crudes was made the subject of a special study.[9] The percentage varied from 0·5–3·7 by volume.

The average proportion of naphthenes in straight run petrols is 20–50 per cent by volume (Chapter 2); cracked petrols, which are not suitable sources for the isolation of naphthenes owing to presence of olefins, contain 10–20 per cent by volume of naphthenes (Chapter 7).

3. Isolation of naphthenes

The boiling points of the simpler naphthenes are given alongside the corresponding paraffins and aromatics in Appendix 1. The boiling points of these petroleum naphthenes up to C_7 to C_8 are repeated in Table 50 below with the nearest boiling important petroleum hydrocarbon.

TABLE 50

Boiling points of lower naphthenes, etc., in petroleum

Naphthene	b.p. ° C.	Nearest boiling non-naphthene hydrocarbon	b.p. ° C.
Cyclopentane	49·3	2 : 2-Dimethylbutane . .	49·7
Methylcyclopentane . . .	71·8	*n*-Hexane	68·7
Cyclohexane	80·7	Benzene	80·1
1 : 1-Dimethylcyclopentane .	87·8	2 : 3-Dimethylpentane .	89·8
trans-1 : 3-Dimethylcyclopentane .	90·8	2-Methylhexane .	90·1
cis-1 : 3-Dimethylcyclopentane .	91·7	} 3-Methylhexane .	91·9
trans-1 : 2-Dimethylcyclopentane .	91·9		
cis-1 : 2-Dimethylcyclopentane .	99·5	*n*-Heptane . . .	98·4
Methylcyclohexane . .	100·9	2 : 2 : 4-Trimethylpentane .	99·2

[8] Sachanen, 'Chemical Constituents of Petroleum', *Reinhold*, 1945.

[9] Fischer and Welty, *Chem. Met. Eng.*, 1944, **51**(8), 92.

The boiling points in Table 50 do not indicate all the difficulties of isolation of the individual naphthenes. In admixture with other hydrocarbons, they tend to form azeotropes and other mixtures with abnormal vapour pressures; even the very simple mixture, benzene-cyclohexane, forms an azeotrope. Straight fractional distillation is inadequate to separate any naphthene occurring in crude petroleum in the pure state; separation of naphthenes from aromatics can be carried out by solvent extraction and is relatively easy by azeotropic or extractive distillation. Separation of naphthenes from paraffins is somewhat more difficult using these methods, but is still practicable. For example, the relative volatility of *n*-hexane-methylcyclopentane, is 1·10; extractive distillation in presence of aniline raises it to 1·45. Similarly, the relative volatility for *n*-heptane-methyl-cyclohexane is raised from 1·08 to 1·52 in presence of aniline.

A chemical method of separation of cyclohexanes from paraffins by dehydrogenation to aromatics, separation of the aromatic, and hydrogenation to the cyclohexane is a possible method of preparing particular cyclohexanes. A method depending on isomerisation has also been worked out. Separation of cyclohexane from paraffins associated with it in a narrow boiling cut has been described, depending on isomerisation of the cyclohexane to methylcyclopentane, which boils 9° c. lower, separation of the methylcyclopentane from the paraffins by precision fractionation and then isomerising the isolated methylcyclopentane back to cyclohexane.[10]

Reasonably pure cyclohexane has been obtained from a naphthene cut containing 30 per cent hexanes, 37 per cent of methylcyclopentane, 20 per cent cyclohexane and 7 per cent of benzene by removing the benzene with sulphuric acid, destroying the paraffins by a brief thermal cracking operation at 550–650° c. in 10–20 seconds, and finally removing any benzene formed in this cracking process. Cyclohexane of better than 95% purity is said to be obtained by this method.

4. Reactions of naphthenes

The naphthenes undergo all the chemical reactions of paraffins dealt with in Chapters 4–6, although little work has been carried out on their reactions in the vapour phase. In the liquid phase, they chlorinate readily, can be nitrated and sulphonated with difficulty, undergo various reactions activated with ultra-violet light, such as with sulphur dioxide and chlorine to give sulphonyl chlorides, and can be oxidised. Owing to its symmetry, cyclohexane has been chosen in many academic studies as a model of the behaviour of paraffin hydrocarbons. The hydrogen atoms are all alike and there are no end groups or tertiary carbon atoms to complicate reactivity.

The most important outlet for naphthenes in the petroleum chemical field is the liquid phase air oxidation of cyclohexane; in presence of polyvalent metal salts such as those of cobalt, a mixture of cyclohexanol and

---

[10] Shell Development, U.S.P. 2382446.

cyclohexanone is obtained by decomposition of the primarily formed hydro-peroxide, as explained in Chapter 4, p. 55.

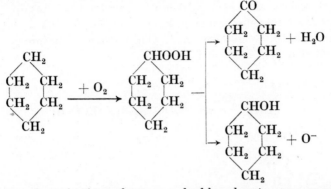

These products in themselves are valuable solvents; even more important, they are intermediates for adipic acid, the starting material for the synthesis of nylon. So far as nylon is concerned, it is reported that a considerable proportion of American production is made from petroleum cyclohexane. It would appear that the necessary rigid purification has been achieved at a sufficiently low cost to displace benzene from petroleum or coal.

Cyclohexane can be oxidised with air in one step directly to adipic acid but the yields are lower than 35 per cent; with nitric acid, cyclohexane will give 30 per cent adipic acid in one operation or 45 per cent in two operations.[11] Technically, the oxidation of cyclohexane is carried out in two steps, using air to make a cyclohexanol-cyclohexanone mixture, and using nitric acid for the second stage of the oxidation.

Conditions used by I.C.I. for the manufacture of adipic acid from cyclohexane have been outlined by Lindsay.[12] The air oxidation is carried out to the extent of oxidising only 5–12 per cent of the cyclohexane. The crude cyclohexanol-cyclohexanone mixture, which also contains other cyclohexyl derivatives, was oxidised with 50% nitric acid in the presence of a mixed copper-vanadium catalyst at about 80° c. The process is preferably operated continuously under a positive pressure. The yield of adipic acid was of the order of 1 lb./lb. crude oxidation mixture

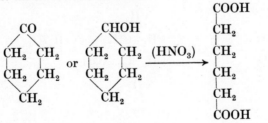

[11] du Pont, U.S.P. 2228261.
[12] Lindsay, Chemical Engineering Science, 1954, **3**, Supplement, p. 78; I.C.I. B.P. 567525; 572260; 633354.

Cyclohexanone and other cyclic ketones can also be oxidised with air in the liquid phase under pressure in the presence of metal catalysts to give dicarboxylic acids. The usual conditions are temperatures up to 200° c. at 25 atma. air pressure, using manganese or cobalt salts as catalysts.[13] Cyclopentanone gives glutaric acid, and methylcyclohexanone, methyl adipic acid. The yields appear to be rather low:

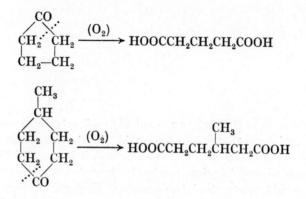

Another route to dicarboxylic acids from cyclic ketones is by reaction with carbon dioxide in presence of suitable catalysts. Aqueous cyclohexanone heated for twenty hours at 200° c. under carbon dioxide pressure in presence of reduced manganese chromite and some free acetic acid gives pimelic acid in good yield.[14]

$$\text{(cyclohexanone ring)} + CO_2 + H_2O \rightarrow HOOCCH_2CH_2CH_2CH_2CH_2COOH$$

A further outlet for cyclohexanone, also in the synthetic fibre field, is its use for manufacture of caprolactam, an intermediate for polyamide fibres :[15]

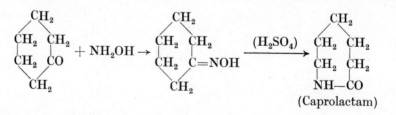

(Caprolactam)

---

[13] I.G., U.S.P. 2005183.
[14] du Pont, U.S.P. 2390576.
[15] C.I.O.S. 29/62.

Vapour phase air oxidation of cyclohexanes has been described. Methyl-cyclohexane mixed with air (1 vol. naphthene : 5 vol. air) passed over silver oxide on asbestos at 400–500° c. gave methylcyclohexanones, the hydrogen atom attached to the tertiary carbon atom rather surprisingly not being preferentially attacked.[16]

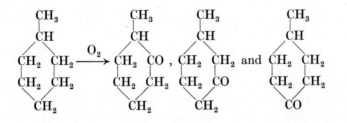

The nitration of cyclohexane was studied by Grundman and Halden-wanger.[17] The partial reduction of nitrocyclohexane to cyclohexylhydroxy-lamine as an intermediate for caprolactam gave overall yields too low to compete with the cyclohexanone oxime route.

The effect of heat on naphthenes should also be mentioned. The catalytic dehydrogenation of cyclohexanes to benzenes above 300° c. has already been referred to. At 500° c. and above in the absence of a catalyst, cyclo-hexane decomposes with rupture of the ring in two different ways without formation of benzene. In one way, it gives butadiene, ethylene and hy-drogen. In the other, two molecules of propylene are formed.[18]

$$
\begin{matrix}
\overset{CH_2}{\diagup} \\
CH_2 \quad CH_2 \\
CH_2 \quad CH_2 \\
\diagdown CH_2 \diagup
\end{matrix}
\longrightarrow
\begin{matrix}
\overset{CH_2}{\diagup} \\
CH \\
CH \\
CH_2
\end{matrix}
\;+\;
\begin{matrix}
CH_2 \\
\| \\
CH_2
\end{matrix}
\;+\; H_2 . \qquad \qquad (9)
$$

$$
\begin{matrix}
\overset{CH_2}{\diagup} \\
CH_2 \quad CH_2 \\
CH_2 \quad CH_2 \\
CH_2
\end{matrix}
\longrightarrow
\begin{matrix}
CH_3 \\
\diagup \\
CH \\
\| \\
CH_2
\end{matrix}
\;+\;
\begin{matrix}
CH_2 \\
\| \\
CH \\
\diagup \\
CH_3
\end{matrix}
. \qquad \qquad (10)
$$

[16] Phillips Pet., U.S.P. 2386372.

[17] Grundman and Haldenwanger, *Angew. Chem.*, 1950, **62**, 556; Grundman, *Angew. Chem.*, 1950, **62**, 558.

[18] Kuchler, *Trans. Faraday Soc.*, 1939, **35**, 874.

It might be mentioned that cyclohexene at low pressures in the temperature range 500–600° c. undergoes decomposition (9) almost exclusively, giving only butadiene and ethylene.[18]

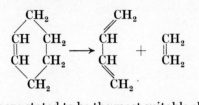

In fact, cyclohexenes are stated to be the most suitable class of hydrocarbon for purely thermal cracking to butadiene.

Cyclopentanes do not give either aromatics or butadiene on thermal treatment. As was mentioned earlier in this chapter, the main result of high temperature treatment is fission into two molecules of olefins of lower molecular weight.[2, 18]

CHAPTER 14

AROMATICS

It was mentioned in Chapter 1 that the manufacture of aromatics from petroleum was the sector of the American petroleum chemicals industry which was most recently established. It is only since the end of the war that aromatics from petroleum have proved to be firmly established and not war-time chemicals only. Because of this factor of time, this chapter has had to be entirely recast; it is divided into the following main sections:

1. Benzene, toluene and xylene.
2. Higher aromatics from benzene and toluene.
3. Other routes to higher aromatics.
4. Heterocyclics – Petroleum pyridines.

1. Benzene, toluene and the xylenes

(a) GENERAL

These aromatics are invariably made from naphthenic rich petroleum fractions by isomerisation and dehydrogenation of the naphthene content followed by separation of the aromatic hydrocarbon so produced together with whatever amount of aromatic was originally present in the petroleum fraction. It is only in exceptional cases that a straight run petroleum fraction is sufficiently rich in aromatics to justify separation without further enrichment. One fraction, b.p. 40–180° c., from Conroe, Texas, is recorded as containing 20 per cent by volume of C_6 to C_9 aromatics, an exceptional figure; Borneo petroleum fractions are also rich in aromatics. Normally, high aromatic content is associated with high naphthene content. The range of aromatic contents in American straight run petrols, boiling range, 40–180° c., is given in Table 51.[1]

TABLE 51

Aromatics in American straight run petrols,
boiling range 40–180° C.

Aromatic	% by vol.
Benzene	0·2–1·2
Toluene	0·3–7
Ethylbenzene	0·2–0·9
p-Xylene	0·3–1·8
m-Xylene	0·2–6
o-Xylene	0·2–2
Isopropylbenzene . . .	0·1–0·3
n-Propylbenzene . . .	0·1–0·4

[1] Sachanen, 'Chemical Constituents of Petroleum', *Reinhold*, 1945.

A special study of the toluene content of American crudes was made during the war.[2] The average figure was below 0·5 per cent; the range was 0–2 per cent.

These low concentrations are a fraction of the naphthene content of naphthenic rich straight run fractions, which vary as shown in Table 52. Since substituted cyclopentanes can be made to give the aromatic containing the same number of carbon atoms as the initial cyclopentane, via isomerisation to the corresponding cyclohexane, the naphthenes have been grouped together into those containing six, seven and eight carbon atoms:

TABLE 52

Naphthene content of naphthenic rich
straight run petrols (40–180° C.)

Naphthene	% by vol.
C_6 Naphthenes	6–12
C_7 Naphthenes	10–30
C_8 Naphthenes	10–30

The first step in making benzene, toluene and the xylenes from petroleum is to select a suitable fraction rich in the naphthenes which are the precursors of the aromatics. The second step is to isomerise the C_5 naphthenes and dehydrogenate the combined C_6 naphthenes; the third is to isolate the aromatics from the paraffin hydrocarbons present.

One method of isomerising C_5 naphthenes as a separate operation has already been described in Chapter 13, p. 220. It is now usual to select a dehydrogenation process which simultaneously isomerises the C_5 naphthenes in the same operation.

(*b*) DEHYDROGENATION OF NAPHTHENES

The free energy change in the reaction:

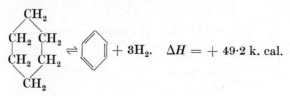

is, according to Chapter 13, p. 218:

$$\Delta G = 52,610 - 94 \cdot 6T$$

$\Delta G = 0$ at 282° c. above which the reaction will proceed to complete dehydrogenation. The equilibrium is favoured by low pressures; in the technical processes for dehydrogenation, pressure is advantageous for

[2] Fischer and Welty, *Chem. Met. Eng.*, 1944, **51(8)**, 92.

operational reasons, necessitating use of considerably higher temperatures than 282° c.

This reaction was established by Zelinski before the first world war, using palladium or platinum as catalyst, and working at 300° c. and atmospheric pressure.

The technical process of dehydrogenation of the C_6 naphthenes in petroleum cuts to aromatics is termed hydroforming. It involves treatment of petroleum fractions, usually boiling within the range 70–200° c., at about 500° c., over dehydrogenation catalysts at moderate pressure and in the presence of hydrogen containing gases. The main reaction is dehydrogenation of cyclohexanes to the corresponding aromatics; in addition, there may be a certain amount of isomerisation of alkyl cyclopentanes to cyclohexanes, and of cyclisation-dehydrogenation of paraffins to aromatics. The principal reaction of paraffins, if they do not pass through unchanged, is cracking to lighter paraffins and olefins, but owing to the high partial pressure of hydrogen, any olefins produced are at once hydrogenated to the corresponding paraffin, and the resultant products are free of olefins; this is believed to be one of the factors responsible for long catalyst life in the hydroforming process, as the absence of olefins reduces coke formation.

The catalyst usually selected is molybdenum trioxide (5–10 per cent) on active alumina, but other Group VIA metal oxides can be used instead of molybdenum oxide. Pressures are 3–25 atma., usually about 15 atma., and the partial pressure of hydrogen is about 40–90 per cent. This hydrogen is obtained from the gases liberated in the process, the surplus being vented for fuel or chemical outlets. The usual temperature range is 480–550° c.; the process is operated cyclically, with regeneration of catalyst every few hours.

The main reaction is highly endothermic ($\Delta H = + 49 \cdot 2$ k. cal./mol aromatic), and use of two or more reactors in series has been described as a method of introducing the required amount of heat at the right temperature level. That dehydrogenation of C_6 naphthenes rather than aromatisation of paraffins is the main reaction is shown by some data given by Fischer and Welty.[2] Under standard hydroforming conditions, 97 per cent of methylcyclohexane was converted to aromatics; under the same conditions with *n*-heptane as feed, only 16 per cent was converted to toluene, most of the heptane suffering extensive cracking.

These hydroforming processes are being displaced by newer methods of catalytic reforming in which recourse is made to Zelinski's original catalyst, platinum. In the Platforming process, the catalyst is platinum supported on fluorine activated alumina; the support functions as a powerful catalyst for the isomerisation of C_5 naphthenes to C_6 naphthenes and also for the isomerisation of straight chain to branch chain paraffins; the original objective of these new processes was to make high grade petrol and aviation fuel.

There are a number of alternative processes in which there is essential combination of an efficient hydrogenation-dehydrogenation ca lyst such as platinum, and an efficient isomerisation catalyst such as activated clay or silica-alumina;[3] the isomerisation is believed to brought about by a carbonium ion mechanism. Essentially these proces are improved variants of hydroforming in which the catalyst life is grea prolonged and the speed of the reactions, particularly the isomerisat reaction, is increased.

The general conditions are:

Temperature	. 450–550° c.
Pressure	. 10–30 atma.
Hydrogen : oil; mol ratio .	. 5–10 : 1

Several reactors are usually operated in series, in view of the hig endothermic nature of the reaction. Catalyst life is long, regeneration be required only every few months.

An example of the performance of this type of process is given by t results at the Marcus Hook refinery of Sun Oil Co., using the Houdrifo process:[4]

Feedstock:	C_6–C_7 *Fraction* (65–103° c.) %	C_8 *Fracti* (113–130° %
Feed composition—		
Paraffins	49	52
Naphthenes	44	40
Aromatics	7	8
Product composition—		
Paraffins	53	52
Naphthenes	4	0
Aromatics	43	48
Yield, aromatics on naphthenes converted . . .	86–87	102

The yield figures suggest that benzene and toluene are obtained in these processes only from naphthenes; with the C_8 aromatics, there is a little dehydrocyclisation of paraffins.

(c) METHODS OF SEPARATION OF THE AROMATICS

The problem is to separate the aromatic from paraffins and occasionally naphthenes of very similar boiling range. The general methods of separation were outlined in Chapter 2; those used for benzene, toluene and the xylenes comprise:

(*i*) Straight fractional distillation.
(*ii*) Azeotropic distillation.
(*iii*) Extractive distillation.
(*iv*) Solvent extraction.
(*v*) Solid adsorption.
(*vi*) Crystallisation.

---

[3] *Pet. Processing*, 1955, **10**, 1162 *seq.*
[4] Beyler, Stevenson and Schuman, *Ind. Eng. Chem.*, 1955, **47**, 740.

(i) Fractional distillation

Straight fractional distillation of petroleum is of value only in preparing concentrates containing individual aromatics or a narrow boiling range of aromatics. Benzene forms azeotropes with methylcyclopentane, with cyclohexane, and probably with n-hexane. Details of these azeotropes are given in Table 53. Although toluene does not form azeotropes with methylcyclohexane, n-heptane or n-octane, the relative volatilities are much smaller than would be expected from the vapour pressures of the pure hydrocarbons.[5]

TABLE 53

Azeotropes of benzene with other C_6 hydrocarbons

Second component with benzene	b.p. of benzene ° c.	b.p. of second component ° c.	b.p. of Azeotrope ° c.	Composition of azeotrope mol % benzene
Methylcyclopentane .	80·1	71·8	71·5	10
Cyclohexane . . .	80·1	80·7	70	50
n-Hexane . . .	80·1	68·7	68·6	3

Fractional distillation has, however, been used successfully for the isolation of pure toluene and of xylenes free from paraffins. The Standard Oil of California group of companies successfully made nitration grade toluene from a cut of crude petroleum during the war years, using the hydroforming process to destroy all hydrocarbons boiling close to toluene.[6] A fraction of California crude petroleum boiling from 83° c. to 110° c., selected to include the dimethylpentanes at the lower end but to exclude large concentrations of non-aromatics boiling near toluene at the upper end, was passed at a total pressure of 13 atma. over a molybdenum oxide-alumina catalyst in the presence of recycled hydrogen at about 540° c. The product was separated into a fraction boiling from 83° c. to 107° c. which was recycled with fresh feed, and a fraction boiling from 107° c. to 110° c. containing 90% toluene. This second fraction was repassed over the catalyst to increase the toluene concentration from 90% to 99%. After repassing, the product was topped, acid treated and re-run to produce nitration grade toluene.

Hydroforming has also been used[7] for converting a narrow boiling cut of C_8 naphthenes into a mixture of o-, m-, and p-xylenes. This process indicates how the difference in boiling points of the naphthenes can be used to prepare or to avoid preparation of specific aromatics. By taking a narrow cut of a naphthenic type straight run petrol of boiling range 110–125° c.

---

[5] Griswold and Ludwig, *Ind. Eng. Chem.*, 1943, **35,** 117.
[6] Burton *et al.*, *Chem. Eng. Prog.*, 1948, **44,** 195.
[7] Standard Oil Development, B.P. 590548.

all the dimethylcyclohexanes were included (except *cis*-1 : 2-dimethylcyclo-
hexane), but ethylcyclohexane, b.p. 132° c., was excluded. This narrow cut
was hydroformed at 480–550° c. under 3–25 atma. pressure in presence of
excess hydrogen, over the usual type of catalyst, 1–10 per cent of the oxides
of molybdenum, chromium or tungsten on alumina, to give the three
xylenes substantially free of ethylbenzene.

A similar process is used by the Sun Oil Co. for making xylenes but not
benzene or toluene.[8] A naphthenic rich fraction is prepared with an end
point of 129° c. This is subjected to one of the new hydroforming processes
and the product worked up in three columns from which are obtained
respectively, light petrol, a naphtha fraction, and the xylenes, with heavy
aromatics as a bottom product from the last column. As the lowest boiling
xylene boils at 136° c., good separation can be achieved in the second
column between the paraffins present in the naphtha and the xylenes.

(*ii*) *Azeotropic distillation*

The usual azeotrope formers employed are methyl ethyl ketone and
methyl alcohol. A list of entrainers forming azeotropes with toluene has
been compiled by Lake.[9] With this aromatic aqueous methyl ethyl
ketone appears the most common azeotropic method; its use on the full
scale has been described.[9, 10] The entrainer takes paraffins and any naphthenes overhead; to economise in steam, it is necessary to start with a
concentrate containing 40 per cent of toluene, and even so, 2–3 vol. of
methyl ethyl ketone/vol. non-aromatic hydrocarbon were required for good
separation.

(*iii*) *Extractive distillation*

The extractive distillation solvent most used is phenol. Mixed cresols
and furfural are occasionally employed. The use of phenol in the manufacture of toluene is described by Dunn,[11] and is used in one of the full-scale
benzene from petroleum plants.

(*iv*) *Solvent extraction*

The solvents chosen must have a high selectivity for aromatics and
must have physical characteristics so that two phases readily separate
within a reasonable range of temperature, say between − 30° c. and
+ 120° c. The solvents suggested for isolating the lower aromatics include
the same range developed for refining of kerosene and lubricating oils—
sulphur dioxide, nitrobenzene, phenol, furfural, etc. The latest solvent used
industrially for extraction of aromatics is aqueous diethylene glycol.

---

[8] *Chem. Eng.*, February 1954, p. 142.
[9] *Trans. Amer. Inst. Chem. Eng.*, 1945, **41**, 327.
[10] *Pet. Refiner*, 1945, **24(12)**, 131.
[11] Dunn *et al.*, *Trans. Amer. Inst. Chem. Eng.*, 1945, **41**, 631.

Aqueous diethylene glycol (the Udex process) possesses the advantage that it can handle wide boiling range stocks to give a mixture of aromatics free from non-aromatics which can then easily be separated. It is believed to operate at or near the boiling point and under slight pressure to avoid loss of aromatic or solvent. The solvent contains 10–12 per cent of water. The solvent is fed at the top of the extraction tower, the aromatic rich feed is introduced near the base. A proportion of the concentrated aromatics are returned to the base, to act as a reflux and sweep out all traces of non-aromatics from the extract. The extract (aromatics plus aqueous diethylene glycol) is distilled, the aromatics going overhead and the diethylene glycol being recycled.[12]

In the Cosden Petroleum Co.'s plant at Big Springs, Texas, the product from Platforming a naphthenic rich feed, containing all the C_6 to C_8 aromatics, is clay treated to destroy traces of diolefins and then subjected to Udex solvent extraction. This gives a mixture of aromatics free from non-aromatics, from which pure benzene, pure toluene and mixed C_8 aromatics were obtained by straightforward continuous fractional distillation. The Sun Oil Co.'s refinery made benzene and toluene in the same way but, as mentioned on p. 234, elected to make the C_8 aromatics as a distinct process, not involving Udex extraction but carrying out the separation of C_8 aromatics from C_8 non-aromatics by distillation before dehydrogenation.

An ingenious method of obtaining substantially pure aromatics is to subject the highly aromatic extract obtained by use of a solvent with high aromatic selectivity to a second extraction with a different solvent with high selectivity for non-aromatics and low selectivity for aromatics. During the war, nitration grade toluene was made from a naphthene cut at the Baytown refinery of Humble Oil in the following way.[13] A cut boiling at 93–121° c., containing about 30 per cent of naphthenes, and 95 per cent of the methylcyclohexane present in the original crude, was hydroformed at 500–550° c., giving a hydroformate containing 21–28 per cent of toluene. This concentrate was extracted at − 32° c. with liquid sulphur dioxide, which gave an extract containing only 65–70 per cent of toluene. The extract was washed with a heavy petroleum oil which extracted the non-aromatics, treated with sulphuric acid, neutralised and re-run. This is the only refinery which uses the double solvent extraction process; it made half the petroleum toluene produced in America during the war. The cycle of operations is indicated in Fig. 28.

The plant is now operated for making 98–99% toluene, 98–99% mixed xylenes, 95% C_9 aromatics and 90% C_{10} aromatics. The composition of the xylenes is 43% *m*-xylene, 20% each of *o*-xylene and ethylbenzene and

---

[12] Thornton, *Pet. Proc.*, 1953, **8**, 384; Jackson, Chadd and Krause, *Pet. Proc.*, 1954, **9**, 233.
[13] Marshall, *Chem. Eng. Prog.*, 1950, **46**, 313.

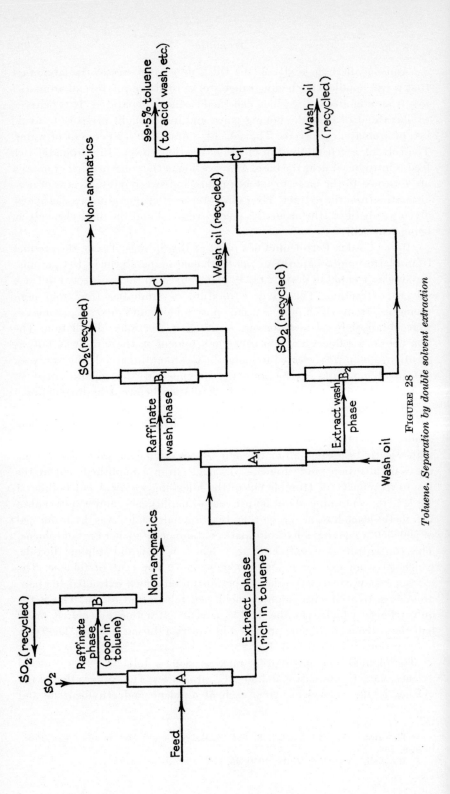

FIGURE 28

Toluene. Separation by double solvent extraction

17% p-xylene. The C_9 and C_{10} aromatics do not require double extraction. By limiting the top temperature of the feed, they require only acid treatment and re-running after the SO_2 extraction.

(v) Solid adsorption

This is used industrially in the Arosorb process, which depends upon the selective adsorption of aromatics on silica gel. It is used in one plant, that of Sun Oil Co., at Marcus Hook, for isolating benzene and toluene from the products of Houdriforming a naphthenic feedstock (p. 232).[14] The product from this process contains about 27 per cent of benzene and toluene, the remainder being paraffins. This is fed to a number of silica gel adsorbers in a cyclical operation consisting of three steps — introduction of feed to the silica gel to give about 70% saturation; displacement of the saturates from the bed with a volatile liquid such as butane or pentane; displacement of the benzene and toluene from the bed with an aromatic of higher boiling point, mixed xylenes being used. The benzene and toluene, separated from paraffins of the same boiling range, can then be purified to nitration grade quality by distillation. For a feed of about 350–400 tons/day three silica gel adsorbers were provided, each 4·5 ft. dia. and 15 ft. high; the cycle time was about 90 minutes. The total weight of silica gel was 15 tons. The approximate rates per pound of silica gel per cycle were:

Feed	.	.	.	0·45 lb.
Push liquid (butane)	.	.	0·12 lb.
Desorbent (xylenes)	.	.	0·62 lb.

For long life of the silica gel, water, olefins, sulphur and nitrogen compounds must be absent. With the new hydroforming processes, the only problem is removal of water.

(vi) Crystallisation

This is used only for isolation of p-xylene from the other C_8 aromatics. Because of the similarity of boiling points, p-xylene cannot be separated from m-xylene by distillation methods, but its relatively high melting point, + 13·3° c., compared with that of m-xylene, − 47·9° c., and those of the other C_8 isomers (o-xylene, − 25·2° c., ethylbenzene, − 95·0° c.), is the basis of the technical processes now used.

Petroleum C_8 aromatics normally contain about 50 per cent m-xylene, 20 per cent each of p-xylene and o-xylene and 10 per cent of ethylbenzene; non-aromatics are sometimes left in as their presence does not obstruct isolation of p-xylene.

The system m-xylene-p-xylene forms a eutectic freezing at − 53° c. containing 13 per cent of p-xylene; the presence of the other isomers depresses the freezing point and slightly decreases the proportion of p-xylene in the eutectic, to about 10 per cent at − 85° c., as shown by the

---

[14] Harper, Olsen and Schuman, *Chem. Eng. Prog.*, 1952, **48**, 276.

dotted line in Fig. 29. The important factors in recovery of *p*-xylene are therefore the initial *m-p-* ratio and the composition of the eutectic. With the figures cited, 50 per cent *m*-xylene; 20 per cent *p*-xylene; 30 per cent other hydrocarbons, the maximum theoretical recovery of *p*-xylene is about 60 per cent with a 13% eutectic and about 70 per cent with a 10% eutectic.

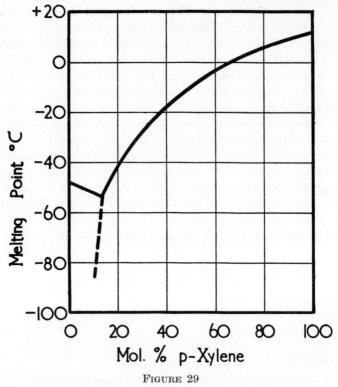

FIGURE 29

m-p-Xylene mixtures. Freezing point curve

Methods of lowering the eutectic composition described in the patent literature include addition of solvents such as toluene, *n*-pentane and isopentane.[15] This improves the recovery of *p*-xylene but involves extra refrigeration costs.

What appears to be an improved method is based on the discovery that carbon tetrachloride forms an equimolar compound with *p*-xylene, melting at − 4° c., but not with *m*- or *o*-xylene.[16] In the ternary system, *m*-xylene, *p*-xylene, carbon tetrachloride, two ternary eutectics exist, one of which,

---

[15] Standard Oil Development U.S.P. 2435792; B.P.M., Belg. Pat. 502208; B.P.M., F.P. 1037648.

[16] Egan and Lutty, *Ind. Eng. Chem.*, 1955, **47**, 250; California Research Corp., B.P. 677368.

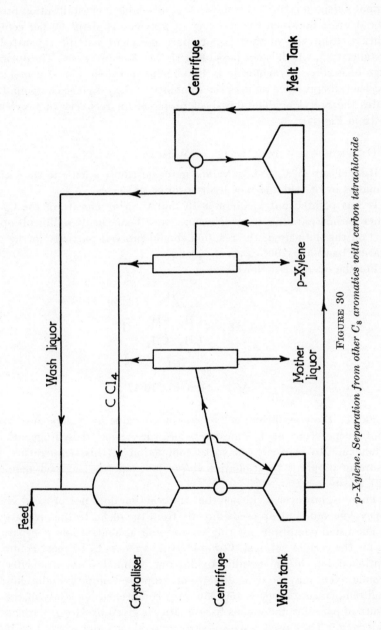

FIGURE 30

p-Xylene. Separation from other C$_8$ aromatics with carbon tetrachloride

Feed

Wash liquor

CCl$_4$

Centrifuge

Melt Tank

p-Xylene

Mother liquor

Crystalliser

Centrifuge

Wash tank

melting at $-76°$ c., contains only 1 per cent of p-xylene (2 per cent on the original xylene mixture). These two factors enable a crystallisation process to be devised in which the recovery of p-xylene is about 90 per cent; in addition, from the mother liquor, pure m-xylene can be separated by crystallisation, which is not possible with the older processes. The optimum usage of carbon tetrachloride is 1 mol : mol p-xylene plus 1·2 mol : mol m-xylene; its presence reduces the solubility of the p-xylene compound and dilutes the m-xylene. The flowsheet proposed for recovery of p-xylene is shown in Fig. 30.

(d) OTHER ROUTES TO C_6 TO C_8 AROMATICS

Ring closure of C_6 to C_8 paraffins may contribute a little to the yield of aromatics in the old and new hydroforming processes.

It was pointed out in Chapter 13 that the ring closure of the C_6 and higher normal paraffins to cyclohexanes was theoretically a difficult operation; on the data used, the reaction should proceed partially in the temperature band 550–700° c. via the olefins.

For the overall reaction:

$$n\text{-}C_6H_{14} \rightleftharpoons \begin{array}{c} CH_2 \\ \diagup \diagdown \\ CH_2 \quad CH_2 \\ | \qquad | \\ CH_2 \quad CH_2 \\ \diagdown \diagup \\ CH_2 \end{array} + H_2$$

$$\Delta G = 11,200 - 10·5T$$

At 500° c., the equilibrium conversion of n-hexane to cyclohexane will be about 40 per cent at 1 atmosphere pressure. Since dehydrogenation of cyclohexane to benzene will go to completion at this temperature, ring closure of paraffins to aromatics via cyclohexanes is thermodynamically quite feasible.

There is, however, evidence that the reaction does not proceed via the free cyclohexane but proceeds directly from the olefin to the aromatic.[17]

The usual conditions for ring closure and aromatisation of n-paraffins call for the correct catalyst. Chromic oxide appears to be most commonly mentioned but other metallic oxides and sulphides are also effective; chromic oxide may be used directly or supported on active alumina; the usual temperature range is 450–550° c. A comprehensive study of the ring closure of paraffins and olefins to aromatics is given by Hoog, Verheus and Zuiderweg.[17] They used a special chromic oxide gel and worked at 465° c. and atmospheric pressure. Their results are summarised in Table 54.

---

[17] Hoog, Verheus and Zuiderweg, *Trans. Faraday Soc.*, 1939, **35**, 993.

Wherever possible, a methylene group reacts in preference to a methyl group, as would be expected in view of the relative reactivity of the CH_2 and CH_3 groups at high temperature (see, *e.g.*, Chapter 5); the recorded ring closure of *n*-decane to methylpropylbenzene with some naphthalene but no diethylbenzene is an exception to this rule.

TABLE 54

Aromatisation of paraffins

Hydrocarbon	Reaction	Degree of aromatisation %	Individual aromatic formed
n-Hexane . . .	CCCCCC	19·5	Benzene
2-Methylhexane . .	CCCCCC C	31	Toluene
n-Heptane . . .	CCCCCCC	36	Toluene
2 : 5-Dimethylhexane .	CCCCCC C C	52	mainly *p*-Xylene
3-Methylheptane . .	CCCCCCC C	35	mainly *o*- and *p*-Xylenes
n-Octane . . .	CCCCCCCC	46	mainly *o*-Xylene
n-Nonane . . .	CCCCCCCCC	58	*o*-Methylethylbenzene with some lower alkyl benzenes

The ring closure of the corresponding olefins was examined under the same conditions; provided the double bond was in the correct position, the olefins aromatised more readily than the paraffins but 2-hexene gave a lower yield of benzene than 1-hexene, presumably due to side reactions occurring during the time required for movement of the double bond to the 1-position.

Further information on the conversion of *n*-heptane to toluene is contained in a paper from the Shell Development laboratories.[18] Operation was carried out at 490° c. and atmospheric pressure with a space velocity of about 0·3 hr.$^{-1}$, using a catalyst composed of 10 per cent chromic oxide on alumina promoted with small amounts of cerium dioxide and potassium

---

[18] Archibald and Greensfelder, *Ind. Eng. Chem.*, 1945, **37**, 356.

oxide.[19] 80% conversion to toluene could be obtained but not maintained, and 40% conversion per pass was aimed at. The yield of toluene on *n*-heptane reacted was about 80–90 per cent. Toluene could be recovered from the reaction products by any of the physical methods outlined in Section 1. The catalyst slowly lost its activity due to carbon formation, and required periodical regeneration. The greater ease of aromatisation of naphthenes compared with paraffins was shown by two observations; traces of sulphate poisoned the catalyst for aromatisation of paraffins but not of naphthenes. Secondly, the ratio of processing time to regeneration time was 20 : 1 for the naphthene reaction but only 6 : 1 for the paraffin reaction.

In the processes described so far, the aromatisation of paraffins is operated at a much lower pressure than the hydroforming of the naphthenes. If the key reaction is the dehydrogenation of the paraffin to an olefin, the reason is obvious; hydroforming conditions are unfavourable to this reaction. At 500° c. and atmospheric pressure, the equilibrium conversion of *n*-hexane to 1-hexene is about 15 per cent from the free energy equation, $\Delta G = 31,660 - 33 \cdot 6T$. At the same temperature, but at a hydrogen pressure of 15 atma., the conversion of *n*-hexane to 1-hexene would be only 0·2 per cent.

Another possibility is the synthesis of aromatics from C_1 to C_4 hydrocarbons. The relative stability of benzene and the lower paraffins is given by the graph of thermodynamic stability of hydrocarbons in Fig. 11, p. 93. Benzene is more stable than methane above 1,100° c. and more stable than any other C_2 and C_3 hydrocarbon above 500° c., indicating that the homologues of methane should give benzene more readily and at lower temperature. This is so.

Dunstan, Hague and Wheeler[20] have published an extensive investigation of the thermal aromatisation of the C_2 to C_6 paraffins. Optimum temperature range was 750–900° c. and the yield of liquid products, a large part of which was aromatic, varied from 20 per cent (ethane) to 35 per cent (*n*-hexane) on feed charged. Frey and Hepp[21] were able to show that the reaction proceeded in at least two steps, a rapid endothermic dehydrogenation to olefins, and a somewhat slower exothermic aromatisation, *e.g.*,

$$CH_3CH_3 \rightarrow CH_2 : CH_2 + H_2. \qquad \Delta H = + 37 \cdot 3 \text{ k. cal.} \qquad (a)$$

$$3CH_2 : CH_2 \rightarrow \bigcirc + 3H_2. \qquad \Delta H = - 17 \cdot 7 \text{ k. cal.} \qquad (b)$$

[19] Shell Development, U.S.P. 2337190–1.
[20] *Ind. Eng. Chem.*, 1934, **26**, 307.
[21] *Ind. Eng. Chem.*, 1932, **24**, 282.

The general picture of the mode of synthesis of aromatics from low molecular weight paraffins is that they arise largely via ethylene and butadiene.

The benzene initially formed can then undergo further reaction to give alkylbenzenes and naphthalene.

The direct production of benzene from ethylene is therefore an obvious target and Dunstan, Hague and Wheeler obtained 30% yields of liquid hydrocarbons, mainly benzene, from ethylene at 800° c. Similar results have been obtained by other workers.

Conversion of acetylene to benzene and other aromatic hydrocarbons is a classical synthesis. The most favourable temperature range is 600–700° c.; the reaction does not appear to have been tried out on the manufacturing scale.

The current importance of *p*-xylene (see p. 246) has led to a number of proposals for its synthesis; the amount available in coal tar is totally inadequate, even in Western Europe, so that at present the products based on *p*-xylene are dependent on the carrying out of rather specialised operations by oil refineries.

The method of making *p*-xylene now used gives a large surplus of *m*-xylene for which there are only relatively low value outlets in fuels and solvents. Isomerisation of this *m*-xylene to the equilibrium *o*-, *m*-, *p*-xylene mixture is therefore an obvious step. The isomerisation can be brought about in the temperature range 350–550° c. using carbonium ion type isomerisation catalysts such as silica-alumina. The equilibrium in this range is very approximately 50 per cent *m*-xylene, and 25 per cent each of *o*-xylene and *p*-xylene. This equilibrium has been achieved for example with *m*-xylene at 450–500° c. and 12 atma. pressure in presence of excess hydrogen over a silica-alumina catalyst, containing some platinum (for other reasons).[22]

Ethylbenzene does not isomerise so readily to the other C_8 aromatics; it appears necessary to operate a two-stage process, the first at low temperature to hydrogenate the ethylbenzene to ethylcyclohexane, and the second stage, at a higher temperature, to isomerise the ethylcyclohexane to mixed dimethylcyclohexanes, followed immediately by dehydrogenation to the equilibrium mixture of xylenes.[22]

Ziegler has proposed to make *p*-xylene from 1-butene by conversion to 1-octene with aluminium trialkyl; this is then ring closed and dehydrogenated to a mixture of *o*- and *p*-xylenes.[23]

p-Xylene is wanted not for itself but as a route to terephthalic acid. Other syntheses of terephthalic acid would, if economically successful, reduce the demand for *p*-xylene; some possibilities are referred to on p. 247.

[22] Pitts, Connor and Leum, *Ind. Eng. Chem.*, 1955, **47**, 770.
[23] *Angew. Chem.*, 1952, **64**, 323.

(e) OUTLETS FOR BENZENE, TOLUENE AND THE XYLENES

(i) *Benzene*

In America, the outlets for benzene in the chemical industry in 1953 and 1954 were as follows.[24]

TABLE 55

Benzene end-uses in the United States

	1953 long tons p.a.	1954 long tons p.a.
Styrene	292,000	254,000
Phenol	143,000	154,000
Synthetic detergents	71,000	74,000
Aniline	42,000	36,000
D.D.T.	26,000	28,000
Chlorobenzenes	28,000	25,000
Maleic anhydride	19,000	18,000
Benzene hexachloride	15,000	15,000
Miscellaneous (nylon, nitrobenzene, diphenyls, solvents)	113,000	110,000
Total	749,000	714,000

The consumption of benzene for chemical purposes in America in 1957 is estimated to be about 1,115,000 tons, an increase of over 50 per cent on 1954. Little difference in percentage distribution is expected; the principal component of the miscellaneous uses is nylon, which will require 100,000 tons benzene in 1957, over 8 per cent of the total consumption.[25]

The normal source of benzene is as a by-product from the coke and coal gas industries. The amount available in America from this source is insufficient now and in the foreseeable future. This is what has led to the development of petroleum benzene in America, despite its higher cost. The production of petroleum benzene in the United States was 180,000 tons in 1953 and 250,000 tons in 1954.

In England, there is 2·5 to 3 times as much by-product benzene as the chemical industry requires. There is at present no case for making benzene from petroleum in the United Kingdom.

(ii) *Toluene*

Toluene end-uses in America in 1950, 1952 and 1954 are shown in Table 56.[26] The explosives outlet in 1952 was entirely for military purposes.

---

[24] *Chem. Week*, March 26, 1955, p. 91.
[25] *Chem. Week*, 1 December, 1956, p. 100.
[26] *Chem. Week*, April 24, 1954, p. 98.

Only about 50,000 tons p.a. toluene enters the chemical industry in the United States;[27] its uses are mainly for nitrotoluene, chlorinated toluenes, and saccharin.

TABLE 56

Toluene end-uses in the United States

	1950		1952		1954	
	long tons	%	long tons	%	long tons	%
1. *Production* . . .	246,000		317,000		515,000	
2. *Outlets—*						
Explosives . .	2,000	1	80,000	26	67,000	13
Aviation fuel . .	90,000	37	128,000	42	237,000	46
Solvents . . .	105,000	44	45,000	15	113,000	22
Chemical synthesis .	45,000	18	55,000	17	67,000	13
Miscellaneous . .	—	—	—	—	31,000	6
Total . . .	242,000		308,000		515,000	

Of the toluene produced in America, about 75 per cent is derived from petroleum, and the remaining 25 per cent from the coke and coal gas industries.

Because there is at present adequate toluene from the coal tar industry in Western Europe, there is no manufacture of toluene from petroleum for chemicals in this region.

(iii) Xylenes

In 1954, American production of xylenes was 350,000 long tons, 90 per cent from petroleum, 10 per cent from coal; 55 per cent was used as a solvent and in the paint industry, 37 per cent as an aviation fuel, and 8 per cent went for isomer separation, other chemical syntheses and miscellaneous outlets.

o-Xylene, which can be separated from the other xylenes by fractional distillation, is used for making phthalic anhydride by air oxidation.[28] In America, about 5 per cent is made this way, requiring about 5,000 tons p.a. o-xylene. Coal-tar naphthalene is the usual source of phthalic anhydride. The outlets of phthalic anhydride are almost entirely in resins and plasticisers.

m-Xylene is only just entering the chemical field. It is being converted

---

[27] Goldstein, *Pet. Times*, April 16, 1954, p. 377.
[28] Levine, *Chem. Eng. Prog.*, 1947, **43,** 168; Ononite, U.S.P. 2521466, U.S.P. 2574511.

to isophthalic acid by liquid phase air oxidation on a scale of some **25,000** tons p.a.:[29]

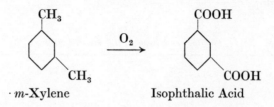

$\cdot$ *m*-Xylene   Isophthalic Acid

This process is carried out by a new oxidation process.[30] The xylenes are reacted at 300–350° c. and 150 atma. pressure with ammonium sulphate and ammonium polysulphide in aqueous solution, some of the water remaining in the liquid phase. A liquid phase process operating under milder conditions, and suitable for mixtures of the xylenes, is being developed. This uses air oxidation in acetic acid solution at about 15–30 atma. pressure and 200° c., with polyvalent metal salts and bromides as activators.[31]

The oxidation of pure *m*-xylene has been made possible by the carbon tetrachloride method of isolating *p*-xylene from C_8 aromatics, which gives pure *m*-xylene as a by-product or co-product. Isophthalic acid is a new industrial chemical, for which outlets are expected in the plastics and plasticiser industries.

p-Xylene is the most important individual xylene, as it is the key raw material for the new British synthetic fibre, Terylene (Dacron in the United States), polyethylene terephthalate. *p*-Xylene is converted to terephthalic acid either by oxidation with nitric acid under pressure,[32] or by a multi-stage air oxidation process which finally yields dimethyl terephthalate (Terylene is made from ethylene glycol and dimethyl terephthalate, not from free terephthalic acid).

One reason for esterifying the *p*-toluic acid, which melts at 180° c., is to enable the second air oxidation to be carried out in the liquid phase at the right temperature.

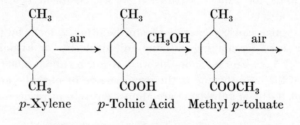

p-Xylene   *p*-Toluic Acid   Methyl *p*-toluate

---

[29] Lum and Carlston, *Ind. Eng. Chem.*, 1952, **44**, 1595.
[30] California Research Corporation, U.S.P. 2722547–9.
[31] Mid-Century Corporation, Belg. Pat. 546191.
[32] du Pont, U.S.P. 2636899.

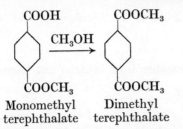

Monomethyl   Dimethyl
terephthalate   terephthalate

It is estimated that some 12,000 tons *p*-xylene were consumed in the United States for terephthalic acid in 1952.

Because the production of xylenes from coal tar in Western Europe is very low, there is insufficient *p*-xylene for this new fibre outlet. Great Britain is obtaining its supplies from the C_8 aromatic fraction of a petroleum refinery platformer; other countries have followed or will follow suit.

The present and future importance of Terylene has directed attention to making both *p*-xylene (p. 243) and terephthalic acid by routes not involving petroleum or coal tar aromatics. Among the syntheses of terephthalic acid which have been suggested are:

(*a*) dimethyl succinate to cyclohexadione dicarboxylate, subsequently dehydrated and hydrogenated:[33]

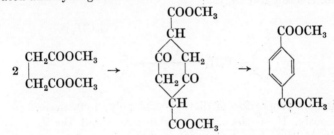

(*b*) phthalic anhydride or benzoic anhydride or benzoic acid carboxylated with carbon dioxide and potassium carbonate:[34]

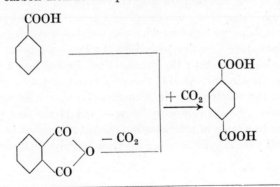

---

[33] I.C.I., Belg. Pat. 519519.
[34] Henkel, Belg. Pat. 522829, 524035.

(*c*) oxidation of *p*-diisopropylbenzene to terephthalic acid with nitric acid[35] and with air.[36]

2. Synthesis of higher aromatics from benzene and toluene

(*a*) ETHYLBENZENE AND STYRENE

Ethylbenzene is wanted for styrene, one of the components of the synthetic rubber manufactured on the largest scale during the war (butadiene-styrene copolymer — GR–S in America, Buna S in Germany). Styrene is also wanted on its own account in the high polymer field, for polystyrene, which is used in the decorative and electrical fields, for interpolymers with butadiene containing a high proportion of styrene, for styrene modified polyesters and for styrene based paints.

Commercial processes include condensation between ethylene and benzene in both the liquid and the vapour phase, and vapour phase condensation between ethyl alcohol and benzene. The liquid phase condensation is the more important process, and the following account is summarised from a description of German work.[37]

The condensation was carried out as a Friedel-Crafts reaction using aluminium chloride as catalyst:

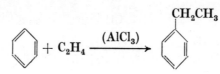

A considerable proportion of diethyl- and polyethylbenzenes are formed simultaneously. If ethylbenzene ethylates at about the same speed as benzene itself, it can be calculated that above about 20 per cent ethylation, formation of polyethylbenzenes will become serious. It is a fortunate circumstance that in this reaction the polyethylbenzenes themselves can be used to ethylate benzene; they are therefore recovered and recycled.

In the process, benzene together with recovered polyethylbenzenes and ethylene were introduced continuously into the base of a tower and fresh aluminium chloride at the top; the products overflowed into a separator, from which the aluminium chloride complex separated as a sludge and was returned to the reactor. The hydrocarbon layer, consisting of about 50 per cent benzene, 33 per cent ethylbenzene and 17 per cent polyethylbenzenes, passed to a train of fractionating columns; the first two columns gave benzene and pure ethylbenzene as overheads. Polyethylbenzenes were

---

[35] I.C.I., Belg. Pat. 536199.
[36] B.P.M., French Application 692428.
[37] C.I.O.S. 27/16.

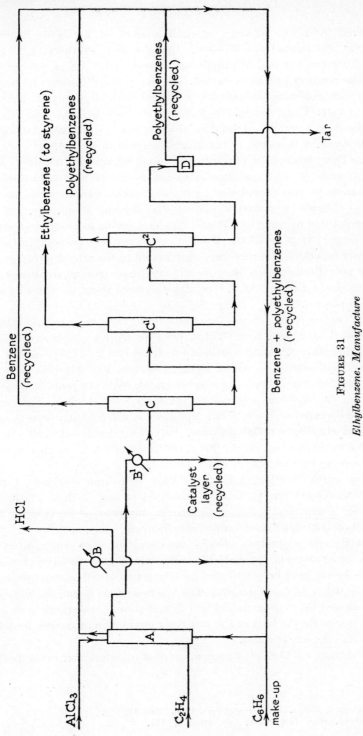

FIGURE 31

Ethylbenzene. Manufacture

recovered from the bottoms, a small amount of tar being discarded. Reaction was carried out at 90° c.; the process is exothermic, 27 k. cal. being liberated per mol of ethylbenzene produced. Cooling was provided after the reaction had once started. The mol ratio of benzene to ethylene in the feed, assuming the polyethylbenzenes were all diethylbenzene, was about 1·7 : 1. The yield of ethylbenzene on both benzene and ethylene was about 95 per cent; aluminium chloride usage was about 0·025 lb./lb. ethylbenzene. A flowsheet of the process is given in Fig. 31.

The Dow process for ethylbenzene, used in America for most of the ethylbenzene for their war-time manufacture of GR–S, is very similar to the German process except that hydrochloric acid, introduced in the form of ethyl chloride, was used to activate the aluminium chloride. The feed ratio was 1 mol benzene to 0·58 mol ethylene, giving as product 51 mol per cent benzene, 41 per cent ethylbenzene and 8 per cent polyethylbenzenes; the lower polyethylbenzenes were recirculated to the ethylation stage. The higher polyethylbenzenes were de-ethylated by vigorous treatment with aluminium chloride at 200° c. Overall yields were about the same as in the German process.[38]

The vapour phase process for ethylbenzene from benzene and ethylene is operated at 275° c. and 60 atm. pressure with a phosphoric acid on kieselguhr catalyst.[39] With a ratio of 4 mols benzene/mol ethylene, the ratio of polyethylbenzene to monoethylbenzene was 1 : 6·05; this ratio was dependent on the benzene to ethylene ratio. With 16 mols benzene/mol ethylene, the ratio of poly/monoethylbenzene was 1 : 20·8. The process could be operated with dilute ethylene gases at a sufficiently high temperature and ethylene partial pressure. Polyethylbenzenes do not ethylate benzene in the vapour phase, but their recirculation tends to reduce the ratio of poly- to monoethylbenzene formed.

It is worth mentioning that one large petroleum company, Cosden, intend to subject the C_8 fraction obtained in one of their Platforming processes to superfractionation, to recover ethylbenzene for styrene. Their C_8 fraction contains 27 per cent of ethylbenzene.

For styrene production, ethylbenzene must be very pure, and in particular must contain no diethylbenzene which goes to divinylbenzene. Two processes have been operated for converting ethylbenzene to styrene; catalytic dehydrogenation operated in America and in Germany, and oxidation followed by hydrogenation and dehydration. Catalytic dehydrogenation was used for the bulk of the American production of styrene for GR–S, and is still the major route.

Conditions for the dehydrogenation of styrene are controlled both by

---

[38] Mitchell, *Trans. Amer. Inst. Chem. Eng.*, 1946, **42**, 293.
[39] *Trans. Amer. Inst. Chem. Eng.*, 1945, **41**, 463.

the theoretical equilibrium and by the thermal stability of the reactants and products. The theoretical equilibrium in the reaction:

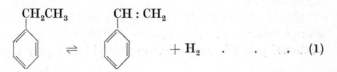

$$\qquad\qquad\qquad\qquad\qquad\qquad\qquad\qquad + H_2 \qquad . \qquad . \qquad . \qquad (1)$$

is $\Delta G = 29{,}720 - 31 \cdot 1T$. At 630° c., this corresponds to 84% conversion at 1 atma. pressure, and to 98% conversion at 0·1 atma. pressure. The equilibrium is more favourable at higher temperatures, but ethylbenzene and styrene are then unstable, suffering thermal cracking to toluene and benzene. The low pressure for good conversion at 630° c. was achieved not by operating *in vacuo*, but by use of steam as inert diluent. This has other advantages; the steam prevents carbon deposition, any carbon being gasified by the water gas reaction. Secondly, the high temperatures required can be obtained without exposing ethylbenzene to an unduly high temperature, by superheating the steam and mixing with relatively cool ethylbenzene vapour. At 630° c. in presence of steam, attainment of equilibrium in reaction (1) was relatively slow when carried out thermally, and recourse to dehydrogenation catalysts was necessary.

The German process[37] used promoted zinc oxide as catalyst† and operated at 40% conversion per pass at 560–600° c. and atmospheric pressure. The steam to ethylbenzene ratio was 1·6 : 1 by weight. The endothermic reaction was carried out in the usual type of multi-tubular reactor; this was constructed of 18/8 austenitic steel, the tubes being lined with a 98 per cent copper-2 per cent manganese alloy to reduce cracking and side reactions. Traces of benzene and toluene were formed but the yield of styrene was over 90 per cent on ethylbenzene reacted. The crude product was worked up in a train of five stills; to reduce polymerisation, most of these stills operated *in vacuo* and were lined with tin. The purity of the final styrene was at least 99·5 per cent.[37]

The American dehydrogenation process,[38] like the ethylation of benzene, was also similar to the German process, although worked out independently. It operated at 630° c. (600–660° c., depending on the age and activity of the catalyst), with 2·6 lb. steam/lb. ethylbenzene, using the Standard Oil Development Co. catalyst No. 1707 developed for the dehydrogenation of *n*-butenes to butadiene (see Chapter 12, p. 197); the conversion per pass was 37 per cent and the yield of finished styrene 90 per cent on ethylbenzene. The ethylbenzene-styrene product from the dehydrogenators was worked up by distillation *in vacuo* in presence of sulphur, a non-volatile inhibitor of polymerisation, and all possible steps were taken

---

† Approximate composition, 85 per cent ZnO, 5 per cent CaO, 5 per cent K_2SO_4, 3 per cent K_2CrO_4, 2 per cent KOH (C.I.O.S. 22/21).

to cut down pressure drop and thus to avoid exposing styrene to a temperature higher than 90° c. The finished styrene was stabilised with *tert*-butylcatechol.

Liquid phase oxidation of ethylbenzene in presence of metal catalysts gives a mixture of acetophenone and phenylmethylcarbinol by the conventional peroxide mechanism explained in Chapter 4, p. 55.

$$
\begin{array}{c}
CH_3 \\
CH_2
\end{array}
 + O_2 \rightarrow
\begin{array}{c}
CH_3 \\
CHOOH
\end{array}
\longrightarrow
\left[
\begin{array}{l}
\begin{array}{c} CH_3 \\ CO \end{array} + H_2O \quad . \quad . \quad (2) \\[2em]
\begin{array}{c} CH_3 \\ CHOH \end{array} + O^- \quad . \quad . \quad (3)
\end{array}
\right.
$$

The active oxygen liberated when phenylmethylcarbinol is formed, reaction (3), oxidises the ethylbenzene to benzoic acid, the proportion of acid corresponding to the amount of carbinol formed, on the assumption that the reaction is:[40]

$$ C_6H_5CH_2CH_3 + 4O^- \rightarrow C_6H_5COOH + CH_2O + H_2O $$

The mixture of ketone and carbinol is hydrogenated to phenyl methyl carbinol which is smoothly dehydrated to styrene in the vapour phase at about 300–350° c. over dehydration catalysts such as active alumina. This process has been operated in America.

The Germans operated the oxidation process to give acetophenone as the main product, working at 115–120° c. and 4·5 atma. air pressure with a mixed metal naphthenate catalyst. At 60% conversion, the yield of acetophenone was 86 per cent; the acetophenone-carbinol ratio was 16 : 1.[41]

In 1955, about 450,000 tons of styrene were made in U.S.A.; 50 per cent went to polystyrene, 40 per cent to GR–S synthetic rubber, and the remainder to high styrene-butadiene copolymers and miscellaneous outlets.[42]

(*b*) ETHYLTOLUENE AND XYLENE; METHYL- AND DIMETHYL-STYRENES

The scale of making styrene and the diversity of its outlets have led to studies of its homologues; their full scale manufacture is being established.

---

[40] Sully, *Trans. Faraday Soc.*, 1946, **42**, 260.
[41] B.I.O.S. 1053.
[42] *Chem. Week*, 24 March, 1956, p. 76.

Toluene is ethylated in the same way as benzene and the ethyltoluene dehydrogenated to methylstyrene. The commercial product made by this route is a mixture of about 65 per cent *m*-methylstyrene and 35 per cent *p*-methylstyrene with only a trace of *o*-methylstyrene.[43]

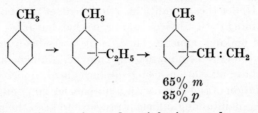

65% *m*
35% *p*

This methylstyrene isomer is used mainly in copolymers for water paints and in polyesters.

A different mixture of isomers is obtained by a totally different synthesis. Ditolylethane is made by reaction between acetylene and toluene in presence of a sulphuric acid-mercury sulphate catalyst; this is then cracked over a kaolin catalyst at 400–600° c. in presence of excess steam to 1 mol of toluene and 1 mol of a mixture of methylstyrenes containing 32 per cent *o*-methylstyrene, 3 per cent *m*-methylstyrene and 65 per cent *p*-methylstyrene.[44] This methylstyrene gives a polymer with an appreciably higher heat distortion temperature than straight polystyrene:

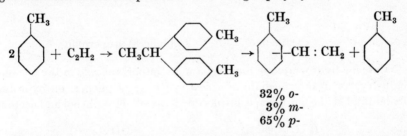

32% *o*-
3% *m*-
65% *p*-

If acetaldehyde is used in the initial step instead of acetylene, the final product contains 85–90 per cent of *p*-methylstyrene, which is not technically desirable for polymerisation; it might be a source of terephthalic acid.

With the xylenes, the ethylation route is not used but the second diarylethane route is. In this case, acetaldehyde and not acetylene gives those isomers which are technically wanted.[44] In a mixture of technical xylenes, the meta isomer reacts the fastest, leaving *o*- and *p*-xylenes in the residue; on pyrolysis nearly pure *m*-xylene is obtained. The dimethylstyrene contains 94 per cent of the 2 : 4-dimethyl isomer and 4 per cent of the 3 : 4-dimethyl isomer. This dimethylstyrene mixture gives a polymer of higher heat distortion temperature than either poly-*o*-methylstyrene or polystyrene.

[43] Boundy and Boyer, 'Styrene', *Reinhold*, 1952.
[44] Dixon and Saunders, *Ind. Eng. Chem.*, 1954, **46**, 652; *Chem. Eng.*, Sept. 1956, p. 118.

(c) CUMENE (ISOPROPYLBENZENE)

Propylene reacts much more readily than ethylene with benzene; the vapour phase isopropylation of benzene is carried out at 250° c. and 25 atma. over a supported phosphoric acid catalyst[39] with refinery propane-propylene. Under these conditions, ethylene does not react so that refinery gases containing both ethylene and propylene, but freed from butenes, can be used for making cumene. There is little tendency to form polyalkyl-benzenes and no problem in isolating cumene. Cumene has also been made by liquid phase alkylation, using sulphuric acid, under conditions similar to the alkylation of isobutane with *n*-butene. 86–90% sulphuric acid is used at 20–50° c., maintaining sufficient pressure to keep the propane-propylene feed in the liquid phase.[45] Complete propylene conversion takes place in the process.

Cumene was made during the war as a component of aviation fuel; it is now one of the raw materials of the chemical industry. Its first outlet was for cumene hydroperoxide, used as the catalyst for the American GR–S synthetic rubber. This was made by blowing with air until a certain percentage of cumene was oxidised, and isolating the peroxide:

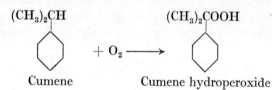

Cumene hydroperoxide now has a more important role in the chemical industry, as an intermediate in a new synthesis of phenol; on hydrolysis under mild acid conditions, it breaks down mainly into phenol and acetone:

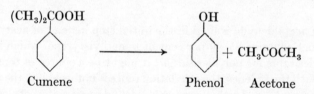

This reaction, discovered by Hock and Lang,[46] has since been developed by Distillers Co. and by the Hercules Powder Co. The series of steps has been outlined by Salt.[47] The peroxide stage is carried out at moderate temperatures in presence of alkalies either in aqueous emulsion or under anhydrous conditions. Conversion is always kept low to reduce by-product formation, the unchanged cumene being separated and recycled. It is

[45] McAllister, Anderson and Bullard, *Chem. Eng. Prog.*, 1947, **43**, 189.
[46] Hock and Lang, *Ber.*, 1944, **77**, 257.
[47] Salt, *Chem. and Ind.*, Aug. 10, 1953, p. 846.

claimed that the peroxide stage proceeds more smoothly in presence of a trace of formaldehyde.[48]

The hydrolysis step is normally conducted with dilute aqueous sulphuric acid. Besides phenol and acetone, by-products such as acetophenone, α-methylstyrene and higher phenols are also formed and have to be removed. The yield of phenol on benzene is about 85 per cent and an equivalent amount of acetone is also obtained.

The hydrolysis step has proved to be corrosive in practice; an improvement claimed is to use non-acidic elements such as sulphur or phosphorus for hydrolysis in boiling hydrocarbon solution[49] instead of aqueous acids.

This cumene to phenol process is a good example of a petroleum chemical process. It uses petroleum propylene and air to oxidise benzene to phenol. Its economics depend upon the realisation obtained for the co-product, acetone, another petroleum chemical. The routes which it threatens are all consumers of heavy inorganic chemicals. They are sulphonation of benzene, followed by caustic fusion; chlorination followed by hydrolysis with aqueous sodium carbonate; chlorination followed by high temperature vapour phase hydrolysis with steam (in this process, the chlorine is a carrier). The direct air oxidation of benzene is not a technical success.

The end-use picture for phenol in the United States in 1954 was on a production of 190,000 tons:[50]

Outlets	% by wt.
Phenol formaldehyde resins	48
Other chemicals (pentachlorphenol, salicylic acid, diphenylol propane, etc.) .	22
Alkylphenols	7
2 : 4-D (selective weed-killer)	6
Export and miscellaneous	17
	100

In 1954, 87 per cent of phenol was made from benzene, 5 per cent from cumene, and 7 per cent was isolated from coal tar. In 1954, American production of cumene was reported as 15,000 tons. This corresponds approximately to the chemical outlets indicated above.

(d) tert-BUTYLBENZENE AND tert-BUTYLTOLUENE

tert-Butylbenzene has been made from isobutene and benzene in the same way as cumene, by vapour phase reaction over a supported phosphoric acid catalyst. It has been used as a component of aviation fuel but has not so far found any chemical outlet.

tert-Butyltoluene is made in the same way. It has been oxidised with

---

[48] Rhone-Poulenc, U.S.P. 2680139.
[49] Rhone-Poulenc, U.S.P. 2668859.
[50] Matthew, Messing and James, *Chem. Eng.*, Nov. 1955, p. 286.

air in the liquid phase at 130–200° c. using cobalt salts as catalysts, to give
p-tert-butylbenzoic acid:

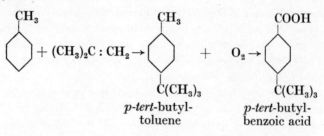

$$p\text{-}tert\text{-butyl-} \qquad p\text{-}tert\text{-butyl-}$$
$$\text{toluene} \qquad \text{benzoic acid}$$

The process is operated to give about 50 per cent conversion per pass.
Moderate pressures of 5–15 atma. are used.[51]

p-tert-Butylbenzoic acid is now available in pilot quantities; it has
potentialities in alkyds and in other directions.

(e) LONG CHAIN ALKYL AROMATICS

Long chain alkyl aromatics are required mainly as intermediates for
detergents. They are made by alkylation of benzene with the alkyl chloride
or with an olefin under Friedel-Crafts conditions.

The process first developed (in the 1930's) was based on chlorinating a
kerosene fraction to 'keryl chloride' which was then condensed with
benzene to 'kerylbenzene'. The kerosene fraction boiled at 220–245° c.
and corresponding to $n\text{-}C_{12}\text{--}C_{13}$ paraffins, which had been solvent and acid
treated to remove aromatics. Chlorination is carried out at 60° c. to give
50 per cent conversion to the mono-chloro-derivative (Chapter 5, p. 75).
This is condensed with excess of benzene using aluminium chloride as
catalyst, at 50° c.[52] Both *n*- and isoparaffins react but what happens to
the naphthenes is not known. The product is worked up to recover 'kerylbenzene' and to recycle the excess of unchanged benzene and kerosene.

The second type of alkylbenzene uses propylene tetramer as the olefin.
The tetramer is added to excess of benzene at 30–60° c. using aluminium
chloride as catalyst; hydrofluoric acid can also be used as the catalyst but
sulphuric acid is unsuitable owing to by-product formation. The product is
neutralised and purified by distillation, the excess benzene being recycled.
The dodecylbenzene, obtained in over 80 per cent yield, boils at 280–320° c.
and contains at least 99 per cent of alkylbenzenes.[53] Propylene tetramer
was chosen as likely to give the most homogeneous branch chain C_{12} alkyl
group. Other branch chain C_{12} olefins, such as triisobutene, tend to fragment
under the reaction conditions, and to give lower alkylbenzenes.

[51] Cole, Fairbairn and Detling, *Chemical Engineering Science*, 1954, **3**, Supplement,
p. 67.
[52] Sharrah and Feigner, *Ind. Eng. Chem.*, 1954, **46**, 248.
[53] Birch, *J. Inst. Pet.*, 1952, **38**, 69.

Either alkylbenzene is sulphonated with 98 per cent sulphuric acid or with oleum below 40° C, to avoid discoloration and fission of the alkyl chain. The sulphonates are isolated by dilution with water, separation of the aqueous layer and neutralisation of the organic layer.

The sodium dodecylbenzene sulphonates are the most widely used synthetic detergents in the United States and Great Britain. Toluene cannot be used in place of benzene for making satisfactory detergents of this class. Propylene trimer is used to a limited extent for detergents.

3. Other routes to higher aromatics

In the technical processes for dehydrogenation of C_6 to C_8 naphthenes dealt with in section 2 (*b*), some C_9 and C_{10} alkylbenzenes are usually obtained. They are isolated and sold in the solvents industry as Hi-Test naphtha in competition with similar fractions from coal tar.

In high temperature cracking and pyrolysis of petroleum fractions, aromatics are invariably obtained to some extent. One example is the Rittman process of vapour phase cracking, designed in 1915 to give maximum aromatics. It operated at 700° c. and 10 atma. pressure and gave a liquid product containing 6–8 per cent benzene, and 4–6 per cent each of toluene and C_8 aromatics.

The formation of aromatics is believed to arise in the same way as in Section 1(*d*), p. 243, by combination of the lower olefins and diolefins produced in the cracking of the high molecular weight paraffins. Aromatics also arise in the more conventional cracking processes, by the mechanisms discussed in Sections 1(*b*) and 1(*d*), dehydrogenation of naphthenes and ring closure-dehydrogenation of paraffins; another way in which the simpler aromatics are formed is by dealkylation of long chain alkyl or polyalkylbenzenes. A simple example is the thermal cracking of styrene and ethylbenzene to toluene and benzene, referred to on p. 251.

A new way of making aromatics from paraffinic hydrocarbons is the Catarole catalytic cracking process, referred to in Chapter 7, p. 99; this operates at 630–680° c. and atmospheric pressure over a copper or copper-iron catalyst. About 40–50 per cent of the feedstock is converted to liquid hydrocarbons which are almost entirely aromatic. From cracking a paraffinic naphtha, b.p. 113–183° c., 37 per cent of liquid products were obtained, of which about half consisted of C_6, C_7, and C_8 benzenoid aromatics; the C_8 fraction contained both ethylbenzene and styrene. Indene and isopropenylbenzene (α-methylstyrene) were present in the next fraction; naphthalene, the two methylnaphthalenes, a number of dimethylnaphthalenes, diphenyl, acenaphthene, fluorene, anthracene, pyrene and chrysene were isolated in appreciable quantity and high purity from the higher fractions;[54] the constituents of this aromatic product resemble, both in

---

[54] *Pet. Times*, 12 October, 1946, p. 1078.

variety and to a lesser extent in composition, the aromatics from the carbonisation of coal, a reaction carried out at a much higher temperature.

Polynuclear aromatics are present in certain types of crude petroleum, and are produced by some specialised cracking processes. High temperature cracking of liquid feed stocks to give, *e.g.*, ethylene, also yield 2–4 per cent of naphthalene and 2–4 per cent of methylnaphthalenes.

Borneo crude oils contain 25–40 per cent aromatics, of which 6–7 per cent belong to the naphthalene series; the following individual members have been isolated:

> Naphthalene
> 1- and 2-methylnaphthalene
> Two dimethylnaphthalenes

2-Isoamylnaphthalene has also been isolated from Burma oil. A straight run kerosene fraction, b.p. 163–300° c., has been shown to contain tetralin and 1- and 2-methyltetralins, as well as naphthalene and the methyl naphthalenes. The 200–230° c. cut from Ponca City distillate contained 0·02 per cent tetralin, 0·1 per cent methyltetralins, 0·03 per cent naphthalene, 0·06 per cent 1-methylnaphthalene, and 0·13 per cent 2-methylnaphthalene.[1]

In the pyrolysis of gaseous hydrocarbons for benzene production (Section 2 (*e*)), the heavy residue boiling above 200° c., from fractionation of the liquid products, consists very largely of polynuclear hydrocarbons, naphthalene and anthracene predominating.[55] Naphthalene, anthracene, and higher polynuclear hydrocarbons are also produced by other high temperature reactions; indeed, the coking of petroleum oils on distillation is regarded as a process of progressive increase in condensation of aromatic nuclei.

Until recently, there was no indication that petroleum sources of these polynuclear aromatics could compete with the existing coal tar sources. We now have the Catarole process (this Chapter, p. 257), which yields from straight chain petroleum fractions an aromatic fraction containing the same hydrocarbons as coal tar, and reports that petroleum companies are planning to isolate naphthalene itself and methylnaphthalenes from petroleum as by-products from the heavy residues of catalytic cracking. They occur at the upper end of the petrol fraction and the lower end of the gas oil fraction.[56]

Substituted polycyclic hydrocarbons with more than one or two methyl groups cannot survive high temperatures, and when these are wanted, they have to be prepared synthetically, using the methods outlined in Section 2 (*e*), p. 256. An example is the manufacture of mono- and di-*sec*-amylnaphthalene from naphthalene and chloropentane or *n*-pentenes.[57]

---

[55] Dunstan and Howes, *J. Inst. Pet. Tech.*, 1936, **22**, 347.
[56] *Chem. Week*, 25 August, 1956, p. 60.
[57] Hunt, *Ind. Eng. Chem.*, 1943, **35**, 1048.

4. Heterocyclics—petroleum pyridines

Formerly, pyridine and the alkylpyridines, like the simpler aromatic hydrocarbons, were available economically only as by-products of the coal-tar industry.

In America, because of the shortage of aromatics from coal, it has been necessary to develop a second route to aromatics from petroleum. The same position is developing there with pyridine and pyridine bases.

The first alkylpyridine which is a petroleum chemical is 2-methyl-5-ethylpyridine. This is made by reaction between excess of ammonia and paraldehyde in the liquid phase at about 200° c.–250° c. and 50 atma. pressure in one hour contact time, using ammonium acetate as catalyst:[58]

$$NH_3 + 4CH_3CHO \longrightarrow \underset{N}{\overset{C_2H_5}{\bigcirc}}_{CH_3} + 4H_2O$$

The yield is about 70–80 per cent, with some 10 per cent of mixed picolines as by-products. The process can be operated continuously.[59]

The main outlets of methylethylpyridine are as an intermediate for nicotinic acid (pyridine-3-carboxylic acid), used for pharmaceuticals, and for substituted vinylpyridines used in the high polymer field. Two different vinylpyridines can be made, 2-methyl-5-vinylpyridine, made by high-temperature dehydrogenation, and 2-vinyl-5-ethylpyridine, by reaction with formaldehyde, followed by dehydration.

Several plants have been built in the United States for manufacture of 2-methyl-5-ethylpyridine.[60]

Because of outlets for pyridine and the picolines in the textile auxiliary and pharmaceutical industries, their synthesis from petroleum sources has been investigated. One plant is believed to be in operation; it may be operating an old synthesis from acetylene and ammonia or a modification of the ammonia-paraldehyde reaction in which a mixture of acetaldehyde and formaldehyde is reacted with ammonia.[61]

---

[58] *Chem. Trade J.*, Nov. 7, 1952, p. 1100.
[59] Distillers, B.P. 534494.
[60] *Chem. Week*, January 31, 1953, p. 30.
[61] Othmer and Levy, *Ind. Eng. Chem.*, 1955, **47**, 789.

CHAPTER 15

ACETYLENE

THE conventional process for the manufacture of acetylene is from calcium carbide, which is made by the action of the high temperature electric arc on lime and coke:

$$CaO + 3C \rightarrow CaC_2 + CO$$
$$CaC_2 + H_2O \rightarrow CaO + C_2H_2$$

On treatment with water, calcium carbide gives concentrated (99%) acetylene directly. The chief factor in the cost is the electric power required for the high temperature and heat of the reaction, and carbide manufacture is therefore usually sited where abundant supplies of cheap hydroelectric power are available, e.g., in Norway and Canada. The power consumption per ton of carbide is about 3,000 kWh, which corresponds to 4·5 kWh per lb. acetylene.[1]

There is a second route to calcium carbide from coal, the thermal carbide process. This involves use of oxygen to burn coke *in situ* to provide the high temperature necessary for making carbide. The process is still in the experimental stage.[1a]

The possibility of manufacture of acetylene from petroleun hydrocarbons for many years attracted great attention and has now been established technically under conditions of free economy. This is an example of a petroleum chemicals process which has long been known but has been reduced to practice mainly because of changes in the relative economics of the alternative processes.

Acetylene is thermodynamically very unstable at ordinary temperatures but, being a highly endothermic compound, it becomes less unstable with rise in temperature. Although it has been synthesised from carbon and hydrogen in the electric arc, it is regarded as unstable with respect to its elements at all temperatures since at temperatures at which ΔG for the reaction (1) approaches 0 (3,940° c.), molecular hydrogen dissociates into monatomic hydrogen:

$$C_2H_2 \rightleftharpoons 2C + H_2. \quad \Delta H_{298} = + 54·2 \text{ k. cal.} \qquad . \qquad (1)$$
$$\Delta G = 53,580 - 13·0T$$

Nevertheless, above about 1,200° c., acetylene becomes the least unstable of the hydrocarbons and therefore synthesis from the other hydrocarbons is possible. The change of relative stability of acetylene with respect to other hydrocarbons is indicated by Fig. 11, p. 93.

---

[1] Hasche, *Chem. Met. Eng.*, 1942, **49**(7), 78.
[1a] Wurster, *Chem. Ing. Tech.*, 1956, **28**, 1.

In making acetylene from hydrocarbon gases, we shall, however, encounter two problems; above 1,200° c., all gas reactions proceed rapidly and the decomposition of acetylene into its elements must be arrested by very short contact time. Secondly, acetylene becomes increasingly unstable below 1,200° c. and other hydrocarbons become more stable; therefore the acetylene has to be quenched quickly to prevent both decomposition and reaction with other gases present. In the synthesis of acetylene from hydrocarbons, there is also an increase in volume due to formation of hydrogen, so operation at reduced pressure or in presence of a diluent should be advantageous.

In considering the theoretical possibility of synthesis of acetylene from hydrocarbons, we shall restrict ourselves to methane, ethane, propane and ethylene. The free energy changes for the reactions are shown in Table 57, based on the data in Table 22, p. 92.

TABLE 57

Thermochemistry and free energy equations in syntheses of acetylene

Reaction	Eqn. no.	ΔH_{298} k. cal.	ΔG	Temperatures at which		
				$K_p = 0 \cdot 1$	$K_p = 1$	$K_p = 10$
				° c.	° c.	° c.
$2CH_4 \rightleftharpoons C_2H_2 + 3H_2$	(2)	90·0	$95,400 - 64 \cdot 0T$	1,120	1,220	1,330
$C_2H_6 \rightleftharpoons C_2H_2 + 2H_2$	(3)	74·4	$78,220 - 63 \cdot 8T$	870	953	1,050
$\frac{2}{3}C_3H_8 \rightleftharpoons C_2H_2 + 1\frac{2}{3}H_2$	(4)	70·7	$73,690 - 63 \cdot 5T$	810	890	977
$C_2H_4 \rightleftharpoons C_2H_2 + H_2$	(5)	41·7	$43,910 - 31 \cdot 6T$	940	1,120	1,350

The equilibrium therefore favours conversion of methane to acetylene above about 1,200° c.; the higher paraffins, being less stable than methane, will give acetylene at lower temperatures. Ethylene will also give acetylene at a lower temperature than methane, but owing to the different slope of the curve of change of free energy against temperature, it is more difficult to drive the conversion of ethylene to completion. These points will be illustrated by consideration of certain of the technical methods of acetylene synthesis.

The problems associated with rapid transfer of heat to flowing gases at high temperatures have been encountered repeatedly in the earlier chapters of this book. The methods used to provide the heat for acetylene synthesis include the conventional method of heating in tubes, by employment of a regenerative furnace, by electric arc and by partial internal combustion. Each of these will be discussed in turn.

Rapid quenching of reactor gases to prevent decomposition of acetylene is relatively easy; it is usually achieved by spraying in water. The final problem is the separation and purification of acetylene, which is obtained as a dilute gas. This is dealt with in Section 4.

1. Direct and regenerative heating

The occurrence of acetylene in detectable traces in the pyrolysis of hydro-carbon oils and gases at and above 800° c. has been mentioned in Chapter 7, p. 101. As the temperature is raised above 800° c., the proportion of acetylene increases but in short contact time ethylene is one of the major products up to about 1,100–1,200° c.

Conditions described for the production of acetylene from methane include temperatures from 1,400° c. to 2,000° c. at very short contact time, a fraction of a second, and preferably at reduced pressure. The maximum possible concentration of acetylene is 25 per cent (equation (2)) and this is not attained in practice.

The translation of a multi-tubular process for this reaction from the laboratory to the large scale is fraught with almost insurmountable prob-lems. The Wulff process started off as a tube process in the early 1920's. Its status in 1942 is described by Hasche[1] and developments in the last few years by Coberly, Bogart and Schiller.[2]

The original process operated above 1,100° c. with a contact time of less than one second, using steam as a diluent to reduce the partial pressure of the hydrocarbon gas. Methane required a temperature of 1,500° c. but the higher hydrocarbons could be pyrolised at about 1,200° c. In the laboratory, carborundum tubes were used, but on the pilot scale, a re-generative furnace built of carborundum bricks was used. This operated on a $4\frac{1}{2}$ minute cycle, three minutes heating and purging, and $1\frac{1}{2}$ minutes cracking.

Average gas compositions reported by Hasche were:

Product gas	Propane (a) % by vol.	Butane (b) % by vol.
H_2	49·8	38·0
CH_4	17·0	26·4
C_2H_2	16·4	12·3
C_2H_4	8·9	17·6
Other gases	7·9	5·7
	100·0	100·0

Notes—
(a) C_3H_8/H_2O ratio, 1 : 6·5; laboratory scale.
(b) Pilot scale.

At this stage, the two main difficulties were the need to use paraffin gases higher than methane, and the fact that about as much ethylene as acetylene was obtained. Both these are due to the problem of obtaining a sufficiently high temperature at atmospheric pressure.

Both difficulties appear to have been resolved by operating under vacuum (about $\frac{1}{2}$ atma.) but still with steam dilution, so as to operate with a very low partial pressure of hydrocarbon gas.[2] About 5 mols steam per mol of hydrocarbon are used, the partial pressure of the hydrocarbon being

      [2] Coberly, Bogart and Schiller, *Pet. Proc.*, 1953, **8**, 377.

less than 0·1 atma. The Wulff furnaces now operate on a four part cycle, a pyrolysis step and a heating step in one direction of the gas flow and a pyrolysis step and a heating step in the reverse direction. Each step is of 1 minute duration; continuous operation is achieved by building the Wulff furnaces in pairs. Gas residence time in the reaction section has been reduced to about 0·03 seconds, which minimises decomposition of acetylene. The furnace chequers are built of 99% alumina. Results from natural gas (95% methane), ethane and propane are summarised in Table 58.

TABLE 58

Acetylene
Wulff Process gas compositions

Product gas composition	Feed gas		
	Natural gas	Ethane	Propane
	vol. %	vol. %	vol. %
H$_2$	59·7	65·0	55·2
CH$_4$	18·5	6·0	15·5
C$_2$H$_2$	6·0	13·0	10·9
C$_2$H$_4$	—	2·0	3·2
N$_2$	2·2	2·2	5·4
CO	10·0	8·4	7·0
Other gases	3·6	3·4	2·8
Overall Acetylene yield, lb./lb. feed gas .	0·26	0·49	0·40

The final figure for acetylene yield given in this table is based on the yield of concentrated acetylene of at least 98% purity.

The ratio of ethylene to acetylene has been greatly reduced. Bearing in mind the cost of purification, methane appears a less attractive feedstock than ethane or even propane.

In Germany, a regenerative process for making acetylene from methane was developed by Ruhrchemie A-G[3]. This operated at 0·1 atma. pressure in vertical towers lined with alumina and sillimanite; the maximum temperature was 1,500–1,600° c., with a two minute cycle, one minute on blow and one on make. The exit gas was water quenched immediately; its average composition was:

Composition	% by vol.
H$_2$	70·7
CH$_4$	15·7
C$_2$H$_2$	9·8
C$_4$H$_2$	0·3
N$_2$	3·5
	100·0

[3] B.I.O.S. 747; B.I.O.S. 1038.

The acetylene was isolated by solution in water under 10 atma. pressure and release in stages. Due to the need to compress the whole of the exit gases from 0·1 atma. to 10 atma. pressure, the total power consumption of the process was high. This process was operated on the pilot scale in Germany and plans had been made for building a plant with a capacity of 1,500 tons p.a. acetylene in Hungary.

A modification of the regenerative process employing the fluid catalyst technique has been described.[4] Heat is supplied to the gases undergoing pyrolysis to acetylene by introduction of a suspension or fluidised mass of refractory solids which is continuously withdrawn from the reactor, re-heated externally by combustion of fuel gas, and recycled to the reactor.

Under these extreme conditions of temperature, involving alternately reducing and oxidising conditions, it seems doubtful whether a suitable inert refractory material has yet been developed.

2. Electric arc

The method of quick heating by passing the gases through an electric arc has been very actively pursued. For some years in the 1930's, a pilot plant was operated in the United States, but the only large scale installation is one built and operated by the Germans at Huls.[5] This had an output of 200 tons-day 97% acetylene, producing hydrogen, ethylene and carbon black as by-products.

The feed gas was either a methane-ethane mixture obtained from the hydrogenation of coal, or methane from a nearby source of natural gas. Reaction was carried out in a 1 m. long water cooled steel tube, 9·5 cm. inside diameter. The electrodes were copper, the high tension lead situated in an expanded head section, and the low tension, which was earthed, being a copper gasket at the top of the steel tube. The feed gases entered an expanded head section, and were given a high velocity swirling motion before passing through the arc zone and down the steel tube; the maximum gas velocity down the reactor tube was over 1,500 miles per hour. The arc operated at 1,000 amp., 7,000 volt D.C., requiring 7,000 kW for a gas input of 2,800 m.^{3}/hr. Mean maximum gas temperature was 1,600° c. and the gases were quenched to 150° c. by a water spray at the bottom of the tube. One arc produced about 15 tons/day acetylene.

The arc was operated to give 50% conversion, the gases being separated and unchanged methane and ethane recycled with fresh make-up hydro-carbon gas. Typical analyses of inlet and outlet gases are given in Table 59.

The outlet gas contained a number of impurities, which required removal; besides carbon black, appreciable quantities of hydrogen cyanide, benzene and naphthalene, a trace of hydrogen sulphide, and some diacety-lene, CH ⋮ CC ⋮ CH, were present.

---

[4] Standard Oil Ind., U.S.P. 2405395.
[5] C.I.O.S. 22/21 and C.I.O.S. 30/83.

After water quenching in the reactor tube, the carbon black was removed in cyclones and water towers, benzene and naphthalene absorbed by scrubbing with oil (which also absorbed much of the diacetylene),

TABLE 59

Acetylene by arc; gas analysis

Individual gases present	Gases from coal hydrogenation[†] $(C_{1 \cdot 1 - 1 \cdot 5})$		Natural gas $(C_{0 \cdot 95})$[†]	
	Analysis of inlet gas* %	Analysis of outlet gas %	Analysis of inlet gas* %	Analysis of outlet gas %
C_2H_2	2·7	16·2	1·5	13·3
Olefins . . .	3·2	3·6	1·4	0·9
CH_4 and homologues .	74·5	25·1	80·2	27·8
H_2	10·9	50·5	2·5	46·0
CO	1·4	1·0	3·0	2·9
CO_2 . . .	0·2	—	0·3	—
O_2	0·2	0·2	0·3	0·2
N_2	6·9	3·4	10·8	8·9

hydrogen sulphide absorbed by iron oxide, and hydrogen cyanide dissolved in water. The purified mixed gases were then treated as described in Section 4 for recovery of acetylene, ethylene and hydrogen, methane and ethane being recycled to the arc.

100 kg. of hydrocarbon gas gave 45 kg. 97% acetylene, 9·2 kg. 98% ethylene, 5·3 kg. carbon black, and 13 kg. 98% hydrogen.

The power consumption in the arc was 4·5 kWh/lb. acetylene produced. The acetylene was dilute, 13–16%, and additional power is required for purification and concentration to give 97% acetylene. One report gives total power consumption of 5·6 kWh/lb. concentrated acetylene.[6] At the beginning of this chapter, the average power requirements for acetylene from carbide were given as 4·5 kWh/lb. concentrated acetylene. However, comparison of the relative costs of the two processes is not as simple as the power consumption figures suggest. Not only may the starting materials be of different value, the arc process gives by-products which may swing the decision in its favour under suitable local conditions.

There are a considerable number of variants of the arc process. Not only can the arc be struck between gases, it has been operated beneath the surface of hydrocarbon liquids such as gas oil or kerosene, the gaseous products of reaction being immediately quenched by contact with cold liquid; other methods of operating the arc process with liquids are by spraying the oil through the arc, or by cooling the gaseous reaction products by pumping cold fresh oil through the electrodes. In all cases, a complex

---

* 50 per cent make up gas + 50 per cent recycle gas.

† Make up gas.

[6] C.I.O.S. 26/51.

gas mixture containing acetylene, not dissimilar in composition to the gas mixtures given in Table 57, is obtained. For these processes, Hasche[1] gives power consumption figures of 4·2–5·4 kWh/lb. acetylene—presumably power consumption in the arc to produce dilute acetylene.

An example in this class is the Schoch process which uses an expanded arc through which paraffin gases or vaporised liquid hydrocarbons are circulated. This process is capable of giving an off gas containing 10–14 per cent of acetylene; from methane, the power consumption in the arc is of the order of 5 kWh/lb. of acetylene.[7]

3. Partial combustion

In Chapter 3, p. 38, the partial internal combustion of methane with oxygen to a mixture of carbon monoxide and hydrogen was described:

$$CH_4 + \tfrac{1}{2}O_2 \rightarrow CO + 2H_2$$

In this process, the endothermic heat of the usual methane steam process was supplied by burning some of the methane within the reaction zone with oxygen.

The possibility of using partial internal combustion of hydrocarbon gases to attain the very high temperatures required for acetylene production has been envisaged for nearly thirty years.

$$CH_4 + \tfrac{1}{2}O_2 \rightarrow CO + 2H_2. \quad \Delta H_{298} = -8\cdot5 \text{ k. cal.}$$
$$2CH_4 \rightarrow C_2H_2 + 3H_2. \quad \Delta H_{298} = +90 \text{ k. cal.}$$

so that mixtures of acetylene with carbon monoxide and hydrogen are produced.

Since the problem is to obtain a temperature of at least 1,500° c., certain operating limitations are imposed. Oxygen has to be used, to avoid dilution of the reacting gases with nitrogen which would absorb part of the heat of partial combustion and would also take part in the reaction. The gases have to be preheated to aid in attainment of the maximum temperature, but the preheat is controlled by the temperature at which the hydrocarbon feed gas starts to crack and by the risk of premature flame initiation.

The ratio of oxygen to hydrocarbon varies with the hydrocarbon used; about 2 vols. of methane are used per vol. of oxygen,[8, 9] but with ethane, only one vol. is used per vol. of oxygen.[10] In both cases, it is necessary to preheat both the hydrocarbon and the oxygen in order to obtain the

[7] University of Texas publication No. 5011, June 1, 1950.
[8] C.I.O.S. 27/84; B.I.O.S. 877.
[9] Bartholome, Chemical Engineering Science, 1954, **3**, Supplement, p. 94; Sachsse, *Chem. Ing. Tech.*, 1954, **26**, 245; Bartholome, *ibid.*, p. 253.
[10] C.I.O.S. 30/103.

required high flame temperature. The problems involved in the design of the plant are firstly to mix the hot gases without flame formation; secondly to design a burner to give a stationary flame and to prevent flash-back; thirdly, to quench the product gases immediately. The acetylene burner designed by the German workers is described in ref. 9.

The methane and oxygen are preheated separately to 600° c. Mixing is achieved at the head of the burner; the gas velocity is then decreased by expansion of the mixing chamber. The burner consists of a ceramic block with many cylindrical channels from each of which the mixed gases emerge as high velocity jets; this prevents flash-back. A flattish flame is formed, a few centimetres deep; due to the high gas velocity, the reaction mixture is homogeneous after the flame zone. Its temperature is of the order of 1,400° c.; it is immediately quenched to 80° c. by water injection. The cracked gas has the following approximate composition:

Composition					*% by vol.*
H_2	.	.	.	.	54
CH_4	.	.	.	.	5
C_2H_2	.	.	.	.	8
CO	.	.	.	.	26
CO_2	.	.	.	.	7
					100

Some carbon is always formed, which is removed by water washing over granular material such as coke. The dilute gas then passes to the concentration and purification section. The full scale burner has a capacity of about 8 tons/day acetylene; each burner has its own preheater, gas cooler and carbon filter. The further concentration of the acetylene is discussed in Section 4, p. 268.

The following figures are quoted for materials and services consumption for making 1 lb. of concentrated acetylene from methane by this process:[9]

Methane	.	.	.	. 4·3 lb.
Oxygen	.	.	.	. 4·9 lb.
Steam	.	.	.	. 4·0 lb.
Power	.	.		0·7–1·0 kWh

The power consumption is therefore a small fraction of that required either by the carbide process or by the electric arc process. The difference, however, is considerably reduced if one takes into account the power required for making the oxygen, and the energy equivalent of the steam.

As would be expected from Table 57 (p. 261), ethane reacts somewhat more readily with oxygen. In the Ludwigshafen process[10] equal volumes of ethane and oxygen, preheated to 400° c., were burnt in a high velocity combustion chamber (gas velocity, 8·5 m./sec.) giving a maximum temperature of 1,500° c.; the gases were immediately water quenched to

100° c., 1·6 volumes of gas being obtained per 0·5 vol. ethane plus 0·5 vol. oxygen; its composition was:

Composition	% by vol.
C_2H_2	9·3
CO_2	4·0
CO	32·3
CH_4	6·0
H_2	48·4
	100·0

The acetylene was extracted by water scrubbing under pressure (see Section 4, below), giving acetylene containing 30 per cent of carbon dioxide. The methane content of the residual gas was removed by a secondary combustion with oxygen to give a mixture of carbon monoxide and hydrogen, available for the usual outlets of 'synthesis gas' (see Chapter 3). Details of plant, burner, and service requirements are given in the report cited.

The partial combustion process using methane from natural gas and 90–95% oxygen has now been established in the United States and Italy as well as in Germany. It gives at least two parts by weight of 'synthesis gas' ($CO + H_2$) per part of acetylene and is therefore adopted where there is a chemical outlet for the synthesis gas for synthetic ammonia or methanol, in which it has a higher value than as fuel gas. The partial combustion process can be looked on as a variant of the methane oxygen process (Chapter 3, p. 38), in which part of the methane is converted to high value acetylene.

4. Separation of acetylene

In all the routes to acetylene from petroleum materials, acetylene is obtained as a dilute gas, at 6–15 per cent concentration, hydrogen being invariably the major constituent of the gas mixture. Other gases present are methane, ethane, ethylene, carbon monoxide, carbon dioxide, and nitrogen.

The usual method of separating acetylene takes advantage of its relatively high solubility in solvents compared with the other gases present. Its solubility in a few solvents at atmospheric pressure is given in Table 60.[11]

The high solubility of acetylene in acetone is taken advantage of in the storage of acetylene under pressure; the acetylene is dissolved in acetone, and the safety is increased by allowing the acetone to impregnate a porous material such as kieselguhr or charcoal, etc.

Claims have been made for the recovery of acetylene by refrigeration and fractionation, and by adsorption on solids such as active charcoal or

---

[11] McKinnis, *Ind. Eng. Chem.*, 1955, **47**, 850.

silica gel. The former method is hampered by the curious properties of solid and liquid acetylene; the solid sublimes at $-83.6°$ c. at 760 mm., and melts at $-81.8°$ c. The latter method is more adapted to removal of

TABLE 60

Solubility of acetylene in some solvents

Solvent	Temperature ° c.	Vol. acetylene (std. conditions)/ vol. solvent
Hexamethylphosphoramide [(CH₃)₂N]₃PO	25	43
Dimethylformamide	25	33
Dimethyl sulphoxide	25	32
Tetramethylene sulphoxide	25	31
Acetaldehyde	25	24
Acetone	25	19
Tetraethylene glycol dimethyl ether	25	19
Triethyl phosphate	25	19
Butyrolactone	25	15
Acetonitrile	25	14
Ethyl alcohol	18	6
Water	20	1
Paraffin oil	0	1

highly unsaturated impurities such as diacetylene, methylacetylene and butadiene from acetylene.[12] Both methods involve the risk of acetylene explosions.

The two main methods of acetylene concentration both use selective absorption by solvents, which is safer. The earlier method used water under pressure; since the war, the tendency has moved to the use of organic solvents.

An example of the use of water is in the concentration of acetylene from the raw gases obtained by the electric arc.[5] Using methane, the outlet gas has the following composition:

Composition	% by vol.
C_2H_2	13·3
CH_4	27·8
C_2H_4	0·9
H_2	46·0
CO	2·9
O_2	0·2
N_2	8·9
	100·0

Removal of carbon black, aromatics, hydrogen sulphide, hydrogen cyanide and part of the diacetylene has been dealt with on p. 265. The principle of the method of recovery of acetylene is solution in water under pressure, followed by release of pressure in stages; this multi-stage let-down effects a further separation of acetylene from the less soluble gases.

[12] I.G., F.P. 716882.

The gases after the preliminary purification were compressed to 19 atma., giving an acetylene partial pressure of 2·5 atma.; the acetylene was dissolved out by counter-current scrubbing with water; the minimum theoretical requirements of water at 18° c. is 37 gal./lb. acetylene.

The non-absorbed gases, consisting principally of hydrogen, methane, ethane, ethylene, and nitrogen with less than 0·1 per cent of acetylene, were passed to a Linde fractionation plant which separated 98% pure hydrogen, 98% ethylene, a methane-ethane fraction, and a nitrogen-carbon monoxide mixture. The methane-ethane fraction was recycled to the arc, and the hydrogen and ethylene fractions used for other chemical syntheses.

Acetylene was recovered from its water solution by release of pressure from 19 atma. in four stages, to 2 atma., 1 atma., 0·15 atma., and 0·05 atma. The first stage release gave 45% acetylene which was recycled to the compressor and water absorber; the second stage gave 90% acetylene, the third and fourth 90–96% acetylene. These three stages were combined and further purified to 97% acetylene. Diacetylene and other highly unsaturated C_3 and C_4 hydrocarbons not removed with the aromatics in the preliminary purification were scrubbed out with oil, followed by sulphuric acid; carbon dioxide was removed by solution in 0·5% aqueous caustic soda. This gave acetylene of 97–98% purity, containing 0–1 per cent carbon dioxide and 2 per cent inerts. When considerable quantities of carbon dioxide are present alongside the acetylene, separation by solution in weak caustic soda appears to present some difficulties.[8] A simplified flowsheet of this method of concentration of acetylene is given in Fig. 32.

Using organic solvents involves removal of both less-soluble and more soluble impurities than acetylene, the same difficulty as in concentration of butadiene; it is solved in a similar way. The less soluble impurities are swept out of the "fat-liquor" by pure acetylene in an intermediate tower, the more soluble impurities are removed from the stripped liquor after removal of acetylene before recycling to the absorption tower.

In all processes it is necessary to remove soot, tar (if present) and diacetylene. The diacetylene is removed by scrubbing with oil or sulphuric acid or by a pre-absorption treatment with a small amount of the selective solvent; in the Wulff process, the diacetylene and any dissolved acetylene is stripped with off gas from the main acetylene absorber and recycled to the process.

The Wulff process gas (Table 58, p. 263) is cleaned up by electrostatic precipitation to remove carbon, diacetylene is then removed, and the acetylene is absorbed in dimethylformamide at 11 atma. pressure and ordinary temperature.[13]

The acetylene-rich dimethylformamide is let down to 1·7 atma. pressure in an intermediate column where gases less soluble than acetylene are

---

[13] Bixler and Coberly, *Ind. Eng. Chem.*, 1953, **45**, 2596.

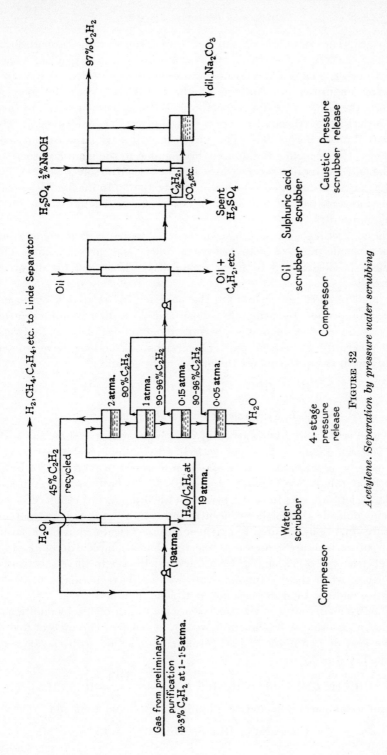

FIGURE 32

Acetylene. Separation by pressure water scrubbing

disengaged. The column is operated so that a considerable proportion of acetylene is also taken overhead; these gases are therefore recycled to the main absorber. The dimethylformamide solution of acetylene is now free of lighter impurities but contains all the methylacetylene; the solution passes to the acetylene stripper, operated at atmospheric pressure, to take pure acetylene overhead, leaving the methylacetylene dissolved in the bottoms dimethylformamide. The methylacetylene is stripped out and rejected before recycling the dimethylformamide to the main absorber.

The current German process[9] uses a two-component solvent, water and a water-miscible organic solvent boiling above 100° c. In the final degassing of this mixture, part of the water is evaporated and removes the more soluble impurities.

These processes give acetylene of 98–99% purity. The remaining impurities include traces of methylacetylene, allene and carbon dioxide. The acetylene has been used both for chemical synthesis and for dissolved acetylene.

A final method is to eliminate the need for the relatively expensive purification section by using the dilute acetylene directly for chemical synthesis. So far, this method has been used only in one plant, at Ludwigshafen, where the gases from partial combustion of methane were reacted directly with steam to convert the acetylene to acetone:[10]

$$2C_2H_2 + 3H_2O \rightarrow CH_3COCH_3 + CO_2 + 2H_2$$

5. Synthesis of higher acetylenes

Acetylene is the only hydrocarbon of its type manufactured on any scale from petroleum sources. Traces of methyl-, ethyl-, vinyl-, and higher acetylenes have been detected in the C_4 fraction obtained in processes for butadiene by pyrolysis (see Chapter 12, p. 203); the highest proportion of any alkylacetylene appears to be 0·1 per cent (1,000 p.p.m.) of ethylacetylene. It seems unlikely that higher concentrations can be expected, as the temperature conditions required to produce alkylacetylenes from more saturated hydrocarbons are so drastic as to cause almost complete decomposition to acetylene and other simpler hydrocarbons. Routes to these substituted acetylenes, when these compounds are wanted, have normally to be by synthesis and not by degradation of petroleum products.

The two main routes to alkylacetylenes are from 1-olefins by addition of one mol of chlorine or bromine followed by removal of two mols of hydrochloric acid or hydrobromic acid, usually by reaction with caustic soda or caustic potash:

$$RCH:CH_2 + Cl_2 \rightarrow RCHClCH_2Cl \xrightarrow{-2HCl} RC:CH$$

or from sodium acetylide and an alkyl halide in liquid ammonia

$$CH:CNa + RCl \rightarrow CH:CR + NaCl$$

The alkylacetylenes are not yet of much importance. It is reported that methylacetylene is made on a petroleum chemical basis.[14] Amylacetylene (1-heptyne), made from petroleum n-heptene, has been used for making the perfumery chemical, methyl octynoate, by the following steps.

$$C_5H_{11}C \vdots CH + Na + CO_2 \rightarrow C_5H_{11}C \vdots CCOONa \rightarrow C_5H_{11}C \vdots CCOOCH_3$$

Unsaturated substituted acetylenes are more important. Monovinylacetylene, $CH_2 \vdots CHC \vdots CH$, is one of the principal chemical outlets for acetylene; its manufacture from acetylene is discussed on p. 279. It is present in traces in some high temperature pyrolysis processes.

Diacetylene, $CH \vdots CC \vdots CH$, is significant because it is the hydrocarbon by-product produced in the largest quantity in all the high temperature processes for making acetylene from methane and the lower paraffins. If wanted, it can be isolated from the concentrated acetylene from the multistage let-down system, before oil and caustic soda scrubbing, by liquefaction at $-78°$ c. and fractionation to separate from methylacetylene and butadiene. Diacetylene boils at $+10.3°$ c.; it is violently explosive. It can be synthesised from butyne diol (see Fig. 33) via 1:4-dichlorobutyne, which gives diacetylene with alcoholic alkalies:

$$CH_2OHC \vdots CCH_2OH \xrightarrow{+\ 2HCl} CH_2ClC \vdots CCH_2Cl \xrightarrow{+\ 2KOH} CH \vdots CC \vdots CH$$

Its chemistry has not been systematically explored.

6. Reactions of acetylene

The main industrial reactions of acetylene are:

(*i*) Chlorination to chlorinated ethylenes as solvents . . . . . . Chapter 10, p. 155
(*ii*) Hydration to acetaldehyde for acetic acid, etc. . . . . . . Chapter 16, p. 288
(*iii*) Vinyl chloride . . . . . Chapter 10, p. 154
(*iv*) Vinyl acetate . . . . . Chapter 18, p. 340
(*v*) Monovinylacetylene for neoprene . . This Chapter, p. 279
(*vi*) Acrylonitrile . . . . . . Chapter 20, p. 370

The first two of these reactions were discovered and developed before the first world war. Vinyl chloride, vinyl acetate and monovinylacetylene were developed between 1930–1940. Acrylonitrile is the most recent addition to these technical products.

---

[14] *Chem. Ind.*, August 1956, p. 424.

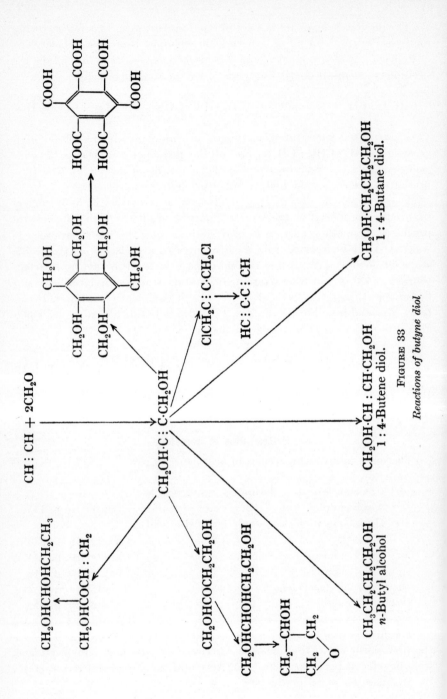

FIGURE 33

Reactions of butyne diol

It is estimated that in 1953, the chemical outlets in America were divided as follows :[15]

Outlet	% offtake
Vinyl chloride . . .	30
Neoprene	28
Trichloroethylene . . .	20
Acrylonitrile	10
Vinyl acetate	8
Others	4
	100

Current developments comprise the synthesis of certain methylstyrenes, described in Chapter 14, p. 253, and the exploitation of some of the reactions of acetylene under pressure, uncovered largely by the researches of Reppe in Germany.

The main lines of Reppe's work[16] were (*a*) addition to aldehydes and ketones, (*b*) polymerisation to cyclic hydrocarbons, (*c*) addition to alcohols, etc., (*d*) reaction with carbon monoxide.

(*a*) ADDITION OF ACETYLENE TO ALDEHYDES AND KETONES

It has long been known that acetylene adds on to aldehydes and ketones, in liquid ammonia in presence of sodium to give ethynyl carbinols, *e.g.*,

$$\begin{matrix} CH_3 \\ >CO + CH:CH \to \\ CH_3 \end{matrix} \quad \begin{matrix} CH_3 \quad OH \\ >C< \\ CH_3 \quad C:CH \end{matrix}$$

Reppe discovered a new and technically better way of bringing about this reaction, and of making it proceed in high yield with the simplest aldehyde, formaldehyde. Reaction is carried out under pressure in aqueous solution in presence of copper acetylide as catalyst. The main product from formaldehyde is 2-butyne-1 : 4-diol (1 : 4-butyne diol), by addition of two mols of formaldehyde to one mol of acetylene:

$$C_2H_2 + 2CH_2O \to CH_2OHC:CCH_2OH$$

The process[17] involves passing acetylene and aqueous formaldehyde co-current downwards over a copper-bismuth catalyst under about 5 atma. total pressure at 90–110° c. The reaction is exothermic, ΔH being − 55 k. cal. for the vapour phase reaction, and − 22 k. cal. for the liquid phase reaction. To control the temperature, the formaldehyde concentration was kept down to a maximum of 12 per cent by recirculation of part of the aqueous butyne diol produced. Two convertors were run in series, with partial reaction in each convertor. A slight excess over theory of

---

[15] Sherwood, *Chimie et Industrie,* January 1955, p. 78.
[16] B.I.O.S. 266; *Ann.,* 1948, 560, 1.
[17] B.I.O.S. 367.

acetylene was used, and the liquors from the convertor contained about 0·5 per cent formaldehyde; excess acetylene was recirculated. The convertor product contained about 33% butyne diol; it was worked up by distillation to remove formaldehyde and propargyl alcohol, which were recirculated, and methyl alcohol. The butyne diol, produced as a 35–40% aqueous solution, was passed on to the next stage.

The catalyst consisted of 12 per cent copper and 3 per cent bismuth in the form of their oxides on granular silica gel; these oxides were converted to the acetylides on contact with acetylene. The actual catalyst was believed to be a complex of one mol of copper acetylide with one mol of acetylene, $CuC_2.C_2H_2$, which was stable only in an atmosphere of acetylene. The bismuth was added as a retarder of cuprene formation. Catalyst life was about two to four months, when cuprene formation led to high pressure drop and low activity.

The yield of butyne diol was 90 per cent on formaldehyde and 80 per cent on acetylene. Its chief outlet in Germany was for manufacture of butadiene, for which the aqueous solution was suitable. Pure butyne diol boils at 145° c./15 mm. and melts at 55° c.

Propargyl alcohol, $CH : CCH_2OH$, is formed to a small extent in this reaction; it can be made the major product by altering the process. Using 40% aqueous formaldehyde diluted with an equal weight of tetrahydrofuran, and operating with excess of acetylene counter-current at 8–10 atma. pressure at 100–110° c., an 80% yield of propargyl alcohol has been obtained. This alcohol boils at 114–115° c./760 mm., and melts at − 17° c.:

$$C_2H_2 + CH_2O \rightarrow CH : CCH_2OH$$

Acetaldehyde also reacts under similar conditions with acetylene, either one or two mols of the aldehyde adding on to give 3-hydroxy-1-butyne or 2 : 5-dihydroxy-3-hexyne:

$$CH_3CHO + CH : CH \rightarrow CH_3CH{<}^{OH}_{C : CH} + CH_3CHO \rightarrow CH_3\underset{OH}{CHC} : C\underset{OH}{CHCH_3}$$

3-hydroxy-1-butyne   2 : 5-dihydroxy-3-hexyne

Plants for butyne diol with a capacity of 25,000 tons p.a. at Ludwigshafen and 5,000 tons p.a. at Schkopau, were built as part of one of the manufacturing processes to butadiene operated in Germany during the second world war. Butyne and butane diols are made on the full scale in U.S.A. The condensation of one and two mols of acetaldehyde with acetylene has been carried out only on the pilot scale.

The scope of reactions of propargyl alcohol, butyne diol and the acetaldehyde condensation products are shown in the attached charts, condensed from German reports.[18] As mentioned earlier, the principal use of butyne

---

[18] C.I.O.S. 24/19.

diol was for manufacture of butadiene, which is described in Chapter 12, p. 208. Figs. 33, 34, and 35 deal with the reactions of butyne diol, butene diol, and 1 : 4-butane diol respectively. Figs. 36 and 37 summarise those of propargyl alcohol and of the acetaldehyde products.

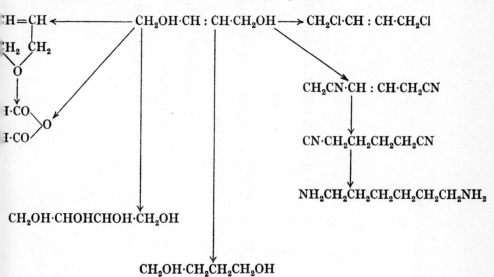

FIGURE 34
Reactions of butene diol

This synthesis is used for the manufacture of butyrolactone, pyrrolidone and vinylpyrrolidone, and polyvinylpyrrolidone (see p. 281).

In this method of condensing aldehydes with acetylene, as well as in other high pressure acetylene reactions, compression and circulation of acetylene at 5–20 atma. pressure were necessary; it was previously considered unsafe to work with acetylene above 1·5 atma. pressure but conditions for safe working were discovered and established in large scale manufacture. The compressors used were the standard direct stroke type, operating at slow speed and with a compression ratio of 2–3 : 1 to provide adequate interstage cooling. Flame arrestors consisting of long tubes packed with wire spirals or Raschig rings were introduced after each compressor. Pipe lines were kept as short and as narrow as possible; large diameter pipes were filled with ¼ in. diameter tubing. These precautions dissipated the heat of decomposition, and prevented explosions, which generated ten times the working pressure; explosions might lead to detonations, developing over one hundred times the working pressure. The plant was built to withstand at least ten times the normal working pressure, provided decomposition of acetylene was limited to explosion, there was an adequate margin of safety.

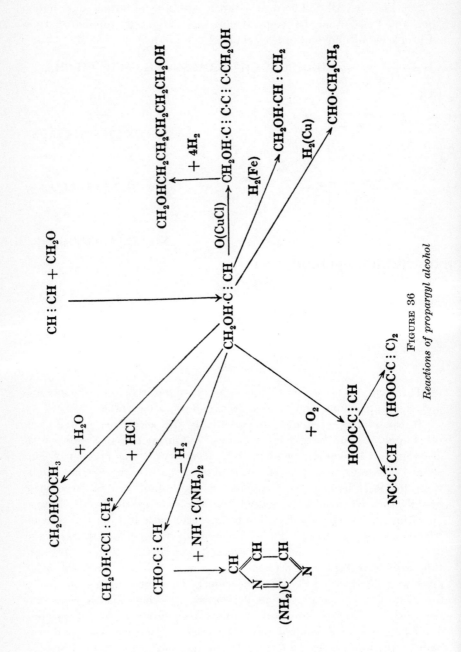

FIGURE 36

Reactions of propargyl alcohol

(*b*) POLYMERISATION OF ACETYLENE

The linear polymerisation of acetylene to monovinylacetylene, divinyl-acetylene, etc., under the influence of acid cuprous chloride as catalyst, was discovered by Nieuwland in America thirty years ago. Acetylene was absorbed in a saturated aqueous solution of cuprous chloride in ammonium or alkali metal chloride; on distillation, unchanged acetylene and polymers, principally divinylacetylene (1 : 5-hexadiene-3-yne) and a tetramer, 1 : 5 : 7-octatriene-3-yne, were obtained. By operating the process continuously and at low conversions of acetylene, it was shown that the primary product was monovinylacetylene, which could be made the main product of reaction. The course of this method of polymerisation could therefore be represented as :

$$CH : CH + CH : CH$$
$$\downarrow$$
$$CH : CCH : CH_2$$

Monovinylacetylene

$$+ \;\Big|\; CH : CH$$

$$CH_2 : CHC \;\vdots\; CCH : CH_2 \qquad\qquad CH : CCH : CHCH : CH_2$$

Divinylacetylene   (3 : 5-hexadiene-1-yne)

(1 : 5-hexadiene-3-yne) $+ \;\Big|\; CH : CH$

$$CH_2 : CHC : CCH : CHCH : CH_2$$

(1 : 5 : 7-octatriene-3-yne)

On the large scale the process can be operated in horizontally agitated catalyst reactors[19] or in a tower type of reactor in which the catalyst circulates counter-current to the gas. The process has to be operated at low conversion to obtain a high ratio of monovinyl- to divinyl-acetylene.

Monovinylacetylene boils at $5\cdot5°$ c.; it is the intermediate for the manufacture of 2-chlorobutadiene (chloroprene) (see Chapter 12, p. 212). Divinyl-acetylene boils at $85\cdot0°$ c.; it has been used for the manufacture of drying oils, and is a convenient route to 3-hexene by partial hydrogenation. Its isomer, 3 : 5-hexadiene-1-yne, $CH_2 : CHCH : CHC \vdots CH$, boils at $83\cdot4°$ c., and is distinguished from divinylacetylene by possession of an acetylenic hydrogen atom.

Under completely different conditions, Reppe obtained cyclic polymers from acetylene.[20] The general method was to react acetylene under pressure at moderate temperature in presence of a catalyst suspended in a solvent. The usual catalyst was nickel cyanide in presence of ethylene oxide or of

---

[19] du Pont, B.P. 401678.
[20] B.I.O.S. 137; F.I.A.T. 967.

calcium carbide; tetrahydrofuran was the preferred solvent. At 60–70° c. and 20 atma. total pressure, a yield of about 70 per cent cyclooctatetraene, C_8H_8, was obtained.

The product made by the Reppe process is identical with the hydrocarbon synthesised by Willstatter over forty years ago by the exhaustive methylation of ψ-pelletierine. It boils at 142–143° c. It is an endothermic compound with a heat of formation of about + 40 k. cal., but the polymerisation of acetylene to cyclooctatetraene is highly exothermic:

$$4C_2H_2 \rightarrow C_8H_8. \quad \Delta H = -170 \text{ k. cal.}$$

On hydrogenation, cyclooctatetraene reacts as (i) giving cyclooctene, cyclooctane, etc. In most of its other reactions, it behaves as 0 : 2 : 4-bicyclo-2 : 4 : 7-octatriene (ii). For example, on chlorination, it gives (iii), which by reduction and oxidation yields hexahydrophthalic acid, (iv).

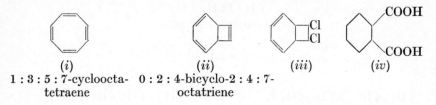

| (i) | (ii) | (iii) | (iv) |
| 1 : 3 : 5 : 7-cyclooctatetraene | 0 : 2 : 4-bicyclo-2 : 4 : 7-octatriene | | |

Despite the large amount of work carried out on cyclooctatetraene in the last fifteen years, no commercial use for it has yet been established.

(c) ADDITION OF ACETYLENE TO ALCOHOLS, ETC.[16]

Addition of acetylene to acids and to certain other compounds containing reactive hydrogen to give vinyl derivatives was already known:

$$\text{RH + HC} \vdots \text{CH} \rightarrow \text{RCH} \vdots \text{CH}_2 \qquad . \qquad . \qquad . \quad (9)$$

This reaction has been extended now to types of organic compounds not previously combined with acetylene. Vinylation† is as general a reaction as sulphonation, nitration, or chlorination.

In the Reppe process, alcohols were reacted with acetylene using an alkali alkoxide as catalyst. Reaction was usually carried out at 150–170° c. and under a total pressure which may be as high as 20 atma., depending on the alcohol used. When working at this pressure, the partial pressure of acetylene was maintained at 12 atma., the remainder being nitrogen as inert diluent. The reaction was carried out by blowing acetylene or acetylene-nitrogen mixtures up a tower co-current to the alcohol; the catalyst was dissolved in the alcohol. The lower alcohols were reacted under pressure, and the vinyl ethers condensed from the exit gases, which were recycled.

---

† The addition of acetylene to a compound containing a reactive hydrogen atom to give a vinyl derivative.

Methyl and ethyl alcohols required 20 atma. pressure, *n*- and isobutyl alcohols, 4 atma., and decahydro-β-naphthol and octadecyl alcohol were vinylated at ordinary pressure. Only one acetylene adds per hydroxyl group, *e.g.*, with methyl alcohol:

$$C_2H_2 + CH_3OH \rightarrow CH_3OCH : CH_2$$

With polyhydric alcohols, either one or two hydroxyl groups can be vinylated.

Methyl vinyl ether boils at $-6°$ c. It is readily hydrolysed with water at atmospheric pressure, giving acetaldehyde and regenerating methyl alcohol:

$$CH_3OCH : CH_2 + H_2O \rightarrow CH_3CHO + CH_3OH$$

This method of hydrating acetylene to acetaldehyde is discussed in Chapter 16, p. 288.

These alkyl vinyl ethers are used for making polymers for various purposes.

Acetylene also adds on to -SH and -NH groups to give S-vinyl and N-vinyl derivatives such as N-vinylcarbazole, 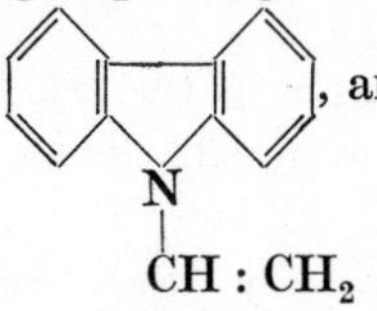 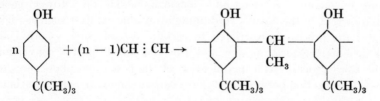, and N-vinyl-pyrrolidone, an intermediate for polyvinylpyrrolidone, used as a blood plasma substitute and an industrial water soluble polymer; the pyrrolidone was made from 1 : 4-butyne diol via 1 : 4-butane diol and 3-butyrolactone (see Fig. 35).

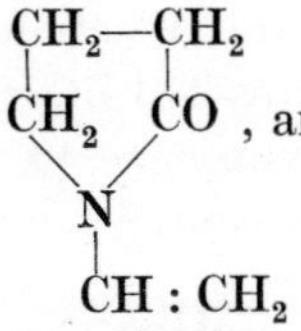

With phenols, acetylene usually substitutes directly into the benzene ring. At 200–240° c. and 15–20 atma. pressure in presence of zinc naphthenate as catalyst, *p-tert*-butylphenol reacts to give a polymer believed to be a substituted ethylidene bis-phenol:

This reaction was used for making a softener for synthetic rubber.

Under special conditions, acetylene can be made to react to give phenyl vinyl ether.

(*d*) REACTIONS OF ACETYLENE WITH CARBON MONOXIDE[16, 21]

Independent of Roelen's discovery of the Oxo reaction (Chapter 11, p. 183), Reppe found that carbon monoxide could be added on to acetylene under simple conditions to give acrylic acid and its derivatives:

$$C_2H_2 + CO + H_2O \rightarrow CH_2 : CHCOOH$$

The reaction is carried out using nickel carbonyl as the source of carbon monoxide, in presence of hydrochloric acid to take up the nickel. It proceeds at 40–50° c. and atmospheric pressure by adding nickel carbonyl slowly to aqueous hydrochloric acid whilst blowing in acetylene continuously; the yield of acrylic acid is almost quantitative. The stoichiometric equations are:

$$C_2H_2 + \tfrac{1}{4}Ni(CO)_4 + \tfrac{1}{2}HCl + H_2O \rightarrow CH_2 : CHCOOH + \tfrac{1}{4}NiCl_2 + \tfrac{1}{4}H_2$$

Nickel carbonyl was regenerated quantitatively from the aqueous solution by converting to the hexammine nickel chloride and reacting with carbon monoxide at 170° c. and 200 atm. pressure:[22]

$$Ni(NH_3)_6Cl_2 + 5CO + 2H_2O \rightarrow Ni(CO)_4 + 2NH_4Cl + (NH_4)_2CO_3 + 2NH_3$$

If the water in the reaction is replaced by alcohols, esters of acrylic acid were obtained. These are more important technically than free acrylic acid.

There are now three ways of carrying out this reaction; originally, acetylene, the alcohol and nickel carbonyl were reacted in presence of an acid such as hydrochloric acid at atmospheric pressure and 40° c.; the yield of ethyl acrylate was reported to be about 80 per cent.[22]

$$CH : CH + \tfrac{1}{4}Ni(CO)_4 + C_2H_5OH + \tfrac{1}{2}HCl \rightarrow$$
$$CH_2 : CHCOOC_2H_5 + \tfrac{1}{4}NiCl_2 + \tfrac{1}{4}H_2$$

The two main drawbacks were the formation of considerable by-product ethyl propionate which is difficult to separate from ethyl acrylate, and the need to recover and convert back to nickel carbonyl large amounts of nickel chloride.

The process was then operated continuously at 150–180° c. and 30 atma. pressure by passing acetylene and carbon monoxide up a tower reactor counter-current to the alcohol containing a suitable catalyst such as nickel chloride; the process is restricted to certain alcohols such as ethyl and butyl alcohols;[23] reaction is slow and proceeds only to partial conversion.

The third process[24] is a modification of the first atmospheric pressure process. The reaction between acetylene, carbon monoxide, nickel carbonyl

[21] B.I.O.S. 355.
[22] B.I.O.S. 358.
[23] F.I.A.T. 933.
[24] *Chem. Eng. News*, February 9, 1953, p. 560; Rohm and Haas Co., U.S.P. 2582911.

and hydrochloric acid is started; free carbon monoxide is then introduced and reacts with the alcohol and acetylene to give the acrylate. In fact, both carbon monoxide and nickel carbonyl contribute to the synthesis; the recommended conditions are to work at 30–50° c., to use a ratio of free carbon monoxide to carbon monoxide content of nickel carbonyl of about 3 : 1, to use some excess of alcohol, and to keep the acetylene and hydrochloric acid ratios approximately stoichiometric according to the chemical equation.

The process is continuous, proceeds to high conversion and yields are 80–90 per cent on acetylene and total carbon monoxide. This process is now in full scale operation in the United States.

Alternative routes to acrylic esters are described in Chapter 18, p. 340.

A number of other new acetylene reactions, based on reactions with iron and cobalt carbonyls, has been disclosed, but none of them has yet been established technically.

CHAPTER 16

ALDEHYDES

1. Formaldehyde

(a) MANUFACTURE

Manufacture of formaldehyde as one of the products of the vapour phase pressure air oxidation of the normally gaseous paraffins has already been discussed in Chapter 4, p. 59. This route is used on the large scale in America, but formaldehyde is usually made by catalytic air oxidation of methyl alcohol over silver or copper catalysts:

$$CH_3OH + \tfrac{1}{2}O_2 \rightarrow CH_2O + H_2O(g). \quad \Delta H = -38 \text{ k. cal.} \quad . \quad (1)$$

The catalyst can be used either in the form of metal gauzes, or as a fixed catalyst on an inert support. The actual temperature of oxidation is about 500–700° c., and it is customary to employ a deficiency of air over that required by equation (1), so that some formaldehyde is formed by dehydrogenation:

$$CH_3OH \rightarrow CH_2O + H_2. \quad \Delta H = +20 \text{ k. cal.} \quad . \quad . \quad (2)$$

Reaction (2) is endothermic, thus tending to offset the highly exothermic reaction (1) and thereby to prevent excessively high temperatures, which leads to decomposition of formaldehyde.

The usual gas mixture fed to the catalyst contains 30–40 per cent by volume of methyl alcohol and 60–70 per cent of air; the exit gas contains 20 per cent hydrogen with a few per cent of carbon dioxide and traces of carbon monoxide and methane; oxygen utilisation is almost complete. The methyl alcohol is not completely consumed, excess being left in to stabilise the aqueous formaldehyde solution obtained. The nett yield of formaldehyde on methyl alcohol consumed is 85–90 per cent. Detailed descriptions of this process are given by Homer[1] and in German reports.[2]

Another type of formaldehyde process is one involving complete conversion of methyl alcohol over vanadium pentoxide alone or mixed with other oxides.[3] A large excess of air is used, the gas mixtures containing only 5–10 per cent by volume of methyl alcohol; the additional operating expenses are said to offset the increased gross yield.[1]

Formaldehyde monomer boils at −19° c. and freezes at −118° c.; it is very unstable, polymerising readily to polyoxymethylenes. Formaldehyde is commercially available as an aqueous solution containing 37 per

---

[1] J. Soc. Chem. Ind., 1941, **60**, 213T.
[2] C.I.O.S. 27/85.
[3] Barrett Co., U.S.P. 1383059; Bakelite Corp., U.S.P. 1913405.

cent by weight of formaldehyde and 6–13 per cent of methyl alcohol, the presence of which retards polymerisation and prevents precipitation of insoluble polymers. 30% and 37% formalin solutions are also marketed substantially free of methyl alcohol (0·5 per cent to 2 per cent content).

Formaldehyde is available as paraform, a solid insoluble mixture of polyoxymethylene glycols, $HO(CH_2O)_nH$, in which $n = 8$ to 100. Paraform is made by distillation and concentration *in vacuo* of aqueous formaldehyde solutions; it contains 93–99% effective CH_2O. Another form in which formaldehyde is being marketed is as the solid cyclic trimer, trioxane:

This melts at 61–62° c. and boils at 115° c., reverting to monomeric formaldehyde in the vapour phase.

(b) Outlets and reactions of formaldehyde

Formaldehyde is used in industry mainly for synthetic resins.

The estimated American production in 1956 is 645,000 tons (37% wt./wt.); the consuming industries and the percentage offtake are:[4]

Industry	% offtake
Phenolic resins	26
Urea resins	23
Melamine resins	6
Ethylene glycol	15
Pentaerythritol	23
Hexamethylene tetramine	4
Miscellaneous, including textiles, dyestuffs, leather and other chemical outlets	3
	100

Outlets in the resins field and for hexamethylene tetramine are outside the scope of this book. Pentaerythritol is referred to later in this chapter (p. 293). We shall limit ourselves here to some reactions of formaldehyde, in which is it used to proceed from the C_1 to the C_2 and higher series.

By condensation of aqueous formaldehyde with carbon monoxide at high pressures and elevated temperatures in presence of an acidic catalyst, glycollic acid is formed:

$$CH_2O + CO + H_2O \rightarrow HOCH_2COOH$$

The usual conditions disclosed in patents are pressures of the order of 700 atm. at 150–200° c., using sulphuric acid or boron trifluoride as

---

[4] *Chem. Week.*, 17 December, 1955, p. 94.

catalysts.[5] With alcohols instead of water, esters of glycollic acid are formed directly.[6]

Glycollic acid can easily be esterified with methyl alcohol to methyl glycollate. This ester on vapour phase hydrogenation, *e.g.*, using copper chromite as catalyst at 200–225° c. and 20–40 atma. pressure, with a large excess of hydrogen, gives ethylene glycol in high yield,[7] with recovery of methyl alcohol, which can be recycled:

$$HOCH_2COOH + CH_3OH \rightarrow HOCH_2COOCH_3$$
$$\xrightarrow{+ 2H_2} HOCH_2CH_2OH + CH_3OH$$

This is one method of making a C_2 chemical, normally available from ethylene, from a C_1 compound. It is operated in America. Other routes to ethylene glycol are discussed in Chapters 10, p. 178, and 19, p. 343.

Secondly, it has long been known that formaldehyde undergoes self-condensation under alkaline conditions to give a series of hydroxyalde-hydes and hydroxyketones up to and beyond the hexoses; this process has been modified to give a route to C_2 to C_4 polyhydroxy compounds. One method of carrying out the condensation is as follows: a solution containing twenty parts (by wt.) of formaldehyde, thirty-two of methyl alcohol, forty-eight of water, and five of the condensation product from a previous condensation, was treated with 0·2 parts of lead oxide (alkaline earth oxides or hydroxides were also claimed) at the boil; the mixture was boiled for between six and seven hours whilst continuously adding a slurry of lime in aqueous ethylene glycol to maintain the pH at 6–6·5; reaction was run to 80–90% utilisation of formaldehyde; the product contained a high propor-tion of C_2, C_3, and C_4 hydroxyaldehydes and ketones.[8] This mixture can be hydrogenated to a mixture of the corresponding di- and polyhydroxy compounds—ethylene glycol, glycerol, and erythritol. It is claimed that the hydrogenation proceeds smoothly and more efficiently after removal of unreacted formaldehyde and of methyl alcohol:[9]

$$CH_2O + CH_2O$$
$$\downarrow$$
$$HOCH_2CHO \xrightarrow{+ H_2} HOCH_2CH_2OH$$
$$+ \downarrow CH_2O$$
$$\begin{matrix} HOCH_2COCH_2OH \\ \text{and} \\ HOCH_2CHOHCHO \end{matrix} \begin{matrix} \xrightarrow{+ H_2} \\ \xrightarrow{+ H_2} \end{matrix} \rightarrow HOCH_2CHOHCH_2OH$$
$$+ \downarrow CH_2O$$
$$HOCH_2CHOHCHOHCHO \xrightarrow{+ H_2} HOCH_2CHOHCHOHCH_2OH, \text{ etc.}$$

[5] du Pont, U.S.P. 2152852, 2153064.
[6] du Pont, U.S.P. 2211625.
[7] du Pont, B.P. 575380.
[8] I.C.I., B.P. 513708.
[9] I.C.I., B.P. 514342.

Other reactions in which formaldehyde has been employed for synthetic processes, dealt with in this book, are:

Condensation with aliphatic nitro compounds to nitroalcohols (Chapter 6, p. 84).

Condensation with olefins and chloroolefins to alcohols, diols and acids (Chapters 11, p. 186, and 10, p. 156).

Condensation with acetylene to propargyl alcohol and butyne diol (Chapter 15, p. 275).

Condensation with aldehydes and ketones (this Chapter and Chapter 17, p. 311).

2. Acetaldehyde

Acetaldehyde is probably the most important of the petroleum aldehydes, as it is the starting point for the manufacture of a wide range of aliphatic chemicals—acids, esters, higher aldehydes and alcohols, butadiene, and so on. Acetaldehyde itself can be manufactured either from ethyl alcohol or from acetylene. It is also obtained from other petroleum sources as one of the products of the controlled air oxidation of the lower paraffin gases (Chapter 4, p. 59).

(a) MANUFACTURE FROM ETHYL ALCOHOL

There are two possible ways of converting ethyl alcohol to acetaldehyde, by dehydrogenation, or by oxidation with air.

For the free energy change in the reaction

$$C_2H_5OH(g) \rightleftharpoons CH_3CHO(g) + H_2(g). \quad \Delta H_{298} = + 15 \text{ k. cal.} \qquad (3)$$

the approximate equation is:[10]

$$\Delta G = 13,600 - 22 \cdot 1T$$

The equilibrium conversions calculated from this equation are given in Table 61.

TABLE 61

Equilibrium in the dehydrogenation of ethyl alcohol

Temperature ° c.	ΔG g. cal./g. mol.	K_p	% conversion of ethyl alcohol
300	+ 900	0·45	55
400	− 1,300	2·7	86
500	− 3,500	9·8	95

The equilibrium is favoured by low pressure.

From Table 61 high conversion of ethyl alcohol will be obtained only above 400° c. In industrial practice, the reaction is carried out at about

---

[10] Ellis, 'Chemistry of Petroleum Derivatives', *Reinhold*, Vol. 2, 1937, p. 1305.

$300°$ c., using a chromium oxide activated copper catalyst, and operating to give 33–50% conversion of ethyl alcohol per pass.[11]

The vapour phase air oxidation of ethyl alcohol:

$$C_2H_5OH(g) + \tfrac{1}{2}O_2 \rightarrow CH_3CHO(g) + H_2O(g). \quad \Delta H_{298} = -43 \text{ k. cal.} \quad (4)$$

is carried out in much the same way as the formaldehyde reaction (2), using silver or copper either as metallic gauze or in the massive form, and operating to balance thermally the exothermic oxidation (4) with the endothermic dehydrogenation (3); for example, the process may be operated with 2 mols air/mol ethyl alcohol at $450°$ c. and 3 atma. pressure over a silver catalyst, giving 20–35% conversion of ethyl alcohol.

In both these processes, the acetaldehyde is separated by distillation from the unchanged ethyl alcohol, which is recirculated.

(b) Manufacture from acetylene

The hydration of acetylene with sulphuric acid in presence of mercuric sulphate as catalyst has been operated on the large scale for over fifty years:

$$CH : CH + H_2O \rightarrow CH_3CHO$$

The process is carried out by passing acetylene counter-current to the acid mercury solution. In German practice,[12] the catalyst solution contained 200 g. $SO_4{''}$, 40 g. Fe (mainly $Fe{'''}$), 0·5 g. $Hg{''}$ and 10 g. $NO_3{'}$ per litre. Reaction was carried out in a rubber lined tower at $94–97°$ c., and 55 per cent of the acetylene introduced was reacted, the excess being recycled after removal of organic products from the gases. The catalyst solution was continuously circulated, a portion being withdrawn periodically for oxidation of $Fe{''}$ to $Fe{'''}$ with nitric acid.

The reacted gases, after removal of traces of mercury in a cyclone, were cooled first to $60°$ c., which condensed out some of the acetaldehyde, and were then washed with the exit liquors from the final scrubber to give 7% aqueous acetaldehyde; the last traces of acetaldehyde were removed by scrubbing with water at $40°$ c., these liquors being used in the previous scrubber. The aqueous acetaldehyde, containing traces of acetone and acetic acid and higher condensation products such as crotonaldehyde, was purified by distillation at 3 atma. pressure. The acetone was taken off in a side stream and worked up in separate columns. The yield of isolated acetaldehyde was 93 per cent on acetylene.

Acetaldehyde can also be obtained from acetylene via methyl vinyl ether which is available from acetylene and methyl alcohol (Chapter 15, p. 281):

$$CH : CH + CH_3OH \rightarrow CH_2 : CHOCH_3 \xrightarrow{\;+ H_2O\;} CH_3CHO + CH_3OH$$

---

[11] Carbide and Carbon, U.S.P. 1977750.
[12] C.I.O.S. 22/21.

The hydrolysis was carried out with 0·28% aqueous sulphuric acid at 80–100° c. under 3·5 atma. pressure[13]. The exit gases were condensed and distilled to separate acetaldehyde from methyl alcohol, slightly acid conditions being used to prevent acetal formation. The overall yield of acetaldehyde on acetylene was 96 per cent. This process avoids use of mercury but appears now to have been discarded.

(c) REACTIONS OF ACETALDEHYDE

Acetaldehyde is a very volatile liquid, b.p. 21° c., normally utilised at the site of manufacture.

The principal outlets of acetaldehyde are in the manufacture of acetic acid and anhydride by oxidation with oxygen (Chapter 18, p. 324), of ethyl acetate by the Tischtschenko reaction (Chapter 18, p. 338), and in the manifold ramifications of the aldol condensation.

American production was estimated at 310,000 tons (100%) in 1954, the outlets being :[14]

Outlet	% offtake
Acetic acid and acetic anhydride	59
n-Butyl alcohol	29
2-Ethylhexanol	7
Pentaerythritol	3·5
Pyridines, chloral, etc.	1·5
	100·0

(i) *The aldol condensation*

Under the influence of small quantities of bases, two molecules of acetaldehyde combine together; one of the three alpha hydrogen atoms of one molecule adds to the oxygen atom and the rest of the molecule to the carbonyl carbon atom of the second molecule to give aldol (2-hydroxy-butyraldehyde); this exists either as the open chain aldehyde form or as a cyclic hemi-acetal :

$$CH_3CHO + HCH_2CHO \rightarrow CH_3CHOHCH_2CHO \rightleftharpoons CH_3\underset{\lfloor——O——\rfloor}{CHCH_2}CHOH \quad (5)$$

Mixed aldol condensations can also be brought about between two dissimilar molecules, and acetaldehyde can supply either the carbonyl group or the alpha hydrogen atom; in condensations involving a series of substituted aldehydes, the ease of supplying the alpha hydrogen is in the order $R_2CHCHO > RCH_2CHO > CH_3CHO$. Except in self-condensation, formaldehyde supplies only the carbonyl group and never the hydrogen atom.

Pure acetaldol boils at 83° c./20 mm. On keeping, it polymerises to the

---

[13] B.I.O.S. 370.
[14] *Chem. Week*, Oct. 9, 1954, p. 93.

crystalline paraldol, a dimer of aldol. This is formed by condensation of the secondary hydroxyl group of one acetaldol molecule with the aldehyde group of another to give a hemi-acetal, which gives paraldol by a similar intramolecular condensation:[15]

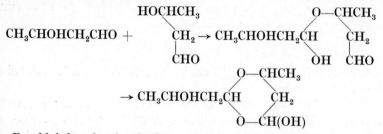

Paraldol therefore is 4-hydroxy-6-methyl-2-(2'-hydroxy-*n*-propyl)-1 : 3-dioxan.

Acetaldol forms 1 : 3-dioxans in the same way with other aldehydes; the most important of these is the compound formed with acetaldehyde itself, 4-hydroxy-2 : 6-dimethyl-1 : 3-dioxan :

This compound is the main component of crude technical acetaldol; on distillation, it breaks down into one molecule of acetaldehyde, which distils off, and one mol of the monomeric aldol. This explains why in technical processes for acetaldol, the conversion of acetaldehyde is reported as 66 per cent or less.

On the large scale, the manufacture of acetaldol is carried out by addition of a trace of alkali hydroxide to acetaldehyde and reacting at 20° c. or lower for a few hours. The process can be operated continuously or batchwise; reaction is exothermic, $\Delta H = -13$ k. cal./g. mol. acetaldehyde, and means must be provided for removing this heat of reaction; in a continuous process, this can be carried out by rapid recirculation of the product.

The process has been worked out for manufacture of both 1 : 3-butane diol via aldol and *n*-butyl alcohol via crotonaldehyde.[16] There are minor differences in the method of making aldol depending upon the end-product desired.

When 1 : 3-butane diol was wanted, the aldol was required to be as free as possible from acetaldehyde, which would be hydrogenated to ethyl alcohol in the next stage. In the Hüls process, the acetaldehyde was dimerised at 20° c., using potassium hydroxide as catalyst, and the conversion

[15] Spath and Schmidt, *Ber.*, 1941, **74**, 859.
[16] B.I.O.S. 1053.

of acetaldehyde was limited to 46 per cent. The catalyst was then exactly neutralised with phosphoric acid, so as to crystallise potassium phosphate, which was removed by centrifuging. If the aldol were too acid, it would dehydrate to crotonaldehyde in the next operation, in which it was heated to 100° c.; if too alkaline, further condensation to high molecular weight resins would take place. Presence of salts of strong acids and weak bases would also bring about side reactions. Crude aldol, analysing as a mixture of 53 per cent acetaldehyde and 47 per cent aldol (but actually containing 71 per cent of the dioxan [6]), was then distilled rapidly at atmospheric pressure, to decompose the dioxan and to remove the acetaldehyde, which was recycled to the dimerising stage. The product from the base of the still, so-called pure 'aldol,' contained 73 per cent aldol, 4–5 per cent acetalde-hyde, 4 per cent crotonaldehyde plus higher condensation products, and 18 per cent water. This product was hydrogenated directly to 1 : 3-butane diol as described in Chapter 12, p. 207.

When *n*-butyl alcohol was the required end-product, the aldolisation was run to 60% conversion, corresponding to a content of 90 per cent of the dioxan (6). The alkaline catalyst was then neutralised with acetic acid or phosphoric acid, a slight excess of the acid added and the crude aldol distilled at once. Distillation under these slightly acid conditions removed the unreacted acetaldehyde and that liberated from the splitting of the dioxan, and simultaneously dehydrated the aldol to crotonaldehyde:

$$CH_3CHOHCH_2CHO \rightarrow CH_3CH : CHCHO + H_2O$$

After removal of all the acetaldehyde, crotonaldehyde was taken over-head as the azeotrope with water, containing 90 per cent of crotonaldehyde. The yield of crotonaldehyde was about 90 per cent on acetaldehyde.

n-Butyl alcohol was made by vapour phase hydrogenation of croton-aldehyde, using copper on silica gel or on pumice as catalyst at 200–240° c. and atmospheric pressure. A certain amount of *n*-butyraldehyde was formed as a by-product, the amount depending upon the temperature and activity of the catalyst. Crotonaldehyde was also hydrogenated to *n*-butyl alcohol in the liquid phase at 100–130° c. and 300 atm. pressure using a promoted nickel-copper catalyst. The American method was to hydrogenate in the vapour phase over a supported nickel chromite catalyst at 180° c. and 3 atma. pressure.[17] The yield of *n*-butyl alcohol was high in all cases:

$$CH_3CH : CHCHO + 2H_2 \rightarrow CH_3CH_2CH_2CH_2OH$$

The principal method of manufacture of *n*-butyl alcohol during the inter-war years was by fermentation of starch, acetone being an important by-product. These methods are being displaced by another petroleum chemical route, the Oxo synthesis from propylene (Chapter 11, p. 183); the fermentation process is still operated in Great Britain.

---

[17] Carbide and Carbon, U.S.P. 1966157.

n-Butyl alcohol is one of the important aliphatic solvents and inter-mediates. The alcohol, the acetate, and di-*n*-butyl phthalate are used on a large scale as solvents and plasticisers in the paints and plastics industries.

The properties and reactions of crotonaldehyde are dealt with later in this chapter, p. 301.

(ii) Mixed aldol condensations

In the aldol process, small amounts of C_6 and C_8 hydroxyaldehydes are always obtained by further condensation of aldol or crotonaldehyde with acetaldehyde. In the 1 : 3-butane diol process, hexane triol and octane tetrol are isolated in the heavy ends; in the *n*-butyl alcohol process, C_6 and C_8 alcohols are produced in traces.

The higher aldehydes can be made by carrying out mixed aldol con-densations under controlled conditions. The condensation between acetal-dehyde and *n*-butyraldehyde can proceed in two ways:

$$CH_3CHO + H\overset{\overset{\displaystyle C_2H_5}{|}}{C}HCHO \rightarrow CH_3CH : \overset{\overset{\displaystyle C_2H_5}{|}}{C}CHO + H_2O \qquad . \qquad (7)$$

$$C_2H_5CH_2CHO + HCH_2CHO \rightarrow C_2H_5CH_2CH : CHCHO + H_2O \qquad (8)$$

As a methylene group is a better source of alpha hydrogens for these aldol condensations than a methyl group, reaction (7) proceeds more readily than reaction (8). German conditions for carrying out this condensation have been described.[18] Five mols of acetaldehyde were condensed with one mol of *n*-butyraldehyde in presence of a trace of caustic soda; the un-saturated aldehydes were isolated and hydrogenated separately using copper on pumice catalyst. The ratio of *n*-hexyl alcohol to 2-ethylbutyl alcohol was reported as 1 : 5, and of C_6 alcohols to C_8 alcohols as 9 : 1.

A similar process is disclosed in the patent literature; thus, *n*-butyralde-hyde is condensed with excess acetaldehyde at 0–10° c. in presence of 0·03–0·04% caustic soda; the product is isolated by neutralisation and pouring into boiling 2% aqueous sulphuric acid. The branch chain unsaturated aldehyde, methylethylacrolein (1-ethylcrotonaldehyde), $\overset{\displaystyle CH_3CH_2CCHO}{\underset{\displaystyle CHCH_3}{\|}}$, b.p. 137° c.,[19] is obtained in good yield.

The hydrogenation of 1-ethylcrotonaldehyde can be stopped at an intermediate stage to give 1-ethylbutyraldehyde (diethylacetaldehyde), $\overset{\displaystyle CH_3CH_2CHCHO}{\underset{\displaystyle C_2H_5}{|}}$. This intermediate boils at 116·8° c. and has been used for making medicinals, plasticisers and resins. On oxidation, it gives 1-ethylbutyric acid (see Chapter 18, p. 331). On further hydrogenation 2-ethylbutyl alcohol is obtained (b.p. 148·9° c.); it is a high boiling alcohol solvent, and has been used for making ester plasticisers.

---

[18] C.I.O.S. 25/20.
[19] Carbide and Carbon, U.S.P. 2175556.

On condensation of acetaldehyde with formaldehyde, the first product which should be formed is 2-hydroxypropionaldehyde:

$$CH_2O + HCH_2CHO \rightarrow CH_2OHCH_2CHO$$

In practice, it cannot be isolated. With excess of formaldehyde in aqueous solution in presence of calcium hydroxide as catalyst, all three alpha hydrogen atoms in acetaldehyde are replaced simultaneously and then the aldehyde group is reduced by a crossed Cannizzaro reaction by a further molecule of formaldehyde, the final product being pentaerythritol, $C(CH_2OH)_4$:

$$3CH_2O + CH_3CHO \rightarrow [(CH_2OH)_3CCHO] + CH_2O \rightarrow (CH_2OH)_4C + HCOOH$$

The process is carried out by adding a mixture of 5 mols aqueous formalin and 1 mol. 99% acetaldehyde to an aqueous slurry of 0·6 mols. of calcium hydroxide at 55° c. After 1 hour, the residual aldehyde content is less than 0·1 per cent. The calcium is removed by precipitation with sulphuric acid, the filtrate and washings concentrated *in vacuo* and the pentaerythritol crystallised out and filtered off, the mother liquor being recycled. The yield on acetaldehyde is over 70 per cent. Sodium hydroxide is also used as the catalyst. The process is operated at a higher temperature than with calcium hydroxide; the yield is higher but the quality of the crude pentaerythritol appears to be lower.[19a] Pentaerythritol melts at 260·5° c.; it is an intermediate for explosives, resins and plasticisers.

Production of pentaerythritol in the United States in 1954 was 25,000 tons, the major proportion of which was used in the resins industry.

In the vapour phase, acetaldehyde and formaldehyde condense to give acrolein, the dehydrated form of the first condensation product, hydroxypropionaldehyde:

$$CH_2O + CH_3CHO \rightarrow (CH_2OHCH_2CHO) \rightarrow CH_2 : CHCHO + H_2O$$

In the German process, a mixture of acetaldehyde and formaldehyde in molar proportions, together with excess steam, were passed over a catalyst of sodium silicate on silica gel at 300° c. and atmospheric pressure. The conversion was 50 per cent, and the ultimate yield of acrolein was 65 per cent on formaldehyde and 75 per cent on acetaldehyde. The acrolein was isolated by condensation of the reaction products, followed by fractional distillation.[20] Other dehydrating catalysts, such as active alumina, give equally good results.

Other routes to acrolein are summarised on p. 299.

Acetaldehyde also undergoes aldol condensations with ketones and with other compounds capable of supplying a reactive hydrogen atom or a carbonyl group.

[19a] Peters and Quinn, *Ind. Eng. Chem.*, 1955, **47**, 1710.
[20] B.I.O.S. 783.

(iii) Other acetaldehyde reactions

Acetaldehyde polymerises readily to the cyclic trimer, paraldehyde:

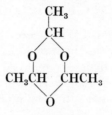

Paraldehyde is a low melting solid boiling at 124·5° c., used as a soporific and in the manufacture of resins and rubber chemicals. It readily regenerates acetaldehyde on heating with a trace of mineral acid. It is used as the source of acetaldehyde in the new petroleum chemical routes to pyridine and alkylpyridines (Chapter 14, p. 259).

Addition of acetylene to give
$$CH_3CHC:CH \atop OH \qquad and \qquad CH_3CHC:CCHCH_3 \atop OH \quad OH$$
has been referred to in Chapter 15, p. 276.

Acetaldehyde adds on carbon monoxide and water to give lactic acid under severe conditions, in presence of sulphuric acid catalyst at about 900 atm. pressure and 150–200° c.:[21]

$$CH_3CHO + CO + H_2O \rightarrow CH_3CHOHCOOH$$

With hydrogen cyanide, acetaldehyde cyanhydrin is obtained. On hydrolysis, this gives lactic acid; it is also an intermediate for one of the routes to acrylonitrile (Chapter 20, p. 371), and with ammonia and amines, it gives aminonitriles which can be hydrolysed to amino-acids (Strecker amino-acid synthesis):

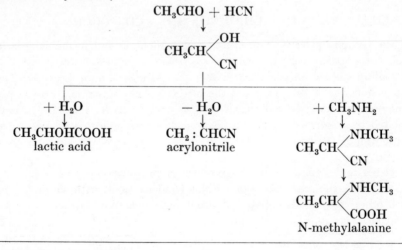

---

[21] du Pont, B.P. 527643.

The potassium salt of N-methylalanine has been used as an absorbent for acid gases such as hydrogen sulphide and carbon dioxide.

Reactions of acetaldehyde are summarised in Fig. 38.

3. Higher aldehydes

A variety of methods is available for the synthesis of the higher aldehydes; they can be built up from the lower aldehydes by the aldol condensation, or from olefins with one less carbon atom, by condensation with carbon monoxide and hydrogen (the Oxo reaction, Chapter 11, p. 183). They can be made from carbon compounds with the same number of carbon atoms, by the catalytic oxidation or dehydrogenation of normal alcohols, or by the isomerisation of olefin oxides (see Chapter 19, p. 361). Some of the lower straight chain aldehydes also occur as by-products in the 'Hydrocol' process (Chapter 3, p. 53) from carbon monoxide and hydrogen and from the controlled air oxidation of propane and *n*-butane (Chapter 4, p. 59).

Propionaldehyde can be made by all these routes; the best method is probably the Oxo reaction on ethylene:

$$CH_2 : CH_2 + CO + H_2 \rightarrow CH_3CH_2CHO$$

It can also be made by isomerisation of propylene oxide or allyl alcohol, by partial reduction of acrolein (from acetaldehyde and formaldehyde or by oxidation of propylene, Chapter 9, p. 148) or of propargyl alcohol (from acetylene and formaldehyde), by direct oxidation of the gaseous normal paraffins and from the 'Hydrocol' process:

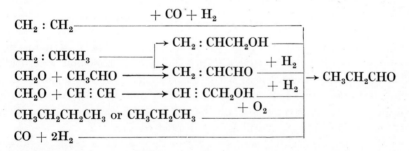

Propionaldehyde boils at 48·8° c. On air oxidation, it gives propionic acid and anhydride (Chapter 18, p. 328). With formaldehyde, it undergoes a pentaerythritol type of condensation to give $CH_3C(CH_2OH)_3$, pentaglycerol, or trimethylolethane, used as a substitute for glycerol in resins, etc.:

$$CH_3CH_2CHO + 3CH_2O \rightarrow CH_3C(CH_2OH)_3 + HCOOH$$

n-Butyraldehye is obtained as a by-product in the hydrogenation of crotonaldehyde to *n*-butyl alcohol (this Chapter, p. 291).

Direct routes from crotonaldehyde include liquid phase hydrogenation at 20–30° c. using a nickel on pumice catalyst,[22] or at 75° c. and 10–12 atma. pressure using nickel suspended in oil;[23] or vapour phase hydrogenation at 80–100° c. over supported nickel chromite,[24] or at 230–250° c. using copper carbonate-sodium silicate catalyst. *n*-Butyraldehyde has also been manufactured by catalytic dehydrogenation of *n*-butyl alcohol using a copper-zinc on pumice catalyst at 300–350° c. and atmospheric pressure, conditions being chosen to give 50% conversion per pass; the yield was 90–95 per cent.[16]

n-Butyraldehyde is now being made in Great Britain and the United States by the Oxo reaction from propylene, carbon monoxide and hydrogen and it seems likely that this route will in time displace the older methods of making both *n*-butyraldehyde and *n*-butyl alcohol. In the reaction, isobutyraldehyde is obtained as well as the normal aldehyde :[25]

$$CH_3CH : CH_2 + CO + H_2 - \begin{cases} \rightarrow CH_3CH_2CH_2CHO \\ \rightarrow CH_3CH(CH_3)CHO \end{cases}$$

Mention should also be made of an ingenious synthesis from ethyl alcohol; reacted at 200° c. under pressure in presence of hydrogen using a copper catalyst promoted with potassium carbonate, it gives a good yield of *n*-butyraldehyde with some C_6 aldehyde.[26] The synthesis presumably proceeds via acetaldehyde and acetaldol :

$$C_2H_5OH \xrightarrow{-H_2} CH_3CHO$$
$$2CH_3CHO \rightarrow CH_3CHOHCH_2CHO$$
$$CH_3CHOHCH_2CHO \xrightarrow{-H_2O + H_2} CH_3CH_2CH_2CHO$$

n-Butyraldehyde boils at 75·7° c. It is used for a variety of industrial purposes; on oxidation with air it gives *n*-butyric acid and anhydride (Chapter 18, p. 331). Condensed with amines, it gives rubber chemicals and resins; with polyvinyl alcohol, it gives polyvinyl butyral. It is also used for making nitriles, hydroxy acids, and by self-condensation or condensation with other aldehydes, for making higher aldehydes.

n-Butyraldehyde condenses with formaldehyde by a pentaerythritol type of condensation to give trimethylolpropane, $CH_3CH_2C(CH_2OH)_3$, an intermediate for synthetic resins. Condensation of *n*-butyraldehyde with acetaldehyde to give *n*-hexenal and 1-ethylcrotonaldehyde was described on p. 292. *n*-Butyraldehyde very readily undergoes self-condensation in presence of a trace of alkali to give 1-ethylhexenal, which can be reduced

[22] C.I.O.S. 26/11.
[23] Distillers, B.P. 478386; 478487.
[24] I.C.I., B.P. 371051–2; Carbide and Carbon, U.S.P. 1724761.
[25] B.I.O.S. 447.
[26] du Pont, U.S.P. 2004350.

in stages to 1-ethylhexaldehyde (1-ethylhexanal) and then to 2-ethyl-hexanol:

$$CH_3CH_2CH_2CHO + \underset{\underset{CH_3CH_2}{|}}{HCHCHO} \xrightarrow{-H_2O} CH_3CH_2CH_2CH : \underset{\underset{CH_3CH_2}{|}}{CCHO}$$

1-ethylhexenal

$$\xrightarrow{+1H_2} CH_3CH_2CH_2CH_2\underset{\underset{CH_3CH_2}{|}}{CHCHO} \xrightarrow{+1H_2} CH_3CH_2CH_2CH_2\underset{\underset{CH_3CH_2}{|}}{CHCH_2OH}$$

1-ethylhexaldehyde   2-ethylhexanol

1-Ethylhexenal (1-ethyl-2-propylacrolein) boils at 175° c. It has been used as a warning agent for fuel gases. 1-Ethylhexaldehyde (technical octaldehyde) boils at 164·1° c. It has been claimed as a solvent, but is of chief value as an intermediate for 2-ethylhexanol and 1-ethylhexoic acid (Chapter 18, p. 331). 1-Ethylhexaldehyde condenses with acetaldehyde to give a product hydrogenated to decylene glycol (b.p. 130° c./3 mm.), a new intermediate:

$$CH_3CHO + \underset{\underset{CHO}{|}}{\overset{\overset{CH_2CH_3}{|}}{HCCH_2CH_2CH_2CH_3}} \rightarrow CH_3\underset{\underset{OH}{|}}{CH}-\underset{\underset{CHO}{|}}{\overset{\overset{CH_2CH_3}{|}}{C}CH_2CH_2CH_2CH_3}$$

$$\xrightarrow{+H_2} CH_3\underset{\underset{OH}{|}}{CH}-\underset{\underset{CH_2CH_2CH_2CH_3}{|}}{\overset{\overset{CH_2CH_3}{|}}{C}}-CH_2OH$$

2-ethyl-2-*n*-butyl-1 : 3-
butane diol
(decylene glycol)

Condensed with acetone and with methyl isobutyl ketone, 1-ethyl-hexaldehyde gives long branch chain secondary alcohols (Chapter 17, p. 312).

2-Ethylhexanol boils at 183·5° c. Its main outlet is for the plasticiser, 2-ethylhexyl phthalate. It is also a useful defoaming and wetting agent and general intermediate. Its ester with maleic acid gives a detergent on sulphonation with sodium bisulphite:

$$2C_8H_{17}OH + \underset{\underset{CHCO}{||}}{\overset{\overset{CHCO}{}}{}}\hspace{-0.3em}\diagdown O \rightarrow \underset{\underset{CHCOOC_8H_{17}}{}}{\overset{\overset{CHCOOC_8H_{17}}{}}{||}} + NaHSO_3 \rightarrow \underset{\underset{SO_2ONa}{|}}{\overset{\overset{CH_2COOC_8H_{17}}{|}}{CHCOOC_8H_{17}}}$$

The self condensation of butyraldehyde can be stopped at the stage of butyraldol, which corresponds to aldol. On hydrogenation, this gives 2-ethyl-1 : 3-hexane diol which is used in insecticide preparations:

$$2CH_3CH_2CH_2CHO \rightarrow CH_3CH_2CH_2CH(OH)CH \overset{C_2H_5}{\underset{CHO}{\big\langle}} \xrightarrow{+ H_2}$$
[butyraldol]

$$CH_3CH_2CH_2CH(OH)CH(C_2H_5)CH_2OH$$
2-ethyl-1 : 3-hexane diol

All these condensation products were based initially on acetaldehyde, but with the development of the Oxo route to *n*-butyraldehyde they are no longer dependent on acetaldehyde.

Isobutyraldehyde can be obtained by the methods indicated above; in Germany it was manufactured by catalytic air oxidation of isobutyl alcohol made from carbon monoxide and hydrogen by the 'Higher Alcohols' synthesis (Chapter 3, p. 45); the oxidation was carried out at atmospheric pressure at 370° c. over a silver gauze catalyst.[27] It is now made alongside *n*-butyraldehyde by the Oxo reaction on propylene (see p. 296).

Isobutyraldehyde boils at 61° c. It is an intermediate for isobutyric acid (Chapter 18, p. 331), and for mono- and di-isobutylamines (Chapter 20, p. 376). With formaldehyde, it gives pentaldol, $(CH_3)_2C\overset{CHO}{\underset{CH_2OH}{\big\langle}}$, a fairly stable compound which can be distilled *in vacuo*. With excess formaldehyde, pentaglycol, $(CH_3)_2C(CH_2OH)_2$ is obtained:

$$(CH_3)_2CHCHO + CH_2O \rightarrow (CH_3)_2C \overset{CH_2OH}{\underset{CHO}{\big\langle}} + CH_2O + H_2O$$

$$\rightarrow (CH_3)_2C \overset{CH_2OH}{\underset{CH_2OH}{\big\langle}} + HCOOH$$

The higher aldehydes, except *n*-heptaldehyde, which is not a petroleum chemical, are not yet of more than academic interest.

4. Glyoxal

Glyoxal, CHOCHO, is the simplest saturated dialdehyde. It is available in tank car quantities, due to the discovery of a new technical synthesis.

The present industrial route, discovered by the Carbide and Carbon Chemicals Co., depends upon the vapour phase oxidation of ethylene glycol in presence of excess air at 250–300° c. over copper as catalyst;[28] traces of halogen compounds such as hydrogen chloride were used to suppress further oxidation of glyoxal, a method recalling the use of ethylene

---

[27] C.I.O.S. 32/107.
[28] U.S.P. 2339282; U.S.P. 2339346–8.

dichloride in the vapour phase oxidation of ethylene to ethylene oxide (Chapter 9, p. 146). The best yield was about 50 per cent.

$$\begin{array}{c} CH_2OH \\ | \\ CH_2OH \end{array} \xrightarrow{\ O_2\ } \begin{array}{c} CHO \\ | \\ CHO \end{array} + 2H_2O$$

Monomeric glyoxal is a yellow solid, m.p. 15° c., b.p. 50·4° c. It normally exists in a variety of polymeric forms. In the ethylene glycol process, glyoxal is obtained as a 30% aqueous solution in which it exists as a series of non-volatile hydrates as in the case of formaldehyde.

Glyoxal is capable of two main technical applications; as an intermediate in chemical synthesis, and as a cross-linking agent for modifying the properties of high polymers. Its first industrial outlet was for the synthesis of pyrazine-2:3-dicarboxylic acid:

This was first manufactured in 1942. It is similar in action to nicotinamide (Vitamin B group) but has certain advantages. The chief outlet of glyoxal is in the dimensional stabilisation of rayon by the 'Sanforset' process, which probably depends upon cross-linking of hydroxyl groups in the rayon molecule. The industrial possibilities of glyoxal have been reviewed.[29]

Methylglyoxal (pyruvic aldehyde), CH_3COCHO, is now available in limited quantities, also as a 30% aqueous solution. It is presumably made in the same way as glyoxal, starting from propylene glycol.

$$\begin{array}{c} CH_3 \\ | \\ CHOH \\ | \\ CH_2OH \end{array} \xrightarrow{+ O_2} \begin{array}{c} CH_3 \\ | \\ CO \\ | \\ CHO \end{array} + 2H_2O$$

It resembles glyoxal in many of its physical and chemical properties.

5. Unsaturated aldehydes

Acrolein (acraldehyde) was originally made by dehydration of glycerol.

$$\begin{array}{c} CH_2OH \\ | \\ CHOH \\ | \\ CH_2OH \end{array} \xrightarrow{- 2H_2O} \begin{array}{c} CH_2 \\ || \\ CH \\ | \\ CHO \end{array}$$

It can also be made by several syntheses from raw materials based on petroleum, such as by condensation of acetaldehyde and formaldehyde (this

---

[29] Field, *Chem. Ind.*, 1947, **60**, 960; Bohmfalk, McNamee and Barry, *Ind. Eng. Chem.*, 1951, **43**, 786.

Chapter, p. 293), by direct oxidation of propylene (Chapter 9, p. 148) and by oxidation of allyl alcohol. It has been manufactured by the Shell Chemical Corporation in America by pyrolysis of diallyl ether (a by-product in the manufacture of allyl alcohol from allyl chloride) at 520° c. and 3 atma. pressure:[30, 31]

$$(CH_3CH : CH_2)O \rightarrow CH_2 : CHCHO + CH_3CH : CH_2 + H_2$$

The overall yield of acrolein is 86 per cent on diallyl ether reacted, the conversion per pass being 90 per cent. This route has been displaced by Shell Development themselves, who improved the direct oxidation of propylene with air (Chapter 9, p. 148). Propylene oxidation can now be accepted as the most economic large-scale route to acrolein.

Acrolein boils at 52·5° c. It first attracted attention as a war gas. It polymerises readily, but the polymers have not yet gained any importance. It has recently been employed as a bifunctional reagent in the high polymer field. Condensed with pentaerythritol, it gives a glass-clear polymer, both the aldehyde group and the double bond reacting with the hydroxyl groups in the pentaerythritol.[32] Other outlets are in the fields of insecticides and pharmaceuticals, for example, for the synthesis of the growth accessory substance, methionine, $CH_3SCH_2CH_2CH(NH_2)COOH$.

Acrolein is now moving out of the field of specialty and small tonnage chemicals. It is the basis of a second Shell Development route to synthetic glycerol for which a plant to make about 15,000 tons p.a. is being planned (Chapter 10, p. 169);[33] the process could involve making allyl alcohol without having to pass through allyl chloride, by selective hydrogenation of acrolein, *e.g.*, with isopropyl alcohol.[34]

$$CH_2 : CHCHO \xrightarrow{+ H_2} CH_2 : CHCH_2OH$$

Other possibilities are the synthesis of acrylonitrile from acrolein, ammonia and air[35] (see also Chapter 20, p. 371):

$$CH_2 : CHCHO + NH_3 + \tfrac{1}{2}O_2 \rightarrow CH_2 : CHCN + 2H_2O$$

of making 1 : 2 : 6-hexane triol, *via* acrolein dimer, a polyol alternative to trimethylolethane and -propane for use in the synthetic resin industry, and of glyceraldehyde, from acrolein and hydrogen peroxide:[36]

$$CH_2 : CHCHO + H_2O_2 \rightarrow CH_2OHCHOHCHO$$

Propargyl aldehyde, $CH : CCHO$, if wanted, could be made from propargyl alcohol, $CH : CCH_2OH$ (Chapter 15, p. 275).

[30] Watson, *Chemical Engineering*, 1947, **54(12)**, 106.
[31] Shell Development, U.S.P. 2309576.
[32] F.I.A.T. 67.
[33] *Chem. Week*, April 23, 1955, p. 30.
[34] Shell Development, B.P. 619014.
[35] Distillers, B.P. 709337.
[36] Shell Development, U.S.P. 2718529.

The manufacturing process for crotonaldehyde, $CH_3CH : CHCHO$, from acetaldehyde was described on p. 291. Although its chief outlet is as an intermediate for n-butyl alcohol and n-butyraldehyde, it has been used for the manufacture of crotonic acid by liquid phase oxidation, of maleic anhydride by vapour phase oxidation (Chapter 18, p. 335), and of 3-ethoxy-butyl alcohol (1 : 3-butane diol monoethyl ether), a solvent, by addition of ethyl alcohol to give 2-ethoxybutyraldehyde, followed by hydrogenation :[16]

$$CH_3CH : CHCHO + 3C_2H_5OH \rightarrow CH_3CH(OC_2H_5)CH_2CH(OC_2H_5)_2 \xrightarrow[\text{(acid)}]{+ H_2O}$$

$$CH_3CH(OC_2H_5)CH_2CHO \xrightarrow{+ H_2} CH_3CH(OC_2H_5)CH_2CH_2OH$$

The CH_3 next to the conjugated system can take part in aldol condensations. Crotonaldehyde dimerises to octatrienal, $CH_3(CH : CH)_3CHO$, and with acetaldehyde gives hexadienal, $CH_3(CH : CH)_2CHO$. These reactions are possible routes to the straight chain saturated aldehydes, $CH_3(CH_2)_nCHO$, and the straight chain saturated alcohols,

$$CH_3(CH_2)_nCH_2OH$$

Crotonaldehyde has also been used for synthesis of certain 1-substituted butadienes :

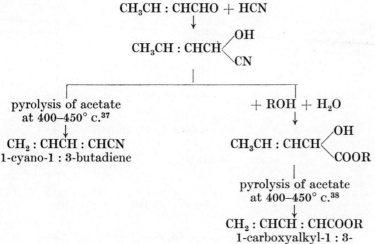

These processes are not operated on any appreciable scale.

Of the two unsaturated aldehydes isomeric with crotonaldehyde, vinyl-acetaldehyde $CH_2 : CHCH_2CHO$ is unknown. The branch chain isomer,

---

[37] I.C.I., B.P. 515737; B.P. 520272.
[38] I.C.I., B.P. 523080.

methacrolein, $CH_2 : C(CH_3)CHO$, is made by catalytic air oxidation of methallyl alcohol, or by dehydration of β-methylglycerol:

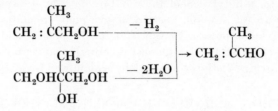

It can also be prepared by catalytic air oxidation of isobutene (Chapter 9, p. 149):

$$CH_2 : \overset{\overset{\displaystyle CH_3}{|}}{C}CH_3 \xrightarrow{\ + O_2\ } CH_2 : \overset{\overset{\displaystyle CH_3}{|}}{C}CHO$$

The higher unsaturated aldehydes are not yet of any interest.

The boiling points of the lower saturated and unsaturated aldehydes are given in Table 62.

TABLE 62

Boiling points of lower aldehydes

Name	Formula	b.p., ° c./760 mm.
1. *Saturated aldehydes*—		
Formaldehyde . . .	CH_2O	$- 19$ (monomer)
Acetaldehyde . . .	CH_3CHO	21
Propionaldehyde . . .	CH_3CH_2CHO	48·8
n-Butyraldehyde . . .	$CH_3CH_2CH_2CHO$	75·7
Isobutyraldehyde . . .	$\overset{\displaystyle CH_3}{\underset{\displaystyle CH_3}{}}{>}CHCHO$	61
1-Ethylbutyraldehyde . . .	$CH_3CH_2\underset{\displaystyle \mid}{C}HCHO$ CH_3CH_2	116·8
1-Ethylhexaldehyde . . .	$CH_3CH_2CH_2CH_2\underset{\displaystyle \mid}{C}HCHO$ CH_3CH_2	164·1
Glyoxal	$OHCCHO$	50·4 (monomer) (m.p. 15° c.)
2. *Unsaturated aldehydes*—		
Acrolein	$CH_2 : CHCHO$	52·5
Crotonaldehyde . . .	$CH_3CH : CHCHO$	104
Methacrolein . . .	$CH_2 : \underset{\displaystyle \mid}{C}CHO$ CH_3	73·5
1-Ethylcrotonaldehyde . (methylethylacrolein)	$CH_3CH : \underset{\displaystyle \mid}{C}CHO$ CH_3CH_2	137·3
1-Ethylhexenal . . (ethylpropylacrolein)	$CH_3CH_2CH_2CH : \underset{\displaystyle \mid}{C}CHO$ CH_3CH_2	175
Propargyl aldehyde . (propiolic aldehyde)	$CH : CCHO$	61

CHAPTER 17

KETONES

THE most important ketone is acetone, and its manufacture and principal reactions will be described in some detail as they are typical of the higher members of the series.

1. Manufacture of acetone

The main petroleum route to acetone is from isopropyl alcohol (Chapter 8, p. 135); just as primary alcohols can be converted to aldehydes by dehydrogenation or by air oxidation (Chapter 16), secondary alcohols such as isopropyl alcohol can be converted to ketones.

(a) DEHYDROGENATION OF ISOPROPYL ALCOHOL

For the reaction,

$$(CH_3)_2CHOH(g) \rightleftharpoons (CH_3)_2CO(g) + H_2 \qquad . \qquad . \qquad (1)$$

Parks and Huffman[1] calculate:

$$\Delta H = 13,500 + 4 \cdot 0T$$
$$\Delta G = 13,500 - 4 \cdot 0T \ln T - 3 \cdot 0T$$

These equations have been used to calculate the equilibrium conversion of isopropyl alcohol to acetone at atmospheric pressure over a range of temperatures (Table 63).

TABLE 63

Equilibrium in the dehydrogenation of isopropyl alcohol to acetone

Temperature ° c.	ΔH g. cal./mol	ΔG g. cal./mol	K_p	% conversion to acetone
227	15,500	— 500	1·6	78·5
327	15,900	— 3,700	20·4	97·6
427	16,300	— 7,000	$1 \cdot 55 \times 10^2$	99·8
527	16,700	— 10,400	$6 \cdot 8 \times 10^2$	100

Conversion will therefore approach completion above about 350° c.; the equilibrium is more favourable than in the corresponding dehydrogenation of ethyl alcohol to acetaldehyde (Table 61, p. 287).

From the patent literature the two catalysts most often referred to are metallic copper and zinc oxide. Copper is stated to suffer from the drawback of loss of activity and zinc oxide has a tendency to lead to some dehydration

---

[1] 'Free Energies of Some Organic Compounds', *Chemical Catalog Co.*, 1932.

of the alcohol to propylene. The preferred industrial process seems now to be dehydrogenation, using a zinc oxide or promoted zinc oxide catalyst. One advantage over the alternative process of oxidation referred to below is that pure hydrogen is produced as a by-product.

In Germany,[2] dehydrogenation of isopropyl alcohol to acetone was conducted in connection with the utilisation of C_3–C_4 olefins from the atmospheric pressure Fischer-Tropsch process (Chapters 3, p. 50 and 8, p. 136). The dehydrogenation was carried out in a stream of hydrogen, using zinc oxide as catalyst (made by heating pumice impregnated with zinc acetate) at 380° c. Owing to the endothermic nature of the reaction (see Table 63), a multitubular reactor was used with long narrow tubes heated by circulating flue gas. The actual conversion was 98 per cent; at 380° c. K_p will be about 63, and even with 10 mols hydrogen/mol of isopropyl alcohol + acetone, the equilibrium conversion will exceed 99 per cent.

The catalyst slowly lost its activity owing to deposition of carbon or tars and required periodical regeneration by burning off the deposit with dilute oxygen containing gases. The total catalyst life was six months.

Half the acetone produced was isolated by cooling the reactor gases; the remainder was scrubbed out with cold water giving a 20% aqueous solution, which was rectified. The exit gas was 99% pure hydrogen containing only traces of propylene and acetone; a portion was recycled and the remainder was available for chemical syntheses.

(b) Oxidation of isopropyl alcohol

The oxidation of isopropyl alcohol with air is carried out over metallic catalysts. The reaction is highly exothermic:

$$(CH_3)_2CHOH(g) + \tfrac{1}{2}O_2 \rightarrow (CH_3)_2CO(g) + H_2O(g). \quad \Delta H_{298} = -43 \text{ k. cal.} \quad (2)$$

and some difficulty has been experienced in avoiding decomposition due to excessive temperatures. Combined oxidation and dehydrogenation has been proposed to make the total reaction more or less autothermic on the lines of the similar processes for conversion of primary alcohols to aldehydes (Chapter 16).

The metallic catalysts suggested cover the usual range—copper, silver, nickel, platinum, etc. Silver gauzes have been used for the oxidation of the isopropyl alcohol-water azeotrope to acetone, the reaction temperature being 650° c.[3]

(c) Other routes to acetone

Acetone is being obtained as a co-product of two petroleum chemical processes, the phenol from cumene process (Chapter 14, p. 254)

---

[2] B.I.O.S. 131.
[3] I.C.I., U.S.P. 2015094.

and hydrogen peroxide by oxidation of isopropyl alcohol (Chapter 8, p. 137). In making phenol from cumene, 0·7 tons of acetone are obtained for one ton of phenol; in the hydrogen peroxide route, theoretically 1·7 tons of acetone are obtained for one ton of 100% hydrogen peroxide. These amounts of acetone are inevitable, and must be sold; acetone from cumene represents a reduction of the market for acetone from isopropyl alcohol. Acetone is also obtained from petroleum sources as a by-product from the 'Hydrocol' process from carbon monoxide and hydrogen (Chapter 3, p. 53) and from the air oxidation of propane and butane (Chapter 4, p. 59).

Acetone has been made on a large scale in various countries from three other starting materials, ethyl alcohol, acetylene and acetic acid, all of which can be regarded as available from petroleum. It seems likely that these three syntheses proceed through a common intermediate.

Ethyl alcohol is converted to acetone, carbon dioxide and hydrogen by passage with steam at 470° c. over a catalyst of iron oxide promoted with lime.

The overall reaction is:

$$2C_2H_5OH + H_2O \rightarrow CH_3COCH_3 + CO_2 + 4H_2 . \qquad (3)$$

Reaction may proceed through the following cycle:

$$C_2H_5OH \rightarrow CH_3CHO + H_2 . \qquad (4)$$

$$2CH_3CHO \rightarrow CH_3COOC_2H_5 + H_2O \rightarrow CH_3COOH + C_2H_5OH \qquad (5)$$

$$2CH_3COOH \rightarrow CH_3COCH_3 + CO_2 + H_2O . \qquad (6)$$

In place of (5), the acetaldehyde may be converted directly to acetic acid by oxidation with steam:

$$CH_3CHO + H_2O \rightarrow CH_3COOH + H_2 \qquad (7)$$

Acetone is isolated as a 5% aqueous solution by scrubbing the exit gases with water. The yield of isolated acetone on ethyl alcohol is 86 per cent.[4] The catalyst loses its activity owing to carbon deposition and requires periodical regeneration by burning in air; its total life is six months.

Acetylene is converted to acetone by passage with excess steam over a catalyst of mixed iron oxide-zinc oxide supported on steel balls, also at the same temperature, 470° c., as in reaction (3). The overall reaction is:

$$2C_2H_2 + 3H_2O \rightarrow CH_3COCH_3 + CO_2 + 2H_2$$

Its probable course is:

$$C_2H_2 + H_2O \rightarrow CH_3CHO$$

followed by the sequence (5) and (6) or (7) and (6).

Acetone is again isolated by scrubbing the exit gases with water, being

---

[4] Jones, *Ind. Chem.*, April 1946, p. 195.

obtained as a 10% aqueous solution. The yield of acetone on acetylene is 85 per cent. The catalyst also loses its activity as with the ethyl alcohol process and requires periodical regeneration with air.[4, 5] This process was operated successfully with gases containing only 8 per cent of acetylene obtained by partial combustion of methane with oxygen (Chapter 15, p. 272).[6] The catalyst used was zinc oxide and the temperature range in the reactor was 350–450° c. Owing to the large volumes of inert gas, the aqueous acetone obtained by water scrubbing contained only 3 per cent of acetone.

The acetone making step in both these processes is probably the decarboxylation of acetic acid. Conversion of acetic acid to acetone by heating the metal salts such as calcium acetate is well known. The direct vapour phase decarboxylation of acetic acid to acetone, reaction (6), was carried out in Germany by passing acetic acid vapour over cerium oxide on pumice at 400–450° c., and atmospheric pressure;[7] the yield was 95 per cent.

The last route to acetone is the classical Weizmann fermentation of starch to give a mixture consisting of 60 per cent *n*-butyl alcohol, 30 per cent acetone and 10 per cent ethyl alcohol, operated during the first world war for acetone and subsequently for *n*-butyl alcohol with acetone as a by-product. The output of acetone by this process is tied to the outlets for *n*-butyl alcohol.

B. Properties and reactions of acetone

Acetone is a colourless liquid, b.p. 56·1° c., completely miscible with water and most organic solvents. It possesses very good solvent powers and this is taken advantage of in a wide range of industries, such as in the manufacture of cellulose acetate, in the paint and plastics industries and in the refining of lubricating oil.

In its reactions, acetone displays the properties of a keto group and of two active methyl groups alpha to the > CO group. It undergoes the aldol condensation (Chapter 16, p. 289) both with itself and with other molecules which supply either the hydrogen atom to the keto group of acetone or accept a hydrogen atom from one of its methyl groups. Another important series of derivatives is based on its pyrolysis.

(a) ALDOL CONDENSATIONS

(i) *Self-condensation*

Acetone undergoes self-condensation to give two distinct series of derivatives depending upon whether an alkaline catalyst is used, when two or three molecules of acetone link up, or whether an acid catalyst is used, when three molecules join up.

---

[5] Morrison, *Chem. and Ind.*, 1941, **19**, 387.
[6] C.I.O.S. 30/103.
[7] B.I.O.S. 1053.

With a trace of alkali, acetone condenses to give diacetone alcohol:

$$\underset{CH_3}{\overset{CH_3}{>}}CO + CH_3COCH_3 \xrightarrow{\text{(alkali)}} \underset{CH_3}{\overset{CH_3}{>}}C(OH)CH_2COCH_3$$

The reaction is reversible, and the conversion at equilibrium is low, 12 per cent at 15–20° c. and 16 per cent at 0° c. The diacetone alcohol should be separated quickly from the excess acetone which is recycled. Catalysts which have been mentioned are lime, caustic soda, barium hydroxide or soda-lime; the process can be operated batchwise or continuously.[7, 8]

Diacetone alcohol boils at 166° c. and is completely miscible with water and many organic solvents. Whilst used as a solvent for several plastics, and for pentachlorophenol, its chief outlets are as an intermediate for other acetone derivatives.

On reduction, for example by hydrogenation at 70–80° c. in the liquid phase under 35 atma. pressure using Raney nickel, it gives 2-methyl-2 : 4-pentane diol:[7]

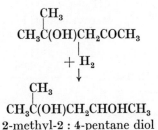

$$CH_3\overset{CH_3}{\underset{|}{C}}(OH)CH_2COCH_3$$
$$+ H_2 \downarrow$$
$$CH_3\overset{CH_3}{\underset{|}{C}}(OH)CH_2CHOHCH_3$$
2-methyl-2 : 4-pentane diol

This is one of the simpler 1 : 3-glycols and can be employed as a solvent and for making ester plasticisers; it boils at 196° c. On liquid phase dehydration at 120° c. with hydrochloric acid or iodine, it gives a mixture of 1 : 3- and 1 : 1-dimethyl-1 : 3-butadienes,[8a] which has attracted interest as a constituent of an all-diene synthetic rubber (see Chapter 12, p. 211).

On heating with weak acids such as oxalic acid, diacetone alcohol loses one molecule of water to give mesityl oxide:

$$\underset{CH_3}{\overset{CH_3}{>}}C(OH)CH_2COCH_3 \xrightarrow{-H_2O} \underset{CH_3}{\overset{CH_3}{>}}C : CHCOCH_3$$
mesityl oxide

This process can be combined with the diacetone alcohol process by acidification at the completion of the aldol condensation, and heating to 120° c. to split off water from the diacetone alcohol and to distil out the unchanged acetone, which is recycled.[9]

---

[8] B.I.O.S. 1652: Shell Development, U.S.P. 2130592: Distillers, B.P. 402788.
[8a] Shell Development, B.P. 572602.
[9] Degussa, U.S.P. 1925317.

Mesityl oxide boils at 128–129° c.; it is soluble in water to the extent of only 3 per cent. It is used to reduce evaporation of surface coating solvents, and to improve flow, especially in nitrocellulose and vinyl type lacquers; its chief value is as an intermediate for saturated ketones and alcohols. On mild hydrogenation, it gives methyl isobutyl ketone, $CH_3{\diagdown}\atop{CH_3{\diagup}}$CHCH$_2$COCH$_3$, b.p. 116° c., a solvent for the paint trade, also used as a dewaxer and in paint removers. On vigorous hydrogenation, methyl isobutyl carbinol (methyl amyl alcohol), b.p. 131·8° c., is obtained. This is used as a medium boiling alcohol solvent, as a frother in ore flotation and for making xanthates and organic esters, of which the most important is the acetate, methyl amyl acetate, b.p. 146·3° c., medium boiling ester solvent:

$$CH_3{\diagdown}\atop{CH_3{\diagup}}C:CHCOCH_3 \xrightarrow{\;+\,H_2\;} CH_3{\diagdown}\atop{CH_3{\diagup}}CHCH_2COCH_3$$

Methyl isobutyl ketone
(4-methylpentan-2-one)

$$\xrightarrow{\;+\,H_2\;} CH_3{\diagdown}\atop{CH_3{\diagup}}CHCH_2CHOHCH_3 \xrightarrow{\;+\,CH_3COOH\;} CH_3{\diagdown}\atop{CH_3{\diagup}}CHCH_2CHCH_3$$
$$\underset{OCOCH_3}{|}$$

Methyl isobutyl carbinol
(Methyl amyl alcohol;
4-methylpentan-2-ol)

Methyl isobutyl
carbinol acetate
(Methyl amyl
acetate; 4-methyl-
pentanyl-2-acetate)

A method of proceeding from C_3 compounds to C_2 and C_4 compounds is by pyrolysis of mesityl oxide at 300–500° c., especially in presence of phosphoric acid catalysts.[10] The mesityl oxide splits into one molecule of isobutene and one molecule of keten (reactions of keten are dealt with in this Chapter, p. 315):

$$CH_3{\diagdown}\atop{CH_3{\diagup}}C:CH \vdots COCH_3 \rightarrow CH_3{\diagdown}\atop{CH_3{\diagup}}C:CH_2 + CH_2:C:O$$

Self condensation of two mols of mesityl oxide under alkaline conditions,

---

[10] Shell Development, U.S.P. 2143489.

e.g., with calcium carbide, followed by hydrogenation, gives the C_{12} ketone, 2 : 6 : 8-trimethyl-4-nonanone:

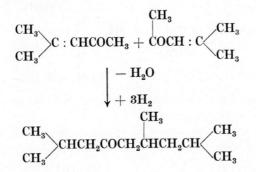

Under more drastic conditions of alkaline condensation three molecules of acetone link up to give the cyclic ketone, isophorone:

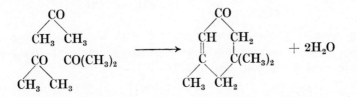

The usual conditions are to heat acetone in the liquid phase in presence of sodium alkoxides or sodium amide as catalyst, removing the water of condensation as formed, or to heat with aqueous caustic soda at 150–170° c. under pressure. These methods give considerable quantities of phorone (see below), the open chain isomer of isophorone:

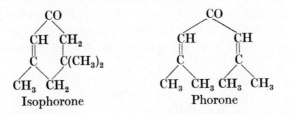

Isophorone   Phorone

Another method is to react acetone in the vapour phase at 350–400° c. over a catalyst of calcium carbide or calcium hydroxide, preferably kept from caking by agitation in a ball mill; this method can also be used for the higher methyl ketones.[11]

Isophorone boils at 215° c.; it is used as a solvent for vinyl resins and

---

[11] Carbide and Carbon, U.S.P. 2183127.

paints. On hydrogenation, it gives $3:3:5$-trimethylcyclohexanol, m.p. $40°$ c., b.p. $198°$ c.:

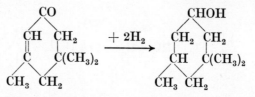

This has been used as a substitute for menthol and camphor, as a hydraulic brake fluid and in textile soaps.

Isophorone can be converted to aromatic compounds by pyrolysis at $670°$ c. with 2–3 seconds' contact time, when $1:3:5$-xylenol is obtained:[12]

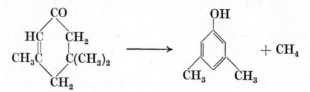

and by vapour phase catalytic reaction with ammonia, using mixed catalysts, such as alumina plus dehydrogenating metals; the temperature range specified is 400–$650°$ c.:[13]

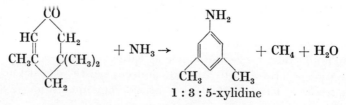

$1:3:5$-xylidine

Under acid conditions, the main product of self-condensation of acetone is phorone, from three mols of acetone. The reaction can be formulated as proceeding via mesityl oxide; the methyl group next to the $> CO$ group in mesityl oxide then condenses with a third acetone molecule:

$$\underset{CH_3}{\overset{CH_3}{>}}CO + CH_3COCH_3 \xrightarrow{-H_2O} \underset{CH_3}{\overset{CH_3}{>}}C:CHCOCH_3 + CO\underset{CH_3}{\overset{CH_3}{<}}$$

$$\xrightarrow{-H_2O} \underset{CH_3}{\overset{CH_3}{>}}C:CHCOCH:C\underset{CH_3}{\overset{CH_3}{<}}$$

Phorone

Phorone boils at $198°$ c. On mild hydrogenation it gives diisobutyl ketone, $CO[CH_2CH(CH_3)_2]_2$, b.p. $168°$ c., a stable slow evaporating solvent.

---

[12] Shell Development, B.P. 584256.
[13] Shell Development, B.P. 586518.

More vigorous reduction gives diisobutyl carbinol, $CHOH[CH_2CH(CH_3)_2]_2$, b.p. 178·8° c., a paint solvent.

Under much more severe conditions, with concentrated sulphuric or hydrochloric acids, three molecules of acetone also condense, but mesitylene, 1 : 3 : 5-trimethylbenzene, is the main product. This synthesis may proceed by condensation of one of the methyl groups attached to the isopropyl group in mesityl oxide with the keto group of the third acetone molecule :

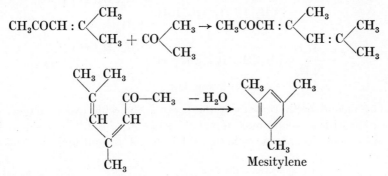

The overall yield of mesitylene is only about 30 per cent.

(ii) Mixed aldol condensations

In the mixed aldol condensation between acetone and aldehydes, the aldehyde always supplies the more reactive keto group, and the acetone, the alpha hydrogen atoms.

With formaldehyde under mild alkaline conditions, one mol of acetone can be made to add from one to seven mols of formaldehyde,[14] the final product being anhydroenneaheptitol (3 : 3 : 5 : 5-tetrakishydroxymethyl-4-pyranol) :

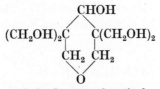

Anhydroenneaheptitol

Only this last compound is of any technical interest; its value as a polyhydric alcohol for synthetic resins is being explored. Reaction between acetone and acetaldehyde does not give rise to useful products, but with higher aldehydes, the condensation has been more successful and has been used for building up long branch chain secondary alcohols which are commercially available.

---

[14] Walker, 'Formaldehyde', *Reinhold*, 1944.

On condensation of 1-ethylhexaldehyde (derived from acetaldehyde, Chapter 16, p. 297) with acetone under mild conditions, a keto alcohol is formed, which readily loses water and can be dehydrated and dehydrogenated in one step to 5-ethyl-2-nonanol (technical undecanol):

$$CH_3COCH_3 + OHCCH \underset{C_2H_5}{\overset{CH_2CH_2CH_2CH_3}{<}}$$

$$\rightarrow CH_3COCH_2CHOHCH \underset{C_2H_5}{\overset{CH_2CH_2CH_2CH_3}{<}}$$

$$\xrightarrow[+\,2H_2]{-\,H_2O} CH_3CHOHCH_2CH_2CH \underset{C_2H_5}{\overset{CH_2CH_2CH_2CH_3}{<}}$$

5-ethyl-2-nonanol

The second methyl group of the acetone molecule can undergo condensation with a second molecule of the same or of a different aldehyde; technical heptadecanol, 3 : 9-diethyl-6-tridecanol, is built up in the following way:

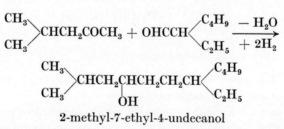

$$CH_3COCH_3 + OHCCHC_4H_9 \quad \underset{+\,H_2}{\overset{-\,H_2O}{\xrightarrow{\hspace{1cm}}}} \quad CH_3COCH_2CH_2CH \underset{C_2H_5}{\overset{C_4H_9}{<}}$$

$$\underset{CH_3CH_2}{\overset{CH_3CH_2}{>}}CHCHO + CH_3COCH_2CH_2CH \underset{C_2H_5}{\overset{C_4H_9}{<}} \quad \underset{+\,2H_2}{\overset{-\,H_2O}{\xrightarrow{\hspace{1cm}}}}$$

$$\underset{CH_3CH_2}{\overset{CH_3CH_2}{>}}CHCH_2CH_2\underset{OH}{\overset{}{C}}HCH_2CH_2CH \underset{C_2H_5}{\overset{C_4H_9}{<}}$$

3 : 9-diethyl-6-tridecanol

Related to these reactions is the synthesis of tetradecanol (2-methyl-7-ethyl-4-undecanol) from methyl isobutyl ketone and 1-ethylhexaldehyde:

$$\underset{CH_3}{\overset{CH_3}{>}}CHCH_2COCH_3 + OHCCH \underset{C_2H_5}{\overset{C_4H_9}{<}} \quad \underset{+\,2H_2}{\overset{-\,H_2O}{\xrightarrow{\hspace{1cm}}}}$$

$$\underset{CH_3}{\overset{CH_3}{>}}CHCH_2\underset{OH}{\overset{}{C}}HCH_2CH_2CH \underset{C_2H_5}{\overset{C_4H_9}{<}}$$

2-methyl-7-ethyl-4-undecanol

All these long branch chain secondary alcohols are intermediates for surface active compounds. They have been used as anti-foaming agents, *e.g.*, in penicillin manufacture, and for plasticisers, cosmetics, flotation agents and insecticides, etc.

With ammonia, acetone gives diacetoneamine and triacetoneamine by addition to two and three molecules of acetone respectively.

Diacetonamine   Triacetonamine

Triacetonamine can also be made by direct addition of ammonia to phorone. It is an intermediate for pharmaceuticals.

Aromatic bases condense similarly with acetone under the influence of acidic catalysts, but the diacetoneamine transiently formed undergoes ring closure to give dihydroquinoline derivatives which are antioxidants for rubber, etc., *e.g.*, with aniline:

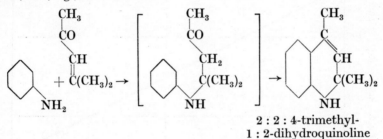

2 : 2 : 4-trimethyl-
1 : 2-dihydroquinoline

With chloroform, acetone gives the pharmaceutical, chloretone:

$$\underset{CH_3}{\overset{CH_3}{>}}CO + CHCl_3 \rightarrow \underset{CH_3}{\overset{CH_3}{>}}C(OH)CCl_3$$

and also under the influence of an alkaline catalyst, acetone condenses with ethyl acetate to give the simplest 1 : 3-diketone, acetyl acetone:

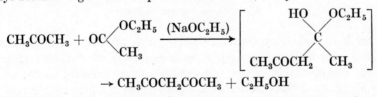

$$\rightarrow CH_3COCH_2COCH_3 + C_2H_5OH$$

Acetyl acetone can also be made by pyrolysis of isopropenyl acetate (this Chapter, p. 317), at 450–500° c. and 1–2 seconds' contact time.[15]

$$\underset{\overset{\|}{CH_2}}{CH_3COCOCH_3} \rightarrow CH_3COCH_2COCH_3$$

Acetyl acetone is an intermediate for pharmaceuticals; its metal chelate compounds have been used as additives for petrol and fuel oil.[16]

---

[15] Boese, U.S.P. 2395800.
[16] *Chem. Ind.*, Sept. 1949, p. 331.

(*b*) Pyrolysis of acetone

(*i*) *Keten*

On heating acetone above 500° c., it undergoes pyrolysis into keten and methane:

$$CH_3COCH_3 \rightarrow CH_2 : C : O + CH_4. \quad \Delta H = + 20 \text{ k. cal.}$$

This process has been established as the first step in the manufacture of acetic anhydride from acetone in both the United States and Great Britain. The development of the British plant built by Courtaulds after

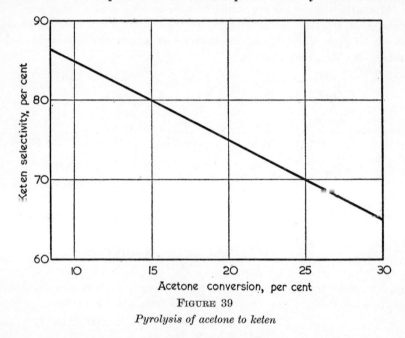

FIGURE 39

Pyrolysis of acetone to keten

the war is described by Daraux.[17] High yields of keten on acetone were obtained only at low conversion per pass; Daraux' data are given in Fig. 39. The process is carried out at atmospheric pressure and at a temperature of about 650–850° c. with a conversion of up to 25 per cent per pass. Courtaulds used 25–30 per cent chromium nickel austenitic steel for the cracking coils; alternative materials are copper[18] or chromium-aluminium or chromium-nitrogen steels.[19]

Catalysts have been claimed for the keten reaction. According to the Ketoid Co.,[20] metal sulphates stable at 700° c. are effective catalysts;

---

[17] Daraux, *J. Appl. Chem.*, 1953, 241.
[18] Carbide and Carbon, U.S.P. 1975663.
[19] Eastman-Kodak, U.S.P. 2232705.
[20] U.S.P. 1602699.

volatile catalysts have also been claimed such as esters of phosphoric acid,[19] or diacetyl,[21] but neither type appears to be used. Some of these suggestions were no doubt based on methods adopted in practice in the similar reaction, the pyrolysis of acetic acid to keten (Chapter 18, p. 327).

For the isolation of keten, the cracked gas must be quenched immediately to prevent decomposition or polymerisation. Courtaulds quench or shock-cool by injection of excess acetic acid to obtain acetic anhydride. After passing through a separator, the vapours at 150° c., still containing some keten, are condensed when the keten present reacts with the excess acetic acid to give acetic anhydride. The mixture of acetic acid, acetic anhydride, acetone and other impurities is then distilled for isolation of the anhydride and for recovery and recycling of the unchanged acetone and acetic acid.

Where keten is to be isolated, the exit gases are immediately quenched with excess of inert solvent, such as acetone, the time from furnace exit to contact with the liquid absorbent being 0·03 sec.[22]

(ii) Properties and reactions of keten

Keten is a gas boiling at $-41°$ c./760 mm. and freezing at $-134°$ c.[15] It reacts with most compounds containing a replaceable hydrogen atom to give acetyl derivatives:

$$RH + CH_2 : C : O \rightarrow RCOCH_3$$

Two of its outlets are for making acetic anhydride and acetic acid esters:

$$CH_2 : C : O + CH_3COOH \rightarrow (CH_3CO)_2O$$
$$CH_2 : C : O + ROH \rightarrow CH_3COOR$$

These reactions are discussed in Chapter 18, p. 327 and 339, but it might be remarked here that keten is not as reactive as it is reputed to be; thus, the acetylation of alcohols with keten requires the presence of a catalyst such as sulphuric acid to proceed to completion.

Solutions of keten readily polymerise at ordinary temperatures. The dimer, diketen, is industrially important and can be made by keeping 5–10% solutions of keten in acetone,[23] or in diketen itself,[24] at temperatures between 0° c. and 50° c. for limited periods.

Diketen boils at 127° c.; it is best represented by the structure:[25]

$$CH_2 : C\!\!-\!\!CH_2$$
$$O\!\!-\!\!CO$$

[21] Rice and Waters, U.S.P. 2305652.
[22] Carbide and Carbon, U.S.P. 1942110.
[23] Carbide and Carbon, B.P. 410394; I.C.I., B.P. 550486.
[24] Cons. f. Elektrochem., B.P. 498280.
[25] Boese, *Ind. Eng. Chem.*, 1940, **32**, 16; Hurd and Blanchard, *J. Amer. Chem. Soc.*, 1950, **72**, 1461.

Diketen adds on to alcohols to give esters of acetoacetic acid, to aromatic amines to give acetoacetic arylamides, and to aromatic hydrazines to give methylarylpyrazolones. These are used as intermediates for dyestuffs, pigments and pharmaceuticals, and are all manufactured from diketen as an alternative to the old routes from ethyl acetoacetate made by the Claisen self-condensation of ethyl acetate.

Diketen is sufficiently stable for certain of these derivatives to be made in the presence of water; *p*-sulphophenylmethylpyrazolone can be made from diketen and phenylhydrazine-*p*-sulphonic acid in water suspension at room temperature.

Diketen can be condensed with aromatic hydrocarbons to give 1 : 3-diketones; with benzene in presence of two mols of aluminium chloride, benzoyl acetone is obtained:

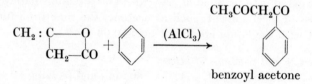

benzoyl acetone

Diketen can be further polymerised under the influence of basic catalysts, *e.g.*, tertiary amines, to give dehydracetic acid:

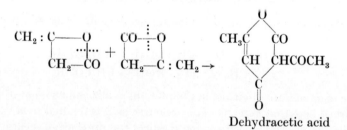

Dehydracetic acid

Possible outlets for dehydracetic acid and other reactions of diketen are discussed by Boese.[25]

The chief outlets for keten are therefore based upon its acetylating powers and on its dimer, diketen. For such a molecule, its other reactions are curiously limited; the only one which is of technical interest is condensation with formaldehyde in presence of aluminium chloride at room temperature to give the new lactone, 2-propiolactone:[26]

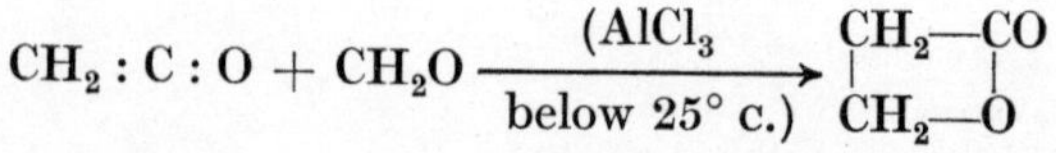

$$CH_2 : C : O + CH_2O \xrightarrow[\text{below } 25° \text{ c.)}]{(AlCl_3} \begin{matrix} CH_2\text{---}CO \\ | \qquad | \\ CH_2\text{---}O \end{matrix}$$

2-Propiolactone boils at 155° c./760 mm. with decomposition. It reacts

[26] Goodrich, U.S.P. 2356459.

with most compounds containing a mobile hydrogen atom to give 2-substituted propionic acids:

$$\begin{matrix} CH_2\text{---}CO \\ | \qquad | \\ CH_2\text{---}O \end{matrix} + RH \rightarrow RCH_2CH_2COOH$$

The lactone is commercially available in America. Under appropriate conditions, it reacts with alcohols to give acrylates:[26a]

$$\begin{matrix} CH_2\text{---}CO \\ | \qquad | \\ CH_2\text{---}O \end{matrix} + ROH \rightarrow CH_2 : CHCOOR + H_2O$$

Other commercial routes to acrylates are summarised in Chapter 18, p. 340.

Other reactions of potential interest are: acetylation of acetone to give isopropenyl acetate:

$$CH_3COCH_3 + CH_2 : C : O \rightarrow CH_3\text{---}\underset{\underset{CH_2}{\|}}{C}OCOCH_3$$

It can be made in 90 per cent yield by reaction between excess acetone and keten at 60–68° c. in presence of acetylsulphoacetic acid as catalyst.[27] Isopropenyl acetate boils at 96° c. It is a powerful acetylating agent; on pyrolysis it gives acetyl acetone (this Chapter, p. 313), and it reacts with acetone to give 2 : 2-dimethylacrylic acid (see Chapter 18, p. 334).

(iii) Dimethylfuran

On pyrolysis above 700° c. for contact times of not more than 0·15 second, acetone gives 2 : 5-dimethylfuran,[28] a reaction which can be formulated:

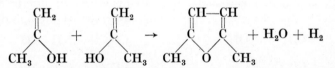

This is another example of entry into the furan series from the aliphatic series; the synthesis of tetrahydrofuran from acetylene and formaldehyde was referred to in Chapter 12, p. 208.

Dimethylfuran is hydrolysed with acidified hot water to acetonyl acetone, the simplest 1 : 4-diketone:

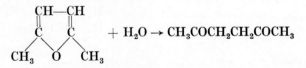

[26a] *Chem. Week*, 29 December, 1956, p. 75.
[27] Hagemeyer and Hull, *Ind. Eng. Chem.*, 1949, **41**, 2920.
[28] Carbide and Carbon, U.S.P. 2098592.

Acetonyl acetone boils at 191° c. and is completely miscible with water; it has been claimed as a solvent for cellulose acetate and other polymers.

(c) OTHER REACTIONS OF ACETONE

One of the important reactions of acetone is addition of hydrogen cyanide to give acetone cyanhydrin. On combined hydrolysis, dehydration and esterification with alcohols and sulphuric acid, it gives the esters of methacrylic acid[29] (α-methylacrylic acid), e.g.,

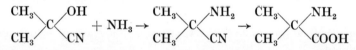

$$\begin{array}{l} CH_3 \\ \!\!\!\!\!\!\!\!\!\!\!\!\!\!>CO + HCN \rightarrow \\ CH_3 \end{array} \quad \begin{array}{l} CH_3 \quad OH \\ \!\!\!\!\!\!\!\!\!\!\!>C< \\ CH_3 \quad CN \end{array} + CH_3OH + H_2SO_4$$

$$\rightarrow CH_2 : \overset{\overset{\displaystyle CH_3}{|}}{C}COOCH_3 + NH_4HSO_4$$

The overall yield of methyl methacrylate on cyanhydrin is about 80 per cent.[30]

The esters of methacrylic acid, particularly methyl methacrylate, are valuable monomers for polymerisation. Free methacrylic acid can be made by hydrolysis of acetone cyanhydrin with sulphuric acid in absence of an alcohol (see also Chapter 18, p. 334).

Acetone cyanhydrin reacts with ammonia and with primary and secondary amines to give aminonitriles which can be hydrolysed to the corresponding aminoacids:

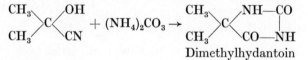

$$\begin{array}{l} CH_3 \quad OH \\ \!\!\!\!\!\!\!\!\!\!\!>C< \\ CH_3 \quad CN \end{array} + NH_3 \rightarrow \begin{array}{l} CH_3 \quad NH_2 \\ \!\!\!\!\!\!\!\!\!\!\!>C< \\ CH_3 \quad CN \end{array} \rightarrow \begin{array}{l} CH_3 \quad NH_2 \\ \!\!\!\!\!\!\!\!\!\!\!>C< \\ CH_3 \quad COOH \end{array}$$

With ammonium carbonate, dimethylhyantoin, an intermediate for resins and for the bleaching agent, dichlorodimethylhydantoin, is obtained:

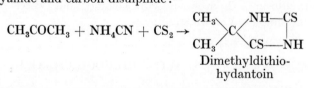

$$\begin{array}{l} CH_3 \quad OH \\ \!\!\!\!\!\!\!\!\!\!\!>C< \\ CH_3 \quad CN \end{array} + (NH_4)_2CO_3 \rightarrow \begin{array}{l} CH_3 \quad NH-CO \\ \!\!\!\!\!\!\!\!\!\!\!>C< \quad | \\ CH_3 \quad CO-NH \end{array}$$

Dimethylhydantoin

Dimethyldithiohydantoin is obtained similarly from acetone, ammonium cyanide and carbon disulphide:[31]

$$CH_3COCH_3 + NH_4CN + CS_2 \rightarrow \begin{array}{l} CH_3 \quad NH-CS \\ \!\!\!\!\!\!\!\!\!\!\!>C< \quad | \\ CH_3 \quad CS-NH \end{array}$$

Dimethyldithio-
hydantoin

This compound is an intermediate for pharmaceuticals.

[29] I.C.I., B.P. 419457.
[30] C.I.O.S. 29/62.
[31] Carrington, *J. Chem. Soc.*, 1947, 681.

Acetone adds acetylene under the influence of alkaline catalysts to give 3-methyl-3-hydroxy-1-butyne:

$$\begin{array}{c}CH_3\\ \end{array}\!\!\!\Big\rangle CO + CH:CH \rightarrow \begin{array}{c}CH_3\\ \end{array}\!\!\!\Big\rangle C \Big\langle \begin{array}{c}OH\\ C:CH\end{array}$$

On semi-hydrogenation and dehydration, this gives isoprene (Chapter 12, p. 211):

$$\begin{array}{c}CH_3\\ CH_3\end{array}\!\!\!\Big\rangle C \Big\langle \begin{array}{c}OH\\ C:CH\end{array} \xrightarrow{\;+\,H_2\;} \begin{array}{c}CH_3\\ CH_3\end{array}\!\!\!\Big\rangle C \Big\langle \begin{array}{c}OH\\ CH:CH_2\end{array} \xrightarrow{\;-\,H_2O\;} CH_2:\overset{\displaystyle CH_3}{C}CH:CH_2$$

Acetone reacts readily with mercaptans to give mercaptals, used in the synthesis of Sulphonal:

$$\begin{array}{c}CH_3\\ CH_3\end{array}\!\!\!\Big\rangle CO + \begin{array}{c}HSC_2H_5\\ HSC_2H_5\end{array} \xrightarrow{\;-\,H_2O\;} \begin{array}{c}CH_3\\ CH_3\end{array}\!\!\!\Big\rangle C \Big\langle \begin{array}{c}SC_2H_5\\ SC_2H_5\end{array} \xrightarrow{\;(+\,O_2)\;} \begin{array}{c}CH_3\\ CH_3\end{array}\!\!\!\Big\rangle C \Big\langle \begin{array}{c}SO_2C_2H_5\\ SO_2C_2H_5\end{array}$$
$$\text{Sulphonal}$$

The normal product of reduction of acetone is isopropyl alcohol, but under special alkaline conditions, *e.g.*, with magnesium, two molecules link up to give pinacol (2 : 3-dimethyl-2 : 3-butane diol):

$$CH_3\!-\!\overset{\displaystyle CH_3}{CO} + \overset{\displaystyle CH_3}{CO}\!-\!CH_3 \xrightarrow{\;+\,H_2\;} CH_3\!-\!\underset{\displaystyle OH}{\overset{\displaystyle CH_3}{C}}\!-\!\underset{\displaystyle OH}{\overset{\displaystyle CH_3}{C}}\!-\!CH_3$$

On dehydration, pinacol loses two molecules of water to give 2 : 3-dimethyl-1 : 3-butadiene, a step used in Germany during the first world war in the manufacture of 'methyl rubber':

$$CH_3\!-\!\underset{\displaystyle OH}{\overset{\displaystyle CH_3}{C}}\!-\!\underset{\displaystyle OH}{\overset{\displaystyle CH_3}{C}}\!-\!CH_3 \xrightarrow{\;-\,2H_2O\;} CH_2{=}\overset{\displaystyle CH_3}{C}\!-\!\overset{\displaystyle CH_3}{C}{=}CH_2$$

On treatment with acids, pinacol undergoes the pinacoline rearrangement with loss of one molecule of water to give pinacoline (methyl *tert*-butyl ketone):

$$CH_3\!-\!\underset{\displaystyle OH}{\overset{\displaystyle CH_3}{C}}\!-\!\underset{\displaystyle OH}{\overset{\displaystyle CH_3}{C}}\!-\!CH_3 \xrightarrow[\text{(tr. acid)}]{\;-\,H_2O\;} CH_3CO\overset{\displaystyle CH_3}{\underset{\displaystyle CH_3}{C}}\!-\!CH_3$$

The reaction of keten with acetone to give isopropenyl acetate has been referred to on p. 317.

The industrially important reactions of acetone are summarised in Fig. 40.

The end-use pattern of acetone in America in 1951, when 230,000 tons were consumed, is shown below:[32]

Outlets	% offtake
(a) Chemical outlets	
Methyl isobutyl ketone and carbinol	29·9
Methyl methacrylate	5·4
Isophorone and phorone	4·2
Mesityl oxide and diacetone alcohol (direct sales) . .	3·8
Methylpentane diol	2·1
Chloroform	1·9
Acetyl acetone	1·0
Miscellaneous	4·9
	53·2
(b) Cellulose acetate (partly as solvent, partly for acetic anhydride)	30·1
(c) Solvent for paints, dissolved acetylene and miscellaneous .	16·7
	100·0

3. Higher saturated ketones

The secondary alcohols made by hydration of the C_4 to C_6 normal olefins (Chapter 8) are converted to the corresponding straight chain ketones in the same way as acetone by vapour phase dehydrogenation or catalytic air oxidation. Dehydrogenation of *sec*-butyl alcohol to methyl ethyl ketone proceeds at a slightly lower temperature than with isopropyl alcohol, 350° c. as against 380° c., and is believed to be the preferred process.

The technical C_5 and C_6 normal ketones are mixtures corresponding in composition to the alcohols from which they are made. According to Brooks,[33] these alcohols are dehydrogenated to the corresponding ketones over brass as catalyst at 455–485° c.

The main outlets for these ketones are in the solvents field.

Methyl ethyl ketone boils at 80° c.; it undergoes most of the reactions of acetone but has not been widely used as a raw material for organic synthesis.

On pyrolysis, it is stated to give methylketen,[34] an intermediate for propionic anhydride (see Chapter 18, p. 330):

$$CH_3CH_2COCH_3 \rightarrow CH_3CH : C : O + CH_4$$

It is used almost entirely in the solvent industry. Production in the United States in 1954 was about 90,000 tons, the end-use pattern being:[35]

Outlets	% offtake
Solvent for nitrocellulose lacquers . .	38
Solvent for polyvinyl chloride lacquers .	37
Solvent for other resins . . .	2
Solvent dewaxing . . .	10
Rubber cements	5
Paint remover	3
Miscellaneous	5
	100

---

[32] *Chem. Week*, May 2, 1953, p. 37; see also *Chem. Week*, April 13, 1957, p. 90.
[33] *Ind. Eng. Chem.*, 1935, **27**, 278.
[34] Eastman-Kodak, U.S.P. 2235561.
[35] *Chem. Eng.*, Feb. 1955, p. 272.

The C_5 and higher ketones may also be made in the following ways. Mixed or symmetrical ketones are obtained in high yield by decarboxylation of aliphatic acids. The lower aliphatic acids dehydrate smoothly in the vapour phase using catalysts such as thoria or cerium oxide at 400° c. The long chain acids give ketones on heating in the liquid phase at 200–300° c. in presence of iron oxide. In both cases, mixed ketones can be made by starting with mixtures of acids; for example:

$$2C_2H_5COOH \rightarrow C_2H_5COC_2H_5 + H_2O + CO_2$$
$$2C_{17}H_{35}COOH \rightarrow C_{17}H_{35}COC_{17}H_{35} + H_2O + CO_2$$
$$C_2H_5COOH + C_3H_7COOH \rightarrow C_2H_5COC_3H_7 + H_2O + CO_2$$

The lower ketones are of some interest as solvents. The long chain ketones have been used in the wax industry.

The synthesis of acetone from ethyl alcohol has been described earlier in this Chapter. This reaction also proceeds with the higher primary alcohols. *n*-Butyl alcohol passed over oxides of zinc, iron, etc., at 400–500° c. gives di-*n*-propyl ketone,[36] a high boiling solvent for paints. It boils at 144° c.

$$2C_4H_9OH + H_2O \rightarrow C_3H_7COC_3H_7 + CO_2 + 4H_2$$

4. Unsaturated ketones

The complex unsaturated ketones arising by self-condensation of acetone, mesityl oxide and phorone, have already been discussed. The simplest unsaturated ketone is methyl vinyl ketone, $CH_3COCH : CH_2$. This may be made from acetone and formaldehyde or by hydration of monovinylacetylene by sulphuric acid in presence of a mercury catalyst:

$$CH_2 : CHC : CH + H_2O \xrightarrow{\text{(H}_2\text{SO}_4,\ \text{Hg)}} CH_2 : CHCOCH_3$$

It boils at about 80° c. and has attracted some interest for polymerisation. The hydrogen atom on the —CH group is mobile and will condense with formaldehyde:[37]

$$CH_3COCH : CH_2 + CH_2O \rightarrow CH_3COC : CH_2$$
$$\overset{|}{C}H_2OH$$

Methyl isopropenyl ketone, $\underset{CH_3COC : CH_2}{\overset{CH_3}{|}}$, b.p. 98° c., is obtained from methyl ethyl ketone and formaldehyde.

These and the higher unsaturated ketones are not yet of any importance.

The boiling points of the lower ketones and of the derivatives of acetone containing only keto and hydroxyl groups are given in Table 64.

---

[36] Commercial Solvents, U.S.P. 1978404.
[37] Gault and Germann, *Compt. Rend.*, 1936, **203,** 514.

TABLE 64

Boiling points of some ketones and of some derivatives of acetone

Carbon atoms	Name	Formula	b.p., ° c./760 mm.
C_3	Acetone	CH_3COCH_3	56·1
C_4	Methyl ethyl ketone . .	$CH_3COCH_2CH_3$	79·6
	Methyl vinyl ketone . .	$CH_3COCH : CH_2$	80
C_5	Methyl *n*-propyl ketone (2-pentanone) . .	$CH_3COCH_2CH_2CH_3$	101·7
	Methyl isopropyl ketone .	$CH_3COCH(CH_3)_2$	93
	Diethyl ketone (3-pentanone)	$CH_3CH_2COCH_2CH_3$	102·7
	Acetyl acetone (2 : 4-pentane dione) . . .	$CH_3COCH_2COCH_3$	139
C_6	Methyl *n*-butyl ketone (2-hexanone) . .	$CH_3COCH_2CH_2CH_2CH_3$	127·2
	Methyl *sec*-butyl ketone .	$CH_3COCHCH_2CH_3$ $\mid$ CH_3	118
	Methyl isobutyl ketone .	$CH_3COCH_2CH(CH_3)_2$	116
	Methyl *tert*-butyl ketone (pinacoline) . . .	$CH_3COC(CH_3)_3$	106·2
	Diacetone alcohol . .	$CH_3COCH_2C(CH_3)_2$ $\mid$ OH	166
	2-Methyl-2 : 4-pentane diol	$CH_3CHCH_2C(CH_3)_2$ $\mid\quad\mid$ $OH\quad OH$	196
	Mesityl oxide . . .	$CH_3COCH : C(CH_3)_2$	128–9
	Methyl isobutyl carbinol .	$CH_3CHCH_2CH(CH_3)_2$ $\mid$ OH	131·6
	Acetonyl acetone (2 : 5-hexane dione) . .	$CH_3COCH_2CH_2COCH_3$	191·4
C_7	Methyl-*n*-amyl ketone (2-heptanone) . .	$CH_3COCH_2CH_2CH_2CH_2CH_3$	150
	Di-*n*-propyl ketone (4-heptanone) . .	$CH_3CH_2CH_2COCH_2CH_2CH_3$	144
C_9	Phorone	$(CH_3)_2C : CHCOCH : C(CH_3)_2$	198
	Diisobutyl ketone . .	$(CH_3)_2CHCH_2COCH_2CH(CH_3)_2$	168
	Diisobutyl carbinol . .	$(CH_3)_2CHCH_2CHCH_2CH(CH_3)_2$ $\mid$ OH	178·8
	Isophorone . . .	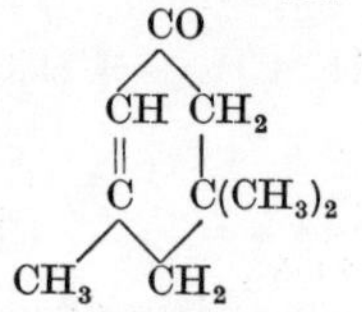 (structure shown below)	215
	Trimethylcyclohexanol .	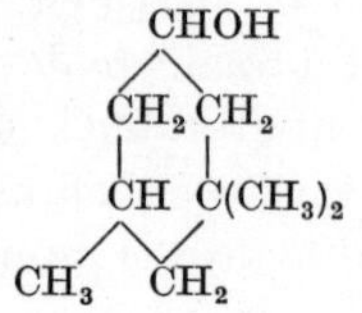 (structure shown below)	198 (m.p. 40° c.)

Isophorone structure:

$$\begin{array}{c} CO \\ \diagup\quad\diagdown \\ CH\quad CH_2 \\ \|\qquad\mid \\ C\quad C(CH_3)_2 \\ \diagup\quad\diagdown \\ CH_3\quad CH_2 \end{array}$$

Trimethylcyclohexanol structure:

$$\begin{array}{c} CHOH \\ \diagup\quad\diagdown \\ CH_2\quad CH_2 \\ \mid\qquad\mid \\ CH\quad C(CH_3)_2 \\ \diagup\quad\diagdown \\ CH_3\quad CH_2 \end{array}$$

CHAPTER 18

ACIDS, ANHYDRIDES AND ESTERS

1. General

THE important methods of making the saturated acids include oxidation of aldehydes, of the lower paraffin gases (Chapter 4, p. 60), and of paraffin wax (Chapter 4, p. 62). Acids are also made by reaction between an alcohol and carbon monoxide or an olefin, carbon monoxide and water.

Another method used in special cases is reaction between a primary alcohol and a caustic alkali at about 250° c. (see p. 328). The hydrolysis of alkyl nitriles is not used for manufacture of saturated acids but combined hydrolysis and dehydration of hydroxynitriles is one of the main routes to unsaturated acids.

2. Formic acid

Formic acid is made by acidification of alkali formates (made from alkali hydroxides and carbon monoxide) or by direct interaction between water and carbon monoxide at high pressure and temperature in the presence of acidic catalysts:

$$CO + H_2O \rightarrow HCOOH$$

It is obtained as a by-product in the pressure air oxidation of the normally gaseous paraffins (Chapter 4, p. 60).

It is the first member of the series of paraffin carboxylic acids, and is distinguished from its higher homologues by possession of reducing properties, a more acid character, and a greater instability. Its chief commercial outlets are in the coagulation of natural rubber latex and as an intermediate for the manufacture of oxalic acid and of formic esters.

3. Acetic acid and acetic anhydride

These are the most important petroleum acidic derivatives owing to the large tonnages consumed in the manufacture of cellulose acetate and of acetic esters. In 1955, America produced 230,000 tons of synthetic acetic acid and 380,000 tons of acetic anhydride.

The commercial routes are summarised below. This scheme omits the small amounts available from the wood distillation industry, from the air oxidation of the lower paraffins or from ethyl alcohol by fermentation— the quick vinegar process. The acetaldehyde used as the main source of acetic acid is usually made from ethyl alcohol or from acetylene; acetaldehyde becoming available from the oxidation of the lower paraffin gases is an additional source of acetic acid.

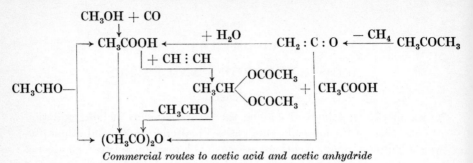

Commercial routes to acetic acid and acetic anhydride

(a) FROM METHYL ALCOHOL AND CARBON MONOXIDE

The free energy change for the reaction

$$CH_3OH(g) + CO \rightarrow CH_3COOH(g)$$

is calculated by Parks and Huffman[1] to be:

$$\Delta G = -29,500 + 33 \cdot 4T$$

At atmospheric pressure, $\Delta G = 0$ at about 610° c.; the equilibrium is favourable below this temperature and is further aided by operation at increased pressure. Nevertheless, the reaction is much more difficult to effect than the change in free energy would suggest.

Krase and Singh[2] investigated the reaction in the vapour phase, working at 300 atm. and 300–500° c. with a phosphoric acid on charcoal catalyst. Only partial conversion to acetic acid was obtained and the catalyst was short lived.

The liquid phase process has been improved by du Pont.[3] The conditions disclosed are similar to those described for reaction between carbon monoxide, olefins and water (Chapter 11, p. 185) and between carbon monoxide and aqueous formaldehyde (Chapter 16, p. 285). Pressures of 700 atm. at 200–250° c. were employed with catalysts such as boron trifluoride used in almost molecular proportions. This involved separation problems as the catalyst formed a complex with the acetic acid. Methyl acetate and more complex products were always formed and the yield of acetic acid was not quantitative. The reaction mixture, containing acetic and other acids, sometimes in aqueous solution, was highly corrosive, and special materials of construction, such as silver liners, were necessary.

(b) FROM ACETALDEHYDE

Direct oxidation of acetaldehyde in the liquid phase with oxygen to acetic acid, using for example manganese acetate as catalyst, is a

[1] 'The Free Energy of some Organic Compounds', *Chemical Catalog Co.*, 1932.
[2] *Ind. Eng. Chem.*, 1935, **27**, 909.
[3] *e.g.*, U.S.P. 2135448; U.S.P. 2135451; U.S.P. 2135453; B.P. 483577.

well-known process operated for many years. Oxygen is used and not air to avoid loss of acetaldehyde in the large volumes of inert nitrogen:

$$CH_3CHO + \tfrac{1}{2}O_2 \rightarrow CH_3COOH \qquad . \qquad . \qquad . \qquad (2)$$

In practice,[4] acetaldehyde containing 0·05–0·1 per cent manganese acetate was oxidised with 2 per cent excess oxygen at 70° c. under sufficient pressure to maintain the acetaldehyde in the liquid phase. The yield of acetic acid was 95 per cent.

This process was completely changed by minor alterations in choice of catalyst and by use of a water removing agent, a mixture of both acetic acid and acetic anhydride being obtained directly. The discovery seems to have been made independently and simultaneously in Canada and Germany. The first step was the use of mixed metal acetates such as manganese + nickel, manganese + copper, or cobalt + copper acetates;[5] the next step was the use of esters[6] for removal of the water found alongside the acetic anhydride:

$$2CH_3CHO + O_2 \rightarrow (CH_3CO)_2O + H_2O \qquad . \qquad . \qquad (3)$$

The esters claimed, such as ethyl acetate, formed azeotropes with the water but not with the acetic acid or acetic anhydride, so that the water of reaction was removed as fast as it was formed. Other water entraining agents can be used such as diisopropyl ether.[7] The ratio of anhydride to acid obtained is dependent on the ratio of ethyl acetate to acetaldehyde used. This is illustrated in Table 65; conditions of oxidation were 50° c. at 5·5 atma. pressure, using 0·04 per cent manganese acetate and 0·1 per cent copper acetate.[8]

TABLE 65

Acetic anhydride formation in oxidation of acetaldehyde

Ratio ethyl acetate/ initial acetaldehyde	Conversion of acetaldehyde %	Yield acetic anhydride on acetaldehyde reacted (remainder is acetic acid) %
20 : 80	80	13·5
40 : 60	80	57
60 : 40	80	64
70 : 30	80	68·5

Both batch and continuous oxidation of acetaldehyde has been operated to give anhydride-acid mixtures. In the batch process,[9] a mixture of acetic

[4] B.I.O.S. 75.
[5] Shawinigan, B.P. 446259.
[6] Shawinigan, B.P. 461808.
[7] Carbide and Carbon, U.S.P. 2320461.
[8] From Shawinigan, U.S.P. 2170002.
[9] C.I.O.S. 27/83.

acid and acetaldehyde in the ratio $1 : 2\cdot3$ was oxidised at $40°$ c. under pressure, using mixed cobalt and copper acetates. A mixture containing 57 per cent acetic acid, 33 per cent acetic anhydride and 10 per cent water was obtained.

In the continuous process,[4] the feed was acetaldehyde with twice its weight of ethyl acetate, using $0\cdot05$–$0\cdot1$ per cent mixed copper-cobalt acetates (ratio $Co : Cu$, $1 : 2$) at $40°$ c. Oxidation was run to 96 per cent completion; the ratio of acetic anhydride to acetic acid produced was $56 : 44$. In the absence of ethyl acetate, it would have been $20 : 80$. During the reaction, acetaldehyde, ethyl acetate and water were continuously distilled and the acetaldehyde-ethyl acetate layer returned to the oxidiser. Present practice is to operate the process to give 70 per cent acetic anhydride and 30 per cent acetic acid.

Even in the direct conversion of acetaldehyde to acetic acid, reaction does not proceed by the simple equation (2), but by the intermediate formation of peracetic acid:

$$CH_3CHO + O_2 \rightarrow CH_3COOOH \qquad . \qquad . \qquad . \qquad (4)$$
$$CH_3COOOH + CH_3CHO \rightarrow 2CH_3COOH \qquad . \qquad . \qquad (5)$$

Peracetic acid itself can be made the main product by carrying out the oxidation at $-15°$ c. in a solvent. This process is now being taken on the large scale; the peracetic acid is to be used for making substituted ethylene oxides by reaction with ethylenic unsaturated compounds.[10] To account for the formation of acetic anhydride, reaction mechanisms have been suggested by Rieche[11] and by Heatley.[12]

Although acetic anhydride is obtained by this reaction, the amount produced is insufficient for its main industrial outlet, the acetylation of cellulose. Other methods are used to make up the deficiency.

(c) ACETIC ANHYDRIDE FROM ACETIC ACID

The old route, reaction between sodium acetate and sulphuryl chloride:

$$2CH_3COONa + SO_2Cl_2 \rightarrow (CH_3CO)_2O + 2NaCl + SO_3$$

is now obsolete. The ethylidene diacetate route,

$$2CH_3COOH + C_2H_2 \rightarrow CH_3CH(OCOCH_3)_2$$

$$CH_3CH(OCOCH_3)_2 \xrightarrow[\text{of catalysts}]{\text{Heat, in presence}} CH_3CHO + (CH_3CO)_2O$$

after a period of quiescence, has been revived as an adjunct of the air oxidation of propane and butane.

---

[10] *Chem. Week*, April 14, 1956; Carbide and Carbon, B.P. 735974.
[11] *Angew. Chem.*, 1938, **51**, 707.
[12] *Can. J. Res.*, 1941, **19B**, 261.

The first stage, reaction between acetylene and acetic acid, is carried out at 60–90° c. and atmospheric pressure using a mercurous salt catalyst. The process can be operated either batchwise or continuously; by adjustment of the ratio of acetylene to acetic acid, vinyl acetate can be made the main product of the reaction (see also p. 340).

Ethylidene diacetate is pyrolysed smoothly by distilling with acidic catalysts such as sodium pyrophosphate or zinc chloride. The yield is as high as 97 per cent at 75% conversion.

The method gives acetaldehyde as a by-product and is operated in conjunction with processes which require acetaldehyde as a raw material, such as its direct oxidation to acetic acid and acetic anhydride.

As explained on p. 340, ethylidene diacetate can also be pyrolysed to vinyl acetate; in this industrial route to vinyl acetate, the ethylidene diacetate is made from acetic acid and acetaldehyde.

The main route to acetic anhydride from acetic acid is by catalytic pyrolysis. This reaction proceeds via keten and in the technical processes, the keten is separated both from the water liberated and from unchanged acetic acid; the anhydride is made by reaction between keten and fresh acetic acid.

$$CH_3COOH \rightarrow CH_2 : C : O + H_2O \quad . \quad . \quad . \quad (6)$$
$$CH_2 : C : O + CH_3COOH \rightarrow (CH_3CO)_2O \quad . \quad . \quad (7)$$

The pyrolysis of acetic acid to keten, reaction (6), is similar in many respects to the pyrolysis of acetone to keten (Chapter 17, p. 314):

$$CH_3COCH_3 \rightarrow CH_2 : C : O + CH_4$$

There are, however, important operating differences; the conversion is much higher, up to 90 per cent, but against this the reaction is carried out at reduced pressure. The problem of constructional materials is less serious. Catalysts are used to assist reaction (6); phosphoric acid and acid phosphates are effective, but have a short life at the high reaction temperature. This was overcome by continuous injection of a volatile phosphorus compound, such as triethyl phosphate.[13] Recombination of keten and water, the reverse of reaction (6), was stopped or retarded by injection of nitrogen bases into the reactor gases.[14]

In a description of the German process,[15] acetic acid, vaporised at 200 mm. pressure, mixed with 0·2 per cent triethyl phosphate, was preheated to 600° c. and pyrolysed at 700–720° c. in a gas-fired or electrically heated furnace constructed of Sicromal 12, a chromium steel containing 23% chromium, 1% silicon, 2·5% aluminium, and no nickel; 0·02 per cent

---

[13] Cons. f. Elektrochem., U.S.P. 2102159.
[14] Cons. f. Elektrochem., D.R.P. 634438.
[15] C.I.O.S. 25/20; F.I.A.T. 145; B.I.O.S. 1050.

by weight of ammonia was injected at the furnace exit and the gases cooled to about 0° c. in multitubular water and brine cooled condensers constructed of V4A austenitic steel. 35% Aqueous acetic acid was drawn off from the bottom of these condensers; from the top, nearly pure keten containing only a little ethylene, methane and carbon monoxide was sent forward to the acetic anhydride stage. The flowsheet of the anhydride stage is shown in Fig. 41.

The anhydride was made in the first and second towers. The third and fourth towers were used for removal of the last traces of acetic acid and anhydride from the tail gases. All these towers operated under reduced pressure, one vacuum pump being used to control all stages from the evaporation of the acetic acid onward.

The acetic anhydride-acetic acid mixture was purified and concentrated to 95% acetic anhydride by vacuum distillation. The absorption towers and final purification still were constructed of copper.

The conversion of acetic acid was about 90 per cent per pass; the yield of acetic anhydride on acetic acid reacted was about 90 per cent.

(*d*) Acetic anhydride from acetone

The pyrolysis of acetone to keten and the conversion of keten to acetic anhydride was described in Chapter 17, p. 315. It is carried out at atmospheric pressure, but owing to the large volumes of inert gas produced in the pyrolysis of acetone, the partial pressure of the keten will be less than 0·5 atma. The working up stage is also more complex, as some acetone is carried through with the keten and inert gases, and many more by-products are formed.

This process requires provision of acetic acid for the other half of the anhydride molecule.

4. Propionic acid and anhydride

Propionic acid can be manufactured by several routes, some of which have been described earlier.

The oxidation of propionaldehyde (routes to propionaldehyde were described in Chapter 16, p. 295) with oxygen proceeds in the same way as with acetaldehyde, to give either propionic acid[16] or propionic acid-anhydride mixtures. The acid or the anhydride can be made by reaction between ethylene, water and carbon monoxide or nickel carbonyl (Chapter 11, p. 185); the acid is one of the products of the pressure air oxidation of *n*-butane (Chapter 4, p. 60). Sodium propionate can be made by reaction between *n*-propyl alcohol and caustic soda; this is a general method available for the synthesis of the higher acids from the corresponding higher primary alcohols, whether straight chain or branch chain. It is carried out

---

[16] Langdon and Schwoegler, *Ind. Eng. Chem.*, 1951, **43**, 1011.

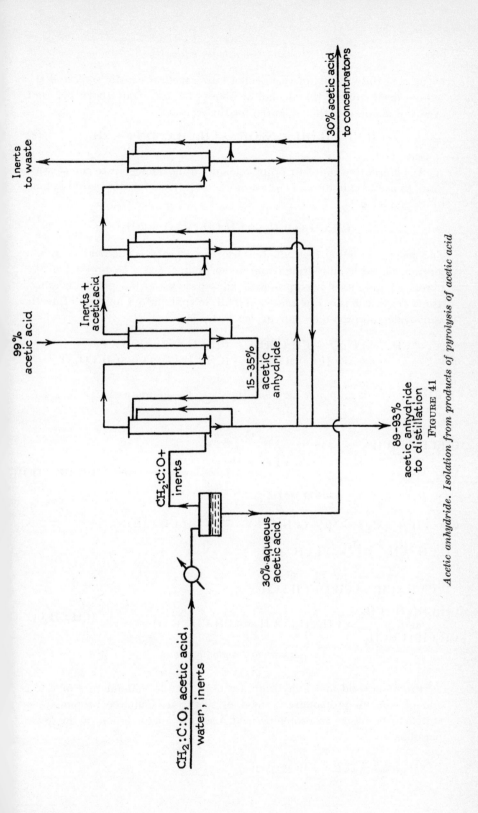

FIGURE 41

Acetic anhydride. Isolation from products of pyrolysis of acetic acid

by passing the vapours of the alcohol into a melt of caustic soda and the sodium derivative of the alcohol at about 250° c.; about 10–20 per cent excess of alkali over that required for the reaction:

$$CH_3CH_2CH_2OH + NaOH \rightarrow CH_3CH_2COONa + 2H_2 \qquad . \qquad (8)$$

is used.

An alternative route to propionic anhydride, analogous to the acetone route to acetic anhydride, is based on the pyrolysis of methyl ethyl ketone to methylketen:[17]

$$CH_3CH_2COCH_3 \rightarrow CH_3CH : C : O + CH_4$$

The gases containing methylketen are reacted with acetic acid to give a mixture of acetic anhydride (from keten produced as a by-product in the pyrolysis) and mixed acetopropionic anhydride with some propionic anhydride. On distillation, the mixed anhydride splits into a mixture of acetic anhydride and propionic anhydride:

$$CH_3CH : C : O + CH_3COOH \rightarrow CH_3CH_2COOCOCH_3$$
$$2CH_3CH_2COOCOCH_3 \rightarrow (CH_3CH_2CO)_2O + (CH_3CO)_2O$$

The sources of propionic acid can therefore be summarised:

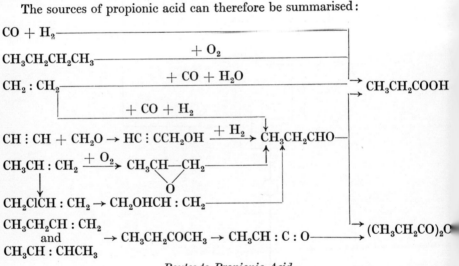

Routes to Propionic Acid

Propionic acid and anhydride are used for the manufacture of esters and of calcium propionate, a food preservative. Cellulose propionate is stated to be based on propionic acid made by air oxidation of the lower paraffins.

---

[17] Eastman-Kodak, U.S.P. 2235561.

5. *n*- and Isobutyric acids

The best route to *n*-butyric acid and its anhydride is probably by oxidation of *n*-butyraldehyde made from propylene by the Oxo reaction (Chapter 11, p. 183) or from acetaldehyde (Chapter 16, p. 296):

$$CH_3CH_2CH_2CHO \xrightarrow{O_2} CH_3CH_2CH_2COOH \text{ and } (CH_3CH_2CH_2CO)_2O$$

The process has been carried out[18] at 30–50° c. using oxygen; a catalyst was not essential, but manganese acetate has been used. The oxidation was run to 90–100% conversion, pure *n*-butyric acid being isolated by distillation and any unchanged *n*-butyraldehyde recycled. The overall yield of *n*-butyric acid was about 90 per cent.

The acid and anhydride are used for the manufacture of butyric acid esters, used as high boiling solvents, and for cellulose acetobutyrate, which is better than cellulose acetate in certain respects.

Isobutyric acid can be made either from isobutyraldehyde or by reaction of carbon monoxide with propylene and water (Chapter 11, p. 185) or with isopropyl alcohol:

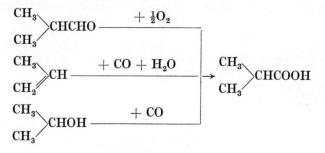

6. Longer chain acids

The medium length acids are manufactured from the branch chain aldehydes built up from acetaldehyde by the aldol condensation (Chapter 16, p. 289) or from the branch chain primary alcohols arising in the 'Higher Alcohols' synthesis from carbon monoxide and hydrogen (Chapter 3, p. 45).

1-Ethylbutyric acid, $CH_3CH_2CH(C_2H_5)COOH$ and 1-ethylhexoic acid, $CH_3CH_2CH_2CH_2CH(C_2H_5)COOH$, are made by oxidation of the corresponding aldehydes, which are both derived from acetaldehyde (Chapter 16, pp. 292, 297). The metal salts of 1-ethylhexoic acid are used as driers; the acid is also used as an intermediate for emulsifying agents and for making plasticisers, *e.g.*, esterification of polyethylene glycols.

1-Ethylbutyric acid is used as an intermediate for plasticisers by esterification of triethylene glycol.

---

[18] B.I.O.S. 1053.

The C_8 and C_{12} primary normal and iso alcohols obtained in the Higher Alcohols synthesis are converted to acids by fusion with caustic soda by the method of reaction (8), p. 330.

Normal long chain fatty acids are made from petroleum starting materials by the oxidation of paraffin wax with air (Chapter 4, p. 62). These can be used as intermediates for the normal long chain fatty alcohols, by catalytic hydrogenation of the esters, or by treatment of the heavy metal salts with hydrogen at high pressure and temperature.[19] They can also be combined with glycerol from propylene (Chapter 10, p. 166) to give an all-synthetic 'natural fat.' The Germans made a synthetic butter by this method, using only the C_{11-12} acids, which was claimed to be superior to natural butter in certain respects, *e.g.*, for diabetics.[20]

Other routes to long chain acids, which may be used where circumstances are favourable, are the oxidation of the aldehydes made by the Oxo reaction from olefins, carbon monoxide and hydrogen (Chapter 11, p. 183), or by reaction between the olefin, carbon monoxide and water.

The boiling points of the lower aliphatic monocarboxylic acids and anhydrides which can be regarded as petroleum chemicals are given in Table 66. Mixed anhydrides have not been included.

TABLE 66
Boiling points of aliphatic acids and anhydrides

Acid	b.p./760 mm. °C.	Anhydride	b.p./760 mm. °C.
Formic . . .	100·7	—	
Acetic . . .	118·1	Acetic	139·5
Propionic . . .	141·4	Propionic . . .	169·0
n-Butyric . . .	163·7	*n*-Butyric . . .	199·5
Isobutyric . .	154·4	Isobutyric . . .	182·5
1-Ethylbutyric . .	194·0	—	
1-Ethylhexoic . .	226·9	—	

It is convenient to include in this section the pilot scale production of *p-tert*-butylbenzoic acid by liquid phase air oxidation of *p-tert*-butyltoluene (from toluene and isobutene, Chapter 14, p. 255):

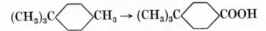

$$(CH_3)_3C\langle\ \rangle CH_3 \rightarrow (CH_3)_3C\langle\ \rangle COOH$$

It is used in improving alkyd type synthetic resins.

7. Polycarboxylic acids

Di- and polycarboxylic acids are important in the high polymer field, especially for polyamide fibres and plastics.

---

[19] Procter and Gamble, B.P. 573788.
[20] C.I.O.S. 31/79.

Adipic acid is the starting material for the synthesis of nylon, poly-hexamethylene adipamide, $(—CO(CH_2)_4CONH(CH_2)_6NH—)_n$; it is also used for making plasticisers, such as dicyclohexyl adipate, and for resins by condensation with polyhydric alcohols such as ethylene glycol (Chapter 19, p. 345). A mixture of isosebacic acids (C_{10} dicarboxylic acids) containing 6–10 per cent of sebacic acid, 72–80 per cent of 1-ethylsuberic acid and 12–18 per cent of 1 : 1-diethyladipic acid is now available starting with butadiene. The dimer is made by reaction with finely divided sodium in an ether solvent in presence of a trace of an aromatic hydrocarbon at $-25°$ c. The disodio derivative is then reacted *in situ* with carbon dioxide.[21]

The main technical route to adipic acid is by the two-stage oxidation of cyclohexane with air and nitric acid (Chapter 13, p. 225).

Pimelic acid, $HOOCCH_2CH_2CH_2CH_2CH_2COOH$, has been made from butadiene and acrylonitrile, which were condensed by the Diels-Alder reaction to give tetrahydrobenzonitrile. On fusion with caustic soda at 250–300° c., the double bond shifted and the ring was opened with simul-taneous hydrolysis of the cyano group.[22]

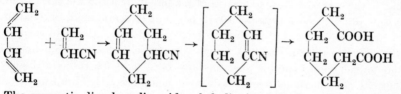

The aromatic dicarboxylic acids, phthalic, isophthalic and terephthalic acids, are important in the high polymer and synthetic fibre fields. Phthalic anhydride is normally made from coal tar naphthalene, but some 5 per cent of United States production is made from petroleum *o*-xylene by vapour phase air oxidation over a vanadium pentoxide catalyst:[23]

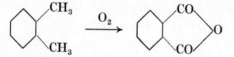

In 1954, total American production of phthalic anhydride was 115,000 tons; of this, 51 per cent was used in resins, 35 per cent in plasticisers and the remainder in dyestuffs and miscellaneous.

Isophthalic acid is made by liquid phase oxidation of petroleum *m*-xylene (Chapter 14, p. 246); its principal outlet is for alkyd resins.[24]

Terephthalic acid is the intermediate for the new British fibre, Terylene (Dacron in the United States), polyethylene terephthalate. Routes to this

---

[21] *Chem. Week*, Dec. 10, 1955, p. 60; U.S. Ind. Chem., F.P. 1093096.
[22] C.I.O.S. 33/50.
[23] Levine, *Chem. Eng. Prog.*, 1947, **43**, 168.
[24] Lum and Carlston, *Ind. Eng. Chem.*, 1952, **44**, 1595; *Chem. Eng.*, March 1956, p. 140.

acid, which at present is manufactured wholly from petroleum *p*-xylene, were summarised in Chapter 14, p. 246.

8. Unsaturated acids

The simplest unsaturated acid, acrylic acid, $CH_2 : CHCOOH$, is made from ethylene cyanhydrin (Chapter 19, p. 357) or from acetylene, carbon monoxide and water (Chapter 15, p. 282).

$$\begin{matrix} CH_2 \\ \| \\ CH_2 \end{matrix} \rightarrow \begin{matrix} CH_2 \\ | \\ CH_2 \end{matrix}\!\!\!> O + HCN \rightarrow \begin{matrix} CH_2OH \\ | \\ CH_2CN \end{matrix} \xrightarrow[-NH_3]{+H_2O} \begin{matrix} CH_2 \\ \| \\ CHCOOH \end{matrix}$$

$$\begin{matrix} CH \\ \| \| \\ CH \end{matrix} + CO + H_2O \rightarrow \begin{matrix} CH_2 \\ \| \\ CHCOOH \end{matrix}$$

Acrylic acid polymerises readily but is less important than its esters (see p. 340).

Crotonic acid, $CH_3CH : CHCOOH$, is manufactured by liquid phase oxidation of crotonaldehyde with oxygen at 20° c. in presence of copper acetate-manganese acetate as catalyst.[18, 25] The reaction is much slower than in the corresponding oxidation of acetaldehyde. Crotonic acid obtained by this process contains some 10–12 per cent of acetic acid, derived from the acetaldehyde present in the crude crotonaldehyde; this acid is suitable as a chemical intermediate. A range of crotonic esters has been made for commercial trial. Crotonic acid has also been used for resins although it does not polymerise as readily as acrylic acid. The CH_3 group in crotonic acid and certain of its derivatives, which are present in the conjugated system, $CH_3CH : CH\underset{\underset{X}{|}}{C} : O$, has some of the properties of an alpha CH_3 group and will undergo Claisen-type condensations with esters under favourable circumstances.

Methacrylic acid, $CH_2 : C(CH_3)COOH$, is best made by hydrolysis and dehydration of acetone cyanhydrin (Chapter 17, p. 318) with sulphuric acid:

$$CH_3COCH_3 + HCN \rightarrow \begin{matrix} CH_3 \\ \diagdown \\ CH_3 \diagup \end{matrix} C \begin{matrix} \diagup OH \\ \diagdown CN \end{matrix} \xrightarrow[-NH_3]{+H_2O} \begin{matrix} CH_3 \\ | \\ CH_2 : CCOOH \end{matrix}$$

The free acid and its salts have been polymerised, but these derivatives are less important than the polymers of methacrylic acid esters.

The higher olefinic monocarboxylic acids appear to have some potential outlets, *e.g.*, 2 : 2-dimethylacrylic acid, $(CH_3)_2C : CHCOOH$, which is of interest in the medicinals field; this acid can be made from acetone and keten:

$$\begin{matrix} CH_3 \\ \diagdown \\ CH_3 \diagup \end{matrix} CO + CH_2 : C : O \rightarrow \begin{matrix} CH_3 \\ \diagdown \\ CH_3 \diagup \end{matrix} C : CHCOOH$$

---

[25] C.I.O.S. 22/21; B.I.O.S. 758.

Many of these acids can be built up by synthesis from intermediates derived from petroleum; they can also be made from natural sources.

Turning to acids of the acetylene series, propiolic acid (propargylic acid), $CH : CCOOH$, can be made by a variety of synthetic routes, including the action of carbon dioxide on sodium acetylide:

$$CH : CNa + CO_2 \rightarrow CH : CCOONa$$

The reaction may be carried out in dioxan solution below 90° c. at 35–70 atma.; some acetylene dicarboxylic acid, $HOOCC : CCOOH$, is also formed.[26]

The most important unsaturated polycarboxylic acid is maleic acid, *cis*-ethylene-1 : 2-dicarboxylic acid. The anhydride is manufactured by catalytic vapour phase air oxidation of benzene over vanadium pentoxide catalyst at 400–450° c. and atmospheric pressure, with a contact time of about 0·1 sec. :

$$\bigcirc + 4\tfrac{1}{2}O_2 \rightarrow \begin{array}{c} CHCO \\ \| \qquad \rangle O \\ CHCO \end{array} + 2CO_2 + 2H_2O$$

The catalytic vapour phase oxidation of *n*-butenes (Chapter 9, p. 149) and of crotonaldehyde[27] is no longer operated.

The main outlet for maleic anhydride is in the high polymer field, for alkyd resins, polyesters and soil conditioners. It is also used as an intermediate for certain anionic detergents and for succinic acid. American production in 1952 was about 17,500 tons.

Fumaric acid, *trans*-ethylene-1 : 2-dicarboxylic acid, $\begin{array}{c} HCCOOH \\ \| \\ HOOCCH \end{array}$,

the more stable geometrical isomer of maleic acid, use of which is also growing, is usually made by fermentation processes.

9. Esters

(*a*) GENERAL METHODS

The general method of making esters is by reaction between an alcohol and an acid in presence of an acidic catalyst such as sulphuric acid:

$$ROH + R^1COOH \rightleftharpoons ROOCR^1 + H_2O \qquad . \qquad . \qquad (9)$$

In the esterification of ethyl alcohol with acetic acid, the equilibrium constant at ordinary pressure at the boil is about 4. From equimolar proportions of either acid and alcohol, or of ester and water, the equilibrium mixture will contain about $\tfrac{2}{3}$ mol of ester, $\tfrac{2}{3}$ mol water, $\tfrac{1}{3}$ mol acid and $\tfrac{1}{3}$ mol alcohol. The equilibrium can be pushed farther to the right hand side of

---

[26] Union Carbide, U.S.P. 2205885.
[27] C.I.O.S. 27/85; B.I.O.S. 739.

equation (9), *i.e.*, towards complete esterification, by removal of the water of reaction or of the ester as formed (whichever is the more volatile) or by use of excess alcohol. All these methods are used depending on the physical properties of the materials being handled; since most esters are higher boiling than water, the usual method to complete esterification is by azeotropic removal of the water as it is formed. According to Brooks,[28] the important acetic esters are manufactured in over 95% yield, using 0·5% sulphuric acid as catalyst and removing the water overhead as the azeotrope with the ester.

Esterification can be operated as a continuous process, the water or ester formed being removed overhead to complete reaction. Leyes and Othmer,[29] who investigated making *n*-butyl acetate by continuous esterification and rectification of *n*-butyl alcohol and acetic acid, found that long contact and attainment of mass action equilibrium on each plate was not necessary, a five plate column giving almost complete reaction with a reasonable hold-up period.

Esterification is a slow reaction, and use of a catalyst is essential. The usual catalyst is sulphuric acid; other acidic catalysts and alkaline catalysts such as caustic soda are also effective.

Esters can be made from alcohols which normally react with difficulty with acids, by ester interchange. By reaction between an ester and an alcohol, the alcohol radical present in the original ester can be displaced:

$$RCOOR^1 + R^2OH \rightleftharpoons \left[RC\!\!\begin{array}{l} \diagup OH \\ \!\!-OR^1 \\ \diagdown OR^2 \end{array} \right] \rightleftharpoons RCOOR^2 + R^1OH \qquad (10)$$

The usual catalyst in ester interchange reactions is an alkali hydroxide or alkoxide. By use of excess of the higher boiling alcohol, R^2OH, and continuous removal of the lower boiling alcohol, R^1OH, the equilibrium in reaction (10) can be pushed completely to the right hand side.

Another technical method of making esters of the less reactive alcohols is from the acid anhydride and the alcohol:

$$(RCO)_2O + 2R^1OH \rightarrow 2RCOOR^1 + H_2O . \qquad . \qquad (11)$$
or
$$(RCO)_2O + R^1OH \rightarrow RCOOR^1 + RCOOH \qquad . \qquad (12)$$

This is the method used for the manufacture of cellulose acetate and for the other technical cellulose esters, the propionate and the acetobutyrate. Cellulose acetate is made by reaction between excess acetic anhydride and cellulose in a solvent for the product such as anhydrous acetic acid or methylene dichloride,[30] in presence of sulphuric acid. Reaction proceeds by equation (12); the product is isolated by partial dilution with water

[28] *Ind. Eng. Chem.*, 1935, **27**, 282.
[29] *Trans. Amer. Inst. Chem. Eng.*, 1945, **41**, 157.
[30] C.I.O.S. 26/75.

and necessarily produces large volumes of dilute acetic acid which have to be concentrated and converted to acetic anhydride, by the processes discussed earlier in this chapter.

Esters are used as solvents in the paint, plastics and other industries; the more high boiling are solvent-plasticisers or plasticisers. Some esters are used in chemical synthesis; ethyl acetate, for example, is an intermediate for ethyl acetoacetate and for acetyl acetone:

$$CH_3COOC_2H_5 + CH_3COOC_2H_5 \xrightarrow{(NaOC_2H_5)} CH_3COCH_2COOC_2H_5 + C_2H_5OH$$

$$CH_3COOC_2H_5 + CH_3COCH_3 \xrightarrow{(NaOC_2H_5)} CH_3COCH_2COCH_3 + C_2H_5OH$$

The boiling points of the esters of the C_1 to C_4 monocarboxylic acids with some of the lower boiling alcohols are given in Table 66.

TABLE 67

Boiling points of some commercial esters

Acid	Ester	b.p. ° c./760 mm.
Formic	Methyl formate	31·8
	Ethyl ,, ...	54·3
	Isopropyl ,, ...	71·3
	n-Butyl ,, ...	106·8
Acetic	Methyl acetate	57·1
	Ethyl ,, ...	77·1
	Isopropyl ,, ...	88·4
	n-Butyl ,, ...	126·5
	sec-Butyl ,, ...	112·4
	Isobutyl ,, ...	116·5
	tert-Butyl ,, ...	95–96
	n-Amyl ,, ...	148
	Technical Amyl acetate	130–150
	sec-Amyl acetate	125–140
Propionic . . .	Methyl propionate . .	79·9
	Ethyl ,, ...	99·1
	Isopropyl ,, ...	111·3
	n-Butyl ,, ...	146·8
	Technical Amyl propionate . .	150–165
n-Butyric . . .	Methyl-n-butyrate . .	102·3
	Ethyl ,, ...	121·3
	n-Butyl ,, ...	166·4
	Isobutyl ,, ...	156·9
	n-Amyl ,, ...	185
	Isoamyl ,, ...	184·8
Isobutyric . . .	Methyl isobutyrate . .	92·6
	Ethyl ,, ...	111·7
	Isopropyl ,, ...	120·8
	Isobutyl ,, ...	148·7

(b) SPECIAL METHODS

Although the esterification of alcohols is the process most widely used on the industrial scale for the manufacture of all types of esters, special methods have been developed and are used for particular classes.

(*i*) *Formic esters from carbon monoxide and alcohols*

Whereas carbon monoxide reacts with alcohols at high pressure and temperature in presence of acid catalysts to give acids, with neutral or oxide catalysts under similar conditions, esters of formic acid are obtained:[31]

$$\text{ROH} + \text{CO} \begin{cases} \xrightarrow{\text{acid catalyst}} \text{RCOOH} \\ \xrightarrow{\text{oxide catalyst}} \text{ROOCH} \end{cases}$$

The probable explanation is that in the acid catalysed synthesis, carbon monoxide is adding to an olefin; in the ester synthesis, the R—O link is not broken.

Methyl formate is made from methyl alcohol and carbon monoxide, using 1 per cent of caustic soda as catalyst at 100–110° c. under 200 atm. pressure in corrosion resistant equipment; the yield is 90 per cent. The reaction is reversible, the equilibrium under the conditions used corresponding to 80% ester:[32]

$$\text{CO} + \text{CH}_3\text{OH} \rightleftharpoons \text{HCOOCH}_3$$

(*ii*) *From an olefin, carbon monoxide and an alcohol*

The synthesis of acids from olefins and carbon monoxide (Chapter 11, p. 185) can be modified by reacting in presence of an alcohol instead of water:

$$\text{RCH} : \text{CH}_2 + \text{CO} + \text{R}^1\text{OH} \rightarrow \begin{array}{l} \text{RCHCH}_3 \\ | \\ \text{COOR}^1 \end{array}$$

Two processes are available for this reaction; it can be carried out under conditions worked out by du Pont,[33] with carbon monoxide at 700–1,000 atm. and 200–300° c. using strong mineral acids as catalysts. Alternatively, nickel carbonyl can be used as the source of carbon monoxide or nickel chloride employed as catalyst (it is converted to nickel carbonyl under the reaction conditions) at about 200–300° c. but at only 150 atm., a considerably lower pressure than is required for the du Pont process.[34] These processes are not thought to be used.

(*iii*) *Tischtschenko synthesis from aldehydes*

The Tischtschenko synthesis of esters from aldehydes is a variant of the Cannizzaro reaction, in which two molecules of aldehyde condense

---

[31] Thorpe, 'Dictionary of Applied Chemistry', *Longmans Green*, 4th Ed., 1940, Vol. 5, p. 323.
[32] C.I.O.S. 26/64; F.I.A.T. 925.
[33] See, *e.g.*, U.S.P. 1924766.
[34] B.I.O.S. 266.

together in the absence of water under the catalytic influence of an aluminium alkoxide, to give the corresponding ester:

$$2RCHO \xrightarrow{Al(OR^1)_3} RCOOCH_2R$$

This process is used for the manufacture of ethyl acetate from acetaldehyde. The catalyst is essentially aluminium ethoxide containing some aluminium chloride and a little zinc oxide or ethoxide. The condensation is carried out in presence of some ethyl acetate and ethyl alcohol by slow addition of acetaldehyde at 0° c. and is run to give 98% conversion; the product is fractionated to give, in order, unreacted acetaldehyde and some ethyl alcohol-ethyl acetate, recycled to the reactors, then 75 per cent ethyl acetate – 25 per cent ethyl alcohol, used for making the catalyst, and finally pure ethyl acetate. The overall yield of ethyl acetate on acetaldehyde is 97–98 per cent.[15]

This method is available for making the symmetrical esters from the higher aldehydes.

Related to this process is the catalytic synthesis of esters from alcohols, using copper or copper chromite as catalyst at about 220° c. under pressure.[35] Ethyl alcohol under these conditions gives a high yield of ethyl acetate, obviously via acetaldehyde:

$$2C_2H_5OH \xrightarrow{-2H_2} 2CH_3CHO \rightarrow CH_3COOC_2H_5$$

(iv) Acetates from keten

Keten, $CH_2 : C : O$, is industrially available by the pyrolysis of acetone (Chapter 17, p. 314) or of acetic acid itself (this Chapter, p. 327). It is a convenient route to acetates since no equilibrium is involved and under suitable conditions, reaction proceeds to completion with molar proportions of reagents:

$$ROH + CH_2 : C : O \rightarrow ROOCCH_3$$

The preparation of *n*-butyl acetate from *n*-butyl alcohol and keten is described by Morey.[36] It was found necessary to use sulphuric acid (0·25 per cent by wt.) as catalyst to ensure complete absorption of keten; under correct conditions, using a continuous counter-current flow process, high yields were obtained.

(v) Unsaturated esters

The scale of production of unsaturated esters is already very considerable, and is likely to grow owing to their importance in the high polymer field.

---

[35] du Pont, U.S.P. 2004350.
[36] *Ind. Eng. Chem.*, 1939, **31**, 1129.

The unsaturation can be either in the alcohol half or in the acid half of the ester. The most important esters of unsaturated alcohols are the vinyl esters; as vinyl alcohol, $CH_2 : CHOH$, is unknown, these are made directly from acetylene and the acid:

$$RCOOH + CH \vdots CH \rightarrow RCOOCH : CH_2$$

The reaction is carried out either in the liquid phase or in the vapour phase, depending on the properties of the acid. Vinyl acetate is usually made in the vapour phase; acetylene and acetic acid vapours, containing excess acetylene, are passed at 170–210° c. over a catalyst of zinc acetate on active charcoal containing 15 per cent by weight of zinc. The exit gases are cooled to 0° c., the surplus acetylene recycled and the vinyl acetate separated by distillation. The yield is 92–95 per cent on acetylene, 97–99 per cent on acetic acid.[37]

Vinyl acetate boils at 72° c.; it is an important monomer, the starting point for polyvinyl acetate, polyvinyl alcohol, polyvinyl acetals and vinyl acetate-vinyl chloride copolymers.

The higher vinyl esters may be obtained similarly, although it is necessary to adopt a liquid phase process as the series is ascended.

An alternative manufacturing process for vinyl acetate, operated in America and Great Britain, is by pyrolysis of ethylidene diacetate with strong acids such as toluene sulphonic acid.[38] As contrasted to the use of ethylidene diacetate as an intermediate for making acetic anhydride from acetic acid (this Chapter, p. 326), the diacetate is made from acetic acid and acetaldehyde, and regenerates acetic acid as a co-product with the vinyl acetate.

$$2CH_3COOH + CH_3CHO \rightarrow CH_3CH(OCOCH_3)_2$$
$$CH_3CH(OCOCH_3)_2 \rightarrow CH_3COOCH : CH_2 + CH_3COOH$$

The esters of allyl alcohol, such as diallyl phthalate, are made by conventional esterification processes; they are finding outlets in the high polymer field.

The technically important esters of unsaturated acids derivable from petroleum sources (this proviso is put in to exclude esters of long chain acids such as the oleates or ricinoleates which are obtained from natural sources) are at present limited to the acrylates, the methacrylates, the maleates and fumarates.

The acrylates and methacrylates are normally made by combined hydrolysis, dehydration and esterification of ethylene cyanhydrin (Chapter 19, p. 357) and acetone cyanhydrin (Chapter 17, p. 318) respectively; outlets for these esters are referred to in the chapters cited.

---

[37] B.I.O.S. 1412.
[38] Brit. Celanese, B.P. 576397.

The more complex esters can be made from the complex alcohol and the lower alkyl acrylate or methacrylate by ester interchange.

Other routes to the acrylates are by the reaction between acetylene, carbon monoxide and an alcohol (Chapter 15, p. 282), and from propiolactone, a reaction product of acetone and keten, and an alcohol (Chapter 17, p. 317).

The maleates and fumarates are made from maleic anhydride or fumaric acid by standard esterification procedures.

CHAPTER 19

OLEFIN OXIDES

1. Ethylene oxide

THE most important of the olefin oxides is the first member of the series, ethylene oxide, $\begin{array}{c} CH_2-CH_2 \\ \diagdown \diagup \\ O \end{array}$. Its importance is due to its relatively low cost and to its versatile reactivity. It is manufactured from ethylene via ethylene chlorhydrin (Chapter 10, p. 177) or by direct catalytic air oxidation (Chapter 9, p. 145):

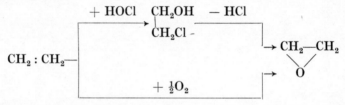

In the United States in 1954, about 59 per cent was made by the chlorhydrin route and 41 per cent by direct oxidation.[1]

Ethylene oxide is a gas at ordinary temperature; it boils at $+ 11°$ c., but is transportable as a liquefied gas. It is toxic and is used as a fumigant, especially for foodstuffs, owing to the ease with which it can be removed. For this purpose, it is employed in admixture with carbon dioxide, usually in the proportion of 10 vol. of ethylene oxide to 90 vol. of carbon dioxide, which gives non-explosive mixtures with air.

However, its chief outlet is as an intermediate for synthesis of new chemicals. It owes its value to a combination of two types of reactivity; firstly, it is capable of combining with compounds containing a replaceable hydrogen atom to give 2-hydroxyethyl derivatives:

$$\begin{array}{c} CH_2 \\ | \quad \diagdown \\ \quad \quad O + RH \rightarrow RCH_2CH_2OH \\ | \quad \diagup \\ CH_2 \end{array}$$

Secondly, it polymerises to give a polyethenoxy chain:

$$n \begin{array}{c} CH_2 \\ | \quad \diagdown \\ \quad \quad O \rightarrow -OCH_2CH_2OCH_2CH_2OCH_2CH_2OCH_2CH_2-etc. \\ | \quad \diagup \\ CH_2 \end{array}$$

This may not be regarded as a true polymerisation, as the configuration of the monomer is not retained in the polymer; the end groups are hydroxyl, and the polymer is really a polyethylene glycol. Ethylene chlorhydrin

---

[1] Matthew, Messing and James, *Chem. Eng.*, Oct. 1955, p. 280.

undergoes most reactions of the first type, but does not give the poly-ethylene glycol reaction except by transient formation of ethylene oxide.

These two types of ethylene oxide reactivity can be combined so that under suitable conditions, a series of derivatives of polyethylene glycols of increasing chain length are obtained:

$$n \begin{array}{c} CH_2 \\ | \\ CH_2 \end{array}\!\!\!\searrow\!\!O + RH \rightarrow RCH_2CH_2OH$$

$$+ RCH_2CH_2OCH_2CH_2OH$$
$$+ RCH_2CH_2OCH_2CH_2OCH_2CH_2OH$$
$$+ \ldots \ldots$$
$$+ RCH_2CH_2(OCH_2CH_2)_{n-2}OCH_2CH_2OH$$

As the number of ethylene glycol groups in the side chain is increased, the water solubility of the polymer undergoes a progressive increase, and any required degree of water miscibility can be obtained.

Carbide and Carbon Chemicals Company were the pioneers of the industrial utilisation of ethylene oxide; the products they manufactured included ethylene glycol, the simpler ethylene glycol ethers and ether-esters, and the ethanolamines. Their publications have been drawn on freely in this chapter. The I.G. were largely responsible for the development of the surface active mono-esters and ethers of the long chain polyethylene glycols.

In addition to these two main types of reaction, ethylene oxide also undergoes a number of other reactions of industrial value.

United States production of ethylene oxide in 1954 was about 260,000 tons. The end-use pattern was:[1]

Outlet	% offtake
Ethylene glycol . . .	64
Glycol ethers and polyglycols .	11
Non-ionic detergents . .	10
Ethanolamines . . .	8
Acrylonitrile	5
Miscellaneous	2
	100

(a) REACTION WITH WATER

From the tonnage standpoint, the most important reaction of ethylene oxide is hydration with water to ethylene glycol:

$$\begin{array}{c} CH_2 \\ | \\ CH_2 \end{array}\!\!\!\searrow\!\!O + H_2O \rightarrow HOCH_2CH_2OH$$

This is carried out in the liquid phase, either under the catalytic influence of traces of acids at 50–100° c., or at about 200° c. under pressure without a catalyst. The second method is usually chosen. With the catalytic route, trouble is encountered with removal of the acid catalyst, necessitating an extra processing operation.[2] In both cases, the second type of ethylene oxide reaction always takes place to some extent, with formation of diethylene glycol, $O(CH_2CH_2OH)_2$, triethylene glycol, $HOCH_2CH_2OCH_2CH_2OCH_2$-CH_2OH, and higher polyethylene glycols. To reduce polyglycol formation as much as possible, the hydration of ethylene oxide is usually carried out with a large excess of water.

Details of one method for the non-catalytic pressure hydration of ethylene oxide have been published.[3, 4] Ethylene oxide mixed with 6 vol. of water (*i.e.*, 14% aqueous ethylene oxide, or about 16 mols of water per mol ethylene oxide) at 22 atma. was reacted at 190–200° c. with a contact time of thirty minutes. The aqueous solution of glycols, after adjusting the pH to 7, was concentrated in a triple effect evaporator, the evaporated 'sweet waters' containing 0·5–1 per cent of ethylene glycol being recycled for mixing with fresh ethylene oxide. The residual glycols containing 15 per cent water were worked up in a train of distillation columns. The glycols were obtained in a weight ratio of approximately thirty-five parts ethylene glycol : four parts diethylene glycol : one part triethylene glycol.[3] The yield of glycols was over 90 per cent on ethylene oxide.

Ethylene glycol can also be made by saponification of aqueous ethylene chlorhydrin (Chapter 10, p. 178):

$$\begin{matrix} CH_2OH \\ | \\ CH_2Cl \end{matrix} + NaHCO_3 \rightarrow \begin{matrix} CH_2OH \\ | \\ CH_2OH \end{matrix} + NaCl + CO_2$$

A further method of manufacture is from carbon monoxide and formaldehyde; these react to give glycollic acid, the methyl ester of which is hydrogenated in the vapour phase to ethylene glycol (Chapter 16, p. 286). In 1954 in the United States, 83 per cent of ethylene glycol was made from ethylene oxide and 17 per cent by the glycollic acid route.[1] This route cannot be used for the manufacture of ethylene oxide; although it is theoretically possible for ethylene glycol to give ethylene oxide at elevated temperatures and low pressures, the main products isolated under these conditions are acetaldehyde or dioxan, which are more stable than ethylene oxide.

Ethylene glycol boils at 197° c.; it is completely miscible with water and alcohol but not with some hydrocarbon solvents. It possesses the typical reactions of an alcohol group, complicated by the presence of a hydroxyl group on the adjacent carbon atom. Thus it forms cyclic acetals and ketals with aldehydes and ketones:

$$\begin{matrix} CH_2OH \\ | \\ CH_2OH \end{matrix} + CH_3CHO \rightarrow \begin{matrix} CH_2O \\ | \quad \diagdown \\ CH_2O \diagup \end{matrix} CHCH_3 + H_2O$$

---

[2] U.S. Ind. Chem., U.S.P. 2135271.
[3] B.I.O.S. 1059.
[4] B.I.O.S. 776.

Dioxolan,
$$\begin{array}{c} CH_2O \\ | \\ CH_2O \end{array}\!\!\!\!\!\!\!\!\!\diagdown CH_2,$$
b.p. 74–75° c., and 2-methyldioxolan,

$$\begin{array}{c} CH_2O \\ | \\ CH_2O \end{array}\!\!\!\!\!\!\!\!\!\diagdown CHCH_3,$$
b.p. 81–82° c., are both commercially available; they are solvents for cellulose esters.

The main outlet for ethylene glycol is as an anti-freeze in radiators of internal combustion engines, *e.g.*, in motor cars and aeroplanes. It is much less volatile than methyl alcohol and has a lower molecular weight than glycerol. It has been used for the preparation of both inorganic and organic esters. The dinitrate is an explosive, being used as a constituent of low freezing dynamites. Acetates and phthalates have been prepared as plasticisers; these can also be made directly from ethylene oxide and the acid or acid anhydride (see p. 352).

Ethylene glycol reacts with polybasic acids to give high molecular weight polyesters:

$$n\mathrm{HOCH_2CH_2OH} + n\mathrm{HOOCRCOOH} \rightarrow$$
$$(-\mathrm{OCH_2CH_2OOCRCO}-)_n + 2n\mathrm{H_2O}$$

which find outlets in a number of industries.

Examples which may be mentioned are:

(*i*) The British synthetic fibre, 'Terylene' (Dacron in the United States), which is based on the polyester from ethylene glycol and terephthalic acid.

(*ii*) A rubbery vulcanisable polyester made from ethylene glycol, adipic acid and a small proportion of naphthalene-1 : 5-diisocyanate, which serves both to elongate the molecule and to permit cross-linking in the vulcanisation step.[5] Vulcaprene A (I.C.I.), a non-diene synthetic rubber, is made from ethylene glycol, adipic acid and hexamethylene diisocyanate.[6]

(*iii*) Norepol, a synthetic factice or rubber substitute of improved properties, which is a polyester from ethylene glycol and polymeric fatty acids.[7]

Another reaction of ethylene glycol is its catalytic vapour phase oxidation to glyoxal (Chapter 16, p. 298):

$$\begin{array}{c} CH_2OH \\ | \\ CH_2OH \end{array} \xrightarrow{+\,O_2} \begin{array}{c} CHO \\ | \\ CHO \end{array} + 2H_2O$$

The end-use pattern of ethylene glycol in America in 1954, when 270,000 tons were made, was:[1]

Outlet	% offtake
Anti-freeze, automobile and other .	80
Industrial explosives . . .	5
Cellophane, etc.	6
For Dacron (Terylene) fibre and film	4
Miscellaneous	5
	100

[5] B.I.O.S. 1166.
[6] Harper, Smith and White, *Rubber Chemistry and Technology*, 1950, **23**, 608.
[7] Cowan, Ault and Teeter, *Ind. Eng. Chem.*, 1946, **38**, 1138.

346
Petroleum Chemicals Industry

Diethylene glycol, $HOCH_2CH_2OCH_2CH_2OH$, b.p. 245·5° c., is a by-product in the manufacture of ethylene glycol by hydration of ethylene oxide; the proportion obtained can be increased by using a higher ratio of ethylene oxide to water. It can also be made by direct interaction between ethylene oxide and ethylene glycol, in the presence or absence of acid catalysts:

$$\begin{matrix} CH_2 \\ | \\ CH_2 \end{matrix}\!\!>\!\!O + HOCH_2CH_2OH \rightarrow HOCH_2CH_2OCH_2CH_2OH$$

Here also, triethylene glycol and higher polyglycols are formed as by-products. In one process,[3] ethylene oxide dissolved in six volumes of 50% aqueous ethylene glycol is reacted at 200° c. and 14 atma. pressure without added catalyst.

Diethylene glycol is used as a humectant, an anti-leak, a solvent, in hydraulic brake fluids, as a softening agent in the textile industry, for gas drying and as an assistant in dyeing and printing. Its esters are important; the dinitrate, like ethylene glycol dinitrate, is an industrial explosive which was used on a large scale in Germany during the recent war. Its esters with monobasic organic acids, for example with acetic acid, are plasticisers. With polybasic acids, it gives polyester resins by polycondensation.

Triethylene glycol, $HOCH_2CH_2OCH_2CH_2OCH_2CH_2OH$, b.p. 287·3° c., and tetraethylene glycol, $HO(CH_2CH_2O)_3CH_2CH_2OH$, b.p. 327·3° c., are also commercial products, used as solvents and plasticisers. Triethylene glycol has outlets in hydraulic brake fluids and in the chemical sterilisation of air. As the size of the molecule increases further, the polyglycol becomes more and more high boiling and viscous. A range of liquid polyethylene glycols of molecular weight 200 to below 1,000, is available for use as plasticisers, as dispersants in plastic compositions and inks, as water soluble lubricants and as humectants. At and above about 1,000 molecular weight, polyethylene glycols are solid at ordinary temperatures. With an average molecular weight of 1,000, the polyglycol has a setting point of 35–40° c.; molecular weight 3,500 sets at 50–55° c., and molecular weight 7,000 at 58–62° c. These high molecular weight polyglycols are waxy solids, soluble to the extent of 50–70 per cent in water, and are used as softening agents, ointment bases, hand creams, and as lubricants in the metal and other industries. A general account of the properties and uses of the solid polyglycols examined in America is given by McClelland and Bateman.[8] Very high molecular weight polyethyene glycols (molecular weight 100,000 or higher) have been made by Staudinger but have not been developed industrially.

For making the liquid polyethylene glycols and the solid polyglycols, the usual process is by passing ethylene oxide into diethylene glycol at

---

[8] *Chem. Eng. News*, 1945, **23**, 247.

120–150° c. and 3 atma. pressure, using caustic soda as catalyst; the higher molecular weight polyglycols were made by passing ethylene oxide into a small amount of preformed polyglycol at 120° c. and 3 atma. pressure, the catalyst being sodium added in the form of sodium methoxide.[9, 10]

A summary of some of the ethylene glycols and their esters which are commercially available is given in Table 68.

TABLE 68

Boiling points and uses of ethylene glycols and their esters

Compound	Formula	b.p. ° c./760 mm.	Uses
1. Glycols—			
Ethylene glycol . .	$HOCH_2CH_2OH$	197	Anti-freeze, intermediate
Diethylene glycol .	$O(CH_2CH_2OH)_2$	245	Solvent-plasticiser, intermediate
Triethylene glycol .	$HO(CH_2CH_2O)_2CH_2CH_2OH$	287	Solvent, etc.
Tetraethylene glycol .	$HO(CH_2CH_2O)_3CH_2CH_2OH$	327	Solvent, etc.
2. Esters—			
Ethylene glycol diacetate	$CH_3COOCH_2CH_2OOCCH_3$	190	Solvent, etc.
Diethylene glycol diacetate	$O(CH_2CH_2OOCCH_3)_2$	250	High boiling solvent
Diethylene glycol monolaurate	$HOCH_2CH_2OCH_2CH_2OCOC_{11}H_{23}$	315–325	Emulsifying and dispersing agent
Diethylene glycol monomyristate	$HOCH_2CH_2OCH_2CH_2OCOC_{13}H_{27}$	—	Emulsifying and dispersing agent
Diethylene glycol monopalmitate	$HOCH_2CH_2OCH_2CH_2OCOC_{15}H_{31}$	—	Emulsifying and dispersing agent
Diethylene glycol monooleate	$HOCH_2CH_2OCH_2CH_2OCOC_{17}H_{33}$	—	Emulsifying and dispersing agent
Diethylene glycol monostearate	$HOCH_2CH_2OCH_2CH_2OCOC_{17}H_{35}$	—	Emulsifying and dispersing agent
Triethylene glycol di-1-ethylbutyrate	$C_5H_{11}COOCH_2CH_2(OCH_2CH_2)_2 \mid C_5H_{11}COO$	358	Plasticiser
Triethylene glycol di-1-ethylhexoate	$C_7H_{15}COOCH_2CH_2(OCH_2CH_2)_2 \mid C_7H_{15}COO$	215/5 mm.	Plasticiser
Polyethylene glycol di-1-ethylhexoate	$C_7H_{15}COOCH_2CH_2(OCH_2CH_2)_n \mid C_7H_{15}COO$	215–290/5 mm.	Non volatile, low temperature flexible, plasticiser

Another derivative of ethylene glycol is the cyclic ether, dioxan

$$ \text{(diethylene-1 : 4-dioxide), } \begin{array}{c} O \\ \diagup \diagdown \\ CH_2 \quad CH_2 \\ | \qquad | \\ CH_2 \quad CH_2 \\ \diagdown \diagup \\ O \end{array} . $$ This is made by dehydration of

ethylene glycol on heating with a few per cent of sulphuric acid, more ethylene glycol being added continuously as the dioxan distils off.[11]

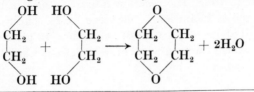

[9] B.I.O.S. 1625.
[10] B.I.O.S. 1651.
[11] I.G., U.S.P. 1939189.

The German process[12] was by adding ethylene oxide to a small amount of 5% aqueous sulphuric acid at 100° c. and 3 atma. pressure; this gave a mixture of polyethylene glycols with the average composition of a tetra-glycol. On completion of this stage, a further quantity of sulphuric acid was added and the solution heated to 150–160° c., when the polyglycols dehy-drated, aqueous dioxan distilling off. The dioxan was finally purified and dried by azeotropic distillation. The yield was 80 per cent on ethylene oxide.

Dioxan can be made directly from ethylene oxide by catalytic dimer-isation in the vapour phase over sodium hydrogen sulphate or other car-bonium ion catalysts:[13]

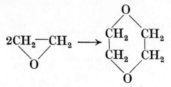

Dioxan boils at 101° c.; it is completely miscible with water (with which it forms an azeotrope containing 81·6 per cent of dioxan and boiling at 87·8° c.) and with most organic solvents. It possesses unusually good sol-vent properties on account of the two ether oxygen atoms. It has a strong tendency to form peroxides and is toxic.

(b) Reactions with alcohols, phenols and acids

In the same way as water reacts with one or more molecules of ethylene oxide, alcohols react to give mono-ethers of ethylene glycol, with mono-ethers of diethylene glycol, triethylene glycol, etc., as by-products:

$$ROH + CH_2{-}CH_2 \rightarrow ROCH_2CH_2OH + CH_2{-}CH_2$$
$$\rightarrow ROCH_2CH_2OCH_2CH_2OH + CH_2{-}CH_2$$
$$\rightarrow ROCH_2CH_2OCH_2CH_2OCH_2CH_2OH, \text{ and so on.}$$

As in the case of ethylene glycol the reaction may be acid catalysed or non-catalytic. The German process involved reacting 1 vol. ethylene oxide with 5–7 vols. of methyl, ethyl, or n-propyl alcohols at 200 to 220° c. and pressures up to 45 atma. The reaction rate was considerably slower than in the non-catalysed hydration of ethylene oxide. The mixed ethers ob-tained contained about 85 per cent of monoether, 10 per cent diether, and 2–3 per cent triether; the total yield of useful ethers was 90–95 per cent on ethylene oxide and on alcohol.[14]

---

[12] B.I.O.S. 1624.
[13] I.G., D.R.P. 597496, 598952.
[14] B.I.O.S. 1618.

The mono-ethers of ethylene glycol and of diethylene glycol are important solvents in the paints trade. The free hydroxyl group in both series can be esterified, *e.g.*, with acetic acid, to give yet a further series of solvents, the ether-esters, *e.g.*,

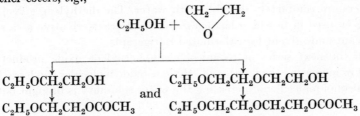

$$C_2H_5OH +$$

Some of the available products are shown in Table 69.

TABLE 69

Boiling points and uses of ethers and ether-esters of the ethylene glycols

Compound	Formula	b.p. ° c./760 mm.	Uses
1. *Derivatives of ethylene glycol*—			
Ethylene glycol methyl ether	$CH_3OCH_2CH_2OH$	125	Solvent, sealing composition, for phthalate, formal and acetal
Ethylene glycol ethyl ether	$C_2H_5OCH_2CH_2OH$	135	Paint solvent; cleaning composition, dyeing and printing assistant
Ethylene glycol n-butyl ether	$C_4H_9OCH_2CH_2OH$	171	In lacquers, soluble mineral oil compositions, dry cleaning soaps
Ethylene glycol 2-ethylbutyl ether	$\frac{C_2H_5}{C_2H_5}{>}CHCH_2OCH_2CH_2OH$	197	Alternative to cyclohexanone and lower ethers of diethylene glycol
Ethylene glycol 2-ethylhexyl ether	$\frac{C_2H_5}{C_4H_9}{>}CHCH_2OCH_2CH_2OH$	228	—
Ethylene glycol methyl ether acetate	$CH_3OCH_2CH_2OCOCH_3$	145	Solvent for cellulose acetate
Ethylene glycol ethyl ether acetate	$C_2H_5OCH_2CH_2OCOCH_3$	156	Solvent for lacquers
2. *Derivatives of diethylene glycol*—			
Diethylene glycol methyl ether	$CH_3OCH_2CH_2OCH_2CH_2OH$	193	High boiling lacquer solvent, intermediate
Diethylene glycol ethyl ether	$C_2H_5OCH_2CH_2OCH_2CH_2OH$	210	Assistant in dyeing, printing, wood staining. For esters, *e.g.*, acetate, phthalate
Diethylene glyco n-butyl ether	$C_4H_9OCH_2CH_2OCH_2CH_2OH$	231	In lacquers, printing inks, speciality soaps, and textile oils
Diethylene glycol methyl ether acetate	$CH_3OCH_2CH_2OCH_2CH_2OCOCH_3$	209	Solvent for lacquers
Diethylene glycol ethyl ether acetate	$C_2H_5OCH_2CH_2OCH_2CH_2OCOCH_3$	218	High boiling solvent-plasticiser in lacquers
Diethylene glycol n-butyl ether acetate	$C_4H_9OCH_2CH_2OCH_2CH_2OCOCH_3$	246	High boiling solvent-plasticiser in lacquers
3. *Derivatives of triethylene glycol*—			
Triethylene glycol methyl ether acetate	$CH_3OCH_2CH_2(OCH_2CH_2)_2OCOCH_3$	244	Solvent for inks, antidusting agent

The diethers of the ethylene glycols are also marketed as solvents; on account of the two ether oxygen atoms, their physical properties are similar to those of dioxan, but their boiling points are higher. Ethylene glycol diethyl ether, $C_2H_5OCH_2CH_2OC_2H_5$, boils at 121° c./760 mm., diethylene glycol diethyl ether, $O(CH_2CH_2OC_2H_5)_2$, at 188° c./760 mm., and tetra-ethylene glycol dimethyl ether, $CH_3OCH_2CH_2(OCH_2CH_2)_3OCH_3$, at 276° c./760 mm. Ethylene glycol diethyl ether is soluble to the extent of 21 per cent in water and is employed as a 'mutual solvent'; the other two diethers are completely miscible with water. The diethylene glycol ether has been used in brushing lacquers, and the tetra- derivative as a rubber lubricant and solvent for chlorinated refrigerants.

In the next series of technical alcohol-ethylene oxide products, the effect of increasing the number of ethylene oxide molecules condensed on to one alcohol molecule in increasing the water solubility is brought out even more clearly.

Long chain fatty alcohols are condensed with 10–40 molecules of ethylene oxide to give detergents for the textile and other industries. The reaction is carried out by passing the ethylene oxide into the alcohol at about 165° c. in presence of basic catalysts. Commercial products include octadecyl alcohol condensed with 20 mols of ethylene oxide and castor oil condensed with 40 mols of ethylene oxide. Any degree of water compatibility or solubility can be obtained by variation of the hydrocarbon chain and of the number of ethylene oxide groups added on. These compounds have the same type of detergent properties as the sodium salts of the fatty acids, *e.g.*, $C_{17}H_{35}COONa$ (sodium stearate) and of the sulphates of the fatty alcohols, *e.g.*, $C_{18}H_{37}OSO_3Na$ (sodium octadecyl sulphate). Like them, the molecule has both an oil soluble part and a water soluble part; what is unique is that the water solubility does not depend upon the salt of an acid group but upon an entirely non-ionic organic fragment. These ethylene oxide condensates are therefore unaffected by such factors as acidity and formation of insoluble heavy metal salts, which interfere with the universal use of the older types of detergents.*

Phenols react in the same way as alcohols to give mono- and poly-glycol ethers. Phenol itself gives 2-phenoxyethyl alcohol, $C_6H_5OCH_2CH_2OH$, b.p. 250° c., marketed as a perfume fixative. This glycol ether is soluble in cold water to the extent of 2·5 per cent by weight.

Much more important are the completely water soluble alkylphenyl ethers of the higher polyethylene glycols.[15, 16] These are made by addition of ethylene oxide to the alkylphenol, using sodium acetate or caustic soda as the catalyst, at such a rate that the temperature is kept around 200° c. The pressure during addition of ethylene oxide is slightly above atmospheric, say 2–2·5 atma.; the reaction is carried out in iron equipment, and liquid ethylene oxide is advantageously used, as the latent heat of evaporation assists in controlling the exothermic heat of reaction. The yield is

---

* For further information, the reader is referred to J. L. Moilliet and B. Collie, 'Surface-Active Agents', E. & F. N. Spon, Ltd., London.

[15] C.I.O.S. 26/2.
[16] B.I.O.S. 418.

quantitative; reaction is very rapid, and any desired number of ethylene oxide molecules can be introduced.

These products are detergents of the same general class as the long chain alcohol-ethylene oxide condensates. The properties can be varied in three ways, by choice of alkylphenol, by the number of ethylene oxide molecules introduced and by sulphation of the phenyl polyglycol ether.

The alkylphenols used are derivatives of phenol or cresol into which one long alkyl chain or two medium length alkyl chains have been introduced; cresol cannot apparently be disubstituted. The free hydroxyl group in the ethylene oxide condensate can be converted to an alkyl hydrogen sulphate by heating with sulphamic acid, NH_2SO_3H, to 120° c., or by reaction in the cold with chlorosulphonic acid.

The sulphates are made only with short or medium chain length polyglycols so as not to upset the hydrophobic/hydrophilic balance of the molecule.

Probably the most important detergents of this class are based upon condensation of 8–15 mols of ethylene oxide with dodecylphenol from propylene tetramer and phenol, and with *tert*-octylphenol or cresol from diisobutylene and the phenol. These are used in both the domestic and industrial detergent markets.

Owing to its high reactivity, ethylene oxide can be condensed with the alcoholic OH groups present in certain natural and synthetic high polymers. Natural or artificial cellulose fibres treated in aqueous alkaline solutions with ethylene oxide give organdie or parchment effects, depending on the degree of substitution;[17] hydroxyethylcellulose is a commercial product, marketed as an 8–10% solution in water. Its outlets include textile and paper sizing, as a printing assistant in place of gums and dextrins, and as an adhesive, thickener and protective colloid. Hydroxyethylated methylcellulose[18] and ethylcellulose are also marketed for similar outlets. Ethylene oxide has been condensed with other polymers containing hydroxyl groups, such as polyvinyl alcohol and starch.

Ethylene oxide adds on to acids in the same way and under similar conditions as it adds to alcohols and phenols, to give the mono-ester of a mono- or polyethylene glycol:

$$RCOOH + n \; \overset{CH_2}{\underset{CH_2}{|}}\!\!\!>\!\!O \rightarrow RCOO(CH_2CH_2O)_{n-1}CH_2CH_2OH$$

With acetic acid, one molecule of ethylene oxide gives mainly ethylene glycol monoacetate:

$$CH_3COOH + \overset{CH_2}{\underset{CH_2}{|}}\!\!\!>\!\!O \rightarrow CH_3COOCH_2CH_2OH$$

[17] I.C.I., B.P. 439880.
[18] B.I.O.S. 185; B.I.O.S. 547.

On further treatment with acetic acid, this gives ethylene glycol diacetate, $CH_3COOCH_2CH_2OCOCH_3$ (see Table 68, p. 347). The diesters of ethylene glycol are obtained directly from ethylene oxide and the acid anhydride:

$$(CH_3CO)_2O + \underset{O}{\overset{CH_2-CH_2}{\diagdown\diagup}} \rightarrow CH_3COOCH_2CH_2OCOCH_3$$

This reaction has also been used for the manufacture of surface active compounds by combining the hydrophobic hydrocarbon grouping present in long chain fatty acids with the hydrophilic grouping present in the polyethylene glycols. Thus oleic acid combined with six molecules of ethylene oxide at 150–160° c. in presence of caustic soda as catalyst gives an emulsifying agent for olein. Stearic acid condensed also with six molecules of ethylene oxide gives a softening agent for rayon.[19]

(c) Reaction with ammonia and with amines

Ethylene oxide reacts with ammonia to give the three ethanolamines, the hydrogen atoms on the nitrogen atom being more reactive than those which are part of the hydroxyl groups created during the reaction:

$$NH_3 + 1\text{-}3 \underset{O}{\overset{CH_2-CH_2}{\diagdown\diagup}} -\!\!\begin{cases} \rightarrow NH_2CH_2CH_2OH & \text{Monoethanolamine} \\ \rightarrow NH(CH_2CH_2OH)_2 & \text{Diethanolamine} \\ \rightarrow N(CH_2CH_2OH)_3 & \text{Triethanolamine} \end{cases}$$

From the patent information, it appears that the velocity of addition of ethylene oxide to each hydrogen atom on the nitrogen is about the same; therefore mixtures of all three ethanolamines will be obtained even with equimolar proportions of reagents. The best conditions for monoethanolamine hence involve use of excess ammonia.

In the German processes for these amines,[3] gaseous ethylene oxide was introduced into aqueous ammonia at 30–40° c. under 3 atma. pressure. The reaction was very exothermic; the temperature was controlled by circulating the reaction mixture through an external cooler. On completion of reaction, excess ammonia and the water originally present were removed and the individual ethanolamines isolated, if desired, by fractional distillation *in vacuo*. The proportions of the individual ethanolamines were varied by altering the ratio of ammonia to ethylene oxide. With $7\frac{1}{2}$ mols ammonia per mol of ethylene oxide, monoethanolamine and diethanolamine were obtained in equal amounts. With a 5 : 1 ratio, diethanolamine was the chief product. With a 2 : 1 ratio, the mixture after removal of ammonia contained 75 per cent triethanolamine, 10 per cent diethanolamine, 5 per cent monoethanolamine, and 10 per cent of higher ethylene oxide ethers of

---

[19] B.I.O.S. 421.

triethanolamine. This mixture was used without further purification as technical triethanolamine.

Monoethanolamine boils at 190·5° c. Its chief outlets are as an acid gas absorbent for removal of hydrogen sulphide, for non-ionic detergents, and as an intermediate for chemical synthesis, *e.g.*, for the explosive 2-nitraminoethyl nitrate, $NO_2NHCH_2CH_2ONO_2$. It is the simplest amino alcohol, and undergoes a number of ring formation reactions. With carbon disulphide, it gives mercaptothiazoline, an accelerator for the vulcanisation of rubber:

$$\begin{matrix} CH_2OH \\ | \\ CH_2NH_2 \end{matrix} + CS_2 \rightarrow \begin{matrix} CH_2S \\ | \hspace{1em} \diagdown \\ CH_2N \hspace{0.5em} \diagup \end{matrix} CSH + H_2O$$

The hydroxyl group can be replaced by chlorine using thionyl chloride to give 2-chloroethylamine:

$$\begin{matrix} CH_2OH \\ | \\ CH_2NH_2 \end{matrix} + SOCl_2 \rightarrow \begin{matrix} CH_2Cl \\ | \\ CH_2NH_2 \end{matrix} + SO_2 + HCl$$

This chloroamine on treatment with caustic soda gives the three-membered heterocyclic ring compound, ethylene imine:

$$\begin{matrix} CH_2Cl \\ | \\ CH_2NH_2 \end{matrix} + NaOH(aq.) \xrightarrow[(60° c.)]{} \begin{matrix} CH_2 \\ | \hspace{1em} \diagdown \\ CH_2 \hspace{0.5em} \diagup \end{matrix} NH + NaCl + H_2O$$

Ethylene imine is better prepared from 2-aminoethyl hydrogen sulphate, $NH_2CH_2CH_2OSO_3H$, made from monoethanolamine either with 100% sulphuric acid or with oleum:

$$\begin{matrix} CH_2OH \\ | \\ CH_2NH_2 \end{matrix} \xrightarrow[\text{or } SO_3]{H_2SO_4} \begin{matrix} CH_2OSO_3H \\ | \\ CH_2NH_2 \end{matrix} \xrightarrow{\text{aq. NaOH}} \begin{matrix} CH_2 \\ | \hspace{1em} \diagdown \\ CH_2 \hspace{0.5em} \diagup \end{matrix} NH$$

Ethylene imine boils at 55–56° c./760 mm. Its physical and chemical properties can be anticipated from its analogy with ethylene oxide, with the important difference that it has a replaceable hydrogen atom on the nitrogen atom. It is extremely toxic and very reactive, readily polymerising by opening of the ring in the same way as ethylene oxide.

The polymers can be made by heating a water solution to about 100° c. under pressure; one industrial outlet is as a paper coating material. The monomer has also been employed in the treatment of textiles. A number of surface active compounds for imparting wash-fast water-proof effects on textiles have been prepared from it.[16]

Diethanolamine boils at 268° c. It is used for liquid detergents and shampoos, for textile specialities, as an acid gas absorbent and as an intermediate for chemicals. On dehydration with sulphuric acid, it gives morpholine:

$$NH\begin{cases} CH_2CH_2OH \\ CH_2CH_2OH \end{cases} \xrightarrow{-H_2O} NH\begin{cases} CH_2CH_2 \\ CH_2CH_2 \end{cases}O$$

Morpholine can also be made from di-2-chloroethyl ether and ammonia, *e.g.*, at pressures in excess of 100 atm. in presence of inert solvents. High yields were obtained by working to partial conversion:[20]

$$O\begin{cases} CH_2CH_2Cl \\ CH_2CH_2Cl \end{cases} + 3NH_3 \rightarrow O\begin{cases} CH_2CH_2 \\ CH_2CH_2 \end{cases}NH + 2NH_4Cl$$

Morpholine boils at 129° c.; aqueous solutions have the curious property of boiling at constant alkalinity. It is marketed as a solvent and corrosion inhibitor. On condensation with one molecule of ethylene oxide, it gives morpholinoethyl alcohol, $O\begin{cases} CH_2CH_2 \\ CH_2CH_2 \end{cases}NCH_2CH_2OH$, b.p. 225° c., an intermediate for pharmaceuticals and rubber chemicals.

Triethanolamine boils at 208° c./10 mm. Its main outlets are in cream shampoos, textile specialities, pest control chemicals, and waxes and polishes.

Triethanolamine and ethylene oxide at the neutral point give tetra-ethanolammonium hydroxide:

$$N(CH_2CH_2OH)_3 + \begin{matrix} CH_2 - CH_2 \\ \diagdown O \diagup \end{matrix} \rightarrow [N(CH_2CH_2OH)_4]^+OH^-$$

This is a strong base; it melts at 128° c., but is commercially available as a 40% solution in aqueous methyl alcohol. On heating in solution, it decomposes, giving weakly basic polyethanolamines, the strong alkaline reaction being destroyed.

In 1956, American production of the ethanolamines was approximately 45,000 tons, of which diethanolamine accounted for 40 per cent, mono-ethanolamine for 34 per cent, and triethanolamine for 26 per cent.[21]

Aliphatic amines react as would be expected; the monoamines give mono- and di-hydroxyethyl derivatives. The secondary amines give a monohydroxyethyl derivative, to which further molecules of ethylene oxide can add to give derivatives of polyethylene glycols:

$$RNH_2 \rightarrow RNHCH_2CH_2OH \rightarrow RN(CH_2CH_2OH)_2, \text{ etc.}$$
$$R_2NH \rightarrow R_2NCH_2CH_2OH \rightarrow R_2NCH_2CH_2OCH_2CH_2OH, \text{ etc.}$$

[20] Goodrich, U.S.P. 2034427.
[21] *Chem. Week*, 24 November, 1956, p. 86.

Products in this class include (Table 70):

TABLE 70

Alkyl substituted ethanolamines

Name	Formula	b.p. ° c./760 mm.	Uses
Methyldiethanolamine	$CH_3N(CH_2CH_2OH)_2$	247	Intermediate for textile agents, insecticides, emulsifiers
Dimethylaminoethyl alcohol	$(CH_3)_2NCH_2CH_2OH$	133·5	Intermediate for above uses; corrosion inhibitor. Esters used in flotation processes
Diethylaminoethyl alcohol	$(C_2H_5)_2NCH_2CH_2OH$	162	Intermediate for antimalarials; fatty esters, emulsifying agents for oils and waxes
Hydroxyethylethylene diamine	$NH_2CH_2CH_2NHCH_2CH_2OH$	244	Intermediate
Dioctylaminoethyl alcohol	$(C_8H_{17})_2NCH_2CH_2OH$	—	Intermediate
Dioctadecylaminoethyl alcohol + 15 mols ethylene oxide	$(C_{18}H_{37})_2N(CH_2CH_2O)_{15}CH_2CH_2OH$	—	Used in textile assistants for acetate rayon

Primary and secondary aromatic amines react in the same way. Aniline gives 2-hydroxyethylaniline, $C_6H_5NHCH_2CH_2OH$, and di(2-hydroxyethyl)-aniline $C_6H_5N(CH_2CH_2OH)_2$. Ethylaniline gives N-ethyl-N-2-hydroxy-ethylaniline, $C_6H_5N(C_2H_5)(CH_2CH_2OH)$. These are intermediates for dyestuffs, especially for acetate silk.

(*d*) REACTIONS WITH OTHER COMPOUNDS CONTAINING REACTIVE HYDROGEN ATOMS

Ethylene oxide adds on to hydrogen sulphide to give monothioethylene glycol and thiodiglycol, and to mercaptans giving alkyl hydroxyethyl sulphides and higher condensation products:

$$RSH + \overset{CH_2-CH_2}{\underset{O}{\diagdown\diagup}} \rightarrow RSCH_2CH_2OH \rightarrow RS(CH_2CH_2O)_nCH_2CH_2OH$$

Monothioethylene glycol is made by passing hydrogen sulphide and ethylene oxide simultaneously into a solvent such as di-(2-hydroxyethyl sulphide) at 35–40° c., using an excess of hydrogen sulphide:[22]

$$\overset{CH_2-CH_2}{\underset{O}{\diagdown\diagup}} + H_2S \rightarrow HOCH_2CH_2SH$$

Monothioethylene glycol boils at 157° c. It is a toxic compound of considerable reactivity. It was used during the war for the manufacture of the growth accessory substance, methionine, $CH_3SCH_2CH_2CH(NH_2)COOH$;[23] methionine can also be made from acrolein.

---

[22] Woodward, B.P. 585655.
[23] Hands, Millidge and Walker, *J. Soc. Chem. Ind.*, 1947, **66**, 365.

More important is the product from two mols of ethylene oxide and one of hydrogen sulphide, thiodiglycol(di-2-hydroxyethyl sulphide):

$$H_2S + 2\ \underset{O}{\overset{CH_2-CH_2}{\diagdown\diagup}} \rightarrow HOCH_2CH_2SCH_2CH_2OH$$

The reaction proceeds slowly in the gas phase but quantitatively in the liquid phase by passing hydrogen sulphide and ethylene oxide simultaneously into thiodiglycol at 90° c.; this has been developed into a continuous process.[24]

Thiodiglycol boils at 168° c./14 mm. It is used as a solvent in printing processes and is an intermediate for 'mustard gas,' di-2-chloroethyl sulphide, $S(CH_2CH_2Cl)_2$. Unlike most aliphatic alcohols, the hydroxyl groups in thiodiglycol are smoothly replaced by chlorine on heating with aqueous hydrochloric acid above 100° c.:

$$HOCH_2CH_2SCH_2CH_2OH + 2HCl \rightarrow ClCH_2CH_2SCH_2CH_2Cl + 2H_2O$$

Analogously to the formation of tetraethanolammonium hydroxide (see p. 354), three mols of ethylene oxide react with hydrogen sulphide to give the strong base, trihydroxyethyl sulphonium hydroxide:

$$H_2S + 3\ \underset{O}{\overset{CH_2-CH_2}{\diagdown\diagup}} + H_2O \rightarrow [(HOCH_2CH_2)_3\overset{+}{S}]OH^-$$

With sodium bisulphite in water solution, ethylene oxide gives sodium isethionate (sodium 2-hydroxyethyl sulphonate):

$$NaHSO_3 + \ \underset{O}{\overset{CH_2-CH_2}{\diagdown\diagup}} \rightarrow HOCH_2CH_2SO_2ONa$$

The reaction is carried out by passing ethylene oxide into 30% aqueous sodium bisulphite at 70° c. under slight pressure, completing at 110° c.[16] Sodium isethionate is used for manufacture of detergents, *e.g.*, the oleyl ester of sodium isethionate, made by reacting the dry sodium salt with oleyl chloride:

$$HOCH_2CH_2SO_2ONa + C_{17}H_{33}COCl \rightarrow C_{17}H_{33}COOCH_2CH_2SO_2ONa$$

The corresponding derivative of methyltaurine ($CH_3NHCH_2CH_2SO_2OH$) is also a commercial detergent; the aqueous solution of sodium isethionate is condensed with a large excess of monomethylamine at 280° c. and 200 atm. pressure. After removal of the excess monomethylamine, the sodium salt of methyl taurine, still in aqueous solution, is condensed with oleyl chloride:

$$HOCH_2CH_2SO_2ONa + CH_3NH_2 \rightarrow CH_3NHCH_2CH_2SO_2ONa + C_{17}H_{33}COCl$$
$$\rightarrow C_{17}H_{33}CON(CH_3)CH_2CH_2SO_2ONa$$

---

[24] Othmer and Kern, *Ind. Eng. Chem.*, 1940, **32**, 160.

Taurine, $NH_2CH_2CH_2SO_2OH$, is made in the same way from sodium isethionate and ammonia and is used for other detergents.

Hydrogen cyanide adds smoothly and exothermically to ethylene oxide in presence of basic catalysts such as diethylamine to give ethylene cyanhydrin:[25]

$$HCN + \underset{O}{CH_2\!-\!CH_2} \rightarrow HOCH_2CH_2CN$$

This reaction can be carried out either batchwise or continuously.

Ethylene cyanhydrin boils at 221° c. It is an important intermediate for making polymerisable monomers. On dehydration, either in the vapour phase over dehydration catalysts such as active alumina at 300° c., or in the liquid phase at the boil under atmospheric pressure using catalysts as varied as metallic tin, magnesium carbonate or sulphamic acid, it gives acrylonitrile, $CH_2 : CHCN$, in yields of 80–90 per cent:

$$HOCH_2CH_2CN \rightarrow CH_2 : CHCN + H_2O$$

Acrylonitrile is used in synthetic rubbers and other high polymers. Its reactions and alternative syntheses are discussed in Chapter 20, p. 370.

Ethylene cyanhydrin can be dehydrated, hydrolysed and esterified in one operation, giving acrylic acid or the alkyl acrylates. The reaction is carried out in the same way as in the preparation of the alkyl methacrylates from acetone cyanhydrin (Chapter 17, p. 318), by heating with concentrated sulphuric acid in the presence of the alcohol, *e.g.*, with methyl alcohol:

$$HOCH_2CH_2CN + CH_3OH + H_2SO_4 \rightarrow CH_2 : CHCOOCH_3 + NH_4HSO_4$$

With aqueous sulphuric acid in absence of alcohol, the free acrylic acid is obtained. This process is the conventional route to acrylic acid and the acrylates. Alternative competing routes are summarised in Chapter 18, pages 334 and 340.

The acrylates are used as intermediates for polymers and copolymers.

Ethylene oxide reacts with the hydrogen halides to give the ethylene halohydrins, a convenient preparative route to ethylene chlorhydrin or ethylene bromhydrin:

$$\underset{O}{CH_2\!-\!CH_2} + HCl \rightarrow HOCH_2CH_2Cl$$

It reacts readily with the sodio derivative of ethyl acetoacetate in ethyl

---

[25] C.I.O.S. 33/50.

alcohol solution at 0° c. to give 1-aceto-3-butyrolactone,[26] which is used as an intermediate for making Vitamin B1 and antimalarial drugs:

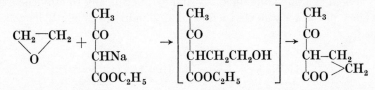

Under favourable conditions, ethylene oxide adds on to hydrocarbons.[27] With excess benzene and aluminium chloride at 0° c., phenylethyl alcohol, a perfumery chemical, is obtained in 55–60% yield:[28]

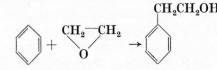

(e) MISCELLANEOUS REACTIONS OF ETHYLENE OXIDE

Addition to active hydrogen atoms does not exhaust the many sided reactivity of ethylene oxide. Of its other reactions, isomerisation to acetaldehyde was at one time of interest; this rearrangement is more significant with the homologues of ethylene oxide:

$$CH_2{-}CH_2 \diagdown O \diagup \rightarrow CH_3CHO. \quad \Delta H = -23\cdot 3 \text{ k. cal.}$$

The reaction is strongly exothermic, and is irreversible under any practical conditions. It proceeds thermally at 300–400° c., or under the influence of dehydrating catalysts such as active alumina or phosphoric acid and metallic phosphates[29] at 150–300° c.; in the latter case, by-products included ethylene glycol and other hydration products.

Ethylene oxide adds on to organic and inorganic acid chlorides to give 2-chloroethyl esters, *e.g.*,

$$CH_2{-}CH_2 \diagdown O \diagup + CH_3COCl \rightarrow ClCH_2CH_2OCOCH_3$$

Phosphorus oxychloride in presence of aluminium chloride gives tri-2-chloroethyl phosphate,[30] a useful plasticiser:

$$3\ CH_2{-}CH_2 \diagdown O \diagup + POCl_3 \rightarrow PO(OCH_2CH_2Cl)_3$$

---

[26] Knunyantz *et al.*, *Brit. Chem. Abs.*, A, 1934, 509.
[27] I.G., U.S.P. 2029618.
[28] B.I.O.S. 1154.
[29] I.G., D.R.P. 528822.
[30] Brit. Celanese, B.P. 475523.

and silicon tetrachloride gives tetra-2-chloroethyl silicate, a trace of hydro-chloric acid acting as catalyst:[31]

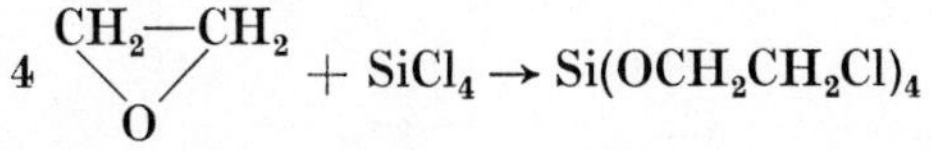

$$4 \quad \underset{O}{\overset{CH_2-CH_2}{\diagdown\diagup}} + SiCl_4 \rightarrow Si(OCH_2CH_2Cl)_4$$

In much the same way, ethylene oxide adds on to aldehydes and ketones in presence of stannic chloride to give dioxolans, which can also be prepared from ethylene glycol and the aldehyde or ketone (this Chapter, p. 344):

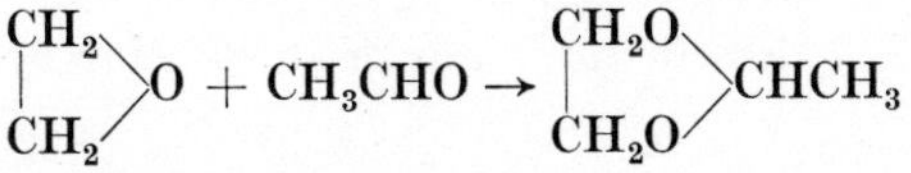

$$\underset{CH_2}{\overset{CH_2}{|}} \!\!\! \diagdown O + CH_3CHO \rightarrow \underset{CH_2O}{\overset{CH_2O}{|}} \!\!\! \diagdown CHCH_3$$

With potassium thiocyanate or thiourea in aqueous solution, ethylene oxide gives ethylene sulphide:

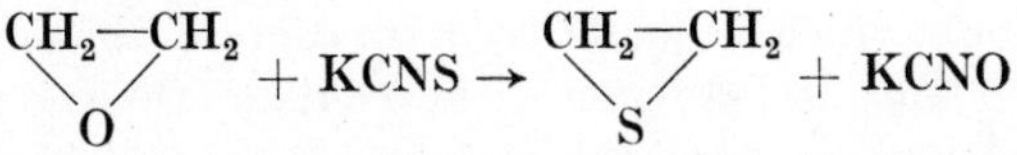

$$\underset{O}{\overset{CH_2-CH_2}{\diagdown\diagup}} + KCNS \rightarrow \underset{S}{\overset{CH_2-CH_2}{\diagdown\diagup}} + KCNO$$

The mechanism of this reaction, which is general for 1 : 2-oxides, is not clear.

Ethylene sulphide boils at 55–56° c./760 mm.; it readily polymerises to polyethylene sulphide, $(—CH_2CH_2S—)_n$, an insoluble infusible white powder, which can also be obtained from 2-hydroxyethyl mercaptan or from ethylene dichloride and sodium sulphide:

$$nHOCH_2CH_2SH \rightarrow (—CH_2CH_2S—)_n + nH_2O$$
$$nClCH_2CH_2Cl + nNa_2S \rightarrow (—CH_2CH_2S—)_n + 2nNaCl$$

The chemical treatment of textile fibres with ethylene sulphide has been claimed.

A summary of the more important reactions of ethylene oxide is given in Fig. 42.

2. Higher olefin oxides

The higher olefin oxides undergo most of the reactions of ethylene oxide. They are somewhat less reactive, and the polymers or polycondensation products are less hydrophilic, owing to the higher proportion of hydro-carbon groups in the molecule.

Of the homologues of ethylene oxide, only propylene oxide is manufac-tured on a large scale. It is made from propylene chlorhydrin (Chapter 10, p. 178) by reaction with aqueous alkali in the same way as ethylene oxide is made from ethylene chlorhydrin. Propylene chlorhydrin reacts twenty times as fast with alkali as ethylene chlorhydrin, a fact which has been utilised in one process[32] for combined manufacture of ethylene oxide and

[31] B.T.H., B.P. 577250.
[32] Wyandotte, U.S.P. 2417685.

propylene oxide from a mixture of ethylene and propylene—transferring the problem of separation from olefins to olefin oxides.

$$\begin{array}{ccc} \mathrm{CH_2Cl} & -\ \mathrm{HCl} & \mathrm{CH_2} \\ | & \xrightarrow{} & | \quad \diagdown \mathrm{O} \\ \mathrm{CH_3CHOH} & & \mathrm{CH_3CH} \diagup \end{array}$$

It arises as one of the minor products of air oxidation of propane (Chapter 4, p. 60). Direct catalytic air oxidation of propylene has been claimed but the methyl group next to the double bond is the part of the molecule which is oxidised, the main product being acrolein (Chapter 9, p. 148).

Propylene oxide boils at 34° c. Its main outlet is as an intermediate; the principal product is propylene glycol, but propylene oxide yields a series of derivatives similar to those which are made from ethylene oxide. Propylene glycol, which is made by hydration of the oxide with water under pressure, boils at 188° c., 9° c. lower than ethylene glycol. Many of its outlets depend upon its relatively low order of toxicity and on the fact that it is practically non-corrosive. Production in America in 1950 was about 40,000 tons, the end-use pattern being:[33]

Outlets	% offtake
Anti-freeze and industrial coolant .	35·3
Resins and plasticisers . .	19·5
Brake and hydraulic fluids .	14·1
Tobacco	8·4
Food industry	7·2
Pharmaceuticals and cosmetics .	6·8
Miscellaneous	8·7
	100·0

Its polyesters with sebacic acid are rubber-like and can be vulcanised with benzoyl peroxide; the corresponding esters with ethylene glycol are rigid plastics, softening above about 74° c., the extra methyl group in propylene glycol conferring sufficient disorder to lower the softening range to below room temperature.[34] Products based on these propylene glycol polyesters are marketed in America as specialty synthetic rubbers. Polypropylene sebacate and adipate are themselves non-migratory plasticisers.

A list of some of the commercial derivatives of propylene oxide is given in Table 71.

A series of higher polypropylene glycols and of monoalkyl ethers of propylene glycol and of dipropylene glycol are also manufactured.

[33] Kern, *Chem. Ind. Week*, 1951, **68(6)**, 61.
[34] Biggs, Erickson and Fuller, *Ind. Eng. Chem.*, 1947, **39**, 1090.

TABLE 71

Propylene oxide and some of its derivatives

Compound	Formula	b.p. °C.	Uses
Propylene oxide . .	$CH_3CH{\diagdown \atop CH_2}O$	34/760 mm.	Intermediate, fumigant
Propylene glycol . .	CH_3CHOH CH_2OH	188/760 mm.	Solvent, anti-freeze
Dipropylene glycol . .	$(CH_3CHOHCH_2)_2O$	232/760 mm.	Plasticiser, high boiling solvent
4-Methyldioxolan . .	$CH_3CH{-}O{\diagdown \atop CH_2{-}O}CH_2$	85/760 mm.	Solvent for cellulose esters
Monoisopropanolamine .	$CH_3CHOHCH_2NH_2$	45/5 mm.	Intermediate, soaps
Diisopropanolamine . .	$(CH_3CHOHCH_2)_2NH$	116/5 mm.	Soaps
Triisopropanolamine . .	$(CH_3CHOHCH_2)_3N$	305/760 mm., m.p. 45° c.	Emulsifying agent; with fatty acids gives soaps completely soluble in hydrocarbons, unlike triethanolamine

Propylene oxide undergoes the same types of polycondensation reactions as ethylene oxide. With alcohols, it gives polypropylene glycol ethers of the general type,

$$RO(CH_2\overset{CH_3}{\underset{|}{C}}HO)_nCH_2\overset{CH_3}{\underset{|}{C}}HOH$$

Where n is large enough, the products are lubricating oils insoluble in water, and having high viscosity index.[35] Alcohols condensed simultaneously with a mixture of ethylene oxide and propylene oxide give lubricating oils soluble in water but also possessing very high viscosity index. The general method of preparation is by reaction between ethylene oxide, propylene oxide and the alcohol at 80–160° c. and 1 to 4 atms. pressure.[36] Some of the products of this reaction are good hydraulic brake fluids.[37] Presumably these products consist of polyglycol ethers with alternate ethylene and propylene groups, *e.g.*:

$$ROCH_2CH_2OCH_2\overset{CH_3}{\underset{|}{C}}HOCH_2CH_2OCH_2\overset{CH_3}{\underset{|}{C}}H \ldots CH_2CH_2OH$$

Similar mixed condensates are made directly from ethylene oxide and propylene oxide;[38] by adjustment of the ratio of the two oxides and of the overall chain length, non-ionic detergents which are solid and not liquid are made industrially.[39]

Another reaction of propylene oxide is its isomerisation, which can be carried out either thermally or catalytically. All three possible products are formed, propionaldehyde, allyl alcohol and acetone.

[35] Carbide and Carbon, B.P. 601419.
[36] Carbide and Carbon, U.S.P. 2425845; U.S.P. 2457139.
[37] Carbide and Carbon, B.P. 584367.
[38] Wyandotte, U.S.P. 2674619; 2677700.
[39] *Chem. Week*, June 19, 1954, p. 78.

In the course of a search for routes to allyl alcohol, Williams[40] described the vapour phase isomerisation of propylene oxide over active alumina at 450–550° c. in presence of excess steam, but obtained propionaldehyde as the main product with only a little allyl alcohol. Other workers have examined the reaction with the object of obtaining maximum yields of propionaldehyde. The I.G. used silica gel or active silicates in presence of inert gases; propylene oxide mixed with eight times its weight of steam at 280° c. over aluminium silicate gave 83 per cent of propionaldehyde with 4 per cent acetone.[41] Carbide and Carbon Chemicals Company used alums or aluminium borate, working either in the vapour phase or the liquid phase. At 280° c. in the vapour phase over potash alum, they obtained 80 per cent propionaldehyde, 2 per cent allyl alcohol, 15 per cent unchanged oxide and some more highly condensed products. At 240° c., using alum suspended in Dowtherm (diphenyl-diphenyl oxide eutectic), they obtained 88 per cent propionaldehyde, 2 per cent allyl alcohol, 10 per cent unchanged oxide and no higher products.[42] With a different catalyst, the course of the isomerisation was completely altered. High yields of allyl alcohol were obtained by vapour phase isomerisation at 240–255° c. using lithium phosphate as catalyst.[43]

$$CH_3CH\underset{\diagdown \diagup}{\overset{}{\underset{O}{}}}CH_2 \rightarrow CH_2 : CHCH_2OH$$

This process was operated for a time on the large scale.

The *n*-butene oxides, isobutene oxide and the higher olefin oxides are obtained by the usual chlorhydrin route. They are not yet important.

The most important substituted olefin oxide is epichlorhydrin, $CH_2\underset{\diagdown \diagup}{\overset{}{\underset{O}{}}}CHCH_2Cl$, made as part of the Shell Development Co.'s route to synthetic glycerol via allyl chloride. Its manufacture and uses are dealt with in Chapter 10, pp. 166, 167.

[40] *Trans. Amer. Inst. Chem. Eng.*, 1941, **37**, 157.
[41] D.R.P. 618972.
[42] U.S.P. 2159507.
[43] Carbide and Carbon, B.P. 603815.

CHAPTER 20

NITRILES AND AMINES

1. Hydrogen cyanide

THE usual route to hydrogen cyanide is by acidification of aqueous sodium cyanide which is manufactured from sodamide and carbon:

$$NaNH_2 + C \xrightarrow{\ -H_2\ } NaCN \rightarrow HCN$$

Hydrogen cyanide can be made by high temperature reaction between various hydrocarbons or carbon itself and nitrogen or ammonia above 1,000° c. Equations (1) to (5) illustrate what may happen:

$$CH_4 + \tfrac{1}{2}N_2 \rightarrow HCN + 1\tfrac{1}{2}H_2 \qquad . \qquad . \qquad . \quad (1)$$
$$CH_4 + NH_3 \rightarrow HCN + 3H_2 \qquad . \qquad . \qquad . \quad (2)$$
$$C_2H_2 + N_2 \rightarrow 2HCN \qquad . \qquad . \qquad . \quad (3)$$
$$C_2H_2 + 2NH_3 \rightarrow 2HCN + 3H_2 \qquad . \qquad . \qquad . \quad (4)$$
$$C + NH_3 \rightarrow HCN + H_2 \qquad . \qquad . \qquad . \quad (5)$$

Using the following equations for the free energies of formation of the four different molecules involved:

CH_4, $\Delta G = -20,920 + 25 \cdot 5T$ from Table 22, p. 92
C_2H_2, $\Delta G = 53,584 - 13 \cdot 0T$,, ,, ,,
HCN, $\Delta G = 32,000 - 10 \cdot 3T$,, Lewis and Randall[1]
NH_3, $\Delta G = -13,400 + 28 \cdot 5T$,, ,, ,, [2]

the free energy changes in the reactions (1) to (5) have been calculated and are given in Table 72. The change in heat content at 25° c. has also been calculated to give an indication of the heat changes involved at reaction temperatures, assuming ΔC_p is nil or relatively small in all cases:

TABLE 72

Free energy of formation of hydrogen cyanide in reactions (1) to (5)

No.	Reaction	ΔG	$\Delta G = 0$ at ° c.	$\Delta H_{25° c.}$
(1)	$CH_4 + \tfrac{1}{2}N_2 \rightarrow HCN + 1\tfrac{1}{2}H_2$	$52,920 - 35 \cdot 8T$	1,205	+ 49 k. cal.
(2)	$CH_4 + NH_3 \rightarrow HCN + 3H_2$	$66,320 - 64 \cdot 3T$	760	+ 60 k. cal.
(3)	$\tfrac{1}{2}C_2H_2 + \tfrac{1}{2}N_2 \rightarrow HCN$	$5,208 - 3 \cdot 8T$	1,090	+ 4 k. cal.
(4)	$\tfrac{1}{2}C_2H_2 + NH_3 \rightarrow HCN + 1\tfrac{1}{2}H_2$	$18,608 - 32 \cdot 3T$	335	+ 15 k. cal.
(5)	$C + NH_3 \rightarrow HCN + H_2$	$45,400 - 38 \cdot 8T$	900	+ 42 k. cal.

Reaction (1) has been carried out by passing methane and nitrogen

---

[1] 'Thermodynamics', *McGraw-Hill*, 1923, p. 590.
[2] 'Thermodynamics', *McGraw-Hill*, 1923, p. 557. Their equation has been reduced to the linear form used, to cover the range 1,000–1,500° K.

through an electric arc;[3] the reactants may be diluted with inert gases. For example, with a mixture of 8·3 per cent methane, 42·7 per cent nitrogen, 33·7 per cent hydrogen and 5·3 per cent carbon monoxide, the production of hydrogen cyanide corresponded to 1 lb./9–10 kWh. This process can be combined with the arc process for making acetylene, and in fact appreciable amounts of hydrogen cyanide are present in the acetylene gases from the arc process when the feed gases contain traces of nitrogen (Chapter 15, p. 264).

Reaction (2) has been investigated by Imperial Chemical Industries[4] and by Bredig *et al.*[5] It proceeds only at temperatures of the order of 1,200–1,500° c., when methane pyrolyses to acetylene, and is carried out in the laboratory by flowing gases through narrow tubes. Reaction (4) also proceeds only at these high temperatures. At the low temperature indicated by the value of ΔG in Table 72, col. 4, the two carbon structure of acetylene is not broken (see this Chapter, p. 369).

Industrially, methane is a much more attractive starting material than acetylene for the synthesis of hydrogen cyanide. Routes (1) and (2) are both highly endothermic and the problem of supplying the large amount of heat at the high temperature of 1,500° c. in a conventional multitubular reactor is more or less insurmountable on the large scale. One solution, use of the electric arc, has already been mentioned. A second solution is internal combustion of a portion of the reactant gases. This method has been applied to reaction (2), and is now the industrial route to hydrogen cyanide from petroleum raw materials. It was developed by Andrussow[6] in the early 1930's by passing ammonia, methane from coal hydrogenation or coke oven gas, and oxygen containing gases over a platinum type catalyst at about 1,000° c. There must be sufficient oxygen present for the reaction:

$$2NH_3 + 3O_2 + 2CH_4 \rightarrow 2HCN + 6H_2O(g). \quad \Delta H = -224 \text{ k. cal.}$$

The current status of the process is indicated by a description of the manufacture of hydrogen cyanide from methanised coke oven gas;[7] the methane content of the coke oven gas is increased by hydrogenation of part of the carbon monoxide also present. The mixture fed to the reactor contained 12–13 per cent of methane, 11–12 per cent ammonia and the remainder mainly dry air; the catalyst is a platinum-rhodium gauze at about 1,000° c. The exit gases, which contain about 8 per cent hydrogen cyanide, are immediately cooled to 150° c. and the unreacted ammonia removed by scrubbing with aqueous ammonium hydrogen sulphate. The hydrogen

[3] Roessler and Hasslacher, U.S.P. 1235342–3.
[4] B.P. 335585; B.P. 335947.
[5] *Z. Elektrochem.*, 1930, **36**, 991.
[6] *Angew. Chem.*, 1935, **48**, 593.
[7] Kautter and Leitenberger, *Chem. Trade J.*, January 22, 1954, p. 197.

cyanide in the ammonia freed gases is absorbed in cold water (5° c.) to give a 3 per cent solution which is distilled to recover hydrogen cyanide of 100 per cent strength. The yield of hydrogen cyanide is 70 per cent on methane, 60 per cent on ammonia. An alternative to recovery of unchanged ammonia as ammonium sulphate is to absorb both the ammonia and the hydrogen cyanide with an aqueous pentaerythritol-boric acid complex. From this solution, the hydrogen cyanide is desorbed under vacuum at 80–90° c.; the ammonia, which forms a salt stable at low temperature, is recovered as such by heating to 130° c. under 3 atma. pressure.[8]

Starting with petroleum natural gas, it appears advantageous to remove all hydrocarbons higher than ethane and to limit the amount of ethane present.[9] The Rohm and Haas plant and process, stated to be the first Andrussow hydrogen cyanide from petroleum methane in the world, has been described.[10] The yields were similar to those in reference 7.

The Andrussow process uses catalysts which are catalysts for the oxidation of ammonia to nitric oxide (part of the standard nitric acid process, Chapter 3, p. 43). The formation of hydrogen cyanide from nitric oxide and organic compounds was observed by Kuhlmann in 1839, and the synthesis of hydrogen cyanide from nitric oxide and methane, etc., over platinum catalysts above 1,000° c. has been patented.[11]

Reaction (5) represents the earliest synthesis of hydrogen cyanide by Clouet in 1791, who passed ammonia over wood charcoal at about 1,000° c.; it has not been developed.

In all these processes, the hydrogen cyanide is obtained in low concentration in the exit gases; it is recovered by absorption in water, as in the Andrussow process.

Hydrogen cyanide has been made directly from ammonia and carbon monoxide over dehydrating catalysts such as alumina:

$$CO + NH_3 \rightarrow HCN + H_2O \qquad . \qquad . \qquad . \qquad (6)$$

and indirectly, via formamide:

$$CO + NH_3 \rightarrow HCONH_2 \rightarrow HCN + H_2O \qquad . \qquad . \qquad (7)$$

In reaction (6), the equilibrium is not favourable; at 450° c., K_p = 0·00048, corresponding to about 2% conversion from equimolar proportions of reactants; there is also a tendency for the hydrogen cyanide to be hydrolised by the water of reaction. Both these defects can be reduced by use of a large excess of carbon monoxide which not only tends to increase

[8] *Pet. Proc.*, March 1955, p. 384.
[9] Rohm and Haas, U.S.P. 2478875.
[10] Sherwood, *Ind. Chem.*, 1953, **29**, 353.
[11] du Pont, B.P. 446277.

the conversion of ammonia but also removes the water liberated, by the water gas shift reaction:

$$CO + H_2O \rightleftharpoons CO_2 + H_2$$

so that the overall reaction can be:

$$2CO + NH_3 \rightarrow HCN + CO_2 + H_2$$

A gas mixture with a carbon monoxide to ammonia ratio of 20 : 1 is stated to give 65% conversion of ammonia to hydrogen cyanide at 700° c. over alumina.[12] The process is economic only where ample supplies of cheap carbon monoxide are available.[7]

The formamide route has been operated in Germany and the United States. Formamide was made from methyl formate (from methyl alcohol and carbon monoxide, see Chapter 18, p. 338) by reaction with ammonia at 60–70° c. under 10–15 atma. pressure to give a yield of 90–95 per cent of formamide:

$$CO + CH_3OH \rightarrow HCOOCH_3 + NH_3 \rightarrow HCONH_2 + CH_3OH$$

The formamide was dehydrated in the vapour phase at 350–370° c. over aluminium phosphate in presence of a large excess of ammonia; the hydrogen cyanide was isolated as aqueous sodium cyanide.[13]

$$HCONH_2 \rightarrow HCN + H_2O \qquad . \qquad . \qquad . \qquad (7)$$

The equilibrium in reaction (7) is given by the equation:[9]

$$\log_{10} K_p = \frac{-23{,}380}{4 \cdot 57T} + 1 \cdot 75 \log_{10} T - \frac{0 \cdot 0046}{4 \cdot 57} T + 3 \cdot 5$$

The calculated conversions at 1 atma. pressure and at 0·02 atma. pressure published in reference (12) are given in Table 73:

TABLE 73

Conversion in dehydration of formamide

Temperature ° C.	% Conversion	
	$P = 1$ atma.	$P = 0 \cdot 02$ atma.
200	8·8	53·1
300	25·0	87·7
400	77·8	99·4
500	96·7	—

The main purpose of the added ammonia was to reduce the partial

---

[12] Thorpe, 'Dictionary of Applied Chemistry', *Longmans Green*, 4th Ed., 1939, Vol. 3, p. 492.

[13] C.I.O.S. 27/92.

pressure of the formamide. A similar result could be achieved by carrying out the dehydration at 3 mm. absolute pressure in the absence of ammonia.[14]

Hydrogen cyanide is a low boiling liquid, b.p. 26° c. It is used for fumigation purposes but its main outlets in the synthetic organic chemicals industry are for the manufacture of nitriles, *e.g.*, acrylonitrile (this Chapter, p. 370), and acetone cyanhydrin (Chapter 17, p. 318).

The scale of manufacture of hydrogen cyanide in America and the increasing proportion made by the Andrussow process from methane is indicated in Table 74.[15]

TABLE 74

Hydrogen cyanide in the United States

Year	Production tons	Proportion from methane %
1950	25,000	12
1951	41,000	53
1952	85,000	68

2. Saturated nitriles

Processes for the manufacture of saturated nitriles are to some extent bound up with processes for amines and for unsaturated nitriles, owing to interchangeability under reaction conditions.

The principal technical routes to saturated nitriles are:

(*a*) from acids and ammonia:

$$RCOOH + NH_3 \rightarrow RCN + 2H_2O$$

(*b*) from chloro-compounds and alkali cyanides:

$$RCl + NaCN \rightarrow RCN + NaCl$$

(*c*) from hydroxy compounds and hydrogen cyanide:

$$ROH + HCN \rightarrow RCN \rightarrow H_2O$$

(*d*) from unsaturated hydrocarbons and ammonia:

$$C_2H_4 + NH_3 \rightarrow CH_3CN + 2H_2$$
$$C_2H_2 + NH_3 \rightarrow CH_3CN + H_2$$

(*e*) from amines by dehydrogenation or oxidation:

$$RCH_2NH_2 \begin{cases} \xrightarrow{-2H_2} RCN + 2H_2 \\ \xrightarrow{+O_2} RCN + 2H_2O \end{cases}$$

---

[14] B.I.O.S. 754.
[15] Reay, *Pet. Times*, March 4, 1955, p. 229.

(a) FROM ACIDS AND AMMONIA

This route is analogous to the academic preparation of nitriles by dehydration of acid amides with phosphorus pentoxide. Technically it is carried out by reaction between excess ammonia and the acid, either in the liquid phase or in the vapour phase in presence of catalysts; the process is applicable not only to the monocarboxylic acids but to dicarboxylic acids to give dinitriles which are important intermediates for polyamide fibres and plastics.

The manufacture of long chain nitriles by circulating excess ammonia through the long chain acids in the liquid phase just below their boiling point, *e.g.*, at 250–350° c., in the presence of dehydrating catalysts, has been claimed.[16] The vapour phase conversion of acids to nitriles has been described by du Pont; catalysts include boron phosphate, working at 350–450° c. for manufacture of both mono- and di-derivatives, such as adiponitrile, $CNCH_2CH_2CH_2CH_2CN$,[17] and silica gel, used for monocarboxylic acids with at least 7 carbon atoms and working in the temperature range, 425–450° c.[18] The Germans made adiponitrile from adipic acid and ammonia in the vapour phase using phosphoric acid on silica gel at 320–390° c.; the catalyst life was six weeks. The yield of pure adiponitrile was over 80 per cent.[19]

(b) FROM CHLORO-COMPOUNDS AND SODIUM CYANIDE

This route has been referred to in Chapter 5, p. 76. Reaction is usually carried out in solution in organic solvents such as ethyl alcohol to reduce side reactions. It can be carried out with both mono- and polychlorides, *e.g.*, ethylene dichloride gives succindinitrile. In one technical process, adiponitrile is manufactured from 1 : 4-dichlorobutane. The process also proceeds under somewhat modified conditions with unsaturated chlorides and dichlorides.

(c) FROM HYDROXY COMPOUNDS AND HYDROGEN CYANIDE

The synthesis of nitriles by direct interaction of hydroxy compounds and hydrogen cyanide is formally possible. It has been realised in effect in the case of dimethyl ether which reacts with hydrogen cyanide in the vapour phase at 290° c. over alumina.[20]

$$(CH_3)_2O + 2HCN \rightarrow 2CH_3CN + H_2O$$

With the higher alcohols, dehydration to olefins is a serious side reaction as in the case of amines (see this Chapter, p. 375).

[16] Armour, U.S.P. 2033536.
[17] U.S.P. 2200734.
[18] U.S.P. 2205076.
[19] B.I.O.S. 368.
[20] I.G., F.P. 799091.

Direct interaction between an alcohol and hydrogen cyanide has been realised in the case of allyl alcohol (see Section 4, p. 372).

(d) FROM UNSATURATED HYDROCARBONS AND AMMONIA

The synthesis of acetonitrile from acetylene and ammonia is well known:

$$C_2H_2 + NH_3 \rightarrow CH_3CN + H_2$$

One method employs a slight excess of acetylene, using dehydrating catalysts such as alumina or silica gel at 300–350° c.[21] Under different conditions, the main products are either the ethylamines, or, as Tschitschibabin showed about forty years ago, pyridine bases such as the picolines.

Formation of nitriles from olefins and ammonia has been referred to in Chapter 11 (p. 188). Acetonitrile can be made the main product. We may include in this sub-section the synthesis of benzonitrile from toluene and ammonia by vapour phase catalytic dehydrogenation:

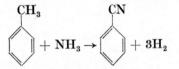

The manufacture of benzonitrile by a petroleum chemical company is carried out as follows. Ammonia and toluene in the mol ratio 1 : 2 are passed at 500–550° c. over a molybdenum oxide on alumina catalyst in short contact time, giving a conversion of 4–6 per cent per pass.[22] The ultimate yield is about 60–85 per cent on each reactant.

(e) BY DEHYDROGENATION OR OXIDATION OF AMINES

The previous section leads naturally to the synthesis of nitriles from amines by dehydrogenation or oxidation. Thus I.G. claim the manufacture of isobutyronitrile from isobutylamine by dehydrogenation over zinc or cadmium phosphates.[23]

$$\begin{matrix} CH_3 \\ \diagdown \\ CH_3 \diagup \end{matrix} CHCH_2NH_2 \rightarrow \begin{matrix} CH_3 \\ \diagdown \\ CH_3 \diagup \end{matrix} CHCN + 2H_2$$

The reaction can also be carried out by vapour phase oxidation over a metallic catalyst such as copper or silver.

3. Substituted nitriles

Substituted nitriles may be obtained by application of the appropriate reaction to a substituted hydrocarbon, or by addition of hydrogen cyanide

---

[21] I.G., D.R.P. 477049.
[22] Denton, Bishop, Caldwell and Chapman, *Ind. Eng. Chem.*, 1950, **42**, 796.
[23] U.S.P. 1684634.

to a reactive molecule, *e.g.*, an aldehyde, ketone or epoxide. These give rise to hydroxynitriles, which are intermediates for unsaturated nitriles, *e.g.*,

$$CH_3CHO + HCN \rightarrow CH_3CH\begin{smallmatrix}OH\\CN\end{smallmatrix} \qquad \text{(Chapter 16, p. 294)}$$

$$\begin{smallmatrix}CH_3\\CH_3\end{smallmatrix}CO + HCN \rightarrow \begin{smallmatrix}CH_3\\CH_3\end{smallmatrix}C\begin{smallmatrix}OH\\CN\end{smallmatrix} \qquad \text{(Chapter 17, p. 318)}$$

$$\begin{smallmatrix}CH_2\\|\\CH_2\end{smallmatrix}O + HCN \rightarrow \begin{smallmatrix}CH_2OH\\|\\CH_2CN\end{smallmatrix} \qquad \text{(Chapter 19, p. 357)}$$

The main technical value of the hydroxynitriles is as a route to unsaturated nitriles, acids and esters. These hydroxynitriles with a hydroxyl group on the carbon atom carrying the nitrile group react readily with ammonia or amines to give α-aminonitriles which can be hydrolised to the corresponding amino acids, *e.g.*,

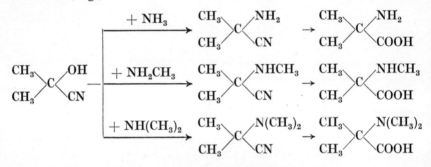

4. Unsaturated nitriles

The most important unsaturated nitrile is the first member of the series, acrylonitrile, $CH_2 : CHCN$. The two main routes to acrylonitrile are by dehydration of ethylene cyanhydrin (from ethylene oxide and hydrogen cyanide, Chapter 19, p. 357) and from acetylene and hydrogen cyanide:

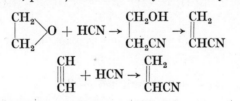

Ethylene cyanhydrin is dehydrated smoothly and in high yield either in the vapour phase or in the liquid phase using the usual dehydration catalysts, as described on p. 357.

There are two methods of addition of hydrogen cyanide to acetylene; the first uses vapour phase reaction at 400–500° c. over barium cyanide catalyst.[24] Yields and conversions are not good, and problems would be encountered in isolation of acrylonitrile from the hot gases; the process is not now operated.

The second is a liquid phase atmospheric pressure low temperature process. The basis is the use of a catalyst, similar to that developed for dimerisation of acetylene to monovinylacetylene (Chapter 15, p. 279), consisting of a hydrochloric acid solution of cuprous chloride maintained at pH 1 by addition of more acid; sodium, potassium and ammonium chlorides can be used in addition, either separately or in combination.[25]

The process was carried out by circulating a large excess of acetylene (10 mols C_2H_2/mol HCN) at 70–90° c. and atmospheric pressure through the catalyst solution in a rubber lined tower reactor. The acrylonitrile was carried away in the exit gases and was scrubbed out with water to give a 1·5% aqueous solution. The excess acetylene was recycled. The aqueous solution was worked up in a train of three distillation columns, the second and third operating under reduced pressure.

The yield of pure acrylonitrile was 80 per cent on acetylene, 85 per cent on hydrogen cyanide.

Other routes to acrylonitrile include:

(*i*) *Dehydrogenation of propionitrile (from propionic acid and ammonia by the process given in Section 2 (a), p. 368):*

$$CH_3CH_2CN \xrightarrow{\ -H_2\ } CH_2:CHCN$$

(*ii*) *Pyrolysis of acetaldehyde cyanhydrin or of its acetate:*

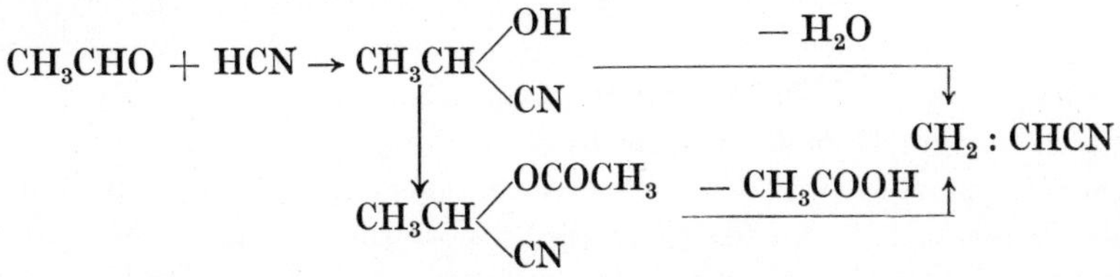

$$CH_3CHO + HCN \rightarrow CH_3CH{\overset{\displaystyle OH}{\underset{\displaystyle CN}{<}}}$$

$$\xrightarrow{\ -H_2O\ }$$

$$CH_3CH{\overset{\displaystyle OCOCH_3}{\underset{\displaystyle CN}{<}}} \quad -CH_3COOH \uparrow \qquad CH_2:CHCN$$

(*iii*) *From propylene and ammonia:*[26]

$$CH_3CH:CH_2 + NH_3 \rightarrow CH_2:CHCN + 3H_2$$

This route, usually carried out in two stages, is unattractive owing to low yields.

(*iv*) *From acrolein:*

Acrolein will shortly be available as a low cost raw material for the chemical industry by the catalytic vapour phase oxidation of propylene

---

[24] Cons. f. Elektrochem., D.R.P. 559734.
[25] C.I.O.S. 26/63; B.I.O.S. 92; B.I.O.S. 1057; F.I.A.T. 836; F.I.A.T. 1025.
[26] *World Pet.*, October 1945, p. 80.

(Chapter 9, p. 148). One of its potential outlets is as an intermediate for acrylonitrile, by reaction with ammonia and air:

$$CH_2 : CHCHO + NH_3 + \tfrac{1}{2}O_2 \rightarrow CH_2 : CHCN + 2H_2O$$

The reaction is carried out in the vapour phase at about 250–500° c. and atmospheric pressure, over oxidation catalysts such as the molybdates or phosphomolybdates. A slight excess of ammonia and air were used; the reagents could be diluted with steam. Conversions were high; the yield on acrolein converted was about 80 per cent.[27]

Outlets for acrylonitrile are referred to in Section 5.

Coming to the C_4 unsaturated nitriles, allyl cyanide is obtained in good yield by reaction between allyl alcohol and cuprous cyanide in the presence of aqueous hydrochloric acid:[28]

$$CH_2 : CHCH_2OH + CuCN + HCl \rightarrow CH_2 : CHCH_2CN + CuCl + H_2O$$

It can also be made from allyl chloride or bromide by reaction with cuprous cyanide but not with sodium cyanide, as the alkaline conditions cause rearrangement of the double bond to crotonic acid nitrile:

$$CH_2 : CHCH_2Cl + NaCN \rightarrow (CH_2 : CHCH_2CN) \rightarrow CH_3CH : CHCN$$

The allyl alcohol reaction has been extended to the synthesis of the dinitrile of dihydromuconic acid, $CNCH_2CH : CHCH_2CN$, from 1 : 4-butene diol, by reaction with hydrogen cyanide in presence of cuprous chloride or cuprous bromide:[29]

$$HOCH_2CH : CHCH_2OH + 2HCN \xrightarrow{\text{(CuCl)}} CNCH_2CH : CHCH_2CN$$

This unsaturated dinitrile can be hydrogenated to hexamethylene diamine in two stages via adiponitrile, $CN(CH_2)_4CN$. This reaction therefore provides a route to hexamethylene diamine from acetylene and formaldehyde (see Chapter 15, p. 274), without the need to synthesise 1 : 4-butane diol or tetrahydrofuran. It is not used; dihydromuconitrile is a technical route to adiponitrile, but it is made from the addition product of butadiene with one mol of chlorine, by reaction with hydrogen cyanide in the presence of cuprous chloride (Chapter 12, p. 214).

Methacrylonitrile, $CH_2 : C(CH_3)CN$, is best obtained from methacryl-amine, $CH_2 : C(CH_3)CH_2NH_2$, by catalytic oxidation with air over copper or silver catalysts:[30]

$$CH_2 : C(CH_3)CH_2NH_2 \xrightarrow{O_2} CH_2 : C(CH_3)CN + 2H_2O$$

The higher unsaturated nitriles have not yet attracted attention.

---

[27] Distillers, B.P. 709337.
[28] Breckpot, *Bull. Soc. Chim. Belg.*, 1930, **39**, 466.
[29] C.I.O.S. 33/50.
[30] Shell Development, B.P. 570835.

5. Outlets for nitriles

The main industrial outlets for the saturated nitriles are for the synthesis of amines by hydrogenation (see Section 6, p. 376) or of acids by hydrolysis.

The most important individual nitrile is acrylonitrile, which enters the high polymer field in synthetic rubbers and in the true synthetic fibres. Its first big use was in the oil resistant butadiene-acrylonitrile synthetic rubbers, Buna N and GR–N. The major outlet now is in the field of fibres, straight polyacrylonitrile (Orlon, etc.) and acrylonitrile copolymers (Acrilan, Dynel, etc.). It is expected that the use of acrylonitrile in fibres will continue to expand and will become increasingly the dominant outlet. Already, in 1954, in the United States, 29,000 tons of acrylonitrile were made, of which about 22,000 tons went to synthetic fibres and about 7,000 tons to making 22,000 tons of GR–N synthetic rubber. In Europe, acrylonitrile fibres have been made on an experimental basis in Germany, and plans for full scale manufacture are being implemented in the United Kingdom, France, Italy, Holland and elsewhere.

Acrylonitrile has other but less important outlets in the high polymer field, in various copolymers. It also has technical possibilities as a new intermediate on account of the ease with which it adds on to compounds with reactive hydrogen atoms to give 2-cyanoethyl derivatives:

$$CH_2 : CHCN + RH \rightarrow RCH_2CH_2CN$$

One of the new developments now being explored experimentally is cyanethylated cotton.

With hydrogen sulphide, acrylonitrile gives thiodipropionitrile, a plasticiser:

$$2CH_2 : CHCN + H_2S \rightarrow S(CH_2CH_2CN)_2$$

Acrylonitrile condenses with hydrogen cyanide in presence of an alkaline catalyst to give succindinitrile, also obtainable from ethylene dichloride and sodium cyanide:

$$\begin{matrix} CH_2 \\ \| \\ CHCN \end{matrix} + HCN \rightarrow \begin{matrix} CH_2CN \\ | \\ CH_2CN \end{matrix}$$

With cyclopentadiene in the presence of an alkaline catalyst (trimethyl-benzyl ammonium hydroxide), all six hydrogen atoms in the diene are replaced to give a hexacyanoethyl derivative:[31]

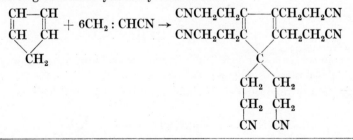

[31] Bruson, *J. Amer. Chem. Soc.*, 1942, **64**, 2457.

In the absence of the catalyst, the normal Diels-Alder adduct is obtained:

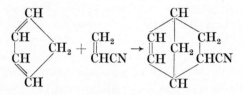

The use of the Diels-Alder adduct of acrylonitrile and butadiene as a source of pimelic acid, $COOH(CH_2)_5COOH$, has been referred to in Chapter 18, p. 333.

The dinitriles are wanted almost exclusively for hydrogenation to the technically important diamines. The most important dinitrile is adiponitrile, $CNCH_2CH_2CH_2CH_2CN$, which contributes half the nylon molecule. There are several routes to adiponitrile. The three operated commercially are from adipic acid and ammonia (p. 368); from the mixed dichlorobutanes obtained by addition of one mol of chlorine to butadiene, reacted with hydrogen cyanide in the presence of cuprous chloride (Chapter 12, p. 214); and from 1 : 4-dichlorobutane and sodium cyanide. The dichlorobutane is made from furfural, a product from waste vegetable matter, but could if economic be manufactured from acetylene and formaldehyde vua 1 : 4 butane diol (Chapter 15, p. 275).

6. Amines

The manufacture of aliphatic amines by reaction of ammonia with alkyl chlorides and with olefin oxides and by the reduction of nitroparaffins and substituted nitroparaffins has already been dealt with in Chapters 5, 6, and 19. Other technical and synthetic routes are:

(*a*) from an alcohol and ammonia;
(*b*) by reductive amination of aldehydes and ketones;
(*c*) by reduction of nitriles;
(*d*) from unsaturated hydrocarbons and ammonia.

(*a*) FROM AN ALCOHOL AND AMMONIA

The reaction:

$$ROH + NH_3 \rightarrow RNH_2 + H_2O \qquad . \qquad . \qquad . \qquad (8)$$

proceeds in the vapour phase under the influence of dehydrating catalysts. Two side reactions occur; dehydration of the alcohol to the olefin, and de-amination of the primary alkylamine to secondary and tertiary amines:

$$RNH_2 \xrightarrow{-NH_3} R_2NH \xrightarrow{-NH_3} R_3N \qquad . \qquad . \qquad (9)$$

To repress dehydration of the alcohol, reaction (8) is carried out at high pressure. It is impossible to stop de-amination, and mixtures of mono-, di- and trialkylamines are always obtained, an equilibrium being set up depending on the ratio of alcohol to total nitrogen. The di- and trialkylamines can therefore be recirculated to increase the proportion of monoalkylamine, if wanted. For example, trimethylamine and methyl alcohol at 300–500° c. over the usual catalysts give a mixture of the three methylamines :[32]

$$(CH_3)_3N + CH_3OH \rightarrow (CH_3)_3N + (CH_3)_2NH + CH_3NH_2$$

Reaction between the lower alcohols and ammonia is usually carried out at about 350–450° c. and up to 100 atm. pressure. The German process for the methylamines[33] involved passing one mol of methyl alcohol with four to five mols of ammonia over alumina on kaolin at 370° c. and 60–200 atm. in a copper-lined reactor. The mixture of the methylamines is separated by distillation under pressure, taking advantage of the abnormal vapour pressures of the methylamines and the formation of an azeotrope between trimethylamine and ammonia. Water was first removed, then the trimethylamine-ammonia azeotrope and excess ammonia. Mono- and dimethylamine were finally separated in a batch still at 5–15 atma. The trimethylamine-ammonia azeotrope was reacted in a separate small converter for partial conversion to mono- and dimethylamine and the product worked up with the main stream.

This general method is applicable to the ethylamines, propylamines and butylamines, but is limited to the lower alcohols owing to various technical problems such as decreasing volatility and increasing tendency to dehydrate to olefin with increasing molecular weight of the alcohol.

(b) REDUCTIVE AMINATION OF ALDEHYDES AND KETONES

A mixture of a $> CO$ compound with ammonia or a primary or secondary amine can be hydrogenated to give a new amine. This reaction is termed reductive amination and can be carried out in one or two steps.

Mignonac was the first to describe the hydrogenation of aldehydes and ketones in presence of ammonia in the liquid phase.[34] Reaction was carried out at ordinary pressure and temperature in the presence of conventional hydrogenation catalysts, such as nickel. In presence of excess ammonia, the main product was the primary amine, *e.g.*,

$$CH_3CHO + NH_3 \xrightarrow{+ H_2} CH_3CH_2NH_2 + H_2O$$

$$\begin{array}{c} CH_3 \\ {>}CO + NH_3 \\ CH_3 \end{array} \xrightarrow{+ H_2} \begin{array}{c} CH_3 \\ {>}CHNH_2 + H_2O \\ CH_3 \end{array}$$

---

[32] Rohm and Haas Co., U.S.P. 2095786; du Pont, U.S.P. 2112970.
[33] C.I.O.S. 32/107.
[34] *Compt. Rend.*, 1921, **172**, 223.

Reaction proceeds equally well with many substituted aldehydes and ketones, provided the substituent is resistant to the hydrogenation conditions; the ammonia can also be replaced by primary and secondary amines to give respectively secondary and tertiary amines. This route can therefore be used for synthesis of a wide range of substituted and unsubstituted symmetrical and unsymmetrical primary, secondary and tertiary amines.

Examples of its use include the synthesis of triethylamine from diethylamine and acetaldehyde. This is carried out in the vapour phase over nickel at 120° c. :[35]

$$CH_3CHO + NH(C_2H_5)_2 + H_2 \rightarrow N(C_2H_5)_3 + H_2O$$

Another vapour phase synthesis is monoisobutylamine from isobutyraldehyde and a large excess of hydrogen and ammonia over nickel-tungsten sulphides at 300° c. and 220 atm. :[33]

$$\begin{matrix} CH_3 \\ \\ CH_3 \end{matrix}\!\!>\!\!CHCHO + NH_3 + H_2 \rightarrow \begin{matrix} CH_3 \\ \\ CH_3 \end{matrix}\!\!>\!\!CHCH_2NH_2 + H_2O$$

Diisobutylamine was manufactured by condensing monoisobutylamine with a second molecule of isobutyraldehyde to give the Schiff's Base, which was hydrogenated with the same catalyst at 200 atm. and about 220° c., presumably in the liquid phase:[33]

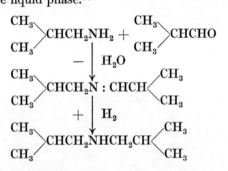

(c) REDUCTION OF NITRILES

The reduction of nitriles to primary amines with alkaline reducing agents such as sodium in alcohol is well known. The reaction is carried out on the technical scale by hydrogenation using the conventional catalysts such as Raney nickel or supported cobalt, preferably in presence of ammonia which reduces the tendency to form secondary and tertiary amines from the primary amine which is the initial product.

The reaction is carried out at moderate temperatures and usually under high pressure; it is reversible at higher temperatures.

Manufacture of primary long chain amines and of primary diamines is probably best effected by reduction of the corresponding nitrile made from

---

[35] I.G., D.R.P. 673017.

the acid by the method of Section 2 (*a*), p. 368 (in the case of diamines there are alternative routes to the dinitrile), *e.g.*,

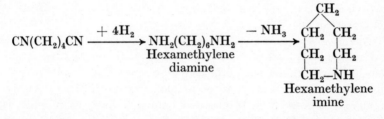

$$C_{17}H_{35}COOH \xrightarrow{\quad NH_3 \quad} C_{17}H_{35}CN \xrightarrow{\quad + 2H_2 \quad} C_{17}H_{35}CH_2NH_2$$

$$HOOCCH_2CH_2CH_2CH_2COOH \xrightarrow{\quad + 2NH_3 \quad} CNCH_2CH_2CH_2CH_2CN$$

$$\xrightarrow{\quad + 4H_2 \quad} NH_2CH_2CH_2CH_2CH_2CH_2CH_2NH_2$$

The manufacture of hexamethylene diamine from adiponitrile has been worked out by du Pont[36] as part of the synthesis of nylon. The German method was by hydrogenation of adiponitrile with cobalt (1 per cent on the nitrile) at 150° c. and 50–200 atm. pressure in presence of ammonia. The yield of diamine was 80 per cent with some 7–10 per cent of hexamethylene imine:[19]

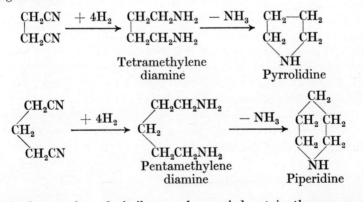

$$CN(CH_2)_4CN \xrightarrow{\quad + 4H_2 \quad} \underset{\substack{\text{Hexamethylene}\\\text{diamine}}}{NH_2(CH_2)_6NH_2} \xrightarrow{\quad - NH_3 \quad}$$

Hexamethylene imine

Tetramethylene diamine (putrescine) and pentamethylene diamine (cadaverine) show a much greater tendency to ring close to the cyclic imines, pyrrolidine and piperidine, but under rigidly controlled conditions, high yields of the diamines are obtainable by hydrogenation of the corresponding dinitriles:

$$\begin{array}{c} CH_2CN \\ | \\ CH_2CN \end{array} \xrightarrow{+ 4H_2} \begin{array}{c} CH_2CH_2NH_2 \\ | \\ CH_2CH_2NH_2 \end{array} \xrightarrow{- NH_3}$$

Tetramethylene diamine — Pyrrolidine

$$\begin{array}{c} CH_2CN \\ \diagup \\ CH_2 \\ \diagdown \\ CH_2CN \end{array} \xrightarrow{+ 4H_2} \begin{array}{c} CH_2CH_2NH_2 \\ \diagup \\ CH_2 \\ \diagdown \\ CH_2CH_2NH_2 \end{array} \xrightarrow{- NH_3}$$

Pentamethylene diamine — Piperidine

The hydrogenation of nitriles can be carried out in the presence of alcohols, aldehydes or ketones to give symmetrical or unsymmetrical secondary and tertiary amines, *e.g.*, with nickel as catalyst at 180–250° c.

---

[36] B.P. 490922; U.S.P. 2166152.

in the vapour phase.[37] Thus triethylamine may be made in high yield from acetonitrile and acetaldehyde:

$$CH_3CN + 2CH_3CHO \xrightarrow{\ +\ 4H_2\ } (C_2H_5)_3N + 2H_2O$$

This method is similar in principle to method (*b*).

(*d*) From unsaturated hydrocarbons and ammonia

The synthesis of nitriles from acetylene or olefins and ammonia was referred to in Section 2 (*d*), p. 369. Amines are intermediates in this process and by suitable modification of conditions may be made the principal products.

For example, by passing acetylene mixed with a large excess of ammonia over a zinc chloride-ammonia catalyst at 280° c., a mixture of the three ethylamines with pyridine bases in the higher boiling fraction was obtained, diethylamine being the principal amine. Above 305° c., acetonitrile was the main product.[38]

Again, in the Sinclair Refining Co.'s process for nitriles from olefins and ammonia at high pressure over hydrogenating-dehydrogenating catalysts, amines can be made the main products and from the published information appear always to occur alongside the nitriles.[26] Other ways of making amines from olefins and ammonia have been dealt with in Chapter 11, p. 188.

7. Outlets for amines

The aliphatic amines are wanted mainly as intermediates.

The primary alkylamines are used for detergents and for a variety of general applications. Methyltaurine, $CH_3NHCH_2CH_2SO_3H$, made from methylamine, ethylene oxide and sodium bisulphite (Chapter 19, p. 356), is converted to a detergent, $C_{17}H_{33}N(CH_3)CH_2CH_2SO_2ONa$, by acylation with oleyl chloride; sarcosine, CH_3NHCH_2COOH, made from methylamine and chloroacetic acid, is converted in the same way to the detergent, $C_{17}H_{33}CON(CH_3)CH_2COONa$. Methylamine is also used as an intermediate for photographic chemicals, medicinals and dyestuffs. *n*-Butylamine is used for dyestuffs, flotation agents, corrosion inhibitors, insecticides and soaps.

The secondary alkylamines find outlets for rubber chemicals, by reaction with carbon disulphide, giving derivatives of dithiocarbamic acids, *e.g.*,

$$(CH_3)_2NH + CS_2 + NaOH \rightarrow (CH_3)_2N\underset{\underset{S}{\|}}{C}SNa \xrightarrow{\ +\ O_2\ } (CH_3)_2N\underset{\underset{S}{\|}}{C}SS\underset{\underset{S}{\|}}{C}N(CH_3)_2$$

Sodium dimethyl   Tetramethyl thiuram
dithiocarbamate   disulphide

---

[37] I.C.I., B.P. 542609.
[38] I.G., B.P. 283163.

These derivatives are also used as pest control chemicals and in the pharmaceutical industry. In America, by 1954, the principal outlets for dimethylamine were for solubilising selective herbicides and for making dimethylformamide, a solvent for the acrylic fibres.

Diethylamine is an intermediate for antimalarials and other pharmaceuticals. Diisobutylamine was used for detergents, by acylation with oleyl chloride followed by sulphation of the double bond in the oleyl radical, *e.g.*:

$$C_8H_{17}\underset{\underset{OSO_3Na}{|}}{C}H(CH_2)_8CON\begin{cases}CH_2CH(CH_3)_2\\CH_2CH(CH_3)_2\end{cases}$$

The tertiary alkylamines have been used for making cationic detergents by condensation with long chain alkyl halides, to give quaternary ammonium salts such as cetyl trimethyl ammonium bromide:

$$(CH_3)_3N + CH_3(CH_2)_{14}CH_2Br \rightarrow [(CH_3)_3NC_{16}H_{33}]^+Br^-$$

An outlet of trimethylamine is for making synthetic agricultural food supplements via choline.

In the United States total production of the three methylamines in 1954 was about 10,000 tons p.a., of which dimethylamine contributed 70 per cent and trimethylamine 20 per cent.[39]

Coming to the polyamines, ethylenediamine, $NH_2CH_2CH_2NH_2$, is used as a solvent for oils, fats, waxes, etc., and as an intermediate for the calcium sequestration agent, ethylenediamine tetracetic acid (EDTA), $(COOHCH_2)_2NCH_2CH_2N(CH_2COOH)_2$; this is made by reaction between the diamine, formaldehyde and hydrogen cyanide, followed by hydrolysis:[40]

$$2HCN + 2CH_2O + NH_2CH_2CH_2NH_2 + 2CH_2O + 2HCN \rightarrow$$

$$(CNCH_2)_2NCH_2CH_2N(CH_2CN)_2 \rightarrow \begin{matrix}HOOCCH_2\\HOOCCH_2\end{matrix}\rangle NCH_2CH_2N\langle\begin{matrix}CH_2COOH\\CH_2COOH\end{matrix}$$

It is also used as an intermediate for a pest control chemical based on its *bis*-dithiocarbamate. During the war, ethylene diamine was used as the basis of the explosive ethylene urea dinitramine:

---

[39] Williams, Willner and Schaefer, *Chem. Eng. News*, Sept. 19, 1955, p. 3982.
[40] B.I.O.S. 421.

Ethylene urea has a peacetime outlet as the source of ethylene urea-formaldehyde resins, widely used in the textile industry.

The polyethylene polyamines, such as triethylene tetramine, $NH_2CH_2CH_2NHCH_2CH_2NHCH_2CH_2NH_2$, and tetraethylene pentamine, $NH_2(CH_2CH_2NH)_3CH_2CH_2NH_2$, obtained as by-products in the ethylene diamine process (Chapter 10, p. 158), are used for making salts with long-chain fatty acids to give soaps. Diethylene triamine is used for the manufacture of a cationic detergent, by condensation with oleic acid or other fatty acid, to give a glyoxalidine derivative:

$$C_{17}H_{33}COOH + \underset{NHCH_2CH_2NH_2}{\overset{\overset{\displaystyle CH_2}{\diagup\diagdown}}{NH_2\ \ CH_2}} \rightarrow C_{17}H_{33}\underset{NCH_2CH_2NH_2}{\overset{\overset{\displaystyle CH_2}{\diagup\diagdown}}{N\ \ \ CH_2}}$$

This is used both in the textile field, and in the oil industry as a lubricant additive.[41] Propylene diamine, $CH_3CHNH_2CH_2NH_2$, made from propylene dichloride and ammonia by the ethylene diamine process (Chapter 10, p. 158), reacts like its lower homologue, but its derivatives are more soluble in oil.

The chief outlet of the higher polyamines is in the polyamide field. Hexamethylene diamine constitutes half the nylon molecule; nylon is actually made by dehydration of the salt from equimolar proportions of hexamethylene diamine and adipic acid:

$$nNH_2(CH_2)_6NH_2 + nHOOC(CH_2)_4COOH$$
$$\rightarrow (-NH(CH_2)_6NHCO(CH_2)_4CO-)_n + 2nH_2O$$

Hexamethylene diamine has also been converted to hexamethylene diisocyanate by treatment with phosgene; the diisocyanate was reacted with dihydric alcohols to give a series of polyurethanes, such as the synthetic fibre, Perlon U, from 1 : 4-butane diol:

$$NH_2(CH_2)_6NH_2 \xrightarrow{(+ COCl_2)} OCN(CH_2)_6NCO$$
$$OCN(CH_2)_6NCO + HO(CH_2)_4OH$$
$$\rightarrow (-O(CH_2)_4OCONH(CH_2)_6NHCOO(CH_2)_4OCONH(CH_2)_6NH-)$$

Hexamethylene diisocyanate is also used for other high polymer reactions.[42]

The boiling points of the more important aliphatic saturated and unsaturated mono- and polyamines are given in Table 75.

---

[41] Carbide and Carbon, U.S.P. 2214152.
[42] C.I.O.S. 29/12; B.I.O.S. 1166.

TABLE 75

Boiling points of some aliphatic amines

Name	Formula	b.p., ° c./760 mm.
1. *Primary amines—*		
Methylamine	CH_3NH_2	− 6·5
Ethylamine	$C_2H_5NH_2$	16·6
n-Butylamine	$CH_3CH_2CH_2CH_2NH_2$	77·8
Isobutylamine	$(CH_3)_2CHCH_2NH_2$	68
2-Ethylhexylamine	$CH_3CH_2CH_2CH_2CHCH_2NH_2$ $\quad\quad\quad\quad\quad\lvert$ $\quad\quad\quad\quad CH_2CH_3$	167–8
2. *Secondary amines—*		
Dimethylamine	$(CH_3)_2NH$	7·4
Diethylamine	$(C_2H_5)_2NH$	55·5
Di-*n*-butylamine	$(CH_3CH_2CH_2CH_2)_2NH$	159–161
Diisobutylamine	$[(CH_3)_2CHCH_2]_2NH$	139–140
Di-2-ethylhexyl-amine	$(CH_3CH_2CH_2CH_2CHCH_2)_2NH$ $\quad\quad\quad\quad\quad\quad\lvert$ $\quad\quad\quad\quad\quad CH_3CH_2$	281·1
3. *Tertiary amines—*		
Trimethylamine	$(CH_3)_3N$	3·5
Triethylamine	$(C_2H_5)_3N$	89·5
4. *Polyamines—*		
Ethylene diamine	$NH_2CH_2CH_2NH_2$	117 (hydrate, b.p. 118° c.)
Diethylene triamine	$NH_2CH_2CH_2NHCH_2CH_2NH_2$	207·1
Triethylene tetr-amine	$NH_2(CH_2CH_2NH)_2CH_2CH_2NH_2$	277·5
Tetraethylene pent-amine	$NH_2(CH_2CH_2NH)_3CH_2CH_2NH_2$	333
Propylene diamine	$NH_2CH(CH_3)CH_2NH_2$	119·7
Tetramethylene di-amine	$NH_2(CH_2)_4NH_2$	158 (m.p. 27° c.)
Pentamethylene di-amine	$NH_2(CH_2)_5NH_2$	178–180
Hexamethylene di-amine	$NH_2(CH_2)_6NH_2$	196 (m.p. 39–40° c.)

CHAPTER 21

CHEMICAL BY-PRODUCTS FROM PETROLEUM REFINING

BESIDES the products manufactured from the gases and other hydrocarbons produced by the petroleum industry, non-hydrocarbon products, which were either present in the original crude petroleum or are produced by the chemical operations of refining, are isolated during the refinery operations. Those products of interest to the petroleum chemicals industry are discussed below—

1. Non-hydrocarbon by-products present in crude petroleum

(a) SULPHUR COMPOUNDS

Most crude petroleums contain sulphur, the amounts ranging from 0·04 per cent in a Pennsylvania oil, to 4·5 per cent in an oil from Mexico; the usual amount is about 1–2 per cent. Hydrogen sulphide is also present in many natural gases.

Elemental sulphur far transcends in magnitude all other chemical by-products of petroleum refining. It is obtained from hydrogen sulphide, which arises in a number of ways—as a constituent of certain natural gases (Table 7, p. 20), in most refinery gases, and as a by-product of some of the new processes of reducing the sulphur content of liquid petroleum fractions such as 'autofining'[1] and 'hydrodesulphurisation.'[2] There are two incentives to make use of the hydrogen sulphide, to reduce atmospheric pollution and because of the world sulphur shortage.

The hydrogen sulphide present in petroleum gases is concentrated by absorption/desorption from aqueous alkaline solutions such as the ethanolamines, and is then converted to sulphur by the Claus process, involving partial combustion with air. This process was developed in England in the nineteenth century for dealing with hydrogen sulphide from gases from the coal industry. In the oil industry, it was first applied to the recovery of sulphur in Iran before the second world war.

The hydrogen sulphide is mixed with air and burnt in a waste heat boiler, the following reactions taking place:

$$H_2S + 1\tfrac{1}{2}O_2 \rightarrow H_2O(g) + SO_2. \quad \Delta H_{400° \text{C}} = -125 \text{ k. cal.} \qquad (1)$$
$$2H_2S + SO_2 \rightarrow 2H_2O(g) + 3S(l). \quad \Delta H_{400° \text{C}} = -35 \text{ k. cal.} \qquad (2)$$

About 60 per cent of the sulphur is condensed in the waste heat boiler. The remaining gases still contain hydrogen sulphide and sulphur dioxide; to bring reaction (2) nearer completion, the gases are passed into a Claus

---

[1] *Chemical and Process Engineering*, 1953, **34**, 180.
[2] *Pet. Times*, April 16, 1954, p. 377.

kiln at about 400° c. where further reaction takes place over a bauxite or alumina catalyst; the residual gases, still containing a little hydrogen sulphide, are mixed with more air, burnt in a line heater and passed into a second Claus kiln. The recovery of sulphur can exceed 90 per cent.

A modern plant for recovery of sulphur from petroleum hydrogen sulphide, that at Fawley, Great Britain, uses a slightly modified process.[3]

Hydrogen sulphide, recovered from waste gases from cracking and hydrodesulphurisation processes by absorption in 20% aqueous diethanolamine, is burnt with the theoretical amount of air to give sulphur and water; this burns all the hydrocarbons present in the feed hydrogen sulphide, preventing coke lay-down on the bauxite catalyst used in the next two stages. About 65 per cent of the hydrogen sulphide feed is converted to sulphur in this stage. The gases leave the burner at about 1,120° c. and pass through a waste heat boiler and a wash tower to condense sulphur as a liquid at 145° c. (minimum viscosity); part of the sulphur is recycled to the top of the tower as wash liquor.

The remainder of the hydrogen sulphide is recovered in a two stage Claus process; the first stage is carried out at 400° c. to decompose all the carbon oxysulphide present, and the second stage at 260–275° c. to give maximum sulphur recovery. After the first stage, the gases are cooled in a waste heat boiler and after the second stage in an economiser before washing out the sulphur produced with liquid sulphur at 145° c. Any sulphur present in the final washed gases is burnt to sulphur dioxide in a tall stack. The total sulphur production is 40 tons/stream day at 99·9% purity and with a recovery of 94 per cent of theory. Over two tons of steam/ton sulphur recovered are also obtained.

In the United States, by-product sulphur from petroleum sources in 1953 was about 350,000 tons, some 6 per cent of total American production. In the United Kingdom over 25,000 tons p.a. of sulphur was recovered from refinery operations. Most of this sulphur is required in the form of sulphuric acid for various petroleum processes, but the petroleum industry need no longer be a nett consumer of sulphur.

The other sulphur compounds present in crude or distilled petroleum, such as mercaptans, sulphides, thiophenes and thiophanes are more of a nuisance to the petroleum refiner than a source of industrial chemicals. Their presence in petrol and oil products is most undesirable; they impart odour, are corrosive and lower octane response to lead tetraethyl. They are normally removed from refinery products in forms in which they are not recovered. Some of the lower sulphur compounds such as the lower alkyl mercaptans have been isolated from petroleum sources and oxidised to alkane sulphonic acids:

$$CH_3SH \xrightarrow{O_2} CH_3SO_2OH$$

---

[3] Edwards *et al.*, *Petroleum*, January 1956, p. 5.

The usual oxidising agent is air with nitric oxide as catalyst. An alkane sulphonic acid with M.W. 110–120 is made commercially from a mixture of C_1–C_3 mercaptans or the corresponding disulphides.[4] The sulphonic acids are strong acids of interest as catalysts, *e.g.*, for olefin polymerisation.

The normal route to these sulphur compounds is by synthesis. When pure methyl mercaptan is wanted, it is made from methyl alcohol and excess hydrogen sulphide over a catalyst. Higher alkyl mercaptans are

manufactured from olefins (Chapter 11, p. 182) and thiophene $\begin{matrix} CH-CH \\ \parallel \quad \parallel \\ CH \quad CH \\ \diagdown \ \diagup \\ S \end{matrix}$ is

made from butane and sulphur (Chapter 6, p. 90).

(*b*) OXYGEN COMPOUNDS

The total oxygen content of petroleum oils is very low, rarely exceeding 1 per cent, and many crudes contain no significant amounts at all. In the primary distillation of crude petroleum, it is possible that a further small proportion of oxygen is taken up especially by the higher boiling fractions.

Traces of the normal aliphatic acids such as heptoic and stearic acids have been reported from a wide range of distillates; reactions of hydroxyl and keto groups have also been recorded, but the only oxygen compounds of technical value obtained from crude petroleums are naphthenic acids and phenols. Where these are present in crude oils, they are isolated at specific stages in the refining.

The naphthenic acids are carboxylic acids of substituted cyclopentanes and cyclohexanes. Their molecular weight ranges from the lowest (cyclopentane carboxylic acid has molecular weight 114) to over 1,000. They occur naturally to the highest extent in naphthenic crude oils.

The principal sources of naphthenic acids are crudes from California, Venezuela and Roumania. The acids important to industry are obtained largely from straight-run gas oil fractions boiling from 200° c. to 370° c.; some acids are isolated from the lighter kerosene cuts. They are isolated from these fractions by extraction with dilute caustic soda, which takes out the commercially important medium molecular weight acids and leaves most of the high molecular weight resinous weaker acids in the hydrocarbon phase. The aqueous solution may be extracted with light naphtha to reduce the oil content of the finished naphthenic acid. The acids are isolated by acidification with sulphuric acid; where special quality is required, the crude acid is then distilled *in vacuo*.

The commercial naphthenic acids have a molecular weight range of 180–350. They are liquids of unpleasant odour and are usually dark in

---

[4] Proell, Adams and Shoemaker, *Ind. Eng. Chem.*, 1948, **40**, 1129.

colour. The lower molecular weight acids are sparingly soluble in water and are distillable at ordinary pressure. A commercial acid of average molecular weight 188 is reported as having a distillation range (10–90 per cent) of 240–300° c.

These acids are a complex mixture; some of the acids definitely identified, mainly by the laborious researches of von Braun in Germany and Lochte in America, include methylcyclopentane and methylcyclohexane carboxylic acids, methylcyclopentane acetic acids, methylcyclohexane acetic acids and more highly alkylated naphthenic acids such as 2 : 2 : 6-trimethylcyclohexane acetic acid:

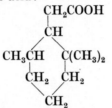

The acids with between eight and twelve carbon atoms are thought to be mainly monocyclic and those with between thirteen and twenty-three carbon atoms mainly bicyclic.

Naphthenic acids are used in industry in the form of their metal salts; the principal outlet is as paint driers. In 1950, when American production of these acids was about 12,000 tons, the end-use pattern was:

Outlet	% usage	Metal salts used
Paint driers	55	Pb, Mn, Co, Zn
Lubricants and detergents . .	15	Pb, Ca
Fungicides and insecticides . .	12	Cu, Zn
Emulsifiers	10	Alkali metals
Miscellaneous	8	—
	100	

The distribution of outlets had hardly changed by 1955.[5]

During the war, aluminium naphthenate had a special outlet for solidifying petrol in incendiary warfare.

Naphthenic acids are isolated from petroleum fractions as an integral part of refinery operations. The amount potentially available is much greater than the amount actually manufactured but separate extraction operations are not worth while.

Phenols are present in the higher fractions of cracked petrol; phenol itself occurs only to a limited extent, the main phenolic constituents in the fraction boiling up to 260° c. being the xylenols. Higher phenols such as polyethylphenols have been reported in kerosene distillates. The phenols are isolated by extraction with caustic soda; if present alongside naphthenic acids, they are separated by taking advantage of their lower acidity.

---

[5] *Chem. Week*, Sept. 24, 1955, p. 105.

A comprehensive investigation on the phenols extracted from a California cracked distillate has been published.[6] The results are summarised in Table 76 and compared with analysis of coal tar phenols boiling in a similar range.

Higher phenols are present in the heavier fractions of this distillate, but their constitution has not yet been worked out.

TABLE 76

Constitution of petroleum and coal tar phenols

Individual phenols present	Petroleum phenols			Coal tar phenols (206–245° c.)
	196–222° c.	215–235° c.	228–258° c.	
	%	%	%	%
Phenol	2·3	—	—	1·8
o-Cresol	28·9	2·0	0·7	12·7
m-Cresol.	7·5	1·1	0·3	16·6
p-Cresol	5·4	0·8	0·2	9·4
2 : 5-Dimethylphenol .	34·2	31·2	4·7	10·8
2 : 4- ,, ,, . .	16·3	14·9	2·3	12·8
2 : 3- ,, ,, . .	0·1	4·5	0·7	—
3 : 5- ,, ,, . .	—	7·8	2·6	12·2
3 : 4- ,, ,, . .	—	3·5	1·4	8·4
2 : 3 : 5-Trimethylphenol .	—	10·4	26·2	—
3-Methyl-5-ethylphenol . .	—	—	—	6·3
% Fraction accounted for .	94·7	76·2	39·1	91·0

It will be noticed from Table 76 that the ratio of the cresols and the xylenols from this particular petroleum source are different from those of the coal tar phenols. For example, there is proportionately much more 2 : 5-dimethylphenol (p-xylenol) in the xylenol fraction of petroleum phenols than in coal tar phenols. The high proportion of 2 : 3 : 5-trimethylphenol (ψ-cumenol) in this source of petroleum phenol is also noteworthy; it is absent in the coal tar phenols. This trimethylphenol is a starting point for the synthesis of Vitamin E (α-tocopherol).

Phenol is not present in sufficient amount in petroleum cresylic acids to be of commercial interest. These acids are also inferior to coal tar cresylic acids owing to a lower proportion of the more valuable m- and p-cresols and a higher content of sulphur compounds. Production of petroleum cresylic acids in America varies from 6,000 tons p.a. to 10,000 tons p.a. Their outlets include the disinfectant and plastics industries.

Oxygen compounds are also present in resins and asphaltic materials in the high boiling fractions of crude petroleum. Their constitution is unknown and certainly very complex, and they are not at present of any interest in synthetic chemistry.

---

[6] Field, Dempster and Tilson, *Ind. Eng. Chem.*, 1940, **32**, 489.

(c) Nitrogen compounds

Appreciable traces of nitrogen are present in some but not all petroleum oils. The highest authentic percentage in any oil is less than 1 per cent. The form in which this nitrogen is combined is not known. The nitrogen derivatives which have been examined have been isolated from distillates and may have been formed during the distillation. They are extracted from distillates with sulphur dioxide or with aqueous sulphuric acid.

The nitrogen bases in oil distillates may be of two types, aromatic and non-aromatic. The aromatic bases are derivatives of pyridine, quinoline and isoquinoline; some of the so-called non-aromatic bases are highly alkylated aromatic bases, which have lost much of their basic character because of the accumulation of alkyl side chains.

Various nitrogen bases from petrol and kerosene, and to a lesser extent from light gas oil, have been identified.[7, 8] They include methyl- and poly-methylpyridines, quinoline, quinaldine and alkyl- and polyalkylquinaldines.

So far no use has been found for petroleum nitrogen compounds in industry. The premium heterocyclic base, pyridine, is not present in significant amounts; coal tar is a richer source of mixed pyridine bases, and where special pyridines are wanted, they may be synthesised, for example, from simpler petroleum chemicals (Chapter 14, p. 259).

2. By-products produced in petroleum refining

Useful by-products are obtained in the sulphuric acid refining of certain petroleum fractions. The treatment of petrol and kerosene fractions with sulphuric acid removes sulphur and nitrogen compounds, and gives rise to polymerisation as well as some sulphonation of hydrocarbons. The sludge obtained is usually worked up for recovery of oil and of sulphuric acid.

However, in the refining of lubricating oil fractions with sulphuric acid to give the so-called 'white oils,' the main chemical by-products of the treatment are sulphonic acids, presumably of aromatic rings present in the original oil.

The petroleum sulphonic acids from white oil manufacture are divided into two classes, those soluble in hydrocarbons, called 'mahogany acids,' and those soluble in water, called 'green acids.' The distinction is relative and is based on the processes of isolation; the names refer to the colour of the products.

The method of making 'white oils' involves drastic treatment of high boiling fractions of naphthenic crude oils with 95% sulphuric acid or 20% oleum. The fraction to be treated is usually deasphaltised by propane treatment or dewaxed. The sulphonation is carried out in several stages

---

[7] Bailey *et al.*, *J. Amer. Chem. Soc.*, 1942, **64**, 909.

[8] Lochte, Thomas and Truitt, *J. Amer. Chem. Soc.*, 1944, **66**, 550.

with removal of the sludge at each stage. Addition of water to the sludge to give 50% sulphuric acid strength leads to separation of the 'green acids' referred to above. Other sulphonic acids remain dissolved in the 'white oil' and have to be removed to complete the refining process. They are usually extracted by water soluble organic solvents such as methyl alcohol or acetone followed by solvent removal and steaming to remove light ends; these oil soluble sulphonic acids are the 'mahogany acids.' The 'white oil' is finally cleaned up with clay or fullers earth.

The water soluble 'green acids' are the less important of the two; they are monobasic sulphonic acids, with a molecular weight range from 150 to about 400. They are essentially surface tension depressants and are used in compounding agricultural sprays and for general cleaning.

The mahogany acids are also monobasic acids, of the approximate formula, $C_nH_{2n-10}SO_3H$, and with molecular weights from 300–500. American consumption during the war was about 22,000 tons p.a., with the following end-use pattern:

Outlets	% offtake
Cutting oils	40
Heavy duty motor oils . . .	30
Rust preventive	12
Textile oils	10
Miscellaneous	8
	100

The calcium and barium salts are used in lubricating oils and the calcium and sodium salts as corrosion inhibitors. Similar acids to the mahogany acids are now being isolated from the aromatic extracts which are by-products in the solvent refining of lubricating oils.

3. Special petroleum fractions

A brief paragraph may be included giving a summary of the petroleum fractions prepared from crude petroleum for other than fuel or lubricating purposes. Solvents are made for the paint and dry cleaning industries by preparing narrow cuts of petrol, usually from straight run sources to avoid presence of the chemically reactive olefins. Petroleum oils are also used in the electrical industry; transformer oils are highly refined fractions of low viscosity, boiling approximately in the gas oil range. For impregnation of paper wrapped cables, highly viscous moderately refined naphthenic oils of high boiling range are used. In the insecticide field, petroleum oils are increasingly used as carriers for active poisons. The oils chosen are those in the heavy kerosene and gas oil range, preferably with a minimum content of aromatics and unsaturateds which damage growing leaves. The 'white oils' referred to above are used as textile lubricants, for medicinal purposes and in the insecticide field.

Reference may also be made here to the petroleum resins made from highly unsaturated cracked petroleum distillates. The lighter fractions from C_4 upwards containing both olefins and diolefins are treated with aluminium chloride which polymerises the unsaturated hydrocarbons. The polymers are separated and treated with superheated steam to give a series of resins melting up to 150° c., used in the paint and plastics industries.

CHAPTER 22

ECONOMICS AND STATISTICS

1. General

THE petroleum chemicals industry is essentially a new large capacity source of some of the bulk raw materials and intermediates required by the chemical industry. Chemicals themselves are intermediates used by other manufacturers in the processing of the final end product and in some form or other are indispensable to most industries.

The main outlets of petroleum chemicals are in those fields where the chemical is the major part of the end-product. The petroleum chemicals industry therefore tends to be concentrated in highly industrialised countries. The principal exception is in the field of nitrogen fertilisers, which find a local market in countries concentrating on agriculture.

There are two reasons for making chemicals from petroleum. The first is because one can make them more cheaply from petroleum than from other raw materials. The second is the assurance of adequate availability and at a reasonably constant price.

Petroleum chemicals have tended to displace the older routes, based primarily on coal and vegetable matter. Besides this competition between starting materials, one also finds, for the same reason of cost, competition within the petroleum chemicals industry between different intermediates, such as between petroleum ethylene and petroleum acetylene.

The growth of petroleum chemicals is due to a combination of two factors: the displacement of older raw materials and the expansion of those end-products which are based on petroleum chemicals as their raw material.

2. Raw materials and intermediates

The three main classes of petroleum chemical raw materials are the lower olefins, the lighter saturated gases and the aromatics.

Of the lower olefins, ethylene, propylene and the butenes, ethylene is the key product. Propylene and the butenes are available from oil refinery operations at little more than fuel value; their real value is based on the return obtained by conversion to petrol by standard processes such as non-selective or selective polymerisation. Ethylene is not obtained solely from waste refinery gases by straight separation, partly because there is not enough available, and partly because the concentration is too low.* Therefore ethylene has to be made by operations specifically devoted to its synthesis—*ad hoc* cracking. It is usually manufactured alongside

---

* As explained in Chapter 7, p. 107, refinery gases are used as a source of both ethylene and ethane but as part of an *ad hoc* cracking and ethylene separation plant.

the chemical unit consuming it because storage and transport costs are high.[1]

The starting points for ethylene are ethane, propane and liquid hydrocarbons. Ethane and propane are available where ample supplies of natural gas exist in excess of the local demand for fuel. The small ethane and propane content of natural gas is extracted, which hardly affects the usage or value of the stripped gas. The cost is therefore the equivalent of methane plus the cost of extraction. This operation is carried out in two types of locality, either in the oilfield itself, or at junctions of the main line gas transmission systems. At present there are only about half a dozen gas systems in the United States carrying such a gas volume as to justify the very expensive chemical plants for making and consuming the ethylene. Ethane and propane give only ethylene, so that there is no problem in finding a profitable outlet for co-products.

In less favoured countries, it is necessary to crack liquid hydrocarbons. This inevitably gives propylene and butenes in an amount of the same order as the ethylene produced. In addition, petrol and heavy fuel oil are also made. It is necessary to provide outlets for propylene and the butenes in the chemical industry, as ethylene alone cannot bear the whole cost of the cracking operation. The need to find profitable outlets for C_3 and C_4 olefins is therefore a limitation on the rate of growth of ethylene chemicals. Highly industrialised countries are now well equipped with refineries and the propylene and butenes available in the refinery off-gases are usually more than sufficient for the foreseeable demands of the chemical industry. The C_3 and C_4 olefin by-products of ethylene cracking plants are therefore worth no more than the C_3 and C_4 olefins in refinery gases.[1]

In Western Europe before the post-war development of petroleum chemicals, ethylene requirements were met by dehydration of ethyl alcohol made by fermentation of imported molasses or from the ethylene fraction obtained in processing coke oven gas for the sake of its hydrogen and methane content for the synthesis of ammonia. In this case, the ethylene fraction was obtained as an inevitable step in working up the coke oven gas and could be given a nominal value. The amount, however, is limited by how much coke oven gas is processed. The method has been widely used in Western Europe but their increasing ethylene requirements have now to be met from oil. Dehydration of ethyl alcohol is becoming obsolete.

The principal outlets for ethylene are synthetic ethyl alcohol, ethylene glycol and other ethylene oxide derivatives, ethyl chloride, vinyl chloride, styrene and polyethylene. In 1954, about 70 per cent of British and American production of ethylene went to ethyl alcohol and ethylene oxide; this proportion is decreasing due to the growth of new products, such as the polyethylenes.

---

[1] Holroyd, *Chem. Age*, June 20, 1953, p. 927.

The principal non-petroleum routes to ethyl alcohol are by fermentation of molasses, a waste vegetable product, or of sulphite liquor from the paper industry. Similarly, there is a non-petroleum route to ethylene glycol, from coal via methyl alcohol and formaldehyde (operated only in the United States). Ethyl chloride is made from ethyl alcohol and from ethane, as well as from ethylene. Vinyl chloride is normally made from acetylene, essentially a product from coal, but in the United States about half their 1954 production was made from ethylene.

There are two routes to ethyl alcohol from ethylene, by hydration with sulphuric acid and by direct hydration; the second route may have the advantage except where there are outlets for by-product dilute sulphuric acid. The main chemical outlets for ethyl alcohol are for acetaldehyde, acetic acid and acetic anhydride, and for *n*-butyl alcohol. Acetaldehyde and acetic acid are also manufactured from acetylene and by direct oxidation of propane and butane. Another route to acetic anhydride starts with propylene from petroleum, via acetone. *n*-Butyl alcohol is now being made from propylene by the Oxo reaction. These alternatives have not retarded the expansion of synthetic ethyl alcohol. Before the war, in the United States only 10 per cent of its ethyl alcohol was made from ethylene; in 1956, the proportion was over 70 per cent. In the United Kingdom no ethyl alcohol was made from ethylene before the war; in 1956 the proportion was 33–40 per cent and new plant has been installed to increase the proportion to 60–70 per cent.

Ethylene oxide is another derivative where there are two approximately balanced competing routes. The original chlorhydrin process gives high yields and can be operated economically in relatively small units but requires large tonnages of the heavy inorganic chemicals, chlorine and lime. The direct oxidation process uses only ethylene and air; the yield is lower and the capital cost is higher than in the chlorhydrin route. The tendency throughout the world seems to be to adopt the direct oxidation route. This may be due to the fact that chlorine manufacture involves disposal of an equivalent of caustic soda, for which a profitable market must be found; even so, in 1954, about 60 per cent of American ethylene oxide was still being made by the chlorhydrin route.

The principal outlet for ethylene oxide is for ethylene glycol, used as a permanent anti-freeze. The market depends on the number of motor cars a head, their size, and the winter weather. These factors favour the United States. Besides glycol, ethylene oxide has a number of other miscellaneous uses, the sum total of which is impressive. These include glycol ethers, ethanolamines, non-ionic detergents, synthetic lubricating oils and acrylonitrile. With the exception of acrylonitrile, which is also made from acetylene, ethylene oxide has to be used for their manufacture.

Ethyl chloride is used almost wholly for tetraethyl lead; styrene is used in the synthetic rubber and plastics fields. Polyethylene is now one of the most important plastics; with the development of new uses for the original polymer and the discovery of new types of polymer, polyethylene may require in the near future as much ethylene as either ethyl alcohol or ethylene oxide.

Propylene is used for acetone, dodecene, *n*-butyl alcohol, glycerol and propylene oxide. Acetone is still the major outlet for propylene; it is used in solvents, for making plastics and for acetic anhydride. Dodecene (propylene tetramer) is the intermediate for the most widely used synthetic detergent, sodium dodecylbenzene sulphonate, an outlet in which there is competition with many other petroleum derived products. *n*-Butyl alcohol is still made by fermentation and from synthetic ethyl alcohol. It is used in the solvent and plasticiser industries. Glycerol is a particularly interesting case. The synthesis of glycerol from propylene via allyl chloride was worked out before the war, but was not established until 1949, when another development of the petroleum chemicals industry, synthetic detergents, affected soap production so seriously as to be one of the main factors threatening a world shortage of glycerol. Glycerol is an inevitable by-product of making soap. It finds many outlets but it is naturally difficult to match consumption and production which used to be fixed by how much soap is made. Glycerol has therefore passed through cyclical phases of feast or famine. Its minimum price from soap is the cost of concentrating it from the lyes obtained in making soap. The maximum price is the level at which it pays the consuming industries to use substitutes. Glycerol is used in a wide range of industries and its use has expanded and will continue to expand at about the same rate as the chemical industry itself. Similarly, soap production could be expected to increase with increasing population and increasing standards of living. This double growth factor was disrupted by the advent of synthetic detergents after the war. Instead of soap usage increasing at the rate of 10 per cent per annum, it has tended to decrease since about 1948. The threat to glycerol supplies was obviated by synthetic glycerol, which by 1956 supplied 40 per cent of America's requirements and 20 per cent of the world's supply. There has been a further development since then; a second route to synthetic glycerol from propylene has been worked out using air as the only other raw material, eliminating the need for making chlorine.

Propylene oxide is made by the chlorhydrin route as in the original ethylene oxide process. Its outlets are similar to those of ethylene oxide, but the market is smaller in the United States; it is about one-fifth that of ethylene oxide.

Outlets for C_4 olefins are dominated by butadiene. A limited amount of butadiene is available in the C_4 fraction obtained by cracking liquid hydrocarbons for ethylene, and can be extracted cheaply because of its high concentration. This was the source of the first butadiene used for synthetic rubber in the United States in 1941–2 and is being used for the British pilot ventures. Where more butadiene is wanted than is available as a by-product, it is made by dehydrogenation of *n*-butenes. The one-stage process from *n*-butane is essentially the same as the butene process and could be used where relative availability would make it the cheaper starting material. Alternative routes to butadiene are from acetylene, used in Germany up to 1945, and from ethyl alcohol, used in the United States for most of the butadiene for synthetic rubber during the war. It is considered that under normal conditions the route from petroleum *n*-butenes is the cheapest. The other chemical outlet for *n*-butenes is for the solvents, *sec*-butyl alcohol and methyl ethyl ketone. Isobutene is used for making Butyl rubber, for polyisobutenes, and for diisobutene, an intermediate for detergents.

The lower saturated hydrocarbon gases are used as starting materials for chemical synthesis only where they are available in surplus quantity at less than fuel value and where they can be used where they are produced. Under these conditions, methane, the principal constituent of natural gas, is the chosen route to ammonia, to methyl alcohol, and under certain conditions, to acetylene. It has opened to petroleum chemicals the field of heavy inorganic chemicals, and is an alternative to the use of coal on which these manufacturers were built up in Western Europe. Already in the United States and Canada, ammonia and methyl alcohol are now made mainly from natural gas methane.

In the United States, in 1954, 86 per cent of its production of synthetic ammonia was made from natural gas, 10 per cent from coke and 4 per cent from by-product hydrogen. Similarly with methyl alcohol, 82 per cent was made from natural gas, 7 per cent from oxidation of propane and butane, 10 per cent from coke, and 1 per cent was non-synthetic. Synthetic methyl alcohol was the principal source of formalin, but 25 per cent of America's formalin was obtained directly from a second petroleum source, the oxidation of propane and butane.[2]

Italy is following suit; and underdeveloped countries which are predominantly agricultural and which are fortunate in possessing reserves of natural gas are using it for synthetic ammonia for fertilisers. In other cases, the shift in Great Britain to residual fuel oil instead of coal for synthetic ammonia will be a forerunner of similar developments here and elsewhere.

Acetylene is made from methane by the partial combustion process in which it is produced as a co-product of gases valuable for synthesis of ammonia and methyl alcohol. The value given to acetylene depends upon whether it or the ammonia is regarded as the premium product; the partial combustion process is always operated in conjunction with plants which use the other gases for chemical synthesis. This process is used in the United States, in Italy and in Germany; even in the United States acetylene from methane represents only 10 per cent of the total acetylene made

---

[2] *Chem. Eng.*, Sept. 1955, p. 266.

there; and the acetylene process is operated only in Texas and Louisiana, which have a unique combination of favourable factors.

The second chemical outlet for the gaseous paraffin gases, other than as feedstock for making ethylene, is air oxidation to a range of C_1, C_2 and C_3 oxygen containing compounds which are also made from methane, ethylene and propylene.

Aromatics are made from petroleum only when the normal source in industrial countries, from coal tar obtained as a by-product of coal carbonisation for town's gas or for the steel industry, is inadequate. This is the position in the United States. Toluene and the xylenes were made from petroleum during and since the war, in amounts greater than from coal carbonisation. Most of the C_7 and C_8 aromatics are used in aviation fuel and the solvent industry. Benzene from petroleum in the United States is more recent and the first important plants were post-war. The chemical industry in America outran the supplies of by-product benzene, and there was a benzene deficit too big to be met by importing from England or Western Europe.

Benzene is more expensive to obtain from petroleum than toluene and xylene. The ratio of C_6 aromatic + naphthene to C_7 and C_8, in naphthenic crudes, is about 1 : 3 : 3, so that in processing a given weight of crude, the recovery of benzene is less, the concentration is lower and the isolation is more expensive. Whilst petroleum toluene and xylene sell at the same price as coal by-product material, petroleum benzene commands a considerable premium over by-product benzene. On the other hand, in Great Britain and Western Europe, the potential production of coal tar benzene is 2·5 times the 1955 consumption for chemicals, so there is no incentive to make it from petroleum. There is at present enough toluene for chemicals but the position on xylene is different. Coal tar contains little xylene; the ratio of benzene, toluene and xylene in British coke oven tar, which is highly aromatic, is 1 : 0.23 : 0.05. Without petroleum xylene, development of the major new petroleum chemical, the synthetic fibre Terylene, might have been hampered.

The principal chemical outlets for benzene are for styrene, phenol and nylon. Toluene is used for dyestuffs intermediates, saccharin and explosives, and the xylenes for phthalic anhydride and Terylene.

Sulphur and carbon black are the largest of the miscellaneous products from petroleum. 5·4 per cent of American and 7 per cent of British consumption of sulphur is now recovered from petroleum and natural gas.

3. End-products of the petroleum chemicals industry

Production of the various classes of synthetic organic chemicals in the United States in 1955[3] gives a picture of the principal outlets for petroleum chemicals.

---

[3] U.S. Tariff Commission, Census of Production of Synthetic Organic Chemicals.

Industry	Total long tons
Flavour and perfumery chemicals . . .	19,000
Lakes and toners	20,000
Medicinals	35,000
Dyestuffs	76,000
Rubber chemicals	79,000
Plasticisers	177,000
Pesticides and other synthetic organic chemicals	226,000
Synthetic detergents and surface active agents .	515,000
Synthetic rubbers	990,000
Plastics and resins	1,670,000

The first seven industries are based primarily on coal tar. They are the chemicals used as catalysts or assistants in making the final article and are employed as a small percentage by weight on the finished product (strictly, plasticisers are an exception as they are frequently used in considerable proportions; their main outlets are directly geared to the plastics industry). In the next three, the chemical is the principal part by weight on the finished product. It is in these fields that expansion leads to a great increase in demand for chemicals and it is here that petroleum as an ample and almost unlimited source of raw materials is mainly used in the chemical industry. To these three must be added the synthetic fibre industry which is not separately classified by the source of statistics used.

(a) SYNTHETIC DETERGENTS

The principal synthetic detergents are the sodium dodecylbenzene sulphonate type, based on propylene tetramer, and (in the United Kingdom and Western Europe) the secondary alkyl sulphate type based on cracking waxy distillates. There are a considerable range of other detergents such as the non-ionic polyethylene oxide ethers and esters and the sulphates of fatty alcohols, which are partly based on petroleum and partly on vegetable matter.

This field is essentially a post war growth. In the United States in 1955, the production of synthetic detergents and surface active agents was about 460,000 tons; of the total detergent market (*i.e.*, soap plus synthetics), the synthetics held 60 per cent. In Great Britain, the position is similar; synthetics hold 40 per cent of the detergent market, production corresponding to about 45,000 tons on a 100 per cent basis; to this tonnage must be added the output of surface active agents used other than in the detergent industry.

Of the different types of synthetic detergent used in the United Kingdom, alkylaryl sulphonates represent 77 per cent (90 per cent of these are based on dodecylbenzene), 15 per cent are secondary alkyl sulphates and 7 per cent nonionics.[4]

The rapid growth of synthetic detergents has led to speeding up the de-rationing of soap and edible fats, to keeping down the cost of edible fats,

---

[4] *Chem. Trade J.*, 22 February, 1957, p. 432.

and to stimulating the manufacture of synthetic glycerol. In the United States, it has produced a large surplus of inedible fatty acids with the curious effect of bringing these acids back into the synthetic detergent market after chemical processing.[5]

(b) SYNTHETIC RUBBERS

This field has hitherto been in effect an American monopoly. Total production has fluctuated since the end of the war between 500,000 tons p.a. and 1,000,000 tons p.a. The main type, representing 70 per cent of all synthetic rubbers, is GR–S, a butadiene-styrene copolymer, of which butadiene and part of the styrene is petroleum based. The other principal types, Butyl and neoprene, account for 8–10 per cent each. Butyl, which is 98 per cent isobutene, 2 per cent isoprene, is entirely petroleum based. Neoprene is at present made from coal via acetylene. Polyisoprene, which will be wholly petroleum based, is still in the experimental stage.

As other countries take up synthetic rubber manufacture, they are almost forced to use petroleum as the source of butadiene, of ethylene (for styrene), of isobutene and of isoprene.

(c) PLASTICS AND RESINS

This field is divided into thermosetting resins and thermoplastics. Without reducing the growth rate of thermosetting resins, thermoplastics have increased and are increasing the faster, so that they are now the senior partner in this field.[6] Thermosetting resins are only incidentally an outlet for petroleum chemicals if phenol is made from petroleum benzene and urea, methyl alcohol or formaldehyde from natural gas.

It is in the faster growing section, the thermoplastics, that petroleum chemicals are most widely used. This field includes polyethylene, polyvinyl chloride and polystyrene, of which the first is wholly petroleum chemical, the second is partly petroleum chemical in the United States but not elsewhere, and the third is partly petroleum chemical. American production of these three thermoplastics alone in 1955 was about 750,000 tons. British capacity for these three resins, already over 100,000 tons p.a., is being expanded rapidly. In addition, there are a number of smaller fields where petroleum chemicals are used as in certain acyclic alkyds, epoxy resins, etc.

(d) SYNTHETIC FIBRES

This class includes both the modified natural polymers such as viscose and acetate rayon and the true synthetic fibres such as nylon, Terylene and Orlon.

Viscose does not use petroleum chemicals. Acetate rayon is a large consumer of acetic anhydride which in the United States and the United Kingdom is now largely a petroleum chemical. Approximately 1 ton of

---

[5] Goldstein, *Pet. Times*, Sept. 18, 1953, p. 920.
[6] Goldstein, *Plastics Institute Transactions*, April 1953, p. 18.

acetic anhydride is used per ton of cellulose acetate. 300,000 tons p.a. acetic anhydride are made in the United States and 50,000 tons p.a. in the United Kingdom. In the rest of the world, the acetic anhydride used is made from coal via acetylene or from fermentation ethyl alcohol.

The true synthetic fibres consume even more chemicals than the modified fibres, because they are built up from the simplest units. In America, nylon is made partly from coal, partly from petroleum and partly from vegetable matter. Petroleum cyclohexane is used for some of the adipic acid half for the nylon molecule and petroleum butadiene for some of the hexamethylene diamine, the other half of the nylon molecule. In the United Kingdom no petroleum chemicals are used for nylon. Terylene (Dacron in the United States) is made wholly from petroleum in both the United Kingdom and the United States. Petroleum p-xylene is the source of the terephthalic acid and petroleum ethylene of the ethylene glycol. Orlon and the other acrylonitrile fibres can be based either on ethylene or acetylene, and the acetylene could be made either from coal or petroleum. In the United States these fibres will be wholly based on petroleum; where the acetylene route is being used, the acetylene is obtained by partial combustion of methane from natural gas. The hydrocyanic acid is also being made from methane.

The scale of requirements is indicated by the facts that the butadiene route to hexamethylenediamine is operated in the United States on a scale adequate for 41,000 tons of nylon per annum; that planned American production of the equivalent of Terylene is 35,000 tons p.a. (the British figure is in excess of 10,000 tons p.a.) and that American production of acrylonitrile fibres in 1955 was 25,000 tons p.a.

4. Petroleum chemicals in individual countries

In including a section of the manufacturing position on petroleum chemicals anywhere in the world, it must be remembered that it is here that information becomes most rapidly out-of-date. We have aimed to give the position as it was known at the end of 1955 except in the case of Great Britain where the new schemes announced up to September, 1956, are included.

(*a*) UNITED STATES OF AMERICA

Statistical information on the American petroleum chemicals industry is based very largely on the United States Tariff Commission Census of Synthetic Organic Chemicals,[3] extracts from which are included in Appendix 4. These annual census reports are, for their purpose, probably the best Government statistics in the world. Because of the complexity of this section of the chemical industry, it is not safe to arrive at overall total outputs by addition, due to what is known as pyramiding or double counting, against which these reports include repeated provisos. There is a second and opposite risk in statistics which is much less frequent; occasionally production figures are too low, usually due to consumption within the reporting manufacturer.

Mainly because of the factor of pyramiding, it is possible only to estimate the actual production of chemicals from petroleum sold either to the rest of the chemical industry or to other industries.

The main outlet for petroleum chemicals is in aliphatic organic chemicals. Allowing for pyramiding, in 1952 the total American output of aliphatic chemicals was 4,200,000 tons, of which 67 per cent was petroleum chemicals. The recorded production was approximately double and the apparent proportion of petroleum chemicals was 80 per cent.

In 1954, the principal aliphatic petroleum chemicals with their sources and main outlets are summarised below:

TABLE 77

American aliphatic chemicals, 1954

Product	Tons p.a.	Source % petroleum	Main outlets
1. Ethylene	1,050,000	100	Ethyl alcohol and ethylene oxide
2. Propylene . . .	530,000	100	Isopropyl alcohol, dodecene, etc.
3. Ethyl alcohol, synthetic .	514,000	100	Acetaldehyde, solvents, etc.
4. Methyl alcohol . .	500,000	92	Formaldehyde and anti-freeze
5. Formaldehyde, 37% . .	460,000	over 90	Plastics
6. Isopropyl alcohol . . .	385,000	100	Acetone
7. Butadiene . . .	360,000	100	Synthetic rubber
8. Acetic anhydride .	308,000	over 80	Cellulose acetate
9. Ethylene glycol . .	284,000	about 80	Anti-freeze
10. Ethyl chloride . . .	244,000	nearly 100	Lead ethyl
11. Ethylene dichloride . .	202,000	100	Vinyl chloride, lead ethyl
12. Acetic acid, synthetic .	200,000	over 80	Plastics, solvents, etc.
13. Butyl alcohols (all) . .	182,000	about 75	Solvents, plasticisers
14. Acetone . . .	180,000	100	Plastics, solvents, etc.
15. Vinyl chloride . . .	175,000	50	Plastics
16. Dodecene (propylene tetramer)	140,000	100	Synthetic detergents

In 1952, the American petroleum chemicals industry produced 2,400,000 tons of inorganic chemicals, 7 per cent of all inorganics. This was comprised almost wholly of about 1,000,000 tons of ammonia, 720,000 tons of carbon black and 300,000 tons of sulphur. By 1954, ammonia from petroleum had increased to about 1,700,000 tons and sulphur to 350,000 tons.[7]

Petroleum aromatic chemicals in 1952 are given as 700,000 tons; they represented about 12 per cent of all American aromatic chemicals. Petroleum based benzene, 115,000 tons, was consumed wholly in the chemical industry. Of the 410,000 tons of toluene and xylene made, only about 10 per cent went into chemicals.[8]

---

[7] *Chem. Week*, January 1, 1955, p. 77.
[8] Goldstein, *Pet. Times*, April 16, 1954, p. 377.

14

The total investment in the American petroleum chemicals industry in 1952 was nearly £900,000,000, of which between 75 per cent and 90 per cent was allocated to the aliphatic sector.

It is estimated that the outlets by value of petroleum chemicals in 1952 were approximately:

Outlets	% by value
Plastics and surface coatings . .	23
Synthetic rubber industry . .	20
Motor cars and aviation . . .	17
Synthetic fibres	15
Agriculture	11
Detergents	2
Miscellaneous	12
	100

The American petroleum chemicals industry is concentrated in Texas and Louisiana, but there has been a tendency to spread outwards, due partly to availability of raw materials on the main gas transmission lines and partly to the need to be near the markets.

From the list of petroleum chemical plants in the United States as at September, 1955,[9] it is possible to present a rough picture of the diversity of their industry. Omitting duplicates, plants closed down, and minor units, of the remaining 263 plants, about 90 were making aliphatic chemicals; aromatics (including phenol, etc.), ammonia and carbon black were each made in 40–50 plants, sulphur was made in over 30 plants, and butadiene and synthetic rubbers in about 30 plants. Several of these petroleum chemical plants were making more than one type of product.

On the forecasts in the Paley report, *Resources for Freedom*, the American petroleum chemicals industry can be expected to expand by 1975 by a factor of 5–10 over 1950, or about 5 over 1954.[10] The principal products are listed below:

TABLE 78

Forward estimates, the United States petroleum chemicals industry

Products	1975 forecast	1954 actual	1950 actual	Increase over 1950	Increase over 1954
	millions tons p.a.			growth rate	
1. *Intermediates*—					
Ethylene . . .	3·0–4·6	1·1	0·75	4–6	2·5–4
Propylene .	1·6	0·5	0·4	4	3
C₄ hydrocarbons .	2·1	—	0·5	4	—
Styrene . .	1·8	0·3	0·25	7	6
p-Xylene . . .	0·3	0·03	—	50	10
Phenol . .	1·25	0·19	0·14	9	7
Acrylonitrile .	0·45	0·03	—	—	15
2. *End uses*—					
Plastics . .	10	1·25	1	10	8
Synthetic rubbers .	2·5	0·65	0·5	5	3·5
True synthetic fibres .	1·8	—	0·07	25	—

[9] *Pet. Proc.*, 1955, **10**, 1413.
[10] Goldstein, *Chem. and Ind.*, Aug. 10, 1953, p. S24.

(b) WESTERN EUROPE

By the middle of 1954, total investment in petroleum chemical plants in Western Europe amounted to nearly £100,000,000, and the combined throughput of liquid and gas feedstocks was about 1,000,000 tons.[11] The United Kingdom had invested 40 per cent of the capital and the throughput was 65 per cent of the European total.

By the end of 1955, investment had increased to £110 million, and in the calendar year, 1955, the total throughout of liquid and gas feedstocks was nearly 1,500,000 tons. Plans for expansion envisage by the end of 1958 additional capital investment of £160 million, and an increase in capacity of 110 per cent by weight; an important part of this expansion will be played by synthetic rubber plants, for which an additional total capacity of 185,000 tons is planned.[12]

(i) The United Kingdom

Aside from some smaller plants, the British petroleum chemicals industry was started on a substantial scale after the war and was concentrated in some six or seven plants. The present and pending plants are shown in Table 79[13], p. 403.

The principal expansions announced by September, 1956, due for completion between 1956 and 1959 were:

(a) *I.C.I., Wilton and Billingham.* Tripling ethylene capacity to over 100,000 tons p.a., mainly for polyethylene.

Production of butadiene and 10,000 tons p.a. butadiene co-polymers. Enlargement of Oxo alcohols plant to 40,000 tons p.a. Manufacture of 60,000 tons p.a. ammonia from residual fuel oil.

(b) *Shell Chemical Co.* 25,000 tons p.a. direct ethylene oxide (by Shell process), with additional ethylene capacity and production of propylene oxide and derivatives from existing chlorhydrin plant (Petrochemicals, Ltd., at Partingdon).

75,000 tons p.a. ammonia from refinery tail gas (Shellhaven), 60,000 tons p.a. to be used by Fisons for fertilisers, remainder for nitric acid.

30,000 tons p.a. dodecylbenzene from petroleum dodecene (Shellhaven).

1,000 tons p.a. low pressure (Ziegler) polyethylene.

(c) *Esso Petroleum Co.* (Fawley, near Southampton). New olefin plant by cracking liquid feedstack. Ethylene for 10,000 tons p.a. polyethylene (Monsanto). Butadiene for 55,000 tons p.a. synthetic rubber (International Synthetic Rubber Corporation). Acrylonitrile (Monsanto).

(d) *British Hydrocarbon Chemicals, Ltd.* (Grangemouth). Enlargement of cracking plant. Synthetic ethyl alcohol doubled. Enlargement of styrene

---

[11] 'The Chemical Industry in Europe', 1954, *O.E.E.C.*, Paris.
[12] 'The Chemical Industry in Europe', October 1956, *O.E.E.C.*, Paris.
[13] Goldstein. *Institute of Petroleum Review*, January 1957, p. 4.

plant to over 30,000 tons p.a. (Forth Chemicals, Ltd.). 12,000 tons p.a. polyethylene (Union Carbide). 10,000 tons p.a. low pressure (Phillips) polyethylene. Propylene tetramer for 10,000 tons p.a., dodecylbenzene (Grange Chemicals, Ltd.). Butadiene for specialist synthetic rubbers.

The bulk of petroleum chemicals goes or will go into plastics, synthetic detergents, solvents, paints, the motor car industry, synthetic rubber and synthetic fibres.

By the end of 1958, the planned capacity will be, very approximately:

Product	Capacity tons p.a.
Ethylene	250,000
Ethyl alcohol (synthetic)	75,000
Ethylene oxide and derivatives	75,000
Ethyl chloride and ethylene dichloride	25,000
Polyethylene	125,000
Styrene	(at least) 40,000
Isopropyl alcohol, acetone, etc.	75,000 to 100,000
C$_4$ Solvents	20,000
Higher Oxo alcohols	30,000
Butadiene	50,000
GR-S and specialty synthetic rubbers	70,000
Dodecylbenzene	(at least) 40,000

In addition, there will be 135,000 tons p.a. ammonia from petroleum, 40,000 tons p.a. by-product sulphur and 75,000–100,000 tons p.a. carbon black.

Between 1948 and 1953, about £40–50 million had been spent in the United Kingdom. By 1959 a further £65–75 million is scheduled for expenditure. Great Britain is now in the second phase of the building up of its petroleum chemicals industry and is keeping its lead over other European countries, which are still in their first phase.

Up to 1953, the expenditure on petroleum chemicals was 20 per cent of the post-war development expenditure of the whole of the British chemical industry. By the end of 1958, the share will have risen to about 25 per cent.

The proportion contributed by petroleum chemicals in Great Britain to industrial organic chemicals was about 33 per cent in 1955. It is likely to approach 67–75 per cent within the next ten years. Most of these petroleum chemicals are aliphatic. Aromatic chemicals are represented by Petrochemicals Ltd's output by the Catarole process, by styrene and by *p*-xylene and terephthalic acid for Terylene. The proportion is a few per cent of that of aromatic chemicals from coal. Inorganic chemicals are or will be represented by a combined total of 250,000–275,000 tons p.a. ammonia, sulphur and carbon black.

(ii) France

The French petroleum chemical plants are shown in Table 80.

United Kingdom Petroleum chemicals industry. Principal plants and products (existing and announced)

Name of company	Location	Operation	C₂'s	C₃'s	C₄'s	Other
British Celanese Ltd.	Spondon, nr. Derby	Cracking liquid feedstock	Ethyl alcohol	Isopropyl alcohol, acetone	—	—
British Hydrocarbon Chemicals Ltd. (Distillers and British Petroleum Co. Ltd.)	Grangemouth	Cracking liquid feedstock	Ethyl alcohol Styrene* Polyethylene†	Isopropyl alcohol Propylene tetramer Dodecyl-benzene‡	Butadiene	—
Imperial Chemical Industries Ltd.	Wilton	Cracking liquid feedstock	Polyethylene, ethylene oxide, ethylene glycol	Isopropyl alcohol and acetone Butyl alcohols	Butadiene	p-Xylene, Terephthalic acid. Medium chain Oxo alcohols
Imperial Chemical Industries Ltd.	Billingham	Gasification of fuel oil	—	—	—	Ammonia
Shell Chemical Manufacturing Co. Ltd.	Stanlow	Refinery gases	Ethyl chloride§ (from ethylene and ethane)	Isopropyl alcohol, acetone and acetone alcohols	sec-Butyl alcohol Methyl ethyl ketone	Detergents from wax cracking, sulphur
Shell Chemical Manufacturing Co. Ltd. (Petrochemicals Ltd.)	Partington, nr. Manchester	Cracking liquid feedstocks	Ethylene oxide, ethylene glycol, glycol ethers, ethanolamines Polyethylene	Isopropyl alcohol, propylene oxide	—	Aromatic hydrocarbons
Shell Chemical Manufacturing Co. Ltd.	Shellhaven, Thames	Refinery tail-gases	—	Dodecylbenzene	—	Ammonia, nitric acid
Esso Standard Oil Co.	Fawley, Southampton	Cracking liquid feedstock	Polyethylene‖	—	Butadiene for synthetic rubber¶‖	Sulphur, acrylonitrile‖

Note:

* Made by Forth Chemicals Ltd. (British Hydrocarbon Chemicals and Monsanto).
† To be made by Union Carbide Ltd.
‡ Made by Grange Chemicals Ltd. (British Hydrocarbon Chemicals and Oronite – Standard Oil of California).
§ Made by Associated Ethyl Corporation Ltd., Ellesmere Port.
‖ To be made by Monsanto.
¶ To be made by International Synthetic Rubber Corporation Ltd.

TABLE 80

French petroleum chemical plants

Name	Location	C₂'s	C₃'s	C₄'s	Others
Shell-St. Gobain .	Petit Couronne and Berre l'Etang	—	Isopropyl alcohol, acetone, etc.	—	Detergents from wax distillates
Napthachimie .	l'Avera	Ethylene oxide and derivatives	Isopropyl alcohol, acetone, etc.	—	—
Standard-Kuhlmann	l'Estaque	—	Dodecylbenzene	—	—
Rhône-Poulenc .	Péage de Rousillon	—	Acetone	—	Phenol
Atlantique-Progil .	Pont de Claix	—	Acetone	—	Phenol
S.I. des Dérivés d'Acétylène (Ugine)	La Chambre	—	Acetone and acetone solvents	—	—

New plant in the next three years will increase the 1954 investment of £16 million by £47 million. The principal new projects will be the manufacture of 40,000 tons p.a. G.R-S. and of 20,000 tons p.a. Butyl rubber from refinery isobutene; other projects are for polyethylene and for ethylene oxide and derivatives.

(iii) West Germany

The main petroleum chemical plants in 1955 were:

(a) *Hüls.* C_1, C_2 and C_3 derivatives from natural gas, C_2—C_4 gases from hydrogenation and oil refineries.

(b) *Rheinpreussen.* Isopropyl alcohol, *sec*-butyl alcohol and methyl ethyl ketone from refinery gases.

(c) *Phenol-Chemie.* Phenol and acetone from cumene.

(d) *Rheinische Olefinwerke* (Badische and Shell). Polyethylene and ethylbenzene from refinery ethylene.

(e) *Hoechst.* Chlorinated methanes from natural gas.

At the end of 1954, capital investment in petroleum chemical plants was £25 million. £9 million was spent in 1955, and a further £32 million is scheduled for expenditure by the end of 1958. Important projects are 45,000 tons p.a. GR-S synthetic rubber (Huls) and low pressure polyethylene (Hoechst and Kohle-Oel Chemie).

(iv) Italy

The petroleum chemical plants in operation in 1954 were those of Montecatini and S.I.S.A.S., in North Italy, making the usual range of C_2, C_3 and C_4 chemicals. In addition, Montecatini make synthetic ammonia, methyl alcohol and acetylene from natural gas.

The capital expenditure of £15 million is to be increased to £45 million due in part to a 30,000 ton p.a. synthetic rubber plant based on natural gas and in part to expansion of existing chemicals from natural gas. By 1957, Italy is expecting to use over 300,000 tons p.a. natural gas for chemicals.

TABLE 81

Petroleum-chemical plants in Canada

Plant number	Company and plant location	Hydrocarbon raw materials	Petrochemical products
1	B. A. Shawinigan Ltd., Montreal, Quebec	Cumene	Phenol, acetone, acetophenone, mesityl oxide, α-methylstyrene
2	British American Oil Co., Montreal, Quebec	Refinery gases	Cumene
3	Cabot Carbon Co. of Canada Ltd., Sarnia, Ontario	Petroleum fractions	Oil furnace blacks
4	Canadian Chemical Co. Ltd., Edmonton, Alberta	Refinery gases, L.P.G.	Formaldehyde, acetaldehyde, propionaldehyde, acrolein, propylene oxide, methanol, acetone, acetic acid, n-propanol, propylene glycol, dipropylene glycol, and mixtures of heavier aldehydes, oxides, alcohols and ketones; pentaerythritol
5	Canadian Industries Ltd., Edmonton, Alberta	Natural gas	Polyethylene
6	Canadian Industries Ltd., Kingston, Ont.	Naphtha	Ammonia
7	Consolidated Mining and Smelting Co. of Canada Ltd., Calgary, Alberta	Natural gas	Ammonia, ammonium nitrate
8	du Pont of Canada Ltd., Maitland, Ontario	Cyclohexane	Hexamethylene diamine and adipic acid
9	Dow Chemical Co. of Canada, Sarnia, Ontario	Refinery gases	Ethylene, ethylene oxide, ethylene glycol, styrene, polystyrene, carbon tetrachloride and other organic chemicals
10	Lubrizol of Canada Ltd., Niagara Falls, Ontario	Petroleum fractions	Lubricating oil additives
11	Polymer Corpn. Ltd., Sarnia, Ontario	Refinery gas	Ethylene, butadiene, styrene, GR-S and butyl synthetic rubbers, other petroleum chemicals
12	Royalite Oil Co. Ltd., Turner Valley, Calgary, Alberta	Natural gas	Sulphur
13	Shell Oil Co. of Canada Ltd., Montreal, Quebec	Refinery gases	Isopropyl alcohol, acetone
14	Shell Oil of Canada Ltd., Jumping Pound, Alberta,	Natural gas	Sulphur
15	Sherritt Gordon Mines, Fort Saskatchewan, Alberta	Natural gas	Ammonia
16	S. Nord Chemical Co., Petrolia, Ont.	Refinery Platformer	Aromatic hydrocarbons
17	Union Carbide Canada, Montreal, Quebec	Ethane, ethylene	Ethylene oxide, ethylene glycol, diethylene glycol, ethylene dichloride, dichloroethyl ether
18	Vosco Industrial Chemical Products Ltd., Montreal, Quebec	Natural gas	Dodecylbenzene and detergents

(v) *Low Countries*

Holland has plants for manufacture of detergents from wax distillates and C_3 solvents from refinery propylene. Investment was £3·5 million. Plants for making intermediates for epoxy resins and detergents and for manufacture of synthetic glycerol, both from refinery propylene, are being built.

Belgium has plans well advanced for making phenol and acetone by the cumene process and ethylene oxide and its derivatives by direct oxidation, both from refinery gases; the capital cost is about £4 million.

(vi) *Denmark*

Denmark is completing a plant to make synthetic ethyl alcohol from refinery gas ethylene.

(c) CANADA

The Canadian petroleum chemicals industry was started during the war for the manufacture of synthetic rubber at Sarnia, Ont. The industry has now expanded and uses all types of raw materials—natural gas, refinery gases, liquid petroleum fractions and special fractions. The position is shown in Table 81.[14]

The capital investment in these plants is over £70,000,000; the total capacity is about 250,000 tons of products.

(d) REST OF THE WORLD

Plants approaching completion include synthetic ammonia for fertilisers from natural gas or refinery gases in Israel, Pakistan and Saudi Arabia, and benzene, toluene, xylene and carbon black from petroleum in Australia. Compared with those countries which are already established in this industry, the combined total capacity being installed is very small.

Other countries for which definite plans have been announced are Japan,[15] Venezuela, Cuba and Brazil.

---

[14] *Pet. Proc.*, 1953, **8,** 713; The Canadian Petrochemical Industry, *Ryerson Press*, Toronto, 1956.

[15] Collingwood, Mackintosh and Steiner, *Pet. Times*, 15 February, 1957, p. 146.

APPENDIX 1

BOILING POINTS OF HYDROCARBONS

Paraffins

NAME	ALTERNATIVE NAME	FORMULA	BOILING POINT AT 760 MM. °C.
Methane	—	CH_4	$-161\cdot5$
Ethane	—	C_2H_6	$-88\cdot6$
Propane	—	C_3H_8	$-42\cdot1$
n-Butane	—	C_4H_{10}	$-0\cdot5$
2-Methylpropane	Isobutane	do.	$-11\cdot7$
n-Pentane	—	C_5H_{12}	$36\cdot1$
2-Methylbutane	Isopentane	do.	$27\cdot9$
2 : 2-Dimethylpropane	Neopentane	do.	$9\cdot5$
n-Hexane	—	C_6H_{14}	$68\cdot7$
2-Methylpentane	Isohexane	do.	$60\cdot3$
3-Methylpentane	Isohexane	do.	$63\cdot3$
2 : 2-Dimethylbutane	—	do.	$49\cdot7$
2 : 3-Dimethylbutane	—	do.	$58\cdot0$
n-Heptane	—	C_7H_{16}	$98\cdot4$
2-Methylhexane	—	do.	$90\cdot1$
3-Methylhexane	—	do.	$91\cdot9$
3-Ethylpentane	—	do.	$93\cdot5$
2 : 2-Dimethylpentane	—	do.	$79\cdot2$
2 : 3-Dimethylpentane	—	do.	$89\cdot8$
2 : 4-Dimethylpentane	—	do.	$80\cdot5$
3 : 3-Dimethylpentane	—	do.	$86\cdot1$
2 : 2 : 3-Trimethylbutane	Triptane	do.	$80\cdot9$
n-Octane	—	C_8H_{18}	$125\cdot7$
2-Methylheptane	—	do.	$117\cdot6$
3-Methylheptane	—	do.	$118\cdot9$
4-Methylheptane	—	do.	$117\cdot7$
3-Ethylhexane	—	do.	$118\cdot5$
2 : 2-Dimethylhexane	—	do.	$106\cdot8$
2 : 3-Dimethylhexane	—	do.	$115\cdot6$
2 : 4-Dimethylhexane	—	do.	$109\cdot4$
2 : 5-Dimethylhexane	—	do.	$109\cdot1$
3 : 3-Dimethylhexane	—	do.	$112\cdot0$
3 : 4-Dimethylhexane	—	do.	$117\cdot7$
2-Methyl-3-ethylpentane	—	do.	$115\cdot7$

Name	Alternative Name	Formula	Boiling point at 760 mm. °c.
3-Methyl-3-ethylpentane	—	C_8H_{18}	118·3
2 : 2 : 3-Trimethylpentane	—	do.	109·8
2 : 2 : 4-Trimethylpentane	Isooctane	do.	99·2
2 : 3 : 3-Trimethylpentane	—	do.	114·8
2 : 3 : 4-Trimethylpentane	—	do.	113·5
2 : 2 : 3 : 3-Tetramethylbutane	—	do.	106·5
n-Nonane	—	C_9H_{20}	150·8
n-Decane	—	$C_{10}H_{22}$	174·1
n-Undecane	—	$C_{11}H_{24}$	195·9
n-Dodecane	—	$C_{12}H_{26}$	216·3
n-Eicosane	—	$C_{20}H_{42}$	342·7
n-Triacontane	—	$C_{30}H_{62}$	446·4
n-Tetracontane	—	$C_{40}H_{82}$	520

2. Naphthenes

Name	Alternative Name	Formula	Boiling point at 760 mm. °c.
Cyclopentane	—	C_5H_{10}	49·3
Cyclohexane	—	C_6H_{12}	80·7
Methylcyclopentane	—	do.	71·8
Methylcyclohexane	—	C_7H_{14}	100·9
Ethylcyclopentane	—	do.	103·5
1 : 1-Dimethylcyclopentane	—	do.	87·8
cis-1 : 2-Dimethylcyclopentane	—	do.	99·5
trans-1 : 2-Dimethylcyclopentane	—	do.	91·9
cis-1 : 3-Dimethylcyclopentane	—	do.	91·7
trans-1 : 3-Dimethylcyclopentane	—	do.	90·8
Ethylcyclohexane	—	C_8H_{16}	131·8
1 : 1-Dimethylcyclohexane	—	do.	119·5
cis-1 : 2-Dimethylcyclohexane	—	do.	129·7
trans-1 : 2-Dimethylcyclohexane	—	do.	123·4
cis-1 : 3-Dimethylcyclohexane	—	do.	120·1
trans-1 : 3-Dimethylcyclohexane	—	do.	124·5
cis-1 : 4-Dimethylcyclohexane	—	do.	124·3
trans-1 : 4-Dimethylcyclohexane	—	do.	119·4
n-Propylcyclopentane	—	do.	130·9
Isopropylcyclopentane	—	do.	126·4
1-Methyl-1-ethylcyclopentane	—	do.	121·5
cis-1-Methyl-2-ethylcyclopentane	—	do.	128·0
trans-1-Methyl-2-ethylcyclopentane	—	do.	121·2
cis-1-Methyl-3-ethylcyclopentane	—	do.	121·4
trans-1-Methyl-3-ethylcyclopentane	—	do.	120·8

Name	Alternative Name	Formula	Boiling Point at 760 mm. ° c.
1 : 1 : 2-Trimethylcyclopentane	—	C_8H_{16}	113·7
1 : 1 : 3-Trimethylcyclopentane	—	do.	104·9

3. Aromatics

Name	Alternative Name	Formula	Boiling Point
Benzene	—	C_6H_6	80·1
Toluene	—	C_7H_8	110·6
Ethylbenzene	—	C_8H_{10}	136·2
o-Xylene	—	do.	144·4
m-Xylene	—	do.	139·1
p-Xylene	—	do.	138·4
n-Propylbenzene	—	C_9H_{12}	159·2
Isopropylbenzene	Cumene	do.	152·4
o-Ethyltoluene	—	do.	165·2
m-Ethyltoluene	—	do.	161·3
p-Ethyltoluene	—	do.	162·0
1 : 2 : 3-Trimethylbenzene	—	do.	176·1
1 : 2 : 4-Trimethylbenzene	—	do.	169·4
1 : 3 : 5-Trimethylbenzene	Mesitylene	do.	164·7
n-Butylbenzene	—	$C_{10}H_{14}$	183·3
Isobutylbenzene	—	do.	172·8
sec-Butylbenzene	—	do.	173·3
tert-Butylbenzene	—	do.	169·1
1 : 2 : 3 : 4-Tetramethylbenzene	Prehnitene	do.	205·0
1 : 2 : 3 : 5-Tetramethylbenzene	Isodurene	do.	198·0
1 : 2 : 4 : 5-Tetramethylbenzene	Durene	do.	196·8

4. Olefins

Name	Alternative Name	Formula	Boiling Point
Ethylene	—	C_2H_4	− 103·7
Propylene	—	C_3H_6	− 47·7
1-Butene	—	C_4H_8	− 6·3
cis-2-Butene	—	do.	+ 3·7
trans-2-Butene	—	do.	+ 0·9
Isobutene	—	do.	− 6·9
1-Pentene	—	C_5H_{10}	21·0
cis-2-Pentene	—	do.	36·9
trans-2-Pentene	—	do.	36·4
2-Methyl-1-butene	—	do.	31·2
3-Methyl-1-butene	—	do.	20·1
2-Methyl-2-butene	—	do.	38·6
1-Hexene	—	C_6H_{12}	63·5

Name	Alternative Name	Formula	Boiling point at 760 mm.
			° c.
1-Heptene	—	C_7H_{14}	93·6
1-Octene	—	C_8H_{16}	121·3
1-Nonene	—	C_9H_{18}	146·9
1-Decene	—	$C_{10}H_{20}$	170·6
1-Eicosene	—	$C_{20}H_{40}$	341·2
1-Triacontene	—	$C_{30}H_{60}$	445
1-Tetracontene	—	$C_{40}H_{80}$	517

5. Diolefins

Name	Alternative Name	Formula	Boiling point at 760 mm.
1 : 2-Propadiene	Allene	C_3H_4	− 34·5
1 : 2-Butadiene	—	C_4H_6	+ 10·9
1 : 3-Butadiene	—	do.	− 4·4
1 : 2-Pentadiene	—	C_5H_8	+ 44·9
cis-1 : 3-Pentadiene	—	do.	44·1
trans-1 : 3-Pentadiene	—	do.	42·0
1 : 4-Pentadiene	—	do.	26·0
2 : 3-Pentadiene	—	do.	48·3
3-Methyl-1 : 2-butadiene	—	do.	40
2-Methyl-1 : 3-butadiene	Isoprene	do.	34·1
Cyclopentadiene	—	do.	42·5

6. Acetylenes

Name	Alternative Name	Formula	Boiling point at 760 mm.
Acetylene	—	C_2H_2	− 84
Methylacetylene	Propyne	C_3H_4	− 23·2
Monovinylacetylene	3-Butene-1-yne	C_4H_4	5
Ethylacetylene	1-Butyne	C_4H_6	8·1
Dimethylacetylene	2-Butyne	do.	27·0
Propylacetylene	1-Pentyne	C_5H_8	40·2
1-Methyl-2-ethylacetylene	2-Pentyne	do.	56·1
Isopropylacetylene	3-Methyl-1-butyne	do.	26·4
Butylacetylene	1-Hexyne	C_6H_{10}	71·3

7. Vinylbenzenes

Name	Alternative Name	Formula	Boiling point at 760 mm.
Styrene	Vinylbenzene	C_8H_8	145·2
1-Methylstyrene	Isopropenyl-benzene	C_9H_{10}	165·4
o-Methylstyrene	*o*-Vinyltoluene	do.	171
m-Methylstyrene	*m*-Vinyltoluene	do.	168
p-Methylstyrene	*p*-Vinyltoluene	do.	169

APPENDIX 2

ROUTES TO PETROLEUM CHEMICALS

This Appendix contains general charts showing the more important routes to petroleum chemicals; for comparison, the main routes to aliphatic chemicals from coal and from fermentation processes are included.

The charts are:

1. Manufacture of gases for chemicals by the cracking of oil.
2. Principal derivatives of acetylene.
3. Principal derivatives of ethylene.
4. Principal derivatives of propylene.
5. Principal routes to aliphatic chemicals from coal and from fermentation processes.

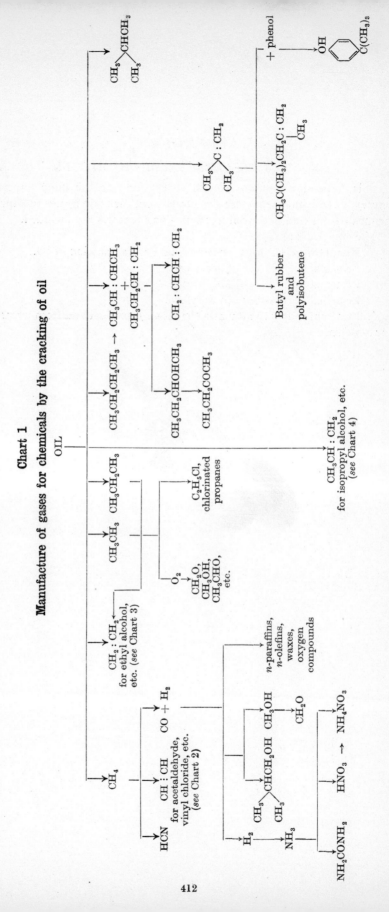

Chart 1

Manufacture of gases for chemicals by the cracking of oil

412

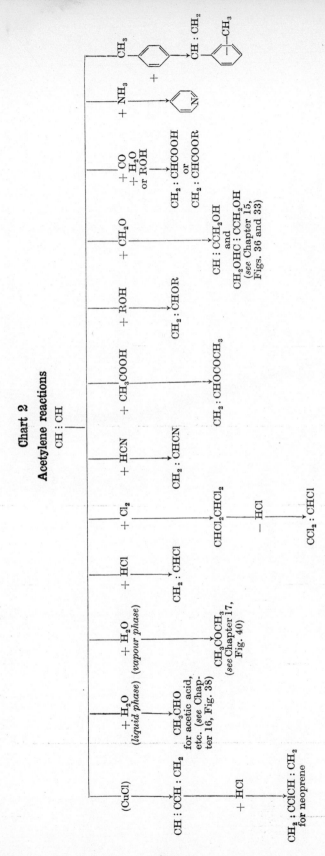

Chart 2

Acetylene reactions

CH : CH

Chart 3

Principal reactions of ethylene

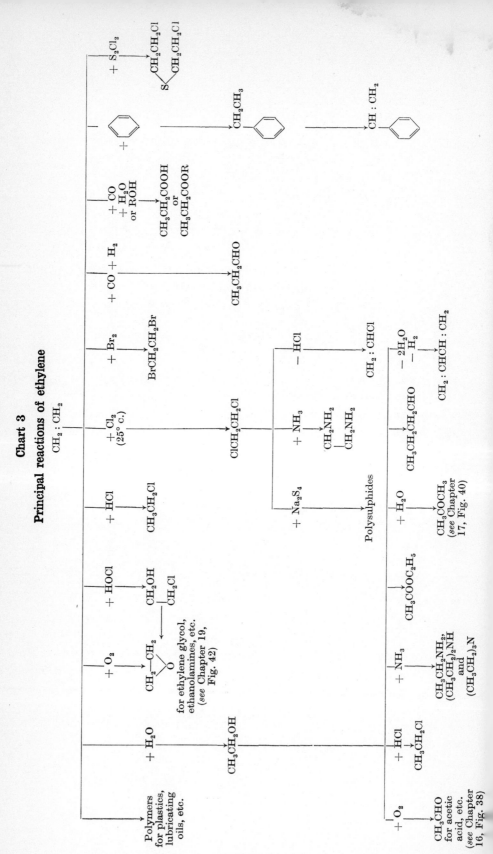

414

Chart 5

Principal routes to aliphatic chemicals from coal and from fermentation processes

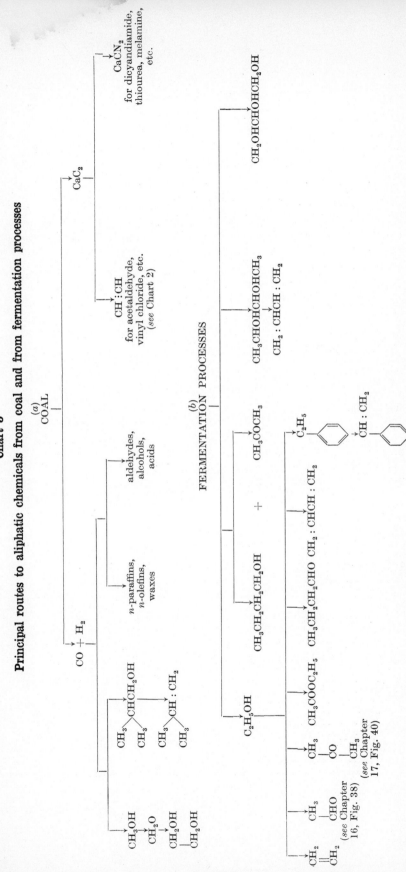

415

APPENDIX 3

STATISTICS OF PETROLEUM PRODUCTION AND CONSUMPTION

Tables 82–85 give useful conversion factors for petroleum products.

Table 86 (*a*) to (*c*) gives world production of petroleum over the period 1861–1955 itemised for individual countries. Table 87 gives a comparison of world oil, hydroelectric power, coal and natural gas production in 1953.

Data on the United Kingdom petroleum industry are given in Table 88 and the consumption of the different petroleum fractions in various countries in 1954 is given in Table 89.

TABLE 82

Conversion factors

(*a*) *Volume*

Unit	U.S. gal.	Imp. gal.	litre	U.S. bbl.	m.^{3}
1 U.S. gal. . .	1	0·833	3·785	0·0238	0·0038
1 Imp. gal. . .	1·201	1	4·546	0·0286	0·0045
1 litre . . .	0·264	0·220	1	0·0063	0·0010
1 U.S. bbl. . .	42·0	35·0	158·8	1	0·159
1 m.^{3} . . .	264·1	220·0	1,000·0	6·29	1

(*b*) *Weight*

Unit	lb.	short ton	metric ton	long ton
1 lb.	1	0·0005	0·00045	0·00044
1 short ton . .	2,000·0	1	0·9072	0·8929
1 metric ton . .	2,204·6	1·1023	1	0·9842
1 long ton . . .	2,240·0	1·1200	1·0161	1

TABLE 83

Crude oil—density of crudes from various countries†

Country	bbl./metric ton	bbl./long ton	lb./bbl.
U.S.A.	7·396	7·51	298
U.S.S.R.	7·290	7·40	302
Venezuela . . .	6·720	6·82	328
Roumania . . .	7·350	7·46	300
Iran	7·552	7·67	292
Iraq	7·481	7·60	295
Netherlands East Indies .	7·811	7·93	282

† Data averaged from Miller, U.S. Bureau of Mines, *International Petroleum Trade*, March 1939, p. 75, and March 1940, p. 128.

TABLE 84

Representative weights of oil products*

Product	U.S. gal./lb.	lb./U.S. gal.	Imp. gal./lb.	lb./Imp. gal.	bbl./ metric ton	metric ton/bbl.
Aviation petrol .	0·171	5·83	0·142	7·01	8·98	0·111
Motor petrol . .	0·162	6·17	0·135	7·41	8·51	0·117
Kerosene .	0·148	6·76	0·123	8·12	7·77	0·129
Gas oil, diesel oil, distillate fuel .	0·138	7·24	0·115	8·70	7·25	0·138
Residual fuel oil .	0·127	7·88	0·106	9·47	6·67	0·150
Lubricating oil .	0·133	7·51	0·111	9·02	6·99	0·143

* Based on data in 'Petroleum Facts and Figures', *American Petroleum Institute*, 7th Ed., 1941.

In America, the density of petroleum products is expressed in terms of A.P.I. gravities; this is a modified Baumé scale, related to specific gravity (60° F./60° F.) by the equation:

$$° \text{A.P.I.} = \frac{141 \cdot 5}{\text{S.G.}} - 131 \cdot 5$$

or

$$\text{S.G.} = \frac{141 \cdot 5}{° \text{A.P.I.} + 131 \cdot 5}$$

The following table† gives the conversion of ° A.P.I. into specific gravity and lb./U.S. gal.

TABLE 85

Conversion of ° A.P.I. against specific gravity

° A.P.I.	S.G.	lb./U.S. gal.
0	1·0760	8·962
5	1·0366	8·634
10	1·0000	8·328
15	0·9659	8·044
20	0·9340	7·778
25	0·9042	7·529
30	0·8762	7·296
35	0·8498	7·076
40	0·8251	6·870
45	0·8017	6·675
50	0·7796	6·490
55	0·7587	6·316
60	0·7389	6·151
65	0·7201	5·994
70	0·7022	5·845
75	0·6852	5·703
80	0·6690	5·568
85	0·6536	5·440
90	0·6388	5·316
95	0·6247	5·199
100	0·6112	5·086

† Condensed from Nelson, 'Petroleum Refinery Engineering', *McGraw Hill*, 1941.

TABLE 86

Production of crude petroleum

(a) Total world production, 1861–1956, in metric tons

Year	1861	1900	1920	1938	1945	1946	1947	1948
Production ('000 metric tons)	287	20,200	94,300	280,500	367,800	390,800	432,200	489,400
Year	1949	1950	1951	1952	1953	1954	1955	1956
Production ('000 metric tons)	485,800	538,300	608,900	640,380	677,600	708,700	795,270	868,900 (est.)

Authority: Petroleum Information Bureau.

TABLE 86 (continued)

(b) Crude oil production in principal producing countries

Country	1938	1946	1947	1948	1949	1950	1951	1952	1953	1954	1955
N. America—											
U.S.A.	170,700	248,200	269,200	293,200	269,800	285,200	324,600	332,300	343,600	338,300	362,720
Mexico	5,500	7,100	8,100	8,600	8,900	10,300	11,100	11,100	10,200	11,900	12,860
Canada	900	1,000	1,000	1,600	2,900	3,900	6,400	8,300	11,000	13,000	17,590
Total	177,100	256,300	278,300	303,400	281,600	299,400	342,100	351,700	364,800	363,200	393,170
S. America—											
Venezuela	28,100	56,700	62,500	70,600	68,500	78,100	89,400	94,900	92,600	99,400	113,210
Colombia	3,100	3,200	3,500	3,400	4,200	4,900	5,600	5,600	5,700	5,800	5,730
Trinidad	2,600	3,000	3,000	2,900	3,000	3,000	3,000	3,100	3,200	3,400	3,560
Rest of S. America	4,900	5,200	5,300	5,800	5,800	6,200	6,400	6,600	7,100	7,700	8,390
Total	38,700	68,100	74,300	82,700	81,500	92,200	104,400	110,200	108,600	116,300	130,890
Europe—											
U.S.S.R.	30,100	22,800	27,100	30,600	33,500	37,500	42,000	47,500	52,000	58,000	70,000
Roumania	6,900	4,400	3,900	4,100	4,100	4,000	4,000	4,000	6,000	7,000	8,000
Austria	60	800	900	900	1,300	1,600	2,100	3,000	3,000	3,000	3,670
Hungary	40	700	600	500	500	500	500	500	600	1,000	1,490
Germany	550	600	600	600	800	1,100	1,400	1,800	2,200	2,700	3,160
U.K.	negligible	60	50	40	50	50	50	60	60	60	60
Rest of Europe	650	440	650	1,060	1,250	1,750	1,550	1,840	2,140	2,840	2,960
Total	38,300	29,800	33,800	37,800	41,500	46,500	51,600	58,700	66,000	74,600	89,340

TABLE 86 (continued)

(b) Crude oil production in principal producing countries (continued)

Country	1938	1946	1947	1948	1949	1950	1951	1952	1953	1954	1955
Middle and Far East—											
Kuwait	—	800	2,200	6,400	12,400	17,300	28,200	37,600	43,300	47,700	54,760
Saudi Arabia	100	8,100	12,100	19,100	23,200	26,600	37,200	40,400	41,400	46,900	47,470
Iraq	4,400	4,700	4,800	3,500	4,200	6,600	8,700	18,900	28,200	30,700	33,700
Iran	10,400	19,500	20,500	25,300	27,200	32,300	16,800	1,000	1,000	3,000	16,160
Qatar	—	—	—	—	100	1,600	2,400	3,300	4,100	4,800	5,450
Bahrain	1,100	1,100	1,300	1,500	1,500	1,500	1,500	1,500	1,500	1,500	1,490
Indonesia	7,400	300	1,100	4,400	5,900	6,500	7,500	8,400	10,200	10,800	11,750
British Borneo	900	300	1,800	2,800	3,400	4,200	5,000	5,100	5,000	4,900	5,380
Egypt	200	1,300	1,300	1,900	2,300	2,400	2,400	2,400	2,400	2,000	1,830
Others	1,900	500	700	600	1,000	1,200	1,100	1,200	1,100	2,300	3,880
Total	26,400	36,600	45,800	65,500	81,200	100,200	110,800	119,800	138,200	154,600	181,870
WORLD TOTAL	280,500	390,800	432,200	489,400	485,800	538,300	608,900	630,400	677,600	708,700	795,270

Authority: Petroleum Information Bureau.

TABLE 86 (continued)

(c) Principal producing countries and their share of world production

Country	1861 Metric tons	1861 % of total	1900 Metric tons	1900 % of total	1920 Metric tons	1920 % of total	1938 Metric tons	1938 % of total	1952 Metric tons	1952 % of total	1953 Metric tons	1953 % of total	1954 Metric tons	1954 % of total	1955 Metric tons	1955 % of total
U.S.A.	285	99·3	8,500	42·0	59,060	62·7	170,700	60·9	332,300	51·9	343,600	50·7	338,300	47·7	362,720	45·7
Venezuela	—	—	—	—	70	—	28,100	10·0	94,900	14·8	92,600	13·7	99,400	14·0	113,210	14·2
U.S.S.R.	—	—	10,400	51·5	3,480	3·7	30,100	10·7	47,500	7·4	52,000	7·7	58,000	8·2	70,000	8·8
Kuwait	—	—	—	—	—	—	—	—	37,600	5·9	43,300	6·4	47,700	6·7	54,760	6·9
Saudi Arabia	—	—	—	—	—	—	—	—	40,400	6·3	41,400	6·1	46,900	6·6	47,470	5·9
Iraq	—	—	—	—	—	—	4,400	1·6	18,900	3·0	28,200	4·2	30,700	4·3	33,700	4·2
Canada	—	—	120	0·6	30	—	900	0·3	8,300	1·3	11,000	1·6	13,000	1·8	17,590	2·2
Mexico	—	—	—	—	23,440	24·9	5,500	2·0	11,100	1·7	10,200	1·5	11,900	1·7	12,860	1·6
Indonesia	—	—	310	1·5	2,280	2·4	7,400	2·6	8,400	1·3	10,200	1·5	10,700	1·5	11,750	1·5
Roumania	2	0·7	250	1·2	1,030	1·1	6,900	2·5	4,000	0·6	6,000	0·9	7,000	1·0	8,000	1·0
Iran	—	—	—	—	1,600	1·7	10,400	3·7	1,000	0·2	1,000	0·1	3,000	0·4	16,160	2·0
Total	287	100·0	19,580	96·8	90,990	96·5	264,400	94·3	604,400	94·4	639,500	94·4	666,600	93·9	748,220	94·0
WORLD TOTAL	287		20,200		94,250		280,500		640,400		677,600		708,700		795,270	

Authority: Petroleum Information Bureau.

TABLE 87

World production of coal, oil and hydroelectric power—1953

Country	Natural gas	Crude petroleum	Coal	Hydroelectric power
	million metric tons			thousand million kWh
U.S.A. . .	185	344	443	109
Rest of America .	21	152	17	67
U.S.S.R. . .	—	52	241	22
U.K. . .	nil	0·06	228	2
West Germany .	0·1	2	125	9
Rest of Europe .	2	5	247	126
Japan . .	0·1	0·3	47	42
Rest of Asia .	1	116	91	4
Other countries .	trace	8	68	7
Total . .	209[1]	679[2]	1,507[3]	388[4]

Authorities:

[1,2] 'Natural gas and crude petroleum', *Petroleum Times.*

[3] 'Coal', *British Iron and Steel Federation Statistical Yearbook*, 1953, Part 2.

[4] 'Hydroelectric power', Various.

TABLE 88

The United Kingdom Petroleum industry

(a) *Imports and refinery production*
(quantities in million gallons)

Product	1938	1948	1950	1952	1954	1955
1. *Imports*[1]—						
Crude oil	568	1,174	2,369	5,927	7,196	7,229
Motor and other spirit . .	1,481	1,214	1,247	558	473	591
Kerosene	205	406	390	403	360	429
Gas oil	158	476	369	210	444	509
Diesel oil	—	} 1,304	573	336	53	59
Fuel oil	686				386	569
Lubricating oil . .	109	86	119	109	114	111
Paraffin wax ('000 tons) .	41	36	30	23	40	38
2. *Refinery production*[2]—						
Motor and other spirit . .	105	198	473	1,545	2,250	2,174
Kerosene . . .	36	34	45	170	211	223
Lubricating oil . . .	39	91	107	92	147	177
Gas/diesel oil . . .	98	236	492	1,025	1,106	1,215
Fuel oil . . .	112	331	902	2,393	2,695	2,425
Solid products ('000 tons) .	624	537	652	730	826	953
3. *Re-exports, oil fuel for bunkers.*	313	468	526	815	913	965

Authorities:

[1] Trade and Navigation Accts.

[2] Petroleum Information Bureau.

TABLE 88 (*continued*)

(*b*) *Sources of principal petroleum products imported into the U.K.*
(million gallons)

Product	1938	1948	1950	1954	1955
1. *Crude oil*—					
Netherlands West Indies and Venezuela	300	337	353	652	862
Iraq	142	193	127	1,339	1,006
Iran	54	247	607	—	326
Peru	22	40	38	36	36
British Commonwealth	20	7	9	110	105
Bahrain, Kuwait, Qatar	—	157	931	4,945	4,631
Saudi Arabia	—	177	278	40	90
2. *Motor spirit*—					
Netherlands West Indies and Venezuela	591	515	595	77	123
Iran	314	214	242	—	—
U.S.A.	317	283	77	52	54
British Commonwealth	99	88	66	126	168
U.S.S.R.	47	9	—	—	—
Roumania	47	22	—	—	—
Bahrain and Kuwait	—	21	92	51	66
Netherlands	—	—	95	95	75
3. *Gas, diesel and fuel oils*—					
Netherlands West Indies and Venezuela	273	858	227	332	334
Iran	198	525	279	—	—
Mexico	36	33	26	—	—
British Commonwealth	130	124	76	132	181
U.S.A.	102	170	39	181	205
Bahrain and Kuwait	—	—	34	26	51
Netherlands	—	—	186	115	219
France	—	—	55	34	90
4. *Lubricating oil*—					
U.S.A.	86	79	95	78	31
Netherlands West Indies	—	7	21	14	18

Authority: Trade and Navigation Accts.

TABLE 88 (*continued*)

(*c*) *C.i.f. values of imported petroleum products, U.K.*
(in pence per Imperial gallon)

Product	1913	1920	1938	1948	1950	1951	1952	1953	1954	1955
Crude petroleum	3·2	13·6	2·2	6·35	7·52	8·87	9·61	7·85	7·36	7·45
Motor spirit	9·0	27·0	4·1	9·49	11·70	13·66	15·27	15·59	14·30	13·53
Kerosene	4·1	17·6	3·5	8·84	10·61	11·99	13·05	11·99	11·28	11·14
Gas oil	2·7	15·0	3·2	8·71	9·88	11·55	13·21	12·17	11·02	10·92
Lubricating oil	8·7	34·1	8·8	21·80	20·40	30·69	29·30	19·86	18·38	19·33
Fuel and diesel oil	2·9	8·8	2·3	7·55	9·13	11·91	11·40	9·82	9·25	—
Paraffin wax (£ per ton)	—	—	15·7	64·21	62·32	76·25	67·93	62·99	71·23	73·90

Authorities:

1913, 1920: Sub-Committee on Oil from Coal (Falmouth Report, 1938, *H.M. Stationery Office*, Cmd. 5665).

1948: *Pet. Times*, Jan. 28, 1939, p. 127.

Other years: *Pet. Times,* Feb. 18, 1955; *Pet. Times,* April 27, 1956.

TABLE 88 *(continued)*

(d) Oil refineries of the United Kingdom

Company	Plant location	Crude capacity b/d	Cracking capacity b/d	Type of refinery*
Esso Petroleum Co.	Fawley	160,000	41,000	*S ; L*
Shell Refining & Marketing	Stanlow	100,000	33,000	*Ch ; S*
,, ,, ,,	Shellhaven	75,000	—	*L ; W*
,, ,, ,,	Ardrossan	3,000	—	—
,, ,, ,,	Heysham	36,000	—	—
British Petroleum Co.	Isle of Grain	92,000	10,000	*S ; L ; W*
,, ,, ,,	Grangemouth	44,000	10,000	*Ch ; S*
,, ,, ,,	Llandarcy	60,000	10,000	*L ; W*
,, ,, ,,	Pumpherston	3,600	1,300	—
Manchester Oil Refinery	Trafford Pk.	3,000	—	*L ; W*
Berry Wiggins	Kingsnorth	2,000	—	—
,, ,,	Weaste	1,600	—	*L*
Lobitos	Ellesmere Pt.	3,800	—	*L ; Sp*
Mobiloil	Coryton	35,000	9,000	*L*
William Briggs	Dundee	700	—	—

* Abbreviations in this column are: *Ch*—chemicals plant, *S*—sulphur, *L*—lubricating oil, *W*—wax, *Sp*—special oils.

Authority: Petroleum Information Bureau.

(e) Oilfields of the United Kingdom[1]

Field	Year opened	Daily average production, b/d July, 1955	Accumulated production, bbl. to 1.7.55
Formby	1939	3	69,000
Eakring	1939	155	1,788,000
Dukes Wood	1941	467	2,999,000
Kelham	1941	330	1,480,000
Caunton	1943	30	209,000
Plungar	1953	25	12,000

[1] *Oil Gas J.*, December 26, 1955.

TABLE 89

Consumption of major petroleum products by leading countries, 1954

(quantities in thousand barrels)

Country	Motor fuel	Kerosene	Distillate fuel oil	Residual fuel oil	Lubri-cating oil	Total
U.S.A. . . .	1,238,346	118,260	526,369	522,099	38,444	2,443,518
Canada. . .	73,922	12,085	47,020	45,380	2,480	180,887
United Kingdom .	57,790	10,550	38,900	67,750	5,820	180,810
France . . .	34,950	757	22,110	54,900	2,870	115,587
Italy (inc. Trieste) .	11,550	1,740	12,414	47,900	990	74,594
Argentina . .	14,100	6,460	9,000	33,750	1,040	64,350
Western Germany .	21,522	377	22,314	16,495	3,067	63,775
Mexico . . .	20,690	7,150	7,080	27,000	800	62,720
Japan . . .	15,100	2,990	7,700	33,700	2,400	61,890
Brazil . . .	23,230	4,175	9,418	19,900	1,320	58,043
Sweden . .	9,575	3,580	16,390	17,120	600	47,265
Australia . .	24,181	3,688	7,950	8,995	1,295	46,109
Netherlands .	7,250	1,790	10,300	17,100	650	37,090
Venezuela . .	10,415	2,888	5,599	14,300	227	33,429
Egypt . . .	2,850	6,160	4,300*	19,500*	250	33,060
India . . .	8,200	10,000	5,850	6,200	1,050	31,300
Belgium/ Luxembourg .	8,468	1,091	7,650	8,940	675	26,824
Malaya . .	3,050	300	5,780	12,990	150	22,270
South Africa . .	10,900	3,950	3,600	2,750	750	21,950
Denmark . .	5,390	840	4,392	7,493	321	18,436
Indonesia . .	4,600	4,661	4,018	4,755	220	18,254
Total 'Free' World.	1,706,851	230,984	858,935	1,156,848	70,874	4,024,492

* Includes transit trade in ships' bunkers.

Note—Motor fuel includes aviation gasoline, other gasolines, and naphtha from crude and natural gasoline, and blended alcohol or benzole. Jet fuel has not been knowingly included with motor fuel or kerosene.

Authority: U.S. Bureau of Mines, World Petroleum Statistics.

APPENDIX 4

STATISTICS OF PRODUCTION OF SYNTHETIC ORGANIC CHEMICALS OF NON-COAL TAR ORIGIN IN U.S.A., 1921–1955

The United States Tariff Commission has reported annually, beginning with 1917, the progress of the American dye and coal tar chemical industry. In 1921 this annual census was extended to include synthetic organic chemicals other than those derived from coal tar (U.S. Tariff Commission, Census of dyes and other synthetic organic chemicals; subsequently re-titled U.S. Tariff Commission, Census of synthetic organic chemicals).

1921 is therefore a logical date from which to show the growth in America of synthetic organic chemicals not based on coal tar. A number of provisos must, however, be borne in mind in interpreting the figures in the following tables; 1921 was an abnormal year, general business activity being considerably lower than in either 1920 or 1922. The bases of the figures have had to be changed from time to time; thus in 1933, rubber chemicals were transferred from coal tar intermediates to coal tar finished products. In 1941, with the realisation that petroleum and coal overlapped, and that both starting materials were used for making the same chemicals, synthetic organic chemicals were divided between cyclic compounds (which were mainly but not wholly derived from coal tar) and acyclic compounds (based mainly on petroleum, carbide and fermentation processes). It need hardly be mentioned that non-coal tar chemicals are not solely based on petroleum or petroleum gases; they include products derived from calcium carbide and from fermentation processes, two sources which in the 1920's supplied the main proportion of non-coal tar chemicals.

All that is claimed for Tables 90–96 presented here is that they give an indication of the rate of growth and of the magnitude of the synthetic organic chemicals industry in the U.S.A.

TABLE 90

Totals of acyclic and of cyclic synthetic organic chemicals manufactured in the United States

(units of million lb.)

Product	1921	1930	1941*	1945	1950	1951	1952	1953	1954	1955
Acyclic products	22	609	5,000	9,650	10,533	11,022	14,716	15,320	19,270	23,211
Cyclic intermediates.	71	291	1,000	2,330	2,484	2,555	3,185	3,495	4,613	6,016
Cyclic finished products	51	142	800	2,700	2,630	2,590	3,203	3,575	4,560	6,107

* Different basis on and after 1941; before 1941, cyclic intermediates and finished products were based on statistics of coal tar chemicals.

TABLE 91

Production of typical coal tar raw materials

Product	1921	1930	1941	1945	1950	1951	1952	1953	1954	1955
Tar,[a] 10^6 U.S. gal. . .	309	647	856	900	750	800	705	833	720	853
Benzole,[b] 10^6 U.S. gal. .	9	20	45	156	176	233	217	210	165	209
Toluole,[c] 10^6 U.S. gal. .	8	12	36	—	38	46	41	41	36	42
Naphthalene, 10^6 lb. .	19	32	198	288	288	355	322	276	317	477

[a] Total coal and coke oven tar only.
[b] Other than motor benzole.
[c] Production from coke ovens only.

TABLE 92

Production of raw materials from petroleum and natural gas for chemical conversion

(units of million lb.)

Product	1945	1950	1951	1952	1953	1954	1955
1. Aromatics and Naphthenes							
Alkyl aromatics . . .	—	—	432	391	405	520	642
Benzene	(a)	73	234	256	462	638	723
Cresylic acid (crude) . .	—	16	20	14	16	22	24
Naphthenic acids . . .	30	25	39	19	23	24	17
Toluene	(a)	329	403	464	836	890	1,038
Xylenes	334	450	464	444	749	726	699
Other aromatics . . .	—	533	5	17	14	19	30
2. Aliphatic hydrocarbons							
Methane	—	—	—	—	—	44	131
Ethane	—	}1,822	1,799	203	145	356	445
Ethylene	308			}1,810	2,136	2,345	3,048
Propane	} 179	999	974	580	1,366	1,675	}3,339
Propylene and propane-propy- lene . . .		694	1,148	996	1,223	1,203	
Butadiene	780	610	1,222	1,106	1,152	809	1,411
n-Butane . . .	255	(b)	(b)	38	418	459	753
1- and 2-butene . . .	306	641	1,136	825	908	1,215	1,172
Isobutene . . .	} 320	387	461	404	156	228	125
Other C_4's . . .					535	853	664
C_5's	—	—	—	15	122	179	251
Diisobutene . . .	—	20	22	25	23	22	—
Dodecene (tetrapropylene) .	—	—	94	115	177	316	372
Nonene (tripropylene) . .	—	—	—	—	61	99	146
Other aliphatic derivatives .	—	337	153	143	222	265	703 (c)
All others . . .	1,060	—	—	—	—	—	—
Total	3,572	6,936	8,606	7,865	11,149	12,907	15,733

(a) Included in "All others".
(b) Included in "Other C_4's".
(c) Includes acetylene and diisobutene.

TABLE 93

Production of some individual non-coal tar synthetic organic chemicals

(units of million lb.)

(a) General products

Product	1930	1940	1945	1950	1951	1952	1953	1954	1955
Acetaldehyde . . .	—	201	—	—	—	—	—	—	—
Acetic acid, synthetic .	—	186	267	441	454	383	478	442	542
Acetic anhydride . . .	—	(a)	525	908	976	686	804	691	842
Cellulose acetate . .	—	—	—	525	552	390	435	364	402
Formaldehyde, 37% wt. . .	41	181	424	835	987	1,022	1,119	1,032	1,259

(a) Production of acetic anhydride in 1939 was 181×10^6 lbs.

(b) Chlorinated compounds

Product	1930	1940	1945	1950	1951	1952	1953	1954	1955
Carbon tetrachloride . . .	34	101	193	217	244	219	260	235	288
Chloroform . . .	2·5	3·1	9·2	20	26	22	26	32	40
Dichloroethyl ether . . .	—	—	—	6	12	12	9	10	—
Ethyl chloride . . .	—	—	—	353	419	442	520	547	542
Ethylene dichloride . .	—	—	(a)	306	436	436	529	452	510
Methyl chloride . . .	2·0	3·0	30	27	37	34	41	33	36
Methylene dichloride . .	—	(b)	—	40	40	55	64	70	74
Perchlorethylene . .	—	—	(c)	—	110	106	153	158	—
Trichlorethylene . . .	—	—	—	—	—	271	323	297	316
Vinyl chloride . . .	—	—	—	250 (d)	431 (d)	321	402	393	529

(a) 106×10^6 lbs. in 1943.
(b) $3·8 \times 10^6$ lbs. in 1941.
(c) 75×10^6 lbs. in 1944.
(d) Including vinylidene chloride.

(c) Alcohols, esters, ethers, ketones

Product	1921	1930	1940	1945	1950	1951	1952	1953	1954	1955
Acetone from isopropyl alcohol	—	—	202 (a)	307	459	538	404	468	404	435
Amyl acetates . . .	—	4·4	—	16	—	11	8	8	—	—
Amyl alcohols . . .	—	—	—	14	17	18	—	21	—	—
Butyl acetates, . .	—	—	(c)	—	90	67	54	62	78	83
n-Butyl alcohol . . .	—	—	100	129	146	153	117	155	194	225
Butyl alcohols, other .	—	—	65	96	177	199	188	237	214	250
Diethylene glycol . .	—	—	—	—	—	50	64	47	36	75
Ethyl acetate, 85% .	5	70	75	106	92	85	72	81	72	77
Ethyl alcohol (synthetic) 100%, C_2H_5OH .	—	—	175	360	735	857	858	1,060	1,152	1,215
Ethyl ether . . .	3	9	(d)	77	38	76	65	47	56	69
Ethylene glycol . .	—	—	(e)	205	519	597	761	624	638	888
Isopropyl alcohol . .	0·2	—	220	491	866	1,075	846	901	859	855
Methyl alcohol, synthetic .	—	49	370	493	902	1,224	1,099	1,116	1,118	1,344
Pentaerythritol . . .	—	—	—	13	36	45	41	56	54	61
Propylene glycol . .	—	—	—	—	79	89	91	60	51	70
Triethylene glycol . .	—	—	—	—	—	—	7	—	17	19
Vinyl acetate . . .	—	—	—	—	—	—	—	—	106	134

(a) Includes fermentation.
(b) 93×10^6 lbs. in 1941.
(c) 7×10^6 lbs. in 1941.
(d) 23×10^6 lbs. in 1941.
(e) 151×10^6 lbs. in 1941.

TABLE 93 (*continued*)

(*d*) *Nitrogen compounds*

Product	1945	1950	1951	1952	1953	1954	1955
Acrylonitrile	—	—	—	—	57	63	118
Amines, total	26	86	106	137	155	142	184
Ethanolamines, total	—	—	—	44	53	63	78
Monoethanolamine	—	—	—	—	20	23	26
Diethanolamine	—	—	—	—	} 33	23	30
Triethanolamine	—	—	—	—		17	22

TABLE 94

Synthetic rubber industry; production of intermediates and synthetic rubbers

(quantities in units of a million lb.)

Product	1945	1950	1951	1952	1953	1954	1955
1. *Intermediates*							
Butadiene (*a*)	1,258	610	1,222	1,106	1,152	809	1,411
Styrene (for GR–S and synthetic resins)	362	539	707	700	798	703	1,014
2. *Synthetic rubbers*							
GR-S	1,621	802	1,561	1,394	1,415	973	1,643
Butadiene/acrylonitrile	18	27	34	36	45	48	71
Butyl	106	125	166	178	176	130	124
Neoprenes	81	112	132	147	180	155	205
Polyvinyl type (*b*)	—	84	90	113	118	105	128
All others (*c*)	78	16	20	21	24	24	40
Total	1,904	1,166	2,003	1,889	1,958	1,435	2,211

(*a*) In 1945, 468×10^6 lbs. from ethyl alcohol, 790×10^6 lbs. from petroleum. Figures for subsequent years are from petroleum only.

(*b*) Includes data for polyvinyl alcohol, butyral and chloride synthetic rubbers.

(*c*) Includes data for chlorinated and cyclo rubbers, polyurethane foams and polysulphide, silicone and polyisobutene synthetic rubbers.

TABLE 95

The plastics industry; production of selected intermediates and plasticisers, plastics and resins

(quantities in units of million lb.)

Product	1945	1950	1951	1952	1953	1954	1955
1. Intermediates—							
Phenol (a)	205	312	388	338	382	418	517
Phthalic anhydride (b) . .	126	216	248	229	227	254	331
Styrene (c)	362	539	707	700	798	703	1,014
p-Xylene	—	—	—	—	—	59	—
2. Plasticisers—							
All cyclic	139	181	204	194	224	228	296
Tricresyl and triphenyl phosphates . . .	14	22	25	24	30	24	43
Phthalate esters . .	99	143	157	150	165	171	213
Dibutyl phthalate . .	46	20	19	18	23	20	24
Di-2-ethylhexyl phthalate	—	61	65	63	51	54	72
Other octyl phthalates .	—	2	8	24	34	34	31
Other phthalates . .	53	60	65	45	57	63	56
All other cyclic plasticisers.	—	16	22	20	29	27	40
Acyclic plasticisers . .	31	63	77	73	69	73	100
Total plasticisers . . .	170	244	281	267	293	301	396
3. Plastics and Resins							
Phenol-formaldehyde type .	188	451	474	393	485	434	563
Alkyds	193	402	440	431	467	453	543
Phthalic . . .	140	333	368	357	391	382	456
Acyclic . . .	53	69	72	74	76	71	87
Polyesters (d) . . .	—	—	—	—	—	49	62
Styrene resins . . .	23	355	394	425	508	481	619
Polystyrene . . .	22	261	272	272	321	328	414
Styrene-butadiene and styrene-divinyl benzene (e)	1	38	57	80	122	123	153
Other styrene types . .	—	56	65	73	26	30	52
Urea and melamine resins .	74	219	237	228	257	265	328
Vinyl resins	123	381	476	420	516	524	703
Polyvinyl chloride and copolymers . . .	84	325	411	356	435	397	527
Polyvinyl acetate . .	39	30	33	34	42	79	73
Other vinyl resins (f) .		26	32	30	39	48	103
Epoxies	—	2	—	—	—	18	22
Silicones	—	—	1·3	1·7	2·5	2	3
Petroleum polymers, coumarones, rosin and tall oil, miscellaneous benzenoid .	128	217	256	244	289	288	361
All others (g) . .	88	121	161	190	253	314	535
Total plastics and resins .	817	2,148	2,439	2,333	2,777	2,828	3,739

(a) Over 90 per cent synthetic; in 1955, 70 × 10⁶ lbs. from cumene.
(b) Proportion from petroleum, about 5 per cent.
(c) Includes styrene for GR–S.
(d) Excludes styrene modified polyesters for surface coatings.
(e) Styrene-divinyl benzene included only for 1953 and 1954.
(f) Polyvinyl alcohol, formal and butyral.
(g) Includes polyethylene, acrylic, polyamide and other non-benzenoid resins; in 1955, 402 × 10⁶ lbs. polyethylene.

T ABLE 96

Surface active agents

Product	1945	1950	1951	1952	1953	1954	1955
Cyclic total	68	383	459	478	594	640	764
Dodecylbenzene sulphonate type	—	262	315	307	364	389	446
Petroleum aromatic sulphonates	15	63	83	85	129	143	125
All other cyclic . . .	53	58	61	86	101	108	193
Acyclic total	93	293	234	263	328	386	389
Esters and ethers non-sulphonated . . .	—	20	21	36	70	88	101
Nitrogen compounds non-sulphonated . . .	—	28	26	37	53	57	65
Sulphated and sulphonated alcohols and esters . .	—	—	—	126	127	130	137
All other acyclic . . .	93	245	187	64	78	109	86
Total	161	676	693	741	922	1,026	1,153

1. NAME INDEX

433

2. INDEX OF PATENT NUMBERS

(a) British Patents.

(b) United States Patents.

3. INDEX OF GERMAN INTELLIGENCE REPORTS

(a) Combined Intelligence Objectives Sub-Committee Reports.

(b) British Intelligence Objectives Sub-Committee Reports.

(c) Field Investigation Agency (Technical) Reports.

4. SUBJECT INDEX